CONVERSION FACTORS

LENGTH
1 meter (m) = 39.37 in. = 3.281 ft = 6.214×10^{-4} mile
1 in. = 0.02540000 m; 1 ft = 0.3048 m; 1 mile = 1,609 m
1 nautical mile = 1,852 m = 1.1508 mile = 6076.10 ft
1 Angstrom (Å) = 10^{-10} m; 1 micron (μ) = 10^{-6} m; 1 millimicron (mμ) = 10^{-9} m
1 mil = 10^{-3} in.; 1 rod = 16.5 ft; 1 fathom = 6 ft

AREA
$1 \text{ m}^2 = 10.76 \text{ ft}^2 = 1{,}550 \text{ in.}^2$
$1 \text{ ft}^2 = 929 \text{ cm}^2$; $1 \text{ in.}^2 = 6.452 \text{ cm}^2 = 1.273 \times 10^6$ circular mils

VOLUME
$1 \text{ m}^3 = 35.31 \text{ ft}^3 = 6.102 \times 10^4 \text{ in.}^3$
$1 \text{ ft}^3 = 0.02832 \text{ m}^3$; 1 U.S. gallon = 231 in.^{3}; 1 liter = 1.000028×10^{-3} m^3 = 61.02 in.^{3}

TIME
1 year = 365.2422 days = 8.766×10^3 hr = 5.259×10^5 min = 3.156×10^7 sec
1 sidereal day (period of earth's revolution) = 86,164 sec

SPEED
1 m/sec = 3.281 ft/sec = 3.6 km/hr = 2.237 mi/hr = 1.944 knot
1 km/hr = 0.2778 m/sec = 0.9113 ft/sec = 0.6214 mi/hr
1 mi/hr = 1.467 ft/sec = 1.609 km/hr = 0.8689 knot

MASS
1 kg = 2.205 lb mass = 0.06852 slug
1 lb mass = 0.4536 kg = 0.03108 slug; 1 slug = 32.17 lb mass = 14.59 kg

DENSITY
$1 \text{ g/cm}^3 = 1{,}000 \text{ kg/m}^3 = 62.43 \text{ lb mass/ft}^3 = 1.940 \text{ slug/ft}^3$
$1 \text{ lb mass/ft}^3 = 0.03108 \text{ slug/ft}^3 = 16.02 \text{ kg/m}^3 = 0.01602 \text{ g/cm}^3$

FORCE
1 newton = 10^5 dynes = 0.1020 kg-wt = 0.2248 lb
1 lb (force) = 4.448 newtons = 0.4536 kg-wt = 32.17 poundals

PRESSURE
$1 \text{ newton/m}^2 = 9.869 \times 10^{-6} \text{ atm} = 1.450 \times 10^{-4} \text{ lb/in.}^2 = 0.02089 \text{ lb/ft}^2$
$\qquad = 7.501 \times 10^{-4} \text{ cm Hg} = 4.015 \times 10^{-3} \text{ in. of water} = 10^{-5} \text{ bar}$
$1 \text{ lb/in.}^2 = 144 \text{ lb/ft}^2 = 6{,}895 \text{ newtons/m}^2 = 5.171 \text{ cm Hg} = 27.68 \text{ in. of water}$
$1 \text{ atm} = 406.8 \text{ in. of water} = 76 \text{ cm Hg} = 1.013 \times 10^5 \text{ newtons/m}^2 = 10{,}330 \text{ kg-wt/m}^2$
$\qquad = 2{,}116 \text{ lb/ft}^2 = 14.70 \text{ lb/in.}^2 = 760 \text{ torr}$

WORK, ENERGY, HEAT
1 joule = 0.2389 cal = 9.481×10^{-4} Btu = 0.7376 ft-lb = 10^7 ergs = 6.242×10^{18} eV
1 kcal = 4,186 joules = 3.968 Btu = 3,087 ft-lb
1 eV = 1.602×10^{-19} joule; 1 unified amu = 931.48 MeV
1 kw-hr = 3.6×10^6 joules = 3,413 Btu = 860.1 kcal = 1.341 hp-hr

POWER
1 hp = 2545 Btu/hr = 550 ft-lb/sec = 745.7 watts = 0.1782 kcal/sec
1 watt = 2.389×10^{-4} kcal/sec = 1.341×10^{-3} hp = 0.7376 ft-lb/sec

ELECTRIC CHARGE
1 coulomb = 0.1 abcoulomb = 2.998×10^9 statcoulombs (esu)
1 faraday = 96,487 coulombs; 1 electronic charge = 1.602×10^{-19} coulomb

ELECTRIC CURRENT
1 ampere = 0.1 abampere (emu) = 2.998×10^9 statamperes (esu)

ELECTRIC POTENTIAL DIFFERENCE
1 abvolt (emu) = 10^{-8} volt; 1 statvolt (esu) = 299.8 volts

CAPACITANCE
1 statfarad (esu) = 1 cm = 1.113×10^{-12} farad (F)

MAGNETIC FLUX
1 weber = 10^8 maxwells = 10^5 kilolines

MAGNETIC INTENSITY B
$1 \text{ newton/amp-m} = 1 \text{ weber/m}^2 = 10{,}000 \text{ gauss} = 10^9 \text{ gamma}$

MAGNETIZING FORCE H
1 amp-turn/m = 0.01257 oersted = 0.01257 gilbert/cm

Elements of Physics

Elements of Physics

ALPHEUS W. SMITH *Professor of Physics, Emeritus*
The Ohio State University

JOHN N. COOPER *Professor of Physics*
U.S. Naval Postgraduate School

Seventh Edition

McGRAW-HILL BOOK COMPANY *New York San Francisco Toronto London*

The role of physics in modern life continues to expand. Since the publication in 1957 of the sixth edition of *Elements of Physics,* space satellites have been launched by the score, and innumerable applications of physics have been made in communications, in transportation, and in industry. A knowledge of the principles of physics is increasingly imperative if one wishes to keep abreast of what is happening in the broad technological segment of human activity. It is the purpose of this book to introduce the student to the fundamental laws of physics and to give him some feeling of their power and beauty. Toward this end, a wealth of applications and examples is introduced, with particular attention to the physics of everyday experience. It is our belief that an understanding of physical phenomena adds a new dimension to the beauty of the rainbow and an enriched appreciation of such scientific advances as those which permit us to view events taking place hundreds of miles away in full color.

This text is written for students who have not studied calculus. The treatment of physical laws and their applications has been handled as quantitatively and rigorously as the mathematical sophistication of the prospective student permits. While there are many situations which can be treated better by use of calculus, there are others in which careful physical reasoning can give a more penetrating understanding of a resulting equation than would the glib application of calculus.

In electricity only mks units are used, while in mechanics both the mks system and the British engineering system of units are stressed. Definitions of key quantities of the cgs system are presented, but no problems are introduced in either cgs electrostatic or electromagnetic units.

Although the overall organization of the book into parts on mechanics, wave motion and sound, heat, light, electricity, and modern physics has been retained, there has been considerable reorganization of material. In particular, many topics have been moved from the section on modern physics to earlier parts. The mechanics section has been extensively reordered, with friction introduced early. The treatment of earth satellites has been expanded with the introduction of material on gravitational potential energy. A major expansion in the section dealing with modern physics comes from the addition of chapters on relativity and on molecules and solids.

There is ample material in this text for three full semesters of study. The classical physics sections alone require a full academic year for reasonably thorough coverage. For a two-semester course which includes considerable modern physics, it is possible to omit many selected chapters without seriously neglecting the background knowledge required for most subsequent chapters. Among the chapters which are sometimes omitted are those on rotational motion, fluids, elastic properties of matter, sound, atmospheric physics, spectra and color, chemical and thermal electromotive forces, generators and motors, and alternating currents. Explanatory material within the chapters that is considered optional reading has been marked with the symbol $<$ at the beginning and a hairline rule at the end.

The junior author is deeply grateful to many persons who have offered constructive criticism of the previous edition and made suggestions for improvement. In particular, he wishes to acknowledge his indebtedness to four former colleagues at Ohio State University: R. A. Oetjen, E. L. Jossem, A. M. Sessler, and R. A. Erickson; to his present colleagues A. R. Frey and L. O. Olsen; to his former student D. L. Shirer of Valparaiso University; to G. M. Koehl of George Washington University; and lastly to an anonymous reviewer, who found faults with the manuscript by the dozens and always proposed ways to correct them. Although Dean Smith has not participated directly in the preparation of this edition of *Elements of Physics,* a sincere effort has been made to retain the spirit and vision with which he imbued the first five editions.

Corrections, criticisms, and suggestions from those who examine or use this book will be greatly appreciated.

John N. Cooper

Monterey, Calif., 1964

ACKNOWLEDGMENTS FOR PHOTOGRAPHS

Figure 1.1	National Bureau of Standards
Figure 8.1	Westinghouse
Figure 8.5	From *PSSC Physics,* D. C. Heath and Company
Figure 8.9	From *PSSC Physics,* D. C. Heath and Company
Figure 12.3	Yerkes Observatory, University of Chicago Press
Figure 12.4	F. N. M. Brown
Figure 12.5	F. N. M. Brown
Figure 12.11	F. N. M. Brown
Figure 12.13	F. N. M. Brown
Figure 13.2	Edgerton, Germhausen, and Grier, Massachusetts Institute of Technology
Figure 13.10	Harold E. Edgerton
Figure 15.9	Macalaster Corporation
Figure 15.10	Vern O. Knudsen, L. P. Delsasso
Figure 17.10	Olin Mathieson Chemical Corporation
Figure 23.7	General Electric Company
Figure 29.5	Glenn A. Fry, Ohio State University
Figure 30.2b	Jenkins and White, *Fundamentals of Physical Optics,* McGraw-Hill Book Company
Figure 30.8	Do-All Company
Figure 30.10	Atomic Laboratories, Inc.
Figure 30.12	Atomic Laboratories, Inc.
Figure 30.13	John M. Stone
Figure 30.15b	John M. Stone
Figure 30.16b	John M. Stone
Figure 31.3	Polaroid Corporation
Figure 31.10	Polaroid Corporation
Figure 31.11	Instrument Division, Budd Company; Zandman Method
Figure 32.4	Mt. Wilson and Mt. Palomar Observatories
Figure 32.7	Kodak Data Book *Color as Seen and Photographed* and Allcolor Company, Inc., by permission
Figure 32.11	L. M. Condax and Eastman Kodak Company

CONTENTS

PART VI MODERN PHYSICS

APPENDIX

PART I   MECHANICS

CHAPTER 1   *Every day we move about, we see, we hear, we interact with our environment in myriad ways.   The science of physics is concerned with the inanimate aspects of the universe and our interactions with it.   How are sound and light produced, propagated, and detected?   How does an automobile engine, an electric motor, or a jet engine operate?   How can the motions of billiard balls, space capsules, and planets be predicted?   These are all questions which can be answered in terms of the principles of physics.   No one who lives a normal, active life can avoid knowing and using physics in a* qualitative *way.   It is the purpose of this book to help you achieve a* quantitative *knowledge of many of the topics of physics and to broaden the range of physical phenomena with which you are acquainted.*

Probably no aspect of physics is more familiar than the motions of objects such as balls or automobiles.   Therefore we start our study with mechanics, *the branch of physics dealing with the forces which act upon bodies and with the responses of the bodies to the forces.   To obtain precise measurements of these responses, we require quantitative comparisons in terms of carefully established standards.   In this first chapter we define the fundamental units of length (the* meter*), of time (the* second*), and of mass (the* kilogram*) in terms of which we can express any quantity which we meet in mechanics.*

Physics and Measurement

1.1 What Is Physics?

In its broadest sense physics is that branch of knowledge which describes and explains the material world and its phenomena.   In terms of this sweeping definition all other physical sciences may be regarded as branches of the basic science *physics*, which a century ago was known as *natural philosophy*.   At present, it is customary to use *physics* in a more restricted sense.   The boundaries between physics and related physical sciences such as chemistry, geology, and astronomy are not definite.   Sharp distinctions between these sciences are neither necessary nor desirable. There are certain aspects of nature, however, which are ordinarily regarded as clearly in the special domain of physics. For convenience, they may be grouped under the headings of mechanics, sound, heat, light, electricity, atomic structure. In addition, several broad areas of knowledge in which physics overlaps related sciences are described by names such as astrophysics, biophysics, chemical physics, and geophysics. Of course, these fields are not distinct, for they merge into one another.

Throughout the ages, men of intelligence have endeavored to explain what went on in the world about them. There has been a never-ending struggle to formulate a systematic set of concepts about the world in which we live. In part, men have been driven by curiosity—an urge to learn "why?" In part, they have been motivated by the conviction that their efforts to understand natural phenomena would lead to the possibility of controlling these phenomena. Thousands upon thousands of men have contributed to the vast store of knowledge and information which constitutes the physics of today. Thousands more are actively working to add new facts to this body of knowledge and to organize facts already known into logical patterns. Physics is growing at an unprecedented rate. It is a science full of life and vigor.

Physics is as old as man's curiosity about his environment and the wealth of processes which it manifests. In the phenomena which impinge on our senses we find many regularities and a great orderliness, suggesting that these phenomena are subject to certain laws. Physical scientists seek to discover these laws of nature, to organize them into a logically elegant structure, and to use them for the benefit of man.

Everyone is familiar with at least some of the regularities of nature. A small child soon learns that released objects fall to the floor; a more mature observer may be impressed by the regularity of the movement of the sun, moon, and stars. To find the relationship between these apparently unrelated processes required the genius of Newton. Yet many an important contribution to physics has been made by men of modest intellectual achievements. In the words of Aristotle,

The search for Truth is in one way hard and in another easy. For it is evident that no one can master it fully nor miss it wholly. But each adds a little to our knowledge of Nature, and from all the facts assembled there arises a certain grandeur.

1.2 The Importance of Physics

As knowledge of physics has grown, men have learned how to apply the laws of nature in ways which have revolutionized our mode of life. For example, in the eighteenth century scientists made great progress in understanding heat. This knowledge led to the development of heat engines, and the use of these engines stimulated further investigations. In the nineteenth century physicists greatly increased their knowledge of electrical phenomena. Application of this knowledge led to the widespread use of electrical energy for light, for heat, for radio and television, and for electric motors. Investigation into the discharge of electricity through gases led to the discovery of X rays, which not only provided a vital tool for the study of crystals and atomic structure, but also paved the way for revolutionary advances in the diagnosis and treatment of diseases. In the twentieth century research in physics has expanded to unprecedented levels and has given us insight into the properties of solids and into the structure of atoms and nuclei.

Progress in physics brings with it progress in commerce and industry, in medicine, and in the related sciences. Much of the difference between the way we now live in the United States and the way the Indians lived 500 years ago is associated with our greater knowledge of physical phenomena and how they may be controlled.

1.3 Physics: A Quantitative Branch of Knowledge

In physics and related sciences, facts and laws are expressed in precise language. For the most part the terms used in physics are defined in a detailed and unambiguous way, so that scientists all over the world mean exactly the same thing by the same term. In order to formulate valid relationships between physical quantities, accurate measurements must be made. Thus, physics is a quantitative science. In 1883, Lord Kelvin emphasized this quantitative aspect in the following words:

I often say that when you can measure what you are speaking about, and express it in numbers, you know something about it; but when you cannot measure it, when you cannot express it in numbers, your knowledge is of a meager and unsatisfactory kind. It may be the beginning of knowledge, but you have scarcely, in your thoughts, advanced to the stage of science, whatever the matter may be.

In making measurements of physical quantities, we ordinarily perform a series of operations which involve the comparison of an unknown quantity with an accepted standard of the same kind. Thus, when we say that a table is 10 feet (ft) long, we mean that a standard of length called a "foot" must be applied to it ten times in succession in order to cover its entire length. Similarly, a body is said to have a mass of 25 kilograms (kg) if its mass is twenty-five times as great as the mass of a standard kilogram.

1.4 Standards of Length and Mass

At one time the length of a king's foot or the span of his hand served as an adequate standard of length, and a selected stone as a standard of mass. However, as commerce between countries increased and as scientists began to make more and more accurate measurements, established standards of length and mass became of increasing importance. The French took the lead in adopting a system of weights and measures which is now almost universally used in scientific work.

French scientists chose as their standard of length one ten-millionth of the distance from the North Pole to the equator measured on a quadrant through Paris, and they fabricated a platinum bar of this length. This bar, known as the *Meter of the Archives,* was adopted by the French government as the national standard of length.

As a standard mass, the French scientists prepared a platinum cylinder which had a mass as near as they could make it to the mass of 1,000 cubic centimeters (cm³) of water at maximum density. This cylinder, known as the *Kilogram of the Archives,* was adopted as the French standard of mass.

In 1875, representatives from many civilized countries met in Paris to discuss international standards of measurement. It was generally agreed that the French units were most suitable and that copies should be made for nations which wished to adopt the *metric system* of units. Thirty bars were made of an alloy of platinum (90 per cent) and iridium (10 per cent). On these bars were marked fine transverse lines separated as nearly as possible by a distance equal to the length of the Meter of the Archives. These new standards were made in 1880, and in 1889 they were distributed to the governments participating in the convention of 1875. The United States obtained two of these standard "meters," of which bar No. 27 was the primary standard of length for the United States until 1960. Bar No. 6 was most nearly equal to the Meter of the Archives, and it was declared the *International Standard Meter.* It is kept at the International Bureau of Weights and Measures at Sèvres, near Paris.

At the same time, 40 standard kilograms, with masses as nearly as possible equal to that of the Kilogram of the Archives, were constructed from the platinum-iridium alloy. The new mass which agreed most closely with the Kilogram of the Archives is now the *International Mass Standard.* The International Standard Kilogram is a cylinder almost 39 mm in diameter and 39 mm in height. Although it was originally intended that the kilogram duplicate the mass of 1,000 cm³ of air-free, distilled water at maximum density, subsequent measurements have shown that a volume of 1,000.028 cm³ of water at maximum density has a mass of 1 kg. This volume is known as the *liter.*

The fundamental unit of mass of the United States is the *kilogram.* The primary mass standard of this country is kilogram No. 20 (Fig. 1.1), one of the two standard masses received by the United States. It is kept at the National Bureau of Standards.

Originally the British pound mass (lbm) was the mass of a cylinder kept in London, while in the United States the pound mass was legally defined as a specified fraction of a kilogram. It turned out that the British and the American mass pounds did not agree exactly. In 1959 this double standard was abandoned, and it was agreed that *the international pound mass is 0.45359237 kg.*

By the middle of the twentieth century the prototype meter bar was no longer good enough as a standard of length. Secondary standards could be compared with it only to an accuracy of roughly one part in

FIGURE 1.1

National standard of mass is the kilogram.

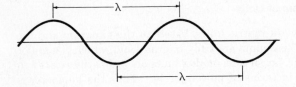

FIGURE 1.2
Wavelength λ is the distance from crest to crest (or trough to trough) of a wave.

10 million, while technological requirements for modern industry called for tolerances of the order of 10^{-7} m. In general, it is desirable that a master standard be at least ten times more accurate than the scientific and industrial measuring systems which are derived from it. As a consequence, at the 1960 International Conference on Weights and Measures the meter was redefined in terms of the wavelength of the orange light emitted by the krypton isotope of mass 86 (Fig. 1.2). Krypton is found in the air, and a standard based on the light from krypton 86 has the advantage that it can never be destroyed, stolen, damaged, or lost. Further, anyone with the appropriate equipment can reproduce the present standard of length, defined as follows:

The meter is a length 1,650,763.73 *times the wavelength of the orange-red light given off by the pure krypton isotope of mass 86 when it is excited in an electrical discharge.*

With this standard of length it is possible to make measurements with an accuracy of the order of 1 part in 100 million.

Although the meter is the national standard of length, most measurements in the United States are made in the British units, which are related to the meter as follows:

One inch is 0.0254 *m, or 2.54 cm.*
One foot is 0.3048 *m, or 30.48 cm.*

1.5 Units of Time

In both the English and metric systems, the *second* is the fundamental unit of time. This unit is defined in terms of the rotation of the earth in the following manner: The time from the instant the center of the sun is on the meridian plane (the meridian plane of an observer is a plane determined by the axis of rotation of the earth and the point at which the observer is located on the earth's surface) until the sun is centered on the meridian the following day is called a *solar day.* For several reasons solar days are not all of identical duration; the average over 1 year is called the *mean solar day.* This period is divided into 24 hr, each hour into 60 min, and each minute into 60 sec. Thus, a solar day contains 86,400 sec. For many years the second was defined as 1/86,400 of a mean solar day.

However, the earth's rotation is subject to small variations which are not thoroughly understood. As a result, the mean solar day is not an entirely satisfactory quantity for defining a standard of time. The 1960 International Conference on Weights and Measures decided on a new definition for the second:

One second is 1/31,556,925.9747 *of the solar year* 1900.

1.6 The MKS System of Units

In most scientific work metric units, based on the kilogram and the meter, are used. These units are truly international, which is a major advantage. Further, larger and smaller units are ordinarily related to the standard units in terms of powers of 10. Thus the kilometer is 1,000 m, while the centimeter is 0.01 m. Table 1.1 lists the prefixes which are used with metric units to indicate multiples and submultiples of standard units.

It is convenient to measure all quantities in mechanics in terms of three standards: one for length, one for mass, and one for time. The *mks system* of units is based on the choice of the *meter*, the *kilogram*, and the *second* as the basic quantities. The meter, kilogram, and second are known as the *fundamental units* of the mks system.

<   Many other systems of units have been devised. For example, the *cgs system* is based on the *centimeter* as the unit of length, the *gram* as the unit of mass, and the *second* as the unit of time. The *British absolute system* has as its fundamental units the *foot*, the *pound-mass*, and the *second*. It is not necessary that the three fundamental units of a system involve length, mass, and time. Indeed, as we shall see, the *British engineering system* is based on the *foot*, the *second*, and the *pound-force*.

1.7 Derived Units

All quantities in mechanics can be expressed in terms of the three *fundamental* units of any system of units. When a quantity is expressed in terms of a combination of the fundamental quantities, its units are referred to as *derived units*. For example, the units of area may be written as the square of units of length. Thus, we may express areas in square meters or square feet. Similarly, the dimensions of volume are lengths cubed—cubic meters, cubic feet, etc. Speed and density are examples of the many quantities in mechanics which are written in terms of derived units.

TABLE 1.1

Factor	Prefix*	Abbreviation	Examples
10^3	kilo-	k	kilogram (kg); kilometer (km)
10^6	mega- (or meg-)	M	megohm (MΩ); million electron volts (MeV)
10^{-2}	centi-	c	centimeter (cm)
10^{-3}	milli-	m	millimeter (mm); milligram (mg)
10^{-6}	micro-	μ	microgram (μg); micron (μ) = 10^{-6} m

* Other prefixes: deka- (10), hecto- (100), giga- (G = 10^9), terra- (T = 10^{12}), deci- (d = 0.1), nano- (n = 10^{-9}), and pica- (p = 10^{-12}).

Speed. The average speed of a body is defined as the ratio of the distance it travels to the time required to pass over that distance. Thus, speed is obtained by dividing a length by a time. Appropriate units of speed are meters per second, feet per second, miles per hour, etc. The speeds of ships and aircraft are often measured in *knots*. One knot is one nautical mile (6,080 ft) per hour.

Example A track star runs a measured mile in 3 min 56 sec. Find his average speed in feet per second.

$$\text{Average speed} = \frac{\text{distance}}{\text{time}} = \frac{5{,}280 \text{ ft}}{236 \text{ sec}}$$
$$= 22.4 \text{ ft/sec}$$

Density. The density of a body is defined as the ratio of its mass to its volume. Thus

$$d = \frac{m}{V} \qquad\qquad\qquad \text{1.1}$$

where d is the density, m the mass, and V the volume. Among the familiar units for density are kilograms per cubic meter, pounds mass per cubic foot, and grams per cubic centimeter.

Example A quantity of mercury has a mass of 2.05 kg and occupies a volume of 151 cm³. What is its density?

$$d = \frac{m}{V} = \frac{2.05 \text{ kg}}{151 \text{ cm}^3} = 0.0136 \text{ kg/cm}^3$$
$$= 13.6 \text{ g/cm}^3 = 13{,}600 \text{ kg/m}^3$$

Example Find the mass of air in a room which is 3.00 by 8.00 by 6.00 m. The density of the air is 1.29 kg/m³.

$$m = dV = 1.29 \text{ kg/m}^3 \times 144 \text{ m}^3 = 186 \text{ kg}$$

The term "density" is often used in conjunction with certain other words to suggest the amount of some quantity per given amount of some other quantity. For example, we use the term *population density* to describe number of people per unit area. In electricity the term *charge density* means the ratio of electric charge to volume, and *surface charge density* is the ratio of electric charge to surface area. The ratio of the weight of an object to its volume is called its *weight density*. The ratio of the mass of a rope to its length is sometimes called its *linear density*. Whenever the word density appears in this text in any sense other than that of mass per unit volume, it will be qualified by an additional word.

1.8 Units and Their Conversion

In the measurement of any physical quantity, the choice of units is ordinarily dictated by convenience and by the habits of the observer. In reporting any measurement, it is important to list not only the number of times the standard unit was included, but also to state what this standard unit is. For example, the height of a man might be 6.08 ft, 73.0 in., 2.03 yd, or 185 cm. The number which describes the height is quite meaningless unless the units which go with the number are known.

We live in a country where most of the everyday measurements are made in the English system, but much scientific work involves metric units. Since anyone who has to deal with scientific phenomena in the United States is essentially forced to use both British and metric units, it is important to be able to transform from one system to another.

It is convenient to convert a quantity from one unit to another in the form of the examples below. Note that one may cancel units just as though they were algebraic quantities. Note further that the factors by which one multiplies are all unity.

Example Convert 60.0 mi/hr to feet per second and meters per second.

$$60.0 \, \frac{\text{mi}}{\text{hr}} = 60.0 \, \frac{\text{mi}}{\text{hr}} \times \frac{1 \, \text{hr}}{3{,}600 \, \text{sec}} \times \frac{5{,}280 \, \text{ft}}{1 \, \text{mile}}$$

$$= \frac{60.0 \times 5{,}280}{3{,}600} \, \frac{\text{mi} \, \text{hr} \, \text{ft}}{\text{hr} \, \text{sec} \, \text{mi}} = 88.0 \, \frac{\text{ft}}{\text{sec}}$$

$$= 88.0 \, \frac{\text{ft}}{\text{sec}} \times \frac{0.3048 \, \text{m}}{1 \, \text{ft}} = 26.8 \, \frac{\text{m}}{\text{sec}}$$

Example The density of aluminum is 2,699 kg/m³. Convert this density to grams per cubic centimeter and to pounds mass per cubic foot.

$$2{,}699 \, \frac{\text{kg}}{\text{m}^3} = 2{,}699 \, \frac{\text{kg}}{\text{m}^3} \times \frac{1 \, \text{m}^3}{(100 \, \text{cm})^3} \times \frac{1{,}000 \, \text{g}}{1 \, \text{kg}}$$

$$= 2.699 \, \frac{\text{g}}{\text{cm}^3}$$

$$2{,}699 \, \frac{\text{kg}}{\text{m}^3} = 2{,}699 \, \frac{\text{kg}}{\text{m}^3} \times \frac{1 \, \text{lbm}}{0.4536 \, \text{kg}} \times \frac{(0.3048 \, \text{m})^3}{1 \, \text{ft}^3}$$

$$= 168.5 \, \frac{\text{lbm}}{\text{ft}^3}$$

1.9 Measurement of Angles

Degrees, minutes, and seconds are familiar units in which angles are measured. A degree is the angle subtended at the center of a circle by an arc of length 1/360 of the circumference of the circle (Fig. 1.3). A minute is 1/60 of a degree, and a second is 1/60 of a minute.

To measure the angle turned through by a rotating wheel, we are likely to use the *revolution*. The angle subtended by the full circumference is one revolution.

Still another unit which is often convenient for measuring angles is the *radian*. *A radian is the angle subtended at the center of a circle by an arc of length equal to the radius.* Thus, the angle AOC of Figure 1.3 is 1 radian, since the arc length AC is equal in length to radius OA.

The angle AOB of Figure 1.3 is represented by θ; in radians it is s (the length of arc AB) divided by the radius R:

$$\theta = \frac{s}{R} \qquad\qquad 1.2$$

The angle θ is the ratio of two lengths; consequently it is *dimensionless.* Since the circumference of a circle is 2π times the radius, it follows that there are 2π radians in a revolution. Hence,

$360° = 2\pi$ radians = 1 revolution

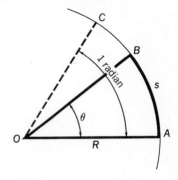

FIGURE 1.3

The radian measure of the angle θ is the arc length AB divided by the radius OA. The arc AC is equal in length to the radius OA, so angle AOC is 1 radian.

1.10 Force

One of the important concepts in physics is that of force. For the moment, we may think of a force as a push or a pull exerted upon some object. The most familiar forces are those which we experience through our own muscular activities. More generally, a force is an action, exerted by one body on another, that tends to change the state of motion of the body acted upon. Thus, when a man throws a baseball, he exerts a force upon it which changes its state of motion. We shall later define force explicitly in terms of effects on the motions of objects.

We know that every body near the surface of the earth is pulled toward the earth by gravitational attraction, which we shall now use to define a unit of force. *The pound-force (lb) is the net gravitational pull of the earth on a standard one-pound mass (lbm) at a specified location* (essentially at mean sea level, 45° north latitude). As we shall see in Chap. 6, the pound-force, the foot, and the second are the fundamental units of the *British engineering system* of units. The pound-force is called a *gravitational* unit because it is defined in terms of the *pull of the earth on a standard mass at a specified location.*

The basic force unit for the mks system is the *newton,* which is properly defined (Sec. 6.4) in terms of its effect on the motion of a one-kilogram mass in a manner which is *independent of the location of this mass.* For this reason it is called an *absolute* unit of force. For the moment it is sufficient to observe that 1 newton = 0.2248 lb.

< The net pull of the earth, at our specified location, on a standard kilogram mass is known as the *kilogram-weight* (1 kg-wt = 9.807 newtons). Although the kilogram-weight is sometimes a convenient force unit, it is not the basic one for any widely adopted system of units. We shall use the *newton* as our force unit for the *metric* system.

FIGURE 1.4

The weight of a body is equal and opposite to the force required to hold the body at rest against the net gravitational pull on it.

Spring balance

Weight, mg

1.11 Weight and Mass

The weight of an object is defined as the net gravitational force of attraction acting on the object (Fig. 1.4). Its value depends on the location. If a good spring balance were calibrated at 45° north latitude and mean sea level and then transported to various points on the earth's surface, it would be found that the pull of the earth on a 1-lb mass would be more than a 1-lb force at the North Pole, but less than 1 lb at the equator or on top of a high mountain. The weight of a body is slightly different on top of Pike's Peak than in New York City. These changes in weight are not large, but they can be detected readily with sensitive instruments. If an object which weighs 6 lb on the earth were taken to the moon, its weight there would be only 1 lb. In principle, we could reduce the weight of a body almost to zero by taking it sufficiently far off in space, as we shall see in Chap. 9.

On the other hand, the mass of a body at rest is the same at all points in the universe. This is one reason that the concept of mass is so important in physics. It is sometimes said that the mass of a body is the "quantity of matter in the body," a property of the body which does not change as long as its speed is negligible compared with the speed of light. An object has mass whether or not it is near enough to the earth to have observable weight. The mass of a body reveals itself as *inertia*—the tendency of matter to resist any change in its state of motion. This important attribute of mass is discussed further in Chap. 6.

The larger the mass of a body, the harder the earth pulls on it. Indeed, the weight of a body at any place is directly proportional to its mass, and the mass of a body is often determined by comparing the pull of the earth on it with the pull on a standard mass at the same place. An unfortunate consequence is that the word "weight" is frequently used improperly in place of mass. For example, an analytical balance typically determines the mass of the unknown in terms of standard masses, yet we carelessly refer to this operation as "weighing" and call the result the "weight" of the unknown.

Questions

1. What are some of the more important characteristics of a physical standard unit?

2. What is your height in meters? Your mass in kilograms?

3. What advantages does the new international standard of length have over the platinum-iridium bar which it replaced? What advantages did the meter bar have over the new standard?

4. What advantages would accrue to the nation if the United States were to adopt the metric system for general commercial and governmental use? What are the disadvantages of abandoning the use of British units of length and force?

5. The sidereal day, widely used by astronomers, is the time interval between two successive passages of a star across the meridian. How many sidereal days are there in one year? Show that the length of a sidereal day is 84,164 sec.

6. In what sense is it true that the earth makes one rotation each 24 hr? In what sense is it false?

7. What repetitive phenomena could serve as reasonable time standards?

Problems

Unless otherwise specified, the numerics stated in the problems should be regarded as valid to as many significant figures as needed. In general, slide-rule accuracy is all that is desired; answers should be given to three (or at most four) significant figures.

1. Mount McKinley is the highest mountain in North America, with an elevation of 6.19 km. Find its altitude in feet. *Ans.* 20,300 ft

2. The highest point in the continental United States is Mount Whitney, with an altitude of 4.4184 km above sea level. Find its altitude in feet.

3. The elevation of Pike's Peak is 14,100 ft above sea level. What is its elevation in meters? *Ans.* 4,300 m

4. The Washington Monument is 169 m high. Find its height in feet.

5. The pages of a 750-page book have a total thickness of 1.50 in. Find the average thickness of a single sheet in microns (1 μ = 10^{-6} m). *Ans.* 102

6. The meter was selected originally as 1/10,000,000 of the distance from the North Pole to the equator along the quadrant of the earth's surface through Paris. Assuming that the earth is spherical, find the radius of the earth in kilometers and in miles.

7. A jet airplane is moving at a speed of 600 mi/hr. Find its speed in feet per second and in meters per second. *Ans.* 880 ft/sec; 268 m/sec

8. The speed of sound in air is 330 m/sec. Find the speed in miles per hour and in feet per second.

9. A swimmer wins the 100-m event with a time of 50 sec. Find his speed in miles per hour and in feet per second. *Ans.* 4.47 mi/hr; 6.56 ft/sec

10. Solid carbon dioxide has a density of 1,530 kg/m^3. What volume would be occupied by 20 cm^3 after evaporation to gas with a density of 1.9 kg/m^3?

11. The gasoline tank of an automobile holds 20.0 gal. If 1 gal is 231 in.^{3}, find the volume of the tank in cubic feet and in cubic meters. *Ans.* 2.67 ft^3; 0.0757 m^3

12. A curve on a scenic highway is 650 ft long and subtends an angle of 44° at the center of the circle of which it is a part. What is the radius of the curve?

13. A circle is 0.400 m in radius. How many radians are subtended at its center by an arc of length 0.300 m? How many degrees? *Ans.* 0.750 radian; 43°

14. The angle subtended by the sun's diameter at the surface of the earth is 0.5°. Find the approximate radius of the sun if it is at a distance of 93,000,000 miles from the earth. The moon subtends essentially the same angle at the earth. What is the approximate radius of the moon if it is 236,000 miles away?

15. In going around a sharp curve, the driver of an automobile turns the steering wheel through an angle of 6.0 radians. Through how many degrees did it turn? Through how many revolutions? If the wheel has a radius of 18 cm, through what distance did a point on the outer edge of the wheel move? *Ans.* 344°; 0.954 rev; 1.08 m

16. The effective radius of the wheel of an automobile is 14 in. Find the angle in radians through which the wheel rotates in going a distance of 1 mile.

17. A rectangular lot has sides 75 ft and 100 ft long. Find the area in square meters. *Ans.* 697 m^2

18. A circle has a diameter of 4 ft. What is its area in square meters? $2.92 \, m^2$

19. A mountain peak 15 km (measured horizontally) away from the observer is sighted from a telescope at an elevation of 400 m above sea level. If the line of sight makes an angle of 12° with the horizontal, find the height of the peak above sea level.

Ans. 3.59 km

20. If one gallon is 231 in.³, find the volume in gallons of an aquarium of dimensions 3 by 2 by 1.5 ft. If 1 ft³ of water weighs 62.4 lb, what weight of water does the tank hold when full?

21. A lake has an area of 5×10^8 m². A layer of water 5 mm thick evaporates from this lake over a hot weekend. What mass of water was evaporated in this period?

Ans. 25×10^8 kg

22. How many tons of water fall on 1 acre (640 acres = 1 square mile) of land during a 1-in. rain if 1 ft³ of water weighs 62.4 lb?

23. An irregular crystal of quartz has a mass of 39.5 g. When it is submerged in water in a test tube of radius 1.5 cm, the water level is observed to rise 2.1 cm. Find the density of the quartz crystal.   *Ans.* 2,660 kg/m³

24. To determine the width of a canyon to be spanned by a horizontal bridge, a distance *AB* of 300 ft is marked off parallel to one edge of the canyon. Point *C* on the opposite side of the canyon is sighted from points *A* and *B*. If *AC* is perpendicular to *AB*, and *BC* makes an angle of 27° with *AB*, what is the width of the canyon?

25. In surveying for a straight road to traverse rough terrain between points *A* and *B* by a series of cuts and fills, a horizontal base line *AC* 200 ft long is laid out. A transit shows that *AB* makes an angle of 38° with *AC*, while *CB* makes an angle of 80° with *CA*. Determine the distance *AB*.   *Ans.* 223 ft

CHAPTER 2 *In the first chapter we learned that quantitative expressions for all the measurable quantities of mechanics can be written in terms of fundamental units of length, time, and mass. For many of the quantities which involve length, such as displacement, velocity, and force, the direction, as well as the magnitude, is important. To add such* vector *quantities we must take appropriate account of the directions, thereby using a form of geometrical addition which we develop and discuss in this chapter.*

Vector Quantities

2.1 Displacement

When a body moves from one location to another, it is said to undergo a *displacement*. Suppose, for example, that a helicopter takes off, flies due east 12 miles, and lands. It has undergone a displacement of 12 miles east. If the helicopter takes off again and flies 25 miles in a straight line before landing, how far is it from its original starting point? A specific answer to this question cannot be given until we have one *additional* piece of information: the direction of this second displacement. From the information now available we can only be sure that the helicopter lies somewhere on a circle with center at B and a radius of 25 miles (Fig. 2.1). *A displacement is completely specified only when we state both its magnitude and direction.* The magnitude consists of a numeral and a unit.

If the second displacement is in the same direction as the first, the helicopter is at point C, and the total displacement is 37 miles east. If the second displacement is in the direction opposite to the displacement AB, the helicopter is at D, and the displacement is 13 miles west. If the displacement is due north, the helicopter is at E, and its distance from the starting point is $R = \sqrt{(25)^2 + (12)^2}$ miles = 28 miles.

Let us now specify the 25-mile displacement to be at an angle of 53°N of E (Fig. 2.2). In our figure we represent each displacement with an arrow pointed in the direction of the displacement and of length proportional to the displacement. One possible way of determining the distance from the starting point to the final position is by making a scaled drawing and measuring the distance with a ruler. However, in most cases it is easier to solve a problem of this type analytically. We observe that the displacement BP of 25 miles at an angle of 53°N of E takes the helicopter a distance BG to the east and a distance GP to the north. By definition (see Mathematical For-

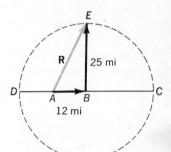

FIGURE 2.1
Successive displacements from point A of 12 miles east and 25 miles in an arbitrary direction could bring a helicopter to any point on the circle DEC.

FIGURE 2.2
Resultant of the displacements 12 miles east and 25 miles 53°N of E is the vector **R**.

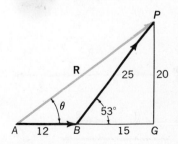

mulas in Appendix) we know that *in any right triangle the sine of an angle is the ratio of the side opposite the angle to the hypotenuse,* while *the cosine is the ratio of the side adjacent to the angle to the hypotenuse.* (A table of sines and cosines may be found in the Appendix.) Therefore $BG/25 = \cos 53° = 0.6$, and $BG = 15$ miles. Similarly $GP/25 = \sin 53° = 0.8$, from which $GP = 20$ miles. Thus, a displacement of 25 miles at an angle of $53°$N of E is equivalent to a displacement of 15 miles east plus a displacement of 20 miles north. We can, if we like, replace our 25-mile displacement with the displacements BG and GP. We observe from Figure 2.2 that the helicopter is now 27 miles east of its original starting point and 20 miles north. The distance AP is therefore given by

$$AP = \sqrt{(27)^2 + (20)^2} \text{ miles} = 34 \text{ miles}$$

From the right triangle AGP we see that $\sin \theta = 20/34 = 0.59$, from which $\theta = 36°$.

2.2 Vectors and Scalars

Physical quantities which have both magnitude and direction and which add like displacements are called vector quantities. A vector quantity can be represented graphically by a directed line segment (arrow) or "line vector." A knowledge of both the magnitude and the direction of a vector quantity is required for its complete description. Vectors in different directions cannot be added, subtracted, multiplied, or divided by the methods of ordinary arithmetic; they must be treated by geometrical techniques. In this chapter we deal with three types of vector quantities: displacements, velocities, and forces. In later chapters, many more vector quantities such as acceleration, momentum, torque, angular velocity, and angular acceleration are introduced.

There are many quantities in physics, such as mass, time, and volume, which have only magnitude and which can be completely specified by a numeral and a dimension. They do not involve any idea of direction. Such quantities are called *scalars.* They obey the ordinary laws of addition, subtraction, multiplication, and division. If 10 gal of gasoline are added to a tank which originally contained 4 gal, the tank contains 14 gal. If a 10-g mass is removed from the pan of a balance which holds 80 g, the mass remaining on the pan in 70 g. These are illustrations of the addition and subtraction of *scalar quantities.*

(a)

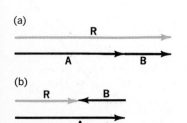

(b)

FIGURE 2.3
Resultant of two displacements:
(*a*) in the same direction,
(*b*) in opposite directions.

FIGURE 2.4
Resultant of two vectors at right angles to one another.
Note that $\mathbf{R} = \mathbf{A} + \mathbf{B} = \mathbf{B} + \mathbf{A}.$

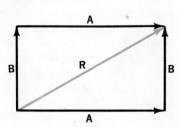

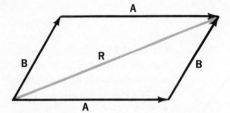

FIGURE 2.5
Resultant of two vectors not at right angles to one another.
$\mathbf{R} = \mathbf{A} + \mathbf{B} = \mathbf{B} + \mathbf{A}.$

Vectors are often denoted in print by boldface type, such as **F** for force, **v** for velocity, etc. Whenever a boldface symbol is used in text or in a formula, it indicates that direction as well as magnitude is of importance. Italic type is used for scalar quantities and for the magnitudes of vectors.

2.3 The Graphical Addition of Vectors

A vector quantity can be represented by a directed line segment or "arrow" pointed in the direction of the vector, of length proportional to the magnitude of the vector. To add two vectors **A** and **B,** we represent each of them with an arrow of scaled length and add them (Figs. 2.3 to 2.5) by placing the tail of the second arrow at the point of the first. Alternatively, we might start with the second vector and add the first, as shown in Figures 2.4 and 2.5. This gives rise to the "vector parallelogram." The vector sum is given by the diagonal **R**. If the graphical representation of the vectors **A** and **B** is performed carefully, the resultant vector **R** can be measured with considerable accuracy. It is customary to call the result of vector addition the *resultant* of the vectors, rather than the sum, to emphasize the geometrical nature of the addition.

To subtract one vector from another, we need only reverse the direction of the vector we wish to subtract and add this negative vector to the first. This is shown schematically in Figure 2.6*a*, where **D** = **A** − **B.** An alternative way of subtracting **B** from **A** is to find that vector **D** which must be added to **B** to give **A** (Fig. 2.6*b*), since **B** + **D** = **A** if **D** = **A** − **B.**

There is no limit to the number of vectors which may be added graphically. If we have four vectors to add together, we may add the third vector to the resultant of the first two, and the fourth vector to the resultant of the first three. For example, suppose that an object has four forces acting upon it: 8 lb east, 5 lb 30° N of E, 7 lb 37° W of

(a)   (b)

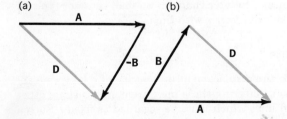

FIGURE 2.6
Subtraction of vector **B** from vector **A** requires: (*a*) adding −**B** to **A,** or (*b*) finding the vector that must be added to **B** to give **A.**

(a)

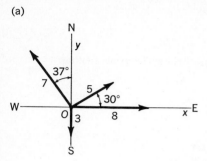

(b)

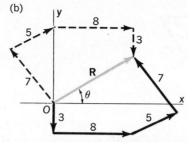

FIGURE 2.7

Independence of order of vector addition is shown by four forces acting upon a body at O in (a), and their resultant in (b).

N, and 3 lb due south, as shown in Figure 2.7. The resultant is given by the vector **R**. The order in which the vectors are added makes no difference in determining the resultant. We shall calculate the value of **R** in Sec. 2.7.

2.4 Velocity

Suppose you take an automobile ride. The distance you travel, as read by the odometer, is a scalar quantity. If at the end of 3 hr you have traveled a distance of 150 miles, your average speed has been 50 mi/hr. Suppose that at this point you are 45 miles due east of your starting point (Fig. 2.8). Then your displacement is 45 miles east. *Displacement* is a vector quantity. It is not necessarily related in any simple way to the total *distance* traversed. The *average velocity* during the trip is *the ratio of the displacement to the time.* In this case the average velocity is 15 mi/hr east. Note that *velocity is a vector quantity,* while *speed is a scalar.* When you return to your starting point, the average *velocity* is zero since the *displacement* is zero; the average speed is very different from zero.

FIGURE 2.8

Displacement is a vector quantity, distance a scalar quantity.

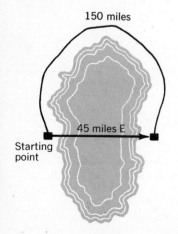

150 miles

45 miles E

Starting point

Example On a transcontinental trip a family begins to drive at 6 A.M. and stops at 5 P.M. In this period the car goes 495 miles and is 350 airline miles southwest of its starting point. Find the average speed and average velocity for the day.

$$\text{Average speed} = \frac{\text{distance}}{\text{time}} = \frac{495 \text{ mi}}{11.0 \text{ hr}} = 45 \text{ mi/hr}$$

$$\mathbf{v}_{av} = \frac{\text{displacement}}{\text{time}} = \frac{350 \text{ mi southwest}}{11.0 \text{ hr}} = 31.8 \text{ mi/hr southwest}$$

In this chapter we shall add velocities, confining ourselves to cases in which the velocity is *uniform* (i.e., in which equal displacements are traversed in equal times). In later chapters we shall consider types of motion in which the velocity varies with time.

2.5 Frame of Reference

Whenever we refer to the displacement or velocity of a body, we are always, by implication, referring these measurements to some other body or framework of lines which must be regarded as fixed. Such a framework is called the *frame of reference*. Some problems can be greatly simplified by the choice of a suitable frame of reference.

With few exceptions we refer quantities to a system of axes fixed on the earth. When we say an object is at rest, we ordinarily mean it is at rest relative to the earth. Relative to the sun it is moving through space at a speed of 19 mi/sec by virtue of the orbital motion of the earth (and at a speed which depends on latitude because of the spin of the earth on its axis). A passenger seated in a train traveling 60 mi/hr is at rest relative to the car and the other passengers. If he walks forward in the car with a speed of 4 mi/hr, his speed relative to the earth is 64 mi/hr.

It is meaningless to speak of the "absolute" position of a body in space or to assign to the body an "absolute" velocity. Any position vector or velocity vector must be specified relative to some frame of reference.

In general, if the velocity of a body B relative to one frame of reference is $\mathbf{v}_{B1}$, its velocity relative to a second frame $\mathbf{v}_{B2}$ is given by the vector equation

$$\mathbf{v}_{B2} = \mathbf{v}_{B1} + \mathbf{v}_{12} \qquad\qquad 2.1$$

where $\mathbf{v}_{12}$ is the velocity of the first frame relative to the second. For example, if an airplane is flying with a velocity $\mathbf{v}_{PA}$ relative to the air, and the air has a velocity $\mathbf{v}_{AG}$ relative to the ground, the velocity $\mathbf{v}_{PG}$ of the plane relative to the ground is given by

$$\mathbf{v}_{PG} = \mathbf{v}_{PA} + \mathbf{v}_{AG} \qquad\qquad 2.1a$$

If $\mathbf{v}_{PA}$ is 300 mi/hr east and $\mathbf{v}_{AG}$ is 50 mi/hr east, $\mathbf{v}_{PG} = 350$ mi/hr east. If $\mathbf{v}_{AG}$ is 50 mi/hr west, $\mathbf{v}_{PG}$ is 250 mi/hr east.

In general, if we have three bodies A, B, and C, and we let $\mathbf{v}_{AB}$ represent the velocity of A relative to B, and so forth, then $\mathbf{v}_{AC} = \mathbf{v}_{AB} + \mathbf{v}_{BC}$. (Note that we add the vectors with the two B's adjoining. This is an example of what is sometimes called the *domino rule* of vector addition.) If we want the velocity of C relative to B, we observe that $\mathbf{v}_{CB} = \mathbf{v}_{CA} + \mathbf{v}_{AB}$. The same rule applies to other vector quantities.

2.6 Rectangular Components of a Vector

Consider a vector $\mathbf{V}$, 5 units in length and directed at an angle of 37°N of E (Fig. 2.9). This displacement is equivalent to displacements of 4 units east and 3 units north. In any problem in which this 5-unit vector occurs, we may replace it with vectors of 4 units east and 3 units north. These two vectors, which are perpendicular to each other, are called the *rectangular components* of the 5-unit vector. By replacing a vector with its rectangular components, we can always reduce any problem in vector addition to a situation in which we are dealing with component vectors, all of which lie either along one line or perpendicular to this line. Thus, the replacement of a vector by suitable components results in the possibility of handling vector additions with a minimum of mathematical complexity.

If we wish to obtain the rectangular components of a vector in any

FIGURE 2.9

Resolution of a vector $\mathbf{V}$ into its rectangular components.

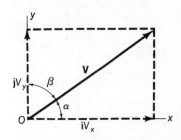

mutually perpendicular directions, we proceed as follows: We place the origin of a rectangular coordinate system at the tail of the vector which we wish to resolve and then drop perpendiculars from the point of the vector to each of the coordinate axes. *The magnitude of the rectangular component in any direction is given by the magnitude of the vector multiplied by the cosine of the angle between the vector and the axis along which we seek the component.*

The vector **V** of Figure 2.9 is the resultant of a vector in the x direction of magnitude V_x and one in the y direction of magnitude V_y. If we let **i**, **j**, and **k** represent vectors of unit length in the x, y, and z directions, respectively, we may write the vector equation

$$\mathbf{V} = \mathbf{i}V_x + \mathbf{j}V_y + \mathbf{k}V_z$$

where $V_x = V \cos \alpha$, $V_y = V \cos \beta$, and $V_z = V \cos \gamma$, γ being the angle between **V** and the z axis. In this text we shall ordinarily confine our attention to problems in which we are concerned with only x and y components.

> **Example** A 50-lb weight rests on an inclined plane (Fig. 2.10) making an angle of 30° with the horizontal. Find the components of the weight parallel and perpendicular to the plane.
>
> We place the origin of a system of axes at the body, with the x axis parallel to the plane. Next we drop perpendiculars from the end of the **W** vector to find the lengths of D and N.
>
> $D = W \cos \alpha = W \sin \theta = 50 \text{ lb} \sin 30° = 25 \text{ lb}$
> $N = W \cos \theta = 50 \text{ lb} \cos 30° = 43.3 \text{ lb}$

< Consider a canalboat as indicated in Figure 2.11, and let a cable pull on it in the direction BC. This force produces two distinct effects on the boat. It moves the boat forward, and it pulls it to the bank. Two separate forces BA and BD might have been applied with the same result. The two forces that would produce the same effect as BC are the components of BC. Similarly, the velocity of the wind propelling a sailboat may be resolved into components perpendicular and parallel to the sail; the force perpendicular to the sail is then resolved into components perpendicular and parallel to the axis of the boat. The component perpendicular to the axis produces little effect because of the shape of the boat.

FIGURE 2.10

Resolution of the weight of an object into components parallel to and perpendicular to an inclined plane.

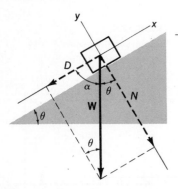

2.7 The Analytical ___ion of Vectors

In adding vectors analytically, it is desirable first to make a rough sketch of the vectors to be added. Then we choose a set of mutually perpendicular axes which appear to be convenient for the problem in question. Usually, this involves a choice of the east-west and north-south axes or vertical and horizontal axes. However, in some cases it may be more convenient to choose a set of mutually perpendicular axes which are oriented in some special way, as in Figure 2.10. Next,

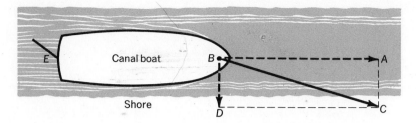

FIGURE 2.11
Components of the force *BC* exerted on a canalboat by a cable.

we find the components of all the vectors along the axes chosen. We then ignore the vectors and work only with the components. We can readily add together all the vector components whose arrows are in the direction of each of the axes, and then find their resultant by the use of the pythagorean theorem.

In general, if we are adding vectors **A**, **B**, and **C**, where $\mathbf{A} = \mathbf{i}A_x + \mathbf{j}A_y$, and so forth, the resultant **R** is given by

$$\mathbf{R} = \mathbf{A} + \mathbf{B} + \mathbf{C}$$
$$= \mathbf{i}A_x + \mathbf{j}A_y + \mathbf{i}B_x + \mathbf{j}B_y + \mathbf{i}C_x + \mathbf{j}C_y$$
$$= \mathbf{i}(A_x + B_x + C_x) + \mathbf{j}(A_y + B_y + C_y)$$

Thus each component of **R** has magnitude equal to the sum of the corresponding components of the vectors added. In dealing with the components of vectors along any given axis, we select one direction as positive; a component in the opposite direction is then assigned a negative sign. Thus, if we have a north-south axis and elect to call north the positive direction, a component of 5 miles southward is written as -5 mi north.

Example Find the resultant of the four forces shown in Figure 2.7.

First we find the x (east) and y (north) components of each force. It is convenient to list them in a table as shown. For the 5-lb force the x component is (5 lb) cos 30° = 4.33 lb, and the y component in pounds is 5 sin 30° = 2.50. For the 7-lb force the x (east) component is (-7 lb) sin 37° $= -4.20$ lb, and the y component is (7 lb) cos 37° = 5.60 lb. In calculating these components we have tacitly assumed that the forces involved were 5.00 and 7.00 lb, i.e., that they were known to three significant figures at least. From the

	Components	
Force, lb	x(east)	y(north)
8 E	8.00	0
5 30°N of E	4.33	2.50
7 37°W of N	−4.20	5.60
3 S	0	−3.00
R	8.13	5.10

table we see that the components of the resultant are 8.13 lb east and 5.10 lb north. The resultant R is given by

$$R = \sqrt{(8.13)^2 + (5.10)^2} \text{ lb} = \sqrt{92.1} \text{ lb} = 9.60 \text{ lb}$$

and the angle between R and the x axis is given by

$$\sin \theta = \frac{5.10}{9.60} = 0.53$$

so that $\theta = 32°\text{N of E.}$

Example In a football game two linemen are assigned to open a hole by blocking a guard. One of them exerts a force of 150 lb straight toward the goal line (Fig. 2.12), and the other exerts a force of 100 lb at an angle of 60° with the goal line. Find the resultant force.

The x component of the 100-lb force is $(100 \text{ lb}) \sin 60° = 86.6 \text{ lb}$. The y component is $(100 \text{ lb}) \cos 60° = 50.0 \text{ lb}$. The net force toward the goal line is then 236.6 lb, while the net force parallel to the goal line is 50.0 lb. The resultant is

$$R = \sqrt{(237)^2 + (50.0)^2} \text{ lb} = \sqrt{58,500} \text{ lb} = 242 \text{ lb}$$

and the angle θ is given by $\sin \theta = 50.0/242 = 0.207$, so that $\theta = 12°$.

Example An airplane cruises at a speed of 300 mi/hr relative to the surrounding air. If the wind is blowing from the southwest at 40 mi/hr, find the direction in which the pilot must point the airplane if he wishes to go due east. What is the velocity of the airplane relative to the ground?

The pilot must fly at an angle θ (Fig. 2.13) south of east such that the southward component of $\mathbf{V}_{PA}$ (velocity of plane relative to air) is exactly equal to the northward component of $\mathbf{V}_{AG}$ (velocity of air relative to ground).

$$300 \sin \theta = 40 \cos 45° = 28.3$$

$$\sin \theta = \frac{28.3}{300} = 0.0943$$

$$\theta = 5°25'\text{S of E}$$

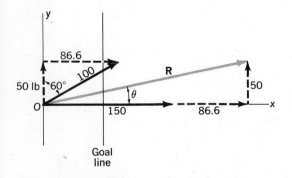

FIGURE 2.12
Finding the resultant force **R** by finding its components parallel to and perpendicular to the goal line.

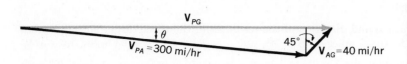

FIGURE 2.13
Flying due east relative to the ground when the wind is blowing from the southwest is accomplished by flying at an angle θ south of east relative to the air.

The velocity $\mathbf{V}_{PG}$ of the airplane relative to the ground is

$$\mathbf{V}_{PG} = (300 \cos \theta + 40 \sin 45°) \text{ mi/hr east}$$
$$= (299 + 28.3) \text{ mi/hr east} = 327 \text{ mi/hr east}$$

Questions

1. Can the vector sum of two unequal forces be zero? Of three unequal forces?

2. Does the odometer of an automobile measure displacement? If not, what does it measure?

3. An airplane has an airspeed of 300 mi/hr, and the wind is blowing with a speed of 50 mi/hr. What is the maximum possible speed of the plane relative to the ground? The minimum possible speed? Could the speed relative to the ground also be 300 mi/hr? If so, explain how.

4. Why does an airplane land and take off into the wind? When a plane is landing on an aircraft carrier, what is the most favorable direction of carrier and plane relative to the wind and to each other? Why?

5. With the aid of a figure explain how an iceboat can sail faster than 10 mi/hr in a 10-mi/hr breeze. What limits the speed which the boat can attain?

Problems

1. An airplane flies 125 miles in a direction 35°E of N. Find the components of its displacement toward the north and toward the east.   *Ans.* 102 miles; 71.8 miles

2. Calculate the horizontal and vertical components of a vector which has a magnitude of 40 ft and makes an angle of 15° with the horizontal.

3. An automobile is driven 7 miles east and then 24 miles north in going from one city to another. How far apart are the two cities?   *Ans.* 25 miles

4. Find the magnitude of the single displacement that is equivalent to successive displacements of 30 m and 50 m, the direction of the second displacement being perpendicular to that of the first.

5. A body is displaced 5 ft east and 12 ft south. What are the magnitude and direction of the resultant displacement?   *Ans.* 13 ft; 22.6°E of S

6. Two forces of 15 lb and 5 lb, with an angle of 90° between them, act on a body. What are the magnitude and direction, with respect to the 15-lb force, of the resultant?

7. A helicopter carrying mail flies 15 miles due north and lands. It then flies 20 miles in a direction 30°N of E. Find (*a*) how far north the helicopter is from its original starting point and (*b*) the magnitude and direction of its resultant displacement.

Ans. 25 miles; 30.4 miles; 35°E of N

8. Find the resultant of the following four displacements: 6 m east, 4 m south, 2 m west, and 3 m south.

9. Find the magnitude and direction of the resultant of the three displacements 3 miles west, 2 miles north, and 5 miles 40°S of W. *Ans.* 6.94 miles; 10°S of W

10. A man pushes along the handle of a lawn mower which makes an angle of 35° with the horizontal ground. One component of the 30-lb force he exerts drives the lawn mower along; another component pushes the lawn mower against the ground. Calculate the force components parallel and perpendicular to the ground.

11. An automobile is driven 15 km east, then 6 km north, and then 7 km west in 20 min. Determine the distance traveled, the displacement, the average speed, and the average velocity. *Ans.* 28 km; 10 km 37°N of E; 84 km/hr; 30 km/hr 37°N of E

12. A boy walks 1,000 m west, 1,500 m south, and then 500 m east in 30 min. Determine the distance traveled, the displacement, the average speed, and the average velocity.

13. Two helicopters take off from the same landing area. One proceeds 5 miles 30°S of W; the second flies 9 miles 45°S of E. Find the displacement of the second helicopter relative to the first. *Ans.* 11.4 miles 20°S of E

14. The current in a river flows north at a rate of 2 mi/hr. A man rows a boat west at a rate of 4 mi/hr relative to the water. Find the speed of the boat relative to the land.

15. A ferryboat goes straight across a river in which there is a current of 5 km/hr. If the speed of the boat relative to the water is 10 km/hr, find the direction in which it is pointed. What is its velocity relative to the earth? *Ans.* 30° upstream; 8.66 km/hr

16. A boat which has a speed of 8 mi/hr crosses a river in which the current is 2 mi/hr. At what angle must the boat be headed to land at a point directly opposite its starting point? What is the speed of the boat relative to the ground?

17. An airplane has a velocity of 100 knots 40°S of E relative to the air. If the wind has a velocity of 20 knots 60°N of E, find the velocity of the airplane relative to the ground. *Ans.* 98.5 knots 28.5°S of E

18. A helicopter has a velocity relative to the air of 50 knots 25°N of W. The velocity of the wind is 20 knots from west to east. Find the velocity of the helicopter relative to the ground.

19. Three football players participating simultaneously in a tackle exert the following forces on the ball carrier: 80 lb north, 100 lb 20°N of E, and 120 lb 35°W of N. Find the resultant of these forces. *Ans.* 214 lb 7°E of N

20. Find the resultant of the following three forces: a force of 60 lb making an angle of 30° with the +x axis, a force of 30 lb making an angle of 135° with the +x axis, and a force of 20 lb making an angle of 240° with the +x axis.

21. An airplane with an air speed of 200 mi/hr is to fly due east. The wind has a speed of 50 mi/hr from 40°N of E. In what direction should the aircraft be pointed? What is the ground speed? *Ans.* 9.3°N of E; 159 mi/hr

22. The pilot of an airplane is trying to keep on a beam toward an airport due east. The air speed of this plane is 200 mi/hr. If the wind is blowing from the north at 30 mi/hr, in what direction must he head the plane? Find the speed relative to the ground.

23. A steamboat (see accompanying figure) is moving eastward with a speed of

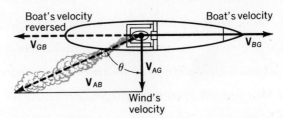

15 km/hr relative to the earth. The wind is blowing from north to south with a speed of 10 km/hr. Find the velocity of the smoke relative to the boat.

Ans. 18 km/hr 56°W of S

24. A steamboat (see accompanying figure) is moving eastward with a speed of 20 mi/hr. The wind is blowing from the north with a speed of 15 mi/hr. Find the velocity of the smoke relative to the boat.

25. A ball is thrown from a moving car with a velocity relative to the car of 40 ft/sec perpendicular to the direction of the car's motion. If the speed of the car is 60 ft/sec, find the velocity of the ball relative to the ground.

Ans. 72 ft/sec at 34° to car's velocity

26. A rope attached to a sled makes an angle of 40° with the ground. With what force must the rope be pulled to produce a horizontal component of 100 newtons? What will then be the vertical component of the force?

27. A boat moves east at a speed of 15 km/hr. The wind is blowing from the northwest at 10 km/hr. To an observer on the boat in what direction does the trail of smoke from the boat lie? What is the speed of the smoke relative to the boat?

Ans. 42°S of W; 10.6 km/hr

28. The velocity of an aircraft relative to the air is 360 mi/hr north. The wind is blowing 50 mi/hr from the south and west with the wind velocity making an angle of 37° with north. Find the velocity of the aircraft relative to the ground.

29. Two trains traveling toward each other leave stations at different times. One train travels at a speed of 60 mi/hr, the other at a speed of 50 mi/hr. The stations are 80 miles apart. How much later should the faster train start in order that the two trains meet halfway between the stations? *Ans.* 8 min

30. Show that if ϕ is the angle between two vectors **A** and **B** when they are placed tail to tail, the magnitude of their resultant is given by $R = \sqrt{A^2 + B^2 + 2AB \cos \phi}$. Show also that the angle θ between **A** and **R** is given by $\tan \theta = (B \sin \phi)/(A + B \cos \phi)$.

CHAPTER 3 *Now that we know how to find the resultant of two or more vector quantities, we are ready to consider the simultaneous action of several forces on a body. Our ultimate objective is to learn how to predict the future motion of any body subject to a known system of forces, provided we know the present position and velocity of the body. At first we consider only the case in which the body remains at rest or moves with constant velocity, reserving cases in which the velocity changes for Chap. 6.*

Systems of Forces

3.1 Force and Motion

FIGURE 3.1
Equilibrium occurs (*a*) for the string of negligible weight when the upward pull of the ceiling is equal and opposite to the downward pull of the ball, and (*b*) for the ball when the upward pull of the string is equal and opposite to its weight.

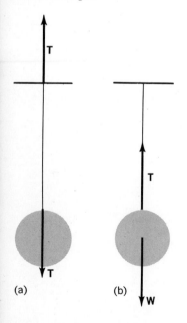

(a)   (b)

The idea of a force as a push or pull is a familiar one. From our everyday experience we know that we must exert forces on bodies whenever we wish to change their state of motion. It is our objective to obtain an understanding of the quantitative relationships between forces and motions, a subject which is called *dynamics*. But first it is desirable that we examine the conditions which must be satisfied in order that a body be at *rest*. This study is known as *statics,* and it is here that we begin our formal development of mechanics.

If a body at rest is to remain at rest, the resultant of all the forces which act on the body must be zero. Similarly, if a body is already in motion and the resultant force acting on it is zero, the velocity of the body remains constant. These statements follow directly from a great generalization known as *Newton's first law* of motion (see Chap. 6). In this chapter and the one which follows we apply the condition that the resultant force acting on a body at rest is zero, but before doing so we pause to distinguish between the forces exerted *on a body* and the forces exerted *by the body.*

3.2 Newton's Third Law

Consider a cord of negligible weight from which a ball is suspended (Fig. 3.1*a*). If the cord is at rest, the upward pull of the ceiling is equal and opposite to the downward pull of the ball. The force exerted on the cord at either end is known as the *tension* in the cord. The cord, subjected to pulls at each end, is said to be "in tension."

We now direct our attention to the ball of Figure 3.1*b*. When the ball hangs at rest, there are two forces acting *on it*: its weight **W**, which is the downward pull of the earth, and the pull **T** of the cord upward. By Newton's first law, the resultant of these two forces must be zero, so they must be equal in magnitude and opposite in direction.

Note that the cord pulls upward on the ball with the force **T,** while the ball pulls downward on the cord with an equal and opposite force. This is an example of the application of Newton's *third law,* which states: *If body A exerts a force on body B, body B exerts an equal and opposite force on body A.* Forces in nature always occur in pairs which are equal and opposite. However, the two members of the pair always act on *different* bodies. In Figure 3.1*a* the ceiling pulls up on the cord, which in turn pulls down on the ceiling with an equal and opposite force.

When you hold this book in your hand, you exert an upward force *on the book;* at the same time the book exerts an equal downward force *on your hand.* If a man pulls *on a rope* with a force of 40 lb, the rope pulls back *on the man* with a force of 40 lb.

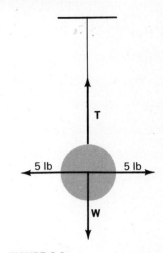

FIGURE 3.2

Exertion of a force to the right on the ball requires an equal force to the left if the ball is to stay at rest.

3.3 Concurrent Forces

When two or more forces act upon a body and the lines of action of these forces pass through a common point, the forces are said to be *concurrent.* By the "line of action" of a force we mean simply the line along which the force acts, extended indefinitely in both directions.

The two forces **W** and **T** acting on the ball of Figure 3.1*b* are concurrent; both act along a line which passes through the center of the ball. Now, suppose that someone were to push on the ball with a force of 5 lb to the right, and you wish to keep the ball at rest. What must you do? Clearly, you must push with a force of 5 lb in the opposite direction (Fig. 3.2). In general, if we wish to keep the ball at rest, we must balance any force applied in any given direction with an equal force in the opposite direction. (Of course, we may replace any force with its rectangular components!)

A body that remains at rest or moves with constant velocity is said to be in a state of *equilibrium* (equal balance). In order that a body be in equilibrium under the influence of any number of concurrent forces, *the vector sum of the forces acting on the body must be zero.* If we draw a vector diagram to represent the forces, the condition that the resultant be zero is equivalent to the condition that the force polygon must close (Fig. 3.3).

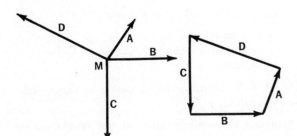

FIGURE 3.3

For a point mass *M* to remain at rest under the influence of forces, the resultant force must be zero so that the force polygon closes.

In treating the equilibrium of any body we must be sure to include all the forces which act *on that body,* and only those forces. The first question to be resolved in working any equilibrium problem is: Of what body is the equilibrium being considered? Then *all* the forces exerted *on this body,* and no other forces, are taken into account.

3.4 Equilibrium under Concurrent Forces

Clearly, if the resultant of all the forces acting on a body is zero, the sum of the rectangular components of these forces along any axis must be zero. Thus, when we resolve the forces into components in mutually perpendicular x and y (and z if necessary) directions, for a body in equilibrium the sum of the x components is zero, or the sum of the components in the $+x$ direction is equal to the sum of the components in the $-x$ direction. Similarly, the sum of the y (and z) components is zero.

Usually, but not always, it is desirable to choose vertical and horizontal axes. In this case:

1. *The sum of all upward force components is equal to the sum of all downward force components.*

2. *The sum of all force components to the right is equal to the sum of all force components to the left.*

In mathematical shorthand these conditions may be written in the form

$$\Sigma F_{\text{up}} = \Sigma F_{\text{down}} \qquad\qquad\qquad 3.1$$
$$\Sigma F_{\text{right}} = \Sigma F_{\text{left}} \qquad\qquad\qquad 3.2$$

where Σ (Greek capital sigma) is a standard abbreviation for "the sum of."

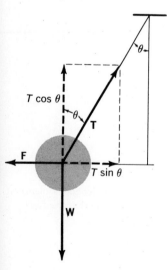

FIGURE 3.4

A ball in equilibrium.

Consider next the case in which the ball of Figure 3.1 is pulled to the left by a horizontal force **F**, as indicated in Figure 3.4. The ball is acted upon by three concurrent forces **F, T,** and **W,** the vector sum of which must be zero.

In treating a problem of this kind it is convenient to resolve the tension **T** into a vertical component $T \cos \theta$ and a horizontal component $T \sin \theta$. If we apply Eqs. (3.1) and (3.2) above, we obtain immediately

$$T \cos \theta = W$$
$$T \sin \theta = F$$

Example If $W = 20.0$ lb and $\theta = 35°$, find F and T.

$$
\begin{array}{ll}
T \cos \theta = W & F = T \sin \theta \\
0.819T = 20.0 \text{ lb} & \quad = 24.4 \text{ lb} \times 0.574 \\
T = 24.4 \text{ lb} & \quad = 14.0 \text{ lb}
\end{array}
$$

Example A weight of 40 lb is supported as shown in Figure 3.5. Find the tension in each rope.

The lower rope supports the 40-lb weight, so the tension in it is 40.0 lb. Now let us consider the knot at which the ropes meet to

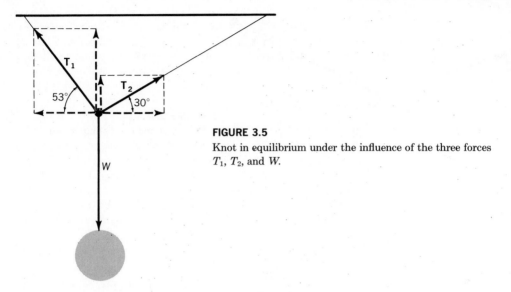

FIGURE 3.5
Knot in equilibrium under the influence of the three forces T_1, T_2, and W.

be the body in equilibrium. It is acted upon by three forces W, T_1, and T_2.

The vertical component of T_1 is $T_1 \sin 53° = 0.800T_1$, and the horizontal component is $T_1 \cos 53° = 0.600T_1$. The vertical component of T_2 is $T_2 \sin 30° = 0.500T_2$, and the horizontal component is $T_2 \cos 30° = 0.866T_2$. Applying the force conditions (3.1) and (3.2) yields

$$0.800T_1 + 0.500T_2 = 40.0 \text{ lb}$$
$$0.866T_2 = 0.600T_1$$

from which $T_1 = 34.9$ lb and $T_2 = 24.2$ lb. Note that the larger force is exerted by the shorter rope in this case.

A force which is equal and opposite to the resultant of two or more forces is called the *equilibrant*. Figure 3.6 shows the resultant and equilibrant of two forces **P** and **Q** which are not mutually perpendicular.

3.5 Friction

Frictional forces play an important role in mechanics, both for moving bodies and for those at rest. Unlike the weight of a body, which is constant at any particular location, we shall find that the frictional force between a body and a surface depends on many factors. For example, when a heavy block of wood is pushed along the top of a table, the amount of frictional resistance depends on the surface of the table, the surface of the block, how clean the surfaces are, the speed of the block, and the force pressing the surfaces together. When a body moves on a surface, there is always such resistance to the

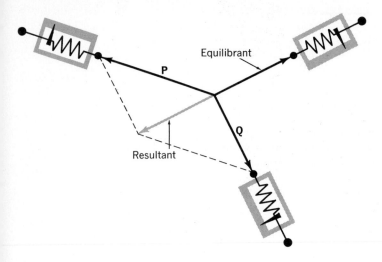

FIGURE 3.6

Resultant and equilibrant of two forces **P** and **Q**.

motion. In many situations friction is undesirable, and elaborate means are employed to make it as small as possible.

Friction has advantages as well as disadvantages. Except for friction between his shoes and the floor, a person would have great difficulty in moving about. When the pavement is covered with ice, friction is small, and walking is difficult. Because of friction, belts cling to pulleys and drive machinery. Without friction the acceleration and the braking of an automobile would require entirely different operations. Screws and nails hold their places in objects into which they are driven by means of friction.

3.6 Kinetic Friction

When an object is sliding over a surface, the direction of the frictional force is always parallel to the surface and opposite to the direction of motion (Fig. 3.7). Let us denote by f the force which is just necessary to overcome the frictional force and keep a body moving with *constant speed* across the surface. It is found experimentally that the force necessary to overcome friction is proportional to the force pressing the surfaces against one another. This fact may be expressed by the equation

FIGURE 3.7

The coefficient of friction is the ratio of the force f required to overcome friction to the force N pressing the surfaces together.

$$f = \mu_k N \qquad\qquad 3.3$$

where N is the force pressing the surfaces together, and μ_k is a constant called the *coefficient of kinetic* (or *sliding*) *friction. The coefficient of kinetic friction between two surfaces is the ratio of the force required to overcome friction to the normal force pressing the surfaces together when one surface is sliding over the other at constant speed.*

For ordinary surfaces the frictional force does not depend on the gross area of the rubbing surfaces. For our rough calculations we usually assume that friction is independent of velocity, although this

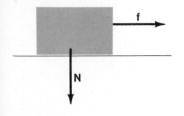

is only a crude approximation. At very low speeds μ_k sometimes increases with speed, but not always; for moderate speeds (an inch per second to a few feet per second) it is often roughly independent of speed; at higher speeds μ_k typically becomes smaller as the speed goes up.

< It should be noted that these statements about friction are worded rather guardedly. This is desirable because the rules which govern friction are only good working approximations. Friction is a very complex phenomenon. Even the smoothest surface is composed of hills and valleys from the microscopic point of view. The actual microscopic area of contact is generally only a tiny fraction of the macroscopic areas of the surfaces. A substantial body of evidence supports the idea that the frictional force is proportional to the area of contact. Ordinarily the frictional force is proportional to the load because the actual contact area is proportional to the load. Apparently, friction arises primarily from adhesion of molecules of the two surfaces which are in contact. Indeed, if we carefully polish and degas two steel surfaces, the friction is tremendously increased over that for rougher surfaces of the same material. Very thin contamination layers can result in large changes in observed friction. Some substances melt and flow under the influence of frictional forces, particularly when high speeds are involved. Such behavior, called *plastic flow,* often lubricates the surface.

It is important to observe that the force N pressing two surfaces together is not necessarily the weight of the sliding object. To move a heavy trunk across a rough floor, one possibility is to pull on the handle as in Figure 3.8a. We resolve the force **F** into two components; the horizontal component f is useful in overcoming the friction, while the vertical component V reduces the force pressing the surfaces together. In this case, $N = W - V$, where W is the weight of the trunk. To move the trunk by pushing downward (Fig. 3.8b) requires a larger force **F'**, since the force N pressing the surfaces together becomes $W + V'$, where V' is the downward component of **F'**.

3.7 The Coefficient of Static Friction

If a body is at rest on a surface, a larger force is required to overcome the friction and put the body in motion than is required to keep the body in motion at constant speed. If we let f_s represent the force necessary to overcome friction in starting the body, we find that this force is also proportional to the force N pressing the surfaces together. Thus,

$$f_s = \mu_s N \qquad\qquad 3.4$$

where μ_s is called the *coefficient of static friction. The coefficient of static friction between two surfaces is the ratio of the force required to overcome friction to the normal force pressing the surfaces together when the surfaces are at rest relative to one another.* Since the force

FIGURE 3.8

The force pressing the surfaces together is (*a*) reduced to $W - V$ by the upward component V of the applied force F, (*b*) increased to $W + V'$ by the downward component V' of the applied force F'.

(a)

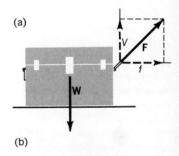

(b)

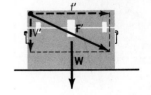

TABLE 3.1   *Approximate Coefficients of Friction*

Surface	μ_k	μ_s	Surface	μ_k	μ_s
Steel on:			Greased surfaces	0.05	0.06
Steel (clean)	0.50	0.75	Rubber tire on:		
Steel (greasy)	0.15	0.20	Dry concrete, low speed	0.7	0.9
Ice	0.01	0.02	Dry concrete, high speed	0.35	0.6
Oak on oak	0.4	0.5	Wet concrete, low speed	0.5	0.7

necessary to overcome static friction is greater than the force necessary to overcome sliding friction, the coefficient of static friction is greater than the coefficient of kinetic friction.   Table 3.1 lists the coefficients of kinetic and static friction for several types of surfaces.

Because static friction is always greater than kinetic friction, a good automobile driver is careful not to keep his wheels locked when he is braking to a stop.   Once the wheels stop rotating, the tires slide over the pavement, and the coefficient of kinetic friction is in effect.   When the wheels are rolling without sliding, the point of contact between tire and pavement is at rest, and the coefficient of static friction is applicable.

If a body is at rest on a surface, the frictional force is just large enough to permit the conditions for equilibrium to be satisfied.   If the body is resting on a horizontal surface and no horizontal forces act, the frictional force is zero.   If the surface is tilted slightly, the frictional force becomes just great enough to prevent the body from sliding. Thus the force of friction can be computed by the relation $f_s = \mu_s N$ only when the body is just at the point of sliding.   The product $\mu_s N$ gives the *maximum* value of the friction when the body is at rest.   The frictional force may be substantially less than this.

⟨ 3.8 Friction on an Inclined Plane

FIGURE 3.9

The frictional force **f** has the same magnitude as D when the block slides down with constant speed.

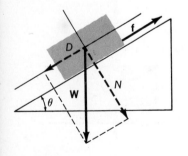

In Figure 3.9 a block of weight W rests on a plane inclined at an angle θ with the horizontal.   Let the angle θ be varied until the block will just slide down the plane with uniform velocity when once started.   Represent this angle by θ_k.   Let D represent the component of the weight down the plane, and N the component of the weight normal to the plane.   The force of friction between the block and plane is parallel to and up the plane.   Since the block experiences no acceleration, the frictional force up the plane is equal to the component of the weight parallel to the plane; thus $D = f_k = W \sin \theta_k$. The force pressing the surfaces together is just the component of the weight perpendicular to the plane, which is $W \cos \theta_k$.   By definition, the coefficient of kinetic friction is

$$\mu_k = \frac{f_k}{N} = \frac{W \sin \theta_k}{W \cos \theta_k} = \tan \theta_k \qquad\qquad \textbf{3.5}$$

The tangent of the angle at which the block slides down the plane with uniform velocity is equal to the coefficient of kinetic friction.

If the angle θ is varied until it is the largest angle at which the block will remain at rest on the plane, the component of the weight parallel to the plane ($W \sin \theta_s$) is equal to the force f_s necessary to overcome static friction, while the force pressing the surfaces together is equal to $W \cos \theta_s$, the component of the weight perpendicular to the plane. The angle θ_s at which we have satisfied these conditions is known as the *angle of repose,* and

$$\mu_s = \frac{f_s}{N} = \frac{W \sin \theta_s}{W \cos \theta_s} = \tan \theta_s \qquad \textbf{3.6}$$

3.9 Reducing Friction

If a layer of liquid is introduced between two surfaces, the liquid flows over the surfaces and adheres to them. Instead of there being friction between two solids, there is friction between layers of the liquid. When oil is poured into the bearings of a machine, it forms layers, and the sliding takes place primarily between layers of oil. Since friction between oil layers is much less than between metal surfaces, the frictional force is decreased. Oil is usually preferred to water as a lubricant, not because there is less friction between oil layers than between water layers, but because oil films have the property of staying between the metal surfaces, while water layers are readily squeezed out.

When frictional forces cannot be reduced sufficiently by lubrication, it is customary to substitute rolling friction for sliding friction. The friction of a solid rolling on a surface is far less than the friction of a solid sliding over the surface. For this reason, automobiles and railroad trains operate on wheels rather than on runners and often use ball bearings or roller bearings at the axles. When a car wheel rolls on a level track, it makes a slight depression in the track, and the wheel is somewhat flattened. As the wheel rolls, it is forced continually to climb out of this depression. This is one reason that even rolling wheels require a force to overcome friction. The amount of depression depends on the nature and area of the surfaces in contact.

Questions

1. A weight is hung from the middle of a rope. Will it ever be possible to get the rope to be horizontal by pulling on the ends? Discuss with a vector diagram.

2. A man lies in a hammock stretched between two trees. Are the supporting ropes more likely to break if the hammock is strung tightly or loosely? Explain using a vector diagram.

3. What is the smallest number of forces, *not all acting in the same plane,* which can put a point mass in equilibrium?

4. If frictional forces are independent of area, why are automobile brake shoes of large area desirable?

5. Under what circumstances will the frictional force on a block on a rough inclined plane be directed down the plane?

6. Show that for a body at rest on a rough horizontal plane no force making an angle with the vertical smaller than the angle of repose can slide the body along the plane.

Problems

1. A pendulum bob with a weight of 20 newtons hangs from a cord. A horizontal force sufficient to bring the cord to an angle of 25° with the vertical is applied to the bob. Find the horizontal force and the tension in the cord. *Ans.* 9.3 newtons; 22.1 newtons

2. The ball of Figure 3.4 has a weight of 4 lb. Find the horizontal force F required to hold the ball at rest with $\theta = 20°$. What is the tension in the cord?

3. A frictionless cart standing on an inclined plane that makes an angle of 10° with the horizontal is kept from rolling downhill by a force of 30 lb applied in a direction parallel to the plane. What is the weight of the cart? *Ans.* 173 lb

4. A block weighing 40 newtons rests on a frictionless plane inclined 20° to the horizontal. It is connected to a weight X by a rope of negligible weight. The rope runs up parallel to the plane and passes over a pulley so that the weight X hangs vertical. What must be the magnitude of the weight if the system is in equilibrium?

5. The end of a horizontal electric transmission line in which there is a tension of 1,000 lb is fastened to the top of a vertical pole and to a guy wire which can sustain a tension of 2,500 lb. What is the smallest angle which the guy wire can make with the pole if there is to be no resultant lateral force on the pole? *Ans.* 23.5°

6. A weight of 5 lb hanging over the edge of a table on a cord is just sufficient to drag a 30-lb body along the horizontal surface of the table with unchanging velocity. What is the coefficient of kinetic friction?

7. A brake shoe is pressed against the rim of a moving wheel with a force of 50 newtons. If the coefficient of kinetic friction between the surfaces is 0.22, how much frictional force is developed? *Ans.* 11 newtons

8. A horizontal force of 15 lb is required to pull a 75-lb trunk along a floor. What is the coefficient of kinetic friction?

9. A box weighing 30 lb is on a horizontal floor. The coefficient of static friction between surfaces is 0.30, and that of sliding friction is 0.25. Find the frictional force under each of the following conditions: (*a*) No additional force is applied; (*b*) a force of 5 lb is applied toward the east; (*c*) a force of 9 lb is applied toward the west; (*d*) a force of 10 lb to the south is applied steadily to the box.
Ans. (*a*) 0; (*b*) 5 lb west; (*c*) 9 lb east; (*d*) 7.5 lb north

10. A carton weighing 180 lb rests on a horizontal loading platform. A horizontal force of 54 lb is required to start the carton in motion, but once it is moving a force of 40 lb is adequate to keep it in motion at constant speed. Find the coefficients of static and kinetic friction.

11. A picture is supported by two wires fastened to the ends of the upper edge of the picture frame, which is horizontal. Each of the wires makes an angle of 70° with the vertical. What is the tension in each wire if the picture weighs 3 lb? *Ans.* 4.4 lb

12. A 5-lb body is supported by two cords, each of which make an angle of 50° with the horizontal. What is the tension in each cord?

13. A bird weighing 1.8 lb alights on a weightless wire midway between two poles 200 ft apart. Because of the weight of the bird, the wire, which was initially horizontal, sags 3 in. What is the tension in the wire due to the weight of the bird?   *Ans.* 360 lb

14. A bird weighing 5 newtons alights on a weightless telephone wire midway between two poles which are 60 m apart. Assume that the wire between the bird and each of the poles forms a straight line. If the center of the wire is 0.12 m below its level at the poles, and if the weight of the wire is neglected, calculate the tension in the wire due to the weight of the bird.

15. An inextensible tow rope 10 m long is stretched taut between a tree and an automobile. A force of 240 newtons at the center of the rope moves it 0.4 m perpendicular to the original line of the rope. Find the force exerted on the tree and on the automobile.
     Ans. 1,500 newtons

16. If the angle of repose for a 10-lb block of metal on an incline is 15°, what force parallel to the incline is necessary to cause the body to begin to move up the incline?

17. The coefficient of sliding friction between a block and the floor is 0.40. If a force of 10 lb acting 37° above the horizontal gives the box a constant velocity, find the weight of the block.   *Ans.* 26 lb

18. What force acting at an angle of 30° above the horizontal is necessary to move a mass of 5 kg with uniform velocity along a horizontal surface, the coefficient of friction being 0.24?

19. Find the tension in each rope of the accompanying figure if the weight *W* is 100 newtons.   *Ans.* (*a*) 71.4, 80.8; (*b*) 125, 75; (*c*) 83.3, 62.5, 29.2 (all in newtons)

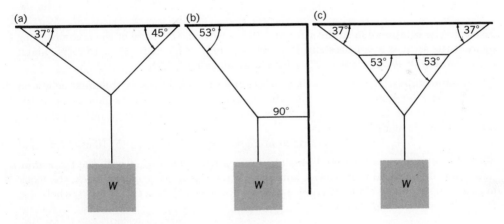

(a) (b) (c)

PROBS. 19 AND 20

20. Find the tension in each rope of the accompanying figure if the weight *W* is 60 lb.

21. A block rests on a plane that is inclined at an angle of 30° to the horizontal. The coefficient of kinetic friction between the block and the plane is 0.15. If the block has a weight of 100 newtons, what force parallel to the incline is necessary to keep it sliding up the plane?   *Ans.* 63 newtons

22. A 50-lb frictionless car rests on an inclined plane that makes an angle of 30° with the horizontal. What force must be exerted to keep it from sliding down the plane if the force is applied so that it makes an angle of 35° downward with the horizontal?

23. A man is pushing a 60-lb box along a level floor with a uniform velocity of 4 ft/sec by exerting a force on the box at an angle of 30° downward from the horizontal. If the coefficient of friction between sliding surfaces is 0.25, what is the magnitude of the force?

Ans. 20.3 lb

24. A force of 50 lb exerted at an angle of 20° above the horizontal is needed to keep a 200-lb block moving along a cement floor. Find the coefficient of kinetic friction.

25. Find the compression in the strut and the tension in the cable of the accompanying figure if the strut is weightless and W is 200 lb. The strut is free to rotate about a pin at the wall so the strut exerts a force only along its length.

Ans. (*a*) 333 lb, 267 lb; (*b*) 346 lb, 400 lb; (*c*) 572 lb, 429 lb

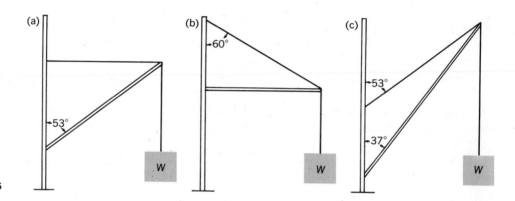

PROBS. 25 AND 26

26. Find the compression in the strut and the tension in the cable of the accompanying figure if the strut is weightless and W is 500 newtons. The strut is free to rotate about a pin at the wall so the strut exerts a force only along its length.

27. A uniform flexible cable of weight W is supported by hooks at the same height on neighboring telephone poles. If the cable makes an angle θ with the horizontal at the hooks, find (*a*) the force exerted on the cable by the hook on the right and (*b*) the tension in the cable at its lowest point.

Ans. (*a*) $W/(2 \sin \theta)$ at angle θ with horizontal; (*b*) $W \cos \theta/(2 \sin \theta)$

28. A block of mass m rests on a rough plane inclined at an angle θ with the horizontal. Show that if a gradually increasing horizontal force F is exerted on the block, the block begins to slide up the plane when $F = mg (\sin \theta + \mu \cos \theta)/(\cos \theta - \mu \sin \theta)$, where μ is the coefficient of static friction.

CHAPTER 4 *In the preceding chapter we learned that if the resultant force on a body is zero, the body maintains a constant velocity (which is zero if the body is initially at rest). However, the body may still have a rotational acceleration about its center of mass. We next consider what condition must be satisfied if there is to be no rotational acceleration, and we develop the general conditions for equilibrium which must be satisfied if a body is to remain at rest or move with constant linear and angular velocities.*

Torque and Equilibrium

4.1 Torque

If two boys who weigh 50 and 60 lb, respectively, sit on opposite ends of a horizontal teeter-totter 12 ft long (Fig. 4.1), we know that the teeter-totter will not remain horizontal; the 60-lb boy will move downward, and the 50-lb boy upward. This occurs even though the upward force exerted by the support is equal to 110 lb (plus the weight of the teeter-totter, which we assume for the moment is negligible). A glance at the figure reveals that the forces are not concurrent and that the conditions required for a body to be at rest under the influence of concurrent forces are not enough to keep the teeter-totter at rest. The weight of the 60-lb boy acts to produce a clockwise rotation about the fulcrum, while the weight of the 50-lb boy acts to produce a rotation in the opposite direction. When both boys are at the ends of the teeter-totter, the two rotational tendencies do not balance each other, and there is a resultant clockwise rotation. We all know from experience that the two boys can sit on the teeter-totter and keep it at rest, provided the heavier boy sits closer to the fulcrum. This suggests that the tendency to produce rotation depends not only on the force acting, but also on a distance.

A simple experiment shows that if the 50-lb boy sits 6 ft from the fulcrum, and the 60-lb boy 5 ft from the fulcrum, the teeter-totter is balanced. We observe that $60 \times 5 = 50 \times 6$. This suggests that the tendency to produce rotation depends on the product of force and distance. We must, however, inquire more closely into how this distance factor is to be determined. Suppose that our teeter-totter is elevated and that the 50-lb boy is suspended from a rope 8 ft long hanging from the end of the teeter-totter (Fig. 4.2). His distance from the fulcrum is then 10 ft. Will the teeter-totter still be balanced? Yes, indeed. An experiment would show that moving the 50-lb boy to this position

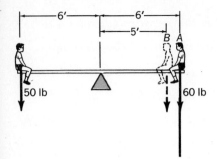

FIGURE 4.1

Rotational equilibrium of the teeter-totter does not occur until the 60-lb boy at *A* moves to *B*.

had no effect on the balance. Thus, it is clear that it is *not* the distance from the fulcrum to the point at which the force is applied which is important; rather, it is the *perpendicular distance from the fulcrum to the line along which the force acts.* This distance is known as the *lever arm. The lever arm for any axis is the perpendicular distance from the axis to the line along which the force acts.*

The product of the lever arm and the force (6 ft and 50 lb for the 50-lb boy on the teeter-totter) is called the *torque.* If the teeter-totter is to be in equilibrium, the clockwise torque about the fulcrum must be balanced by the counterclockwise torque. Not only is the clockwise torque equal to the counterclockwise torque about the fulcrum, but the net counterclockwise torque *about any axis* is equal to the net clockwise torque *about the same axis,* provided the resultant of the forces is zero. For example, if the weight of the teeter-totter itself is negligible, Eq. (3.1) requires that the fulcrum exert an upward force of 110 lb. If we choose an axis through the left end of the teeter-totter, we have a counterclockwise torque of 110 lb × 6 ft = 660 lb-ft and a clockwise torque of 60 lb × 11 ft = 660 lb-ft.

Consider the problem of calculating the torque **L** about an arbitrary axis (Fig. 4.3) exerted by a force **F** acting at a point a distance *r* from this axis. In general, *the torque exerted by a force about a fixed point is the product of the lever arm and the force, where the lever arm is the distance from the point to the line along which the force acts.*

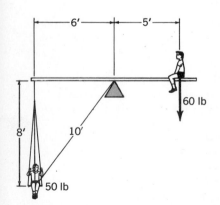

FIGURE 4.2

The torque about the fulcrum depends on the product of the force and the distance from the fulcrum to the line along which the force acts.

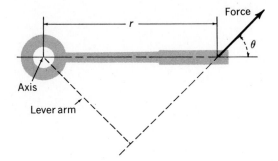

FIGURE 4.3

Torque is the product of the force and the distance from the axis to the line along which the force acts, called the *lever arm*.

Torque is a vector quantity. The direction associated with a torque is the direction in which a right-handed screw would advance if it were turned by the torque (Fig. 4.4). Alternatively, the torque has the direction in which the right thumb points when the right fingers curve to indicate the path along which points of the body would move under the influence of the torque. For the case shown in Figure 4.3 the direction of the torque is out of the page, and its magnitude is

$$L = rF \sin \theta \qquad \qquad \textbf{4.1}$$

Clearly, $F \sin \theta$ is the component of $\mathbf{F}$ perpendicular to the line joining the axis to the point of application of the force.

Since $r(F \sin \theta) = F(r \sin \theta)$, the torque is the product of the force F and the lever arm $r \sin \theta$.

We shall be concerned primarily with forces confined to a single plane. In this case the torques are all perpendicular to the plane containing the forces. In describing the torques, we shall refer to them as clockwise if they act to produce a rotation in the direction in which the hands of a clock move, and counterclockwise if they act in the opposite direction. The actual direction of the torque vector for a clockwise torque is into the plane, and for a counterclockwise torque out of the plane.

As an illustration of the importance of the lever arm in computing the torque, consider the operation of a bicycle. If a boy pushes down

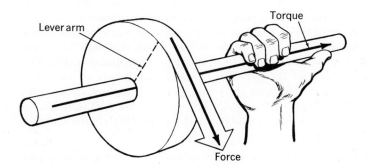

FIGURE 4.4

Torque is a vector quantity. Its direction is that in which a right-handed screw would advance if it were turned by the torque. Alternatively, the direction is pointed by the outstretched right thumb when the fingers of the right hand curve in the direction in which the screw would rotate.

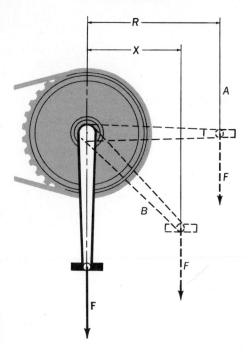

FIGURE 4.5

The vertical force produces no torque when the pedal is straight down; it produces maximum torque when the pedal is at A.

on the pedal with his full weight (Fig. 4.5), the rotational effect produced depends on the location of the pedal. If it is straight down, no rotational effect is produced. The torque in this case is zero, because the lever arm is zero. The maximum torque occurs when the pedal is in the position marked A, since in this position the lever arm is equal to the radius of the pedal. When the pedal is in position B, the lever arm is reduced from R to X.

FIGURE 4.6

The center of gravity of a body may be found by the experiment shown.

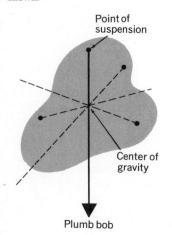

Point of suspension

Center of gravity

Plumb bob

4.2 Center of Gravity

Every particle of an extended body possesses weight, so that the pull of the earth on the body is composed of a large number of forces directed toward the center of the earth. For a body of ordinary size these forces are essentially parallel to one another. The body can, however, be supported in equilibrium by a single upward force, provided its line of action passes through a point called the *center of gravity* of the body. This point can be located as follows:

If we suspend the body from a single point, it comes to rest with a definite orientation. Let us determine a line through the body directed vertically downward from the point of suspension (Fig. 4.6). Next, let us suspend the body from several other points on its surface and, in each case, determine the position of the line through the point of support and directed vertically downward. We find that all the lines determined in this way intersect at a point which is the *center of gravity* of the body.

< The center of gravity of a uniform sphere, cube, or rod is at its geo-

metrical center. The center of gravity of an axe or hammer is nearer the head than the handle. The center of gravity of a telephone pole or a baseball bat lies on the axis, but is closer to the thicker end. The center of gravity of a ring or of a tire is at the geometrical center, which, of course, does not lie in the material of the object. Although the center of gravity is a point fixed relative to the body, it does not necessarily lie within the body.

Since an extended body can be at rest when supported by a single upward force whose line of action passes through the center of gravity, the sum of the clockwise torques due to the individual forces on the particles of the body must be equal to the sum of the counterclockwise torques about an axis through the center of gravity. For any axis the torque due to the weight of the body acting at the center of gravity is equal to the sum of the torques due to the forces of gravity on all the various parts of the body. When we are dealing with the extended body, we may consider all the weight of the body as concentrated at the center of gravity, and we may thus replace the individual forces acting on the many particles of the body with a single force equal to the weight. This is true not only for an axis determined by the center of gravity, but for any axis. *The center of gravity of an object is that point at which we can consider the entire weight of the object to be concentrated for the purpose of computing torques.*

Example Find the center of gravity of two spheres A and B of weights 0.1 and 0.4 newton, respectively, connected by a light (negligible mass) rod 20 cm long (Fig. 4.7).

If the center of gravity is at a point C, the clockwise torque due to the larger weight W_2 about an axis through C is just equal to the counterclockwise torque due to the smaller weight W_1. Then

$$W_1 x_1 = W_2 x_2$$

Since $x_1 + x_2 = 20$ cm $= 0.20$ m,

$$(0.1 \text{ newton})(x_1 \text{ m}) = (0.4 \text{ newton})(0.20 - x_1) \text{ m}$$
$$x_1 = 0.16 \text{ m} = 16 \text{ cm}$$

4.3 Equilibrium

Thus far we have been considering the conditions which must be satisfied in order that a body remain *at rest*. Exactly the same conditions apply to a body which is in motion with *constant velocity*. When we

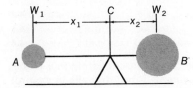

FIGURE 4.7
Center of gravity of two spheres connected by a rod of negligible mass.

ride in an automobile over a smooth road at a constant velocity of 20 mi/hr south, the resultant of the forces which act on us is the same as when we are at rest. As we shall see in Chap. 6, if the resultant force acting on a body is not zero, the body is accelerated.

The condition that the vector sum of the torques on a body be zero in order that there be no rotation for a body at rest can be extended to include bodies rotating about a fixed axis as follows: *If the vector sum of the torques acting on a rigid body is zero, the rotational velocity of the body is constant.* If there is a resultant torque acting on the body, there is a change in its angular velocity, as we shall see in Chap. 10. *A body which has a constant linear velocity and a constant rotational velocity is in a state of equilibrium.* Statics involves a special case of equilibrium, namely, the case in which both the linear velocity and the rotational velocity have the constant value *zero*.

4.4 The Conditions for Equilibrium

In order that a rigid body be in equilibrium, two conditions must be satisfied:

1. *The vector sum (resultant) of all forces acting on the body must be zero.*

2. *The vector sum (resultant) of all torques about any axis must be zero.*

The first condition for equilibrium guarantees that the center of gravity (more accurately the center of mass) of the body moves with constant velocity. The second condition guarantees that the rotational velocity of the body remains constant. In applying the second condition, there is no restriction as to what axis is chosen. It may be through the center of gravity of the body, through one end of the body, or at any convenient place.

In actual practice, it is usually convenient to use the conditions for equilibrium in a slightly different form, but one which is equivalent to the briefer statements above. If we replace forces with their vertical and horizontal components, we may write the conditions for equilibrium in the form:

1. *The sum of all upward forces is equal to the sum of all downward forces.*

The sum of all forces to the right is equal to the sum of all forces to the left.

2. *The sum of all clockwise torques* about any axis *is equal to the sum of all counterclockwise torques* about the same axis.

If we introduce once more the symbol Σ to represent "the sum of," we may write these conditions as

$$\Sigma F_{up} = \Sigma F_{down} \qquad\qquad 4.2$$
$$\Sigma F_{right} = \Sigma F_{left} \qquad\qquad 4.3$$
$$\Sigma \text{ torques}_{clockwise} = \Sigma \text{ torques}_{counterclockwise} \qquad\qquad 4.4$$

These equations are written for the case of forces acting in a plane. The extension to three-dimensional systems is not difficult in that all we need do is (1) add to the first condition for equilibrium that the sum of all components perpendicular to the plane determined by the first two axes add to zero and (2) apply the torque condition for another axis chosen perpendicular to the first axis. It is not necessary that we choose vertical and horizontal axes for applying the conditions for equilibrium, but in the majority of cases this is the most convenient choice.

In working equilibrium problems it is imperative that *all* forces acting on the body in question be considered, and *only* those forces. The first thing one must do is decide what body is to be dealt with. Then it is usually helpful to make a rough sketch of this body, representing all forces acting on it by suitably placed arrows. Next, one resolves all those forces which are neither horizontal nor vertical and replaces them with their components. At this point one is ready to apply the conditions for equilibrium.

Example It is found by weighing that the front wheels of a truck support 3,000 lb and the rear wheels 5,400 lb. If the wheelbase (distance between axles) is 18 ft, find the weight of the truck and the location of the center of gravity (Fig. 4.8).

By Eq. (4.2),

$$3,000 \text{ lb} + 5,400 \text{ lb} = W$$
$$W = 8,400 \text{ lb}$$

Let d be the distance from the front wheels to the center of gravity, and find torques about the front axle as axis. By Eq. (4.4),

$$Wd = 5,400 \text{ lb} \times 18 \text{ ft}$$
$$(8,400 \text{ lb})d = 5,400 \text{ lb} \times 18 \text{ ft}$$
$$d = 11.6 \text{ ft}$$

Example A uniform ladder weighs 60 lb and is 25 ft long. It leans against a smooth (frictionless) wall at a point 24 ft above a cement driveway with its base 7 ft from the wall. A 200-lb man stands 0.6 of the way up the ladder. (*a*) Find the horizontal and vertical components of the force exerted on the ladder by the driveway. (*b*) If the coefficient of static friction between the ladder and the driveway is 0.2, what fraction of the way to the top can the man climb before the ladder slips?

The object in equilibrium is the ladder, and the forces exerted on it are shown in Figure 4.9. H and V are the horizontal and vertical components of the force exerted on the ladder by the driveway.

(*a*) By Eq. (4.2): $V = 200 \text{ lb} + 60 \text{ lb} = 260 \text{ lb}$
By Eq. (4.3): $H = F$

If we choose the base of the ladder as axis, we obtain, by Eq. (4.4),

$$(24 \text{ ft}) F = (200 \text{ lb} \times 4.2 \text{ ft}) + (60 \text{ lb} \times 3.5 \text{ ft})$$
$$F = 43.75 \quad \text{and} \quad H = 43.75$$

Note that we may use any axis for applying Eq. (4.4). It may be

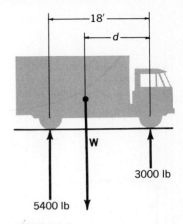

FIGURE 4.8
Center of gravity of a truck.

FIGURE 4.9
Equilibrium of a ladder leaning against a smooth wall.

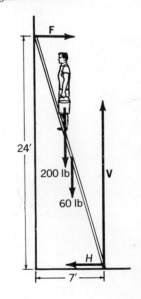

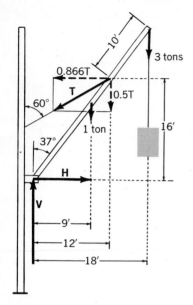

FIGURE 4.10

Equilibrium of a derrick boom.

instructive to try other axes (such as one at the point where the ladder touches the wall or one through the center of the ladder) to assure yourself that we may indeed choose any axis.

(b) H cannot exceed $0.2V = 52$ lb. Applying Eq. (4.4) about the point at which the ladder touches the driveway, and recalling that $H = F$, yields

$$24 \text{ ft} \times 52 \text{ lb} = (60 \text{ lb} \times 3.5 \text{ ft}) + (200 \text{ lb} \times 7q \text{ ft})$$

where q is the fraction of the length of the ladder which the man has climbed. Solving for q gives $q = 0.741$. The ladder slips just before the man has climbed three-fourths of the way to the top!

Example A derrick (Fig. 4.10) has a uniform boom 30 ft long which weighs 1 ton. A load of 3 tons is suspended from the end. The boom is hinged to a vertical mast and held up by a cable which makes an angle of 60° with the mast and which is fastened 10 ft from the end of the boom. If the boom makes an angle of 37° with the mast, find the tension in the cable and the force exerted on the boom by the hinge.

First, we resolve the tension into its horizontal and vertical components, which are $T \sin 60° = 0.866T$ and $T \cos 60° = 0.5T$, respectively. Next let H and V represent the components of the force exerted on the boom by the hinge.

By Eq. (4.2): $V = 3 + 1 + 0.5T$
By Eq. (4.3): $H = 0.866T$

If we choose the hinge as the axis, Eq. (4.4) yields

$$(9 \times 1) + (0.5T \times 12) + (3 \times 18) = (0.866T \times 16)$$
$$T = 8.02 \text{ tons}$$

whence $V = 8.01$ tons, and $H = 6.95$ tons.

Note that we have replaced the force T with its components and then computed the torque due to each component. The resultant of the torques due to the components is equal to the torque due to the original force.

4.5 Types of Equilibrium

The equilibrium of a body may be *stable, unstable,* or *neutral* (Fig. 4.11). When a body returns to its original position after being slightly disturbed, the equilibrium is said to be *stable*. A cone standing on its base is an illustration of this type of equilibrium. When this cone is tilted slightly and released, it returns to its original position.

If the cone rests on its vertex, it can be in equilibrium only when its center of gravity lies directly above the vertex. If it is slightly displaced, the cone falls over; it is in *unstable* equilibrium. A body in unstable equilibrium does not return to the original equilibrium position when slightly displaced, but rather moves farther away. Lastly,

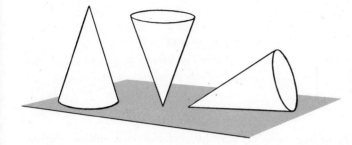

a billiard ball resting on a horizontal table is said to be in *neutral* equilibrium. When it is slightly displaced, it neither returns to its former position nor does it go farther away from the initial position. It remains in any position in which it finds itself. A cylinder or a cone lying on its side on a horizontal surface is also in neutral equilibrium.

The position of the center of gravity is of paramount importance in determining the stability of a body. The lower the center of gravity, the greater the stability of the body and the more difficult it is to overturn it. The body becomes unstable as soon as the vertical line through its center of gravity falls outside its base. The leaning tower of Pisa remains in stable equilibrium because, in spite of its leaning, the line of action of the weight falls inside the base.

4.6 The Stability of Aircraft

An airplane flying horizontally at constant speed is in equilibrium under the influence of four generalized forces: the lift, the weight, the drag, and the thrust (Fig. 4.12). The weight of the airplane may, of course, be regarded as concentrated at the center of gravity. The lift forces, which arise from pressure differences on the wing, fuselage, and

FIGURE 4.12
An aircraft in stable equilibrium. The velocity must be constant.

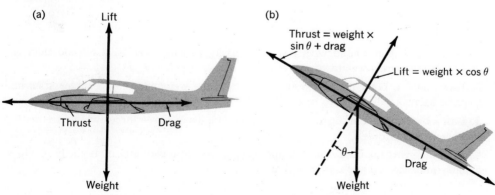

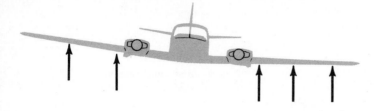

FIGURE 4.13
Lateral stability of an aircraft.

tail sections of the aircraft, may be replaced in a similar way by a resultant lift vector. The friction resulting from the passage of air over the surface of the aircraft gives rise to a net retarding force known as the *drag,* while the aircraft engine, whether it be propeller or jet, provides *thrust* to overcome this drag.

For the aircraft to be longitudinally stable, the resultant of the torques about a transverse axis through the center of gravity must be zero. Note that the conditions for equilibrium must be satisfied over a wide range of speeds and loadings. This can be accomplished by moving aileron, wing, or elevator surfaces in such a way as to keep the lift equal to the weight and the center of lift appropriately placed relative to the center of gravity. When the speed of an aircraft approaches the speed of sound, there may be radical changes in the way in which air flows over the aircraft surfaces. Such changes introduce sudden shifts in the position of the center of lift and thereby introduce large and sudden torques on the aircraft. For this and other reasons, it is dangerous to fly any type of aircraft above a maximum speed which depends upon the design.

Not only must the airplane be stable longitudinally, but also laterally. One way of achieving lateral stability is by having the center of gravity of the aircraft well below the center of lift. Another device which increases the lateral stability is to make the dihedral angle between wing surfaces less than 180° (Fig. 4.13). In this case, when the airplane tilts, the lowered wing has more lift than the raised one, because it presents a greater horizontal area to the air. As a consequence, there is a torque in the direction restoring the aircraft to its stable position.

Questions

1. Why is a wagon loaded with hay more likely to turn over on a hillside than one loaded with an equal weight of gravel?

2. How could a body estimated to weigh 10 lb be weighed using a meter stick and a spring balance calibrated to read only up to 4 lb?

3. Can a body be in equilibrium under the influence of three forces which are neither concurrent nor parallel?

4. Is a ladder resting on a sidewalk and leaning against a wall any more likely to slip as a man climbs toward the top? Explain.

5. Where are the positions of stable, neutral, and unstable equilibrium for a right circular cylinder?

6. A brick rests on a horizontal sidewalk. An identical brick is placed on top of the first with 0.3 of its length overhanging. Can a third brick be added with 0.3 of its length overhanging the second? What is the limiting number which can be assembled in this way and still remain in equilibrium?

Problems

1. When the front wheels of an automobile are run onto a platform scale, the scale balances at 1,500 lb; when the rear wheels are run onto the scale, it balances at 1,200 lb. What is the weight of the automobile, and how far is its center of gravity behind the front axle? The distance between axles is 110 in. *Ans.* 2,700 lb; 49 in.

2. A tapered pole 8 ft long weighs 12 lb. It balances at its mid-point when a 2-lb weight hangs from the slimmer end. Find the center of gravity.

3. Weights of 2.5, 5, 7.5, and 10 newtons are located, respectively, at 25-, 50-, 75-, and 100-cm marks on a meter stick whose weight is negligible. What are the magnitude and location of the single upward force which will balance the system?

Ans. 25 newtons at the 75-cm mark

4. A uniform bar 1 yd long has a weight of 6 lb fastened to it at one end, and a weight of 5 lb at the other end. The bar itself weighs 4 lb. Where could a single force be applied to balance the system, and how great would the force have to be?

5. A wheel of 25 cm diameter has an axle of 3 cm diameter. If a force of 160 newtons is exerted along the rim of the wheel, what is the smallest force exerted on the outside of the axle which will result in zero net torque? *Ans.* 1,333 newtons

6. A 100-lb boy and a 70-lb boy sit at the ends of a 12-ft teeter-totter. At what point should a 50-lb boy sit in order that the teeter-totter be in equilibrium?

7. A square is acted upon by the forces of 4, 6, 8, and 12 lb, respectively, along the four sides. The forces all act to produce rotation in the same direction. If the length of a side of the square is 1.5 ft, what is the resultant torque acting to rotate the square about an axis through its center? *Ans.* 22.5 ft-lb

8. A bar of uniform cross section is carried by two boys, one at either end of the bar. If the bar weighs 50 lb and is 12 ft long, where must a load of 60 lb be hung from the bar so that one boy will carry twice as much as the other?

9. A 50-lb uniform beam 10 ft long is supported at its ends by two walls. Find the forces exerted on the supports when a 200-lb man stands on the beam at a distance of 4 ft from one end. *Ans.* 105 and 145 lb

10. A uniform beam 4 m long weighs 300 newtons and is supported at its ends by two walls. Find the reactions of the walls against the beam when a man weighing 800 newtons stands on the beam at a distance of 3 m from one end.

11. A telegraph pole is placed on a two-wheeled dolly located 2 m from the thicker end, and an upward force of 2,000 newtons at the thinner end is required to keep it horizontal. The pole is 10 m long and weighs 8,000 newtons. Where is the center of gravity?

Ans. 4 m from thicker end

12. A tapered pole which is 14 ft long and weighs 60 lb can be balanced at a point 5 ft from the thicker end. If it were to be supported at its end, how much force would be needed at each end?

13. To a thin circular disk whose radius is 10 cm, there is attached another circular disk of the same material whose radius is 5 cm. Find the center of gravity of the combination if the smaller disk has one point on its circumference at the center of the larger disk.

Ans. 1 cm from center of larger disk, on the line between centers

14. From a circular disk of 20 cm radius there is cut out a circle of 10 cm diameter. Find the center of gravity of the remainder of the disk if the circumference of the hole passes through the center of the disk.

15. From a circular disk whose radius is 40 cm there is cut a circular hole whose radius is 20 cm. Find the center of gravity of the remainder of the disk if the hole has one point of its circumference at the center of the disk.

Ans. 6.7 cm from the center of the disk, on the extension of the line between the center of the disk and the center of the hole

16. A uniform rod 120 cm long has a mass of 3 kg. It has a mass of 5 kg attached to it at one end, a mass of 6 kg at the other end, and a mass of 4 kg in the middle. Find the position of the center of gravity.

17. A cubical box 4 ft on a side weighs 150 lb and rests on a rough floor for which the coefficient of static friction is 0.6. If the center of gravity of the box is at its center, what is the greatest height at which a horizontal force can be applied to slide the box without tipping it? What is the lowest height at which a horizontal 80-lb force can be applied to tip the box?   *Ans.* 3.33 ft; 3.75 ft

18. A uniform horizontal bar 8 ft long weighs 50 lb. Upward forces of 30 and 20 lb are exerted at the ends. Is the bar in equilibrium? Calculate the torque about one end, about the center, and about a point 10 ft from one end of the bar.

19. A 50-lb door 80 in. high and 32 in. wide is hung by two hinges, each of which supports half the weight. If the hinges are 10 in. from the top and 10 in. from the bottom of the door, find the horizontal components of the forces exerted on the door by the hinges. Assume that the center of gravity of the door is at the geometrical center.

Ans. 13.3 lb

20. A uniform 30-lb gate is 4 ft high and 3 ft wide. It is supported by two hinges, the upper of which is 4 in. from the top and bears two-thirds the weight. The lower hinge is 4 in. from the bottom. Find the horizontal and vertical components of the force exerted on the gate by the lower hinge.

21. The horizontal bar AB in the accompanying figure is supported by the cord BC at one end and by a pin at the wall AC at the other end. The bar is of uniform cross section, weighs 25 lb, and is 5 ft long. If θ is 40°, what are the tension in the cord and the horizontal and vertical components of the force exerted on the bar by the pin at A?

Ans. 19.4 lb; 14.9 lb; 12.5 lb

22. In the accompanying figure the uniform horizontal bar 6 ft long weighs 50 lb, and the angle θ is 50°. What is the tension in the cord? What are the horizontal and vertical components of the force exerted on the bar by the pin at A?

23. The 100-lb horizontal bar AB in the accompanying figure is nonuniform, being 10 ft long with its center of gravity 4 ft from the wall. A 120-lb weight is suspended on the

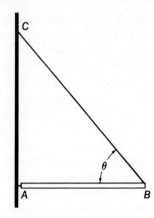

PROBS. 21 TO 24

bar 7 ft from the wall. The angle θ is 60°. What is the tension in the cord BC? Find the horizontal and vertical components of the force exerted on the bar by the pin at A.

Ans. 143 lb; 72 lb; 96 lb

24. The horizontal bar AB in the accompanying figure is nonuniform, being 8 m long with its center of gravity 3 m from the wall. The bar weighs 400 newtons. A 200-newton weight is suspended at the end B of the bar. What is the tension in the supporting cord if θ is 30°? What are the horizontal and vertical components of the force exerted on the bar by the pin at A?

25. Two vehicles are crossing a bridge 60 ft long. A passenger car weighing 3,000 lb is 10 ft from one end. A truck weighing 9,000 lb is 20 ft from the same end. If the bridge is symmetrical with respect to the center and weighs 50 tons, what are the forces on the two supports at the ends of the bridge? *Ans.* 58,500 lb; 53,500 lb

26. If weights A, B, C, D, and E are, respectively, located at distances a, b, c, d, and e from one end of a light bar, use the two conditions for equilibrium to show that the center of gravity is located a distance y from that end of the bar, where

$$y = \frac{Aa + Bb + Cc + Dd + Ee}{A + B + C + D + E}$$

27. A uniform ladder 20 ft long weighs 60 lb. It leans against a vertical frictionless wall with its lower end 12 ft from the wall and its upper end 16 ft from the ground. Draw a sketch showing all forces acting on the ladder. Find the force exerted on the ladder by the wall and the horizontal and vertical components of the force exerted on the ladder by the ground. *Ans.* 22.5 lb; 22.5 lb; 60 lb

28. A uniform 20-ft ladder weighing 40 lb rests against the smooth side of a house so that it makes an angle of 60° with the ground. A 160-lb man stands on the ladder at its center. What is the horizontal force exerted on the ladder by the house? What are the horizontal and vertical components of the force exerted on the ladder by the ground?

29. A ladder (Fig. 4.9) is 25 ft long, has its center of gravity 8 ft from the bottom, and weighs 60 lb. A man weighing 160 lb stands halfway up the ladder, which makes an angle of 20° with the vertical. Find the force exerted on the ladder by the smooth wall and the horizontal and vertical components of the force exerted on the ladder by the ground. *Ans.* 36 lb; 36 lb; 220 lb

30. A uniform ladder weighing 40 lb makes an angle of 60° with a horizontal sidewalk and is leaning against a smooth wall. The ladder is 15 ft long. Calculate the force exerted on the ladder by the wall and the horizontal and vertical components of the force exerted by the ground. If the coefficient of static friction between ladder and sidewalk is 0.30, at what angle with the vertical would the ladder be on the verge of slipping?

31. A uniform 26-ft ladder weighing 50 lb leans against a smooth wall with its base 10 ft from the wall. How far up the ladder can a 200-lb man climb if the maximum horizontal force available at the base is 60 lb? *Ans.* 15.5 ft

32. A uniform ladder 5 m long weighs 100 newtons. It leans against a smooth wall, making an angle of 60° with the horizontal ground. How far up the ladder can a man weighing 800 newtons climb before the ladder slips if the maximum frictional force the ground can provide is 400 newtons?

33. A simple light triangular frame *ABC* (see accompanying figure) is held together by pins. If sides *AB* and *BC* are both 5 ft long while *AC* is 6 ft, find the horizontal and vertical components of the force exerted on the pin at *A* by member *BC* when *W* is 80 lb. What is the tension in member *AC*? *Ans.* 30 lb; 40 lb; 30 lb

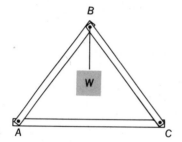

PROBS. 33 AND 34

34. If a light triangular frame *ABC* which is held together by pins (see accompanying figure) is equilateral with sides 2 m in length, and *W* is 100 newtons, find the tension in member *AC* and the compressional force exerted by member *AB*.

35. A horizontal uniform steel beam weighs 300 lb and is 6 ft long. It is supported at a vertical wall by a pin at one end and by a cable making an angle of 37° with the horizontal, attached 1 ft from the other end and running to a clamping point on the wall. A load of 800 lb is suspended from the end of the beam away from the wall. Find the tension in the cable and the horizontal and vertical components of the force exerted on the bar by the pin. What is the direction of the vertical component?
Ans. 1,900 lb; 1,520 lb; 40 lb; downward

36. If the load hanging from the end of the boom of Figure 4.10 were increased from 3 tons to 5 tons, what would be the new magnitudes of *H*, *V*, and *T*?

37. A derrick, similar to that of part (*c*) of the figure for Probs. 25 and 26 in Chap. 3, has a uniform boom 20 ft long which weighs 2,000 lb. A load *W* of 4,000 lb is suspended from one end. Find the tension in the cable and the horizontal and vertical components of the force exerted on the boom by the pin at the base.
Ans. 10,720 lb; 8,570 lb; 12,430 lb

CHAPTER 5 *We know that if the resultant force on a body is zero, the body has a constant linear velocity. What happens if the resultant force is not zero? Then the velocity changes, and the motion is said to be* accelerated. *Before we relate the resultant force on the body to the rate of change of velocity in Chap. 6, we introduce the concept of* acceleration *and consider the motion of a body subject to a constant acceleration. A familiar example is a freely falling ball or projectile.*

Linear Motion

5.1 Types of Motion

As we saw in Chap. 3, the linear velocity of a body is constant when the vector sum of the forces acting on the body is zero. This fact immediately suggests that if the resultant force is not zero, the velocity of the body must be changing. Before we relate this change in velocity to the force, it is important that we develop some of the equations of *kinematics,* the science of motion. In this chapter we deal with some of the simpler but relatively important problems of linear motion. (In order to treat advanced problems in kinematics, it is necessary to use *calculus,* a branch of mathematics developed by Newton and Leibnitz to solve such problems.)

In the motion of an automobile chassis along a straight road or of an elevator up and down in its shaft, all points of the body move along parallel lines. Any object which moves in this way is said to undergo a motion of pure *translation,* or a linear motion. On the other hand, a merry-go-round and the flywheel of a stationary engine revolve about stationary axes. Such a body is said to undergo a motion of *pure rotation,* or an angular motion. All points in the object describe concentric circles about the axis. We shall defer further consideration of rotational motion to Chap. 10 and confine our attention in this chapter to several types of translational motion. If we are dealing with a rigid body, we can always resolve its motion, regardless of how complex it may be, into pure translation of the center of mass and pure rotation about the center of mass. The motion of the wheel of a train or of a boomerang flying through the air may be regarded as a combination of translational and rotational motions.

5.2 Instantaneous Velocity

In dealing with the motion of an object, we shall be concerned with how its displacement and velocity change in time. Suppose we are interested in the motion of an automobile. Let s_0 be the displacement at the instant we start our stop watch, which hereafter reads the time t. We use a subscript zero to indicate the value of any quantity measured at the time $t = 0$. A time t sec later, let the displacement be $\mathbf{s}$ (Fig. 5.1). We have already defined average velocity as

$$\mathbf{v}_{av} = \frac{\mathbf{s} - \mathbf{s}_0}{t} \qquad\qquad 5.1$$

More often than not we shall choose to measure our distances from the point where the automobile is when $t = 0$. Then $\mathbf{s}_0 = 0$, and

$$\mathbf{v}_{av} = \frac{\mathbf{s}}{t} \qquad\qquad 5.1a$$

The velocity of the automobile may well be changing. If so, we may be interested in how fast (and in what direction) it is moving at a given instant—a quantity which we call the *instantaneous velocity*. If we want to know the velocity at a given instant as the car passes a telephone pole, we may proceed as follows: We measure the average velocity of the car in the block containing the telephone pole by dividing the length of the block by the time required to cover the block. This will probably be closer to the velocity at the instant of passing than would the average velocity over some longer period. We might come closer to the instantaneous velocity by determining where the car was 1 sec before it reached the pole and 1 sec after it passed the pole, but this still gives us an average velocity over a 2-sec interval. To get closer to the instantaneous velocity, we measure the displacement over shorter and shorter time intervals. Let $\Delta\mathbf{s} = \mathbf{s}_2 - \mathbf{s}_1$ represent the displacement of the car during a short time interval Δt. (Here we are using the Greek letter Δ as mathematical shorthand to mean "a small change in.") The ratio $\Delta\mathbf{s}/\Delta t$ gives us the average velocity during the time interval $\Delta t = t_2 - t_1$. As we make Δt shorter and shorter, this average velocity comes closer and closer to the instantaneous velocity. We define the instantaneous velocity $\mathbf{v}$ as the limit approached by $\Delta\mathbf{s}/\Delta t$ as Δt becomes smaller and smaller,

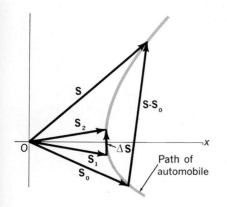

FIGURE 5.1

Average velocity over a time interval t is the ratio of the displacement $\mathbf{s} - \mathbf{s}_0$ to the time; instantaneous velocity is the limit of the ratio $\Delta\mathbf{s}/\Delta t$ as Δt approaches zero.

approaching zero as a limit. We may write this in the form of an equation:

$$\mathbf{v} = \lim_{\Delta t \to 0} \frac{\Delta \mathbf{s}}{\Delta t} \left(= \frac{d\mathbf{s}}{dt} \text{ in calculus notation} \right) \qquad 5.2$$

The instantaneous speed is the magnitude of the instantaneous velocity. The speedometer of an automobile is designed to read instantaneous speed.

5.3 Acceleration

When an automobile is driven in city traffic, its velocity is continually changing. It is zero while the car is waiting for a red light to change; when the traffic light goes green, the velocity is increased for a while and then varies up and down as traffic conditions require until the car is again brought to rest. Figure 5.2 shows a possible pattern for such a motion. Notice that after the first stop light the car picked up speed rapidly, while after the second it gained velocity slowly.

In treating motion in which the velocity is changing, it is convenient to introduce a new term: *acceleration. Acceleration is the time rate of change of velocity.* The word *deceleration* is often used to mean negative acceleration. The average acceleration over any period of time t is the change in velocity divided by the corresponding change in time.

$$\mathbf{a}_{av} = \frac{\mathbf{v} - \mathbf{v}_0}{t} \qquad 5.3$$

In the rather complex motion shown in Figure 5.2 the acceleration varies, and we define instantaneous acceleration $\mathbf{a}$ as

$$\mathbf{a} = \lim_{\Delta t \to 0} \frac{\Delta \mathbf{v}}{\Delta t} \qquad 5.4$$

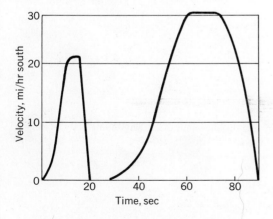

FIGURE 5.2
Velocity plotted as a function of time for an automobile.

From the definition of acceleration we see that it has the units of velocity divided by time, since it tells us how much the velocity changes per unit of time. For example, acceleration may be expressed in feet per second per second (ft/sec^2). In discussing the motion of an automobile, we might measure the change in velocity in miles per hour and the change in time in seconds. Then the acceleration would be in miles per hour per second. If an automobile decelerates from 30 mi/hr to 10 mi/hr in 10 sec, the average acceleration is -20 mi/hr divided by 10 sec, or -2 mi/hr-sec. In metric units we shall most often measure acceleration in meters per second per second.

Example An automobile manufacturer advertises that his product can start from rest and reach 60 mi/hr (88 ft/sec) in less than 11 sec. What minimum average acceleration is required?

$$a_{av} = \frac{v - v_0}{t} = \frac{88 \text{ ft/sec}}{11 \text{ sec}} = 8 \text{ ft/sec}^2$$

$<$ The mathematical treatment of motions in which the acceleration varies irregularly is beyond the scope of this text. We shall confine our discussion to several very important types of motion in which the acceleration is either constant or varies in some relatively simple way. We begin by considering the case in which the acceleration is constant and the motion takes place along a straight line.

5.4 Uniformly Accelerated Rectilinear Motion

If a ball is dropped and its velocity measured as a function of time, it is found that the velocity is 3.2 ft/sec 0.1 sec after release, 6.4 after 0.2 sec, 9.6 after 0.3 sec, and so forth. The velocity and displacement vary with time after release as shown in Figure 5.3. Each tenth of a second the velocity increases 3.2 ft/sec; each second it increases 32 ft/sec.

The acceleration of a freely falling body at mean sea level and 45° latitude is 32.17398 ft/sec^2, or 9.80665 m/sec^2. It varies slightly from

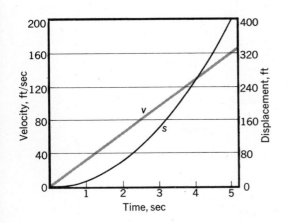

FIGURE 5.3

Velocity and displacement of a freely falling body as functions of time.

place to place for reasons which are discussed in Chap. 9. By a freely
falling body we mean one for which the air resistance is negligible.
Obviously, a feather does not fall through the air with this large
an acceleration because of the substantial air friction, but if it is
released in an evacuated tube, it has the same acceleration as a steel
ball (Fig. 5.4). When a body is falling freely through the air, the
effect of air friction depends on the velocity, size, shape, density, and
surface of the falling object. This friction naturally reduces the
acceleration somewhat for a falling body, but if a ball is thrown
upward, air friction increases the downward acceleration on the way
up. We represent the acceleration due to gravity by g. In our problems on falling bodies we shall take $g = 32.0$ ft/sec^2 or 9.80 m/sec^2,
thereby making the arithmetic of the problems a little simpler.

When the acceleration is constant, the average velocity during any
time interval is given by

$$v_{av} = \frac{v + v_0}{2} \qquad\qquad \text{5.5}$$

If a ball is released from rest and falls for 3 sec, its initial velocity is 0
and its final velocity is 96 ft/sec. During these 3 sec the average
velocity is $(96 + 0)/2 = 48$ ft/sec. Similarly, if an automobile is *uniformly accelerated* from 20 mi/hr to 60 mi/hr, the average velocity
during the acceleration is 40 mi/hr. Equation (5.5) together with the
equations defining average velocity and acceleration are the three
fundamental equations for uniformly accelerated motion. If we measure
displacement from the position of the body at $t = 0$,

FIGURE 5.4
Equal accelerations are measured when a feather and a steel
ball fall in the absence of air
resistance.

$$v_{av} = \frac{s}{t} \qquad\qquad \text{5.1}a$$

$$a = \frac{v - v_0}{t} \qquad\qquad \text{5.3}$$

$$v_{av} = \frac{v + v_0}{2} \qquad\qquad \text{5.5}$$

These basic equations may be combined in many ways; two of the
possibilities are of particular usefulness. They are

$$s = v_0 t + \tfrac{1}{2}at^2 \qquad\qquad \text{5.6}$$
$$v^2 = v_0^2 + 2as \qquad\qquad \text{5.7}$$

Equation (5.6) may be obtained by combining Eqs. (5.1a), (5.3), and
(5.5) as follows:

$$s = v_{av}t \qquad\qquad \text{by Eq. (5.1}a\text{)}$$

$$= \frac{v + v_0}{2}t \qquad\qquad \text{by use of Eq. (5.5)}$$

$$= \frac{v_0 + at + v_0}{2}t \qquad\qquad \text{by use of Eq. (5.3)}$$

$$= v_0 t + \tfrac{1}{2}at^2$$

Equation (5.7) may be derived by multiplying $s = [(v + v_0)/2]t$ by
$a = (v - v_0)/t$ which gives $as = (v^2 - v_0^2)/2$ or $2as = v^2 - v_0^2$.

In the relations developed above, it is important to observe that s is the displacement of the body and not the total distance traversed. For example, if we throw a ball up into the air with a speed of 96 ft/sec and ask what the displacement is at the end of 5 sec, the relations above will provide the answer, which is 80 ft. Figure 5.5 shows the displacement measured upward as functions of time and velocity. During the 5 sec the ball traverses a much greater distance. Indeed, at the end of 3 sec it is at a height of 144 ft.

A second caution has to do with the fact that displacement, velocity, and acceleration are *vector* quantities, and due regard must be given to direction. Which direction one elects to choose as positive is one's own free choice, but once it is decided that upward is positive, any vector quantity which is downward must be given a negative sign. If we return once more to the problem of throwing a ball upward with a speed of 96 ft/sec, we may decide to choose upward as the positive direction. If we do, $v_0 = 96$ ft/sec, but $a = -32$ ft/sec². An alternative choice would be to call downward positive. Then v_0 becomes -96 ft/sec, and $a = +32$ ft/sec².

Equations (5.5) to (5.7) have been developed *only* for the case in which $\mathbf{s}$, $\mathbf{v}$, $\mathbf{v}_0$, and $\mathbf{a}$ all act along the same straight line. If these vectors have different directions but $\mathbf{a}$ is constant, the x components of the vectors satisfy these equations—and so do the y and z components. Indeed, Eqs. (5.5) and (5.6) are valid equations when the quantities are written as vectors, but Eq. (5.7) is not.

Example A baseball is dropped from the top of the Washington Monument, which is 555 ft high. Find how long it takes to reach the ground, its velocity when it hits, and the average velocity during the fall.

Let us take downward as positive. Then $a = 32.0$ ft/sec², $s = 555$ ft, and $v_0 = 0$.

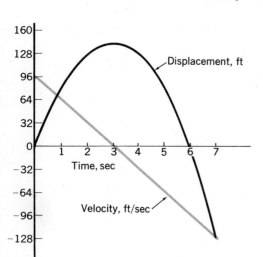

FIGURE 5.5

Displacement and velocity of a ball thrown upward at $t = 0$ with a speed of 96 ft/sec as functions of time.

By Eq. (5.6),

$$s = v_0t + \tfrac{1}{2}at^2$$
$$555 \text{ ft} = 0 + \tfrac{1}{2}(32.0 \text{ ft/sec}^2)t^2$$
$$t^2 = \frac{555 \text{ ft}}{16.0 \text{ ft/sec}^2} = 34.7 \text{ sec}^2$$
$$t = 5.89 \text{ sec}$$

By Eq. (5.7),

$$v^2 = v_0{}^2 + 2as$$
$$= 0 + 2 \times 32.0 \text{ ft/sec}^2 \times 555 \text{ ft}$$
$$= 35{,}500 \text{ ft}^2/\text{sec}^2$$
$$v = 188 \text{ ft/sec}$$

By Eq. (5.1),

$$s = v_{av}t$$
$$555 \text{ ft} = v_{av} \times 5.89 \text{ sec}$$
$$v_{av} = 94 \text{ ft/sec}$$

Check: By Eq. (5.5),

$$v_{av} = \frac{v_0 + v}{2} = \frac{188}{2} \text{ ft/sec}$$

Example A ball is thrown upward from a bridge with a speed of 48 ft/sec. It misses the bridge on the way down and lands in the water 160 ft below. Find how long the ball rises, how high it goes, how long it is in the air, and its velocity when it strikes the water.

Let us take upward as positive. Then $v_0 = 48$ ft/sec, and $a = -32$ ft/sec^2. The ball rises until $v = 0$.

By Eq. (5.3),

$$a = \frac{v - v_0}{t}$$
$$-32 \text{ ft/sec}^2 = \frac{0 - 48 \text{ ft/sec}}{t}$$
$$t = \frac{48 \text{ ft/sec}}{32 \text{ ft/sec}^2} = 1.5 \text{ sec}$$

During this 1.5 sec,

$$v_{av} = \frac{v + v_0}{2} = \frac{0 + 48 \text{ ft/sec}}{2} = 24 \text{ ft/sec}$$

and

$$s = v_{av}t = 24 \text{ ft/sec} \times 1.5 \text{ sec} = 36 \text{ ft up}$$

By Eq. (5.6),

$$s = v_0t + \tfrac{1}{2}at^2$$
$$-160 = 48t + \tfrac{1}{2}(-32)t^2 \qquad \text{(Note that } s \text{ is negative.)}$$
$$t^2 - 3t - 10 = 0$$
$$t = +5 \text{ sec (or } -2 \text{ sec)}$$

(Clearly we want the positive answer here. The negative answer tells us how much before we threw the ball we would have had to fire it upward from the water to have it pass the bridge going 48 ft/sec at $t = 0$.)

By Eq. (5.3),

$$a = \frac{v - v_0}{t}$$

$$-32 \text{ ft/sec}^2 = \frac{v - 48 \text{ ft/sec}}{5 \text{ sec}}$$

$$v = -112 \text{ ft/sec} \qquad \text{(The minus sign means downward.)}$$

Check:

$$s = v_{\text{av}}t = \frac{v + v_0}{2} t$$

$$-160 = \frac{(-112 + 48)}{2} 5$$

$$= -160$$

5.5 Path of a Projectile Fired Horizontally

If a body is projected horizontally from the top of a tower of height h (Fig. 5.6) with a velocity v_x, it continues to move with the same horizontal velocity it had at the beginning of its path (any decrease caused by the resistance of the air is neglected). At the same time the body falls because of the attraction of the earth. Hence, at any instant the velocity of the projectile has two components: a horizontal component which remains constant and a downward component which increases with the time. The horizontal component of the velocity and the horizontal displacement are independent of whether or not the body is falling. Similarly, the vertical components of the displacement, velocity, and acceleration are independent of whether or not the body is moving horizontally.

If a bullet is fired horizontally with a velocity of 2,000 ft/sec, it falls 16 ft in 1 sec, 64 ft in 2 sec, and so forth, just exactly as would a bullet which was simply dropped from the end of the gun. In this case the vertical velocity of the body after t sec is given by $v_y = gt$. The horizontal component of the velocity remains constant, so that the resulting velocity, which is tangent to the path of the body, has a magnitude $v = \sqrt{v_x^2 + v_y^2} = \sqrt{v_x^2 + g^2t^2}$. The horizontal displacement s_x of the body in time t is equal to v_xt, while the distance the body falls in the same time is $s_y = \frac{1}{2}gt^2$.

When an aircraft flying straight and level releases a bomb, the bomb continues to move forward with constant horizontal velocity until it strikes the ground (if air friction is neglected). The downward velocity component, which was zero at release, increases linearly with time because of the acceleration of gravity. In order to hit the target, the bomb must be released some time before the aircraft is directly above the target. The time of release is determined by the velocity of the aircraft and its height above the ground.

FIGURE 5.6

Path of a body projected horizontally. The downward component of the displacement at time t is $\frac{1}{2}gt^2$, while the horizontal component is v_xt.

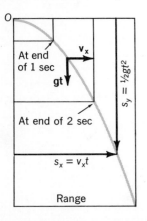

Example   A ball is thrown horizontally with a velocity of 50 ft/sec from a tower 100 ft high.   Find the time of flight, the horizontal range, and the speed of the ball just before it strikes the ground.

Let us choose downward as positive.   For the vertical motion, $a_y = 32$ ft/sec^2, $v_{0y} = 0$, and $s_y = 100$ ft.   By Eq. (5.6),

$$s_y = v_{0y}t + \tfrac{1}{2}a_y t^2$$
$$100 \text{ ft} = 0 + \tfrac{1}{2}(32 \text{ ft/sec}^2)t^2$$
$$t = 2.5 \text{ sec}$$

The horizontal range s_x is the horizontal velocity (which is constant at 50 ft/sec) multiplied by the time of flight.

$$s_x = v_x t = 50 \text{ ft/sec} \times 2.5 \text{ sec} = 125 \text{ ft}$$

Just before hitting, $v_x = 50$ ft/sec, and, by Eq. (5.3),

$$v_y = a_y t = 80 \text{ ft/sec}$$
$$v = \sqrt{v_x{}^2 + v_y{}^2} = \sqrt{(80)^2 + (50)^2} \text{ ft/sec} = 94 \text{ ft/sec}$$

5.6 Projectile Fired at an Angle with the Horizontal

If an object is given a velocity **V** at an angle θ with the horizontal, it follows a parabolic path (Fig. 5.7).   If there were no gravity, this projectile would move along the line **V**t.   In time t the effect of gravity is to bring the projectile a distance $\tfrac{1}{2}gt^2$ below this line.   In treating projectile problems we shall assume that air friction is negligible, that the horizontal component of the velocity remains constant, and that the vertical motion has uniform acceleration **g**.   These are reasonable approximations for our purposes, but they are not entirely justified in many practical situations.

The first step in analyzing the motion of a projectile fired at an angle with the horizontal is to resolve the velocity of projection into vertical and horizontal components.   If the velocity of projection **V** makes an angle θ with the horizontal, the horizontal component is $v_x = V \cos \theta$, the vertical component $v_y = V \sin \theta$.   The horizontal velocity remains constant, but the vertical component changes.   After time t the vertical component is $v_y = V \sin \theta - gt$.   The projectile rises until the vertical

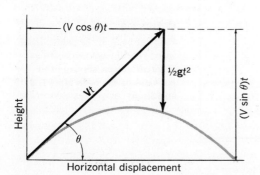

FIGURE 5.7
Path of a body projected at an angle θ above the horizontal axis.

component of the velocity becomes zero. At this instant the height is maximum, and the time of rise t_r is given by

$$0 = V \sin \theta - g t_r \qquad \text{or} \qquad t_r = \frac{V \sin \theta}{g}$$

The total time the projectile is in the air is the sum of the time of rise t_r and the time of fall t_f. Throughout the time of flight the horizontal component of the velocity remains constant at $V \cos \theta$. The horizontal range of the projectile is therefore $V \cos \theta \, (t_r + t_f)$. If the projectile falls to the same height from which it was projected, the time of fall is the same as the time of rise, and the time of flight is given by $t_r + t_f = (2V \sin \theta)/g$. In this case maximum range is attained when $\theta = 45°$ (Fig. 5.8) if air friction is negligible. Note that under these conditions the range is the same for any two complementary angles.

Example A punter kicks a football with a velocity of 80 ft/sec at an angle of 37° with the horizon. Find the time during which the ball rises, how high it goes, and the length of the kick (from punter's toe to receiver's hands).

The vertical component of the initial velocity is (80 ft/sec) sin 37° = 48 ft/sec, and the horizontal component (80 ft/sec) cos 37° = 64 ft/sec. If we choose upward as positive for the vertical motion, $v_{0y} = 48$ ft/sec, and $a_y = -32$ ft/sec². At the top of the path $v_y = 0$; thus, by Eq. (5.3),

$$-32 \text{ ft/sec}^2 = \frac{0 - 48 \text{ ft/sec}}{t}$$

$$t = 1.5 \text{ sec}$$

On the way up, the average velocity is (by Eq. 5.5) 24 ft/sec. Since $s_y = v_{av}t$, we have $s_y = 24$ ft/sec $\times$ 1.5 sec = 36 ft, which is how high the ball goes.

It takes as long for the ball to come down as it did to go up, so that

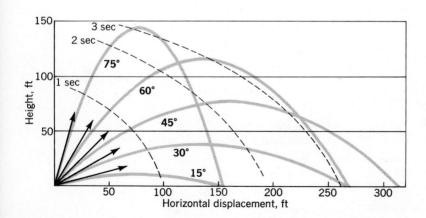

FIGURE 5.8

Paths of balls of the same initial speed (100 ft/sec) projected at different angles, showing the positions of the balls after 1, 2, and 3 sec.

the total time in the air is 3.0 sec. In this time the horizontal velocity is constant at 64 ft/sec, so that

$$s_x = 64 \text{ ft/sec} \times 3.0 \text{ sec} = 192 \text{ ft or } 64 \text{ yd}$$

Example A stone is thrown from the edge of a cliff with a velocity of 50 ft/sec at an angle of 30° above the horizontal. Four seconds later it strikes the ocean below. Find the height of the cliff above the ocean and the horizontal range of the stone.

The vertical component of the initial velocity is 50 sin 30° = 25 ft/sec upward. If we choose upward as positive, $v_{0y} = +25$ ft/sec, and $a_y = -32$ ft/sec². The vertical distance down to the ocean is given by

$$\begin{aligned} s_y &= v_{0y}t + \tfrac{1}{2}at^2 \\ &= (25 \text{ ft/sec} \times 4 \text{ sec}) + \tfrac{1}{2}(-32 \text{ ft/sec}^2 \times 16 \text{ sec}^2) \\ &= +100 \text{ ft} - 256 \text{ ft} \\ &= -156 \text{ ft} \end{aligned}$$

The horizontal range s_x is

$$s_x = v_x t$$

since v_x is constant.

$$\begin{aligned} v_x &= 50 \text{ ft/sec } \cos 30° = 43.3 \text{ ft/sec} \\ s_x &= 43.3 \text{ ft/sec} \times 4 \text{ sec} \\ &= 173 \text{ ft} \end{aligned}$$

Questions

1. If a body has a uniform velocity, what is the relationship among its initial, final, and average velocities? If a body has a uniform acceleration, what is the relationship among its initial, final, and average velocities?

2. Why are the sights on a rifle adjusted when the distance to the target is changed?

3. Draw the path of a stone thrown backwards with a speed of 40 ft/sec from the rear of a train traveling 50 ft/sec (a) from the point of view of the thrower and (b) from the frame of an observer on the ground.

4. What is the effect of air friction on the vertical motion of a baseball? On the horizontal motion? Compare the path of the baseball assuming air friction with the ideal parabolic path by means of a sketch.

5. Under what circumstances may a body have (a) an acceleration but no velocity, (b) an acceleration but constant speed, (c) a velocity but no acceleration, and (d) an acceleration which is constantly changing?

6. If a body is thrown vertically upward and air resistance is not negligible, is the time of rise equal to the time of fall? Which is greater? Explain.

7. For a given initial speed a football kicked at 35° has the same range as one kicked at 55°. Why would the lower trajectory be better for a quick kick when the receiving safety man is close to the line of scrimmage? Why would the higher trajectory be preferred if the receiver is back to catch the ball?

8. Why does an outfielder trying to cut off a run in a baseball game ordinarily try to get the ball to the catcher on the first bounce rather than on the fly?

9. Show that the speed of a ball is the same at any two points on its trajectory which are at the same height. How do the velocities at these two points compare?

Problems

Unless otherwise specified assume that air resistance is negligible and that g is 32 ft/sec^2 or 9.8 m/sec^2.

1. A uniformly accelerated body is moving with a velocity of 3 m/sec south; 5 sec later it has a velocity of 7 m/sec north. What is the acceleration? *Ans.* 2 m/sec^2 north

2. A uniformly accelerated body is moving with a velocity of 12 m/sec west; 5 sec later it has a velocity of 32 m/sec west. What is the acceleration?

3. An airplane starting from rest has a uniform acceleration of 4 ft/sec^2 south. What is its velocity at the end of 30 sec if this acceleration is maintained? *Ans.* 120 ft/sec south

4. During an interval of 10 sec a train on a straight track changes its velocity from 15 to 20 mi/hr. Determine the acceleration and the average velocity during that period, assuming that the change occurred uniformly.

5. A train has an acceleration of 3 ft/sec^2 in a direction opposite that of its motion. How long a time will the train require to stop if it is initially going 61 mi/hr (90 ft/sec)? How far will it travel in this time? *Ans.* 30 sec; 1,350 ft

6. A freight train starts from rest, is uniformly accelerated, and travels 450 ft in 15 sec. Find the acceleration, the average speed, and the final speed.

$\times$ **7.** A particle moves in a straight line with an acceleration of 2 m/sec^2. If it starts from rest, how far does it go in 3 sec? What is its velocity after 3 sec? How long a time is required for the particle to go 25 m? What is its speed as it passes the 25-m point? *Ans.* 9 m; 6 m/sec; 5 sec; 10 m/sec

8. A man has a 120-mile trip to make, of which the first half is over congested highways while the second half is over a good freeway. If he averages 40 mi/hr over the first 60 miles, at what average speed must he drive the remaining 60 miles to average 50 mi/hr for the entire trip?

9. A ball is dropped from a bridge. If it requires 5 sec for the ball to strike the ground below, how high is the bridge in meters? How fast is the ball traveling just before it reaches the ground? *Ans.* 122.5 m; 49 m/sec

10. A small object is given an initial downward velocity of 3 m/sec. (*a*) What is its velocity if it falls freely for 5 sec? (*b*) What is its displacement from the initial position?

$\times$ **11.** If an aircraft lands at a speed of 120 mi/hr (176 ft/sec) and the maximum deceleration which the braking system can produce is 8 ft/sec^2, find the minimum distance in which the plane can be stopped on level ground. How long does it take to bring the aircraft to rest? *Ans.* 1,936 ft; 22 sec

12. A naval aircraft is to be launched by a catapult from a carrier. If the catapult acts over a distance of 150 ft, find the minimum average acceleration which will give the aircraft a speed of 150 ft/sec at launching.

13. The takeoff speed of an airplane is 100 ft/sec. What uniform acceleration must this plane have if it is to become airborne after a 1,000-ft run? How long does the takeoff require?   *Ans.* 5 ft/sec²; 20 sec

14. The maximum deceleration which the tires of an automobile can produce on a certain pavement is 25 ft/sec². Find the minimum distance in which a car traveling 100 ft/sec (68 mi/hr) can be stopped, measuring from the point at which the brakes are first applied. How long does it take?

15. A ball is batted straight up and returns to the level of the batter in 5 sec. How high does the ball travel? What are its velocity and acceleration at the top of its flight? What are its initial and final velocities?

Ans. 100 ft; 0 ft/sec and 32 ft/sec² downward; 80 ft/sec upward and 80 ft/sec downward

16. With what initial velocity will a body moving along a vertical line have to be thrown if after 5 sec it is to be 50 ft above its starting place?

17. In a football game a passer throws the ball with a speed of 60 ft/sec. If he produces speed by moving the ball over a distance of 6 ft along a straight line, find the average acceleration during the throwing operation.   *Ans.* 300 ft/sec²

18. The speed of a baseball pitched by Bob Feller was once determined to be 145 ft/sec. What average acceleration must Feller have given the ball if this speed was produced over a distance of 8 ft?

19. When an aircraft lands on a carrier, it is arrested by a restraining cable which is engaged by a tail hook as the aircraft passes over the cable. If the cable produces an average deceleration of 2.5 g's (80 ft/sec²), how far does the aircraft move after it engages the cable at a speed of 120 ft/sec?   *Ans.* 90 ft

20. At $t = 0$ a body passes $x = 0$ with a velocity $v_x = 20$ m/sec. If the body has a constant acceleration $a_x = -5$ m/sec², find (*a*) the velocity when $t = 2$ sec, (*b*) the position of the body at $t = 2$ sec, (*c*) the time at which the body returns to $x = 0$, and (*d*) its velocity at this time.

21. An automobile starts from rest, maintains a constant acceleration of 5 ft/sec² until its speed is 50 ft/sec, and then continues at this speed. Find the time required for the car to go 1,000 ft.   *Ans.* 25 sec

22. A ball thrown from a tower with an initial velocity of 40 ft/sec downward falls freely for 3 sec. (*a*) What is its speed at the end of this interval? (*b*) How far does it travel?

23. A ball is thrown upward from the roof of a building. It has an initial velocity of 50 ft/sec. How high is the building if on its downward flight it just misses the thrower and falls to the ground 5 sec after it is thrown? With what speed does it strike the ground?   *Ans.* 150 ft; 110 ft/sec

24. A basketball player can reach 8 ft when standing. With what speed must he jump to be able to reach 11 ft?

25. A boy riding a bicycle at a speed of 15 ft/sec passes a parked car. Eight seconds later the car starts and is uniformly accelerated for 10 sec, at which time it passes the cyclist. What was the acceleration of the car?   *Ans.* 5.4 ft/sec²

26. An automobile traveling 45 mi/hr in a 25-mi/hr zone passes a parked patrol car. If the automobile maintains a constant speed and the patrol car a constant acceleration of 8 ft/sec², how long will it take the patrol car to catch the speeding vehicle, assuming the former starts as the latter passes by?

27. A boy on a bridge throws a stone horizontally with a speed of 25 m/sec, releasing the stone from a point 19.6 m above the surface of a river. How far from a point directly below the boy will the stone strike the water? *Ans.* 50 m

28. A bullet has a speed of 2,000 ft/sec as it leaves a rifle. If it is fired horizontally from a cliff 48 ft above a lake, what is the horizontal range of the bullet?

29. A golf ball is driven horizontally with a speed of 30 m/sec from a cliff 40 m high, and it lands on a level plain below. How long a time is the ball in the air? How far from the base of the cliff does it strike the ground? *Ans.* 2.86 sec; 85.7 m

30. A ski jumper takes off from a horizontal jumpoff. He lands 36 ft below the point of takeoff and 90 ft from a vertical line through this point. Find the speed of the skier as he takes off.

31. A bomber flying 600 mi/hr (880 ft/sec) straight and level at an altitude of 40,000 ft releases a bomb. Neglecting air friction (which is far from negligible), find how many miles in advance of the target the bombardier should release the bomb. How would air resistance affect the answer? *Ans.* 8.3 miles; would reduce distance

32. A ball is projected upward from the bottom of a tower that is 400 ft high, and, at the same instant, another ball is dropped from the top of the same tower. If the balls meet at a point halfway between the top and the bottom of the tower, with what initial velocity was the ball projected upward? How high will this ball rise?

33. A baseball is batted with a speed of 100 ft/sec at an angle of 53° with the ground. Find how long the ball is in air, how high the ball goes, how far from the plate it is caught, and the components of the velocity of the ball four seconds after it is hit.
Ans. 5 sec; 100 ft; 300 ft; 60 ft/sec and 48 ft/sec downward

34. At the kickoff a football is given a velocity of 80 ft/sec at an angle of 53° with the horizontal. Find how long the ball is in the air, how high the ball goes, how far from the kickoff point the ball lands, and the magnitude of the velocity of the ball 3 sec after it is kicked.

35. A golf ball is hit with a speed of 128 ft/sec at an angle of 30° with the horizontal from an elevated tee 36 ft above the fairway. How long is the ball in the air? At what horizontal distance from the tee does the ball strike the ground? *Ans.* 4.5 sec; 499 ft

36. A boy kicks a soccer ball off the ground, giving it a speed of 40 ft/sec at an angle of 53° with the horizontal. Find how long a time the ball is in the air, how high it goes, and the horizontal distance it traverses before it strikes the ground.

37. Find the minimum speed with which a baseball must be hit at an angle of 53° with the horizontal to leave the bat at a height of 3 ft and clear a 35-ft screen at a distance of 300 ft from home plate. Assume air friction is negligible. *Ans.* 104 ft/sec

38. A baseball is batted, and 6 sec later it is caught by the center fielder at a distance of 400 ft from the batter. Find the horizontal component of the ball's velocity, how high the ball went, and the vertical component of the velocity as the ball left the bat.

39. A golfer chips a ball high over a sand trap. If the ball leaves his club at an angle of 53° with the horizontal, what velocity must it be given to land 50 yd distant? (Assume the green is at the same level as the initial lie of the ball.) How high does the ball go? How long is it in the air? *Ans.* 70.7 ft/sec; 50 ft; 3.53 sec

40. A golf ball on a level fairway is given an initial velocity of 40 m/sec at an angle of 35° with the horizontal. If air friction is neglected, find (*a*) how long the ball is in the air, (*b*) how high it goes, and (*c*) how far away it lands.

41. A basketball player releases a ball 7 ft above the floor when he is 24 ft from the basket. The ball goes through the rim of the basket 10 ft above the floor 1.5 sec later. Find the horizontal component of the initial velocity, the vertical component of the initial velocity, and the maximum height above the floor reached by the ball.

Ans. 16 ft/sec; 26 ft/sec; 17.6 ft

42. Show that in a frictionless atmosphere the ratio of the maximum height to the horizontal range of a projectile fired at an angle θ above a level field is $(\tan \theta)/4$.

43. A baseball is given a velocity of 100 ft/sec at an angle of 53° above the horizontal. It leaves the bat at a height of 4 ft above the ground. What are its height and distance from home plate (*a*) after 2 sec and (*b*) after 4 sec? Will the ball clear a 20-ft fence 280 ft from the plate for a home run? By how much?

Ans. (*a*) 100 ft, 120 ft; (*b*) 68 ft, 240 ft; yes; about 8 ft

CHAPTER 6 *We wish to be able to predict the motion of any body subjected to a known system of forces. We have learned how to determine the resultant of a system of forces, and we know that the acceleration of the body is zero if the force resultant is zero. But what happens when the resultant is not zero? The answer to this question was formulated in the seventeenth century by Isaac Newton as the second of his three celebrated laws of motion.*

Force and Motion

6.1 Newton's First Law of Motion

It is a familiar fact that the motion of a body is intimately related to the forces which act upon it. However, for many centuries the exact way in which force and motion are related eluded the philosophers who speculated about the relationship. Aristotle expressed the idea that a body in motion comes to rest unless it has a force acting upon it continuously. For centuries men wondered what it was that pushed the planets around in the sky and what made the moon go around the earth. Although brilliant minds worked on the problem, no consistent and acceptable relationship between force and motion was established until the seventeenth century.

Galileo (1564–1642) performed a number of careful experiments on the motions of bodies, and it is largely to his work that we owe the equations of kinematics in the preceding chapter. Galileo studied accelerated motion both by dropping bodies and by rolling balls down inclined planes. He observed that, when friction was very small, a ball would roll for a great distance on a horizontal plane without stopping. Eventually, he became convinced that a ball on a perfectly frictionless horizontal plane would persist forever in its motion at constant speed. This revolutionary idea was one which was to prove most fruitful in developing an understanding of motion. Galileo discovered that bodies do not fall with constant speed; rather they have a *constant acceleration*. This suggested that the pull of the earth produced not the motion itself, but the change in the state of motion.

Isaac Newton (1642–1727) accepted Galileo's conclusions and formulated this idea as his first law of motion, which may be stated as follows:

Every body continues in its state of rest or of uniform velocity in a straight line unless it is compelled to change that state by the application of some resultant external force.

No actual body is ever completely free from external forces, but there are situations in which it is possible to make the resultant force approximately zero. In those cases we find that the body behaves in

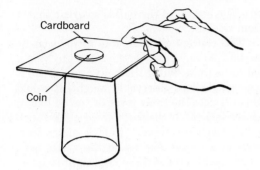

Cardboard

Coin

FIGURE 6.1
Newton's first law states that a body at rest remains at rest unless acted upon by some external unbalanced (i.e., resultant) force.

accordance with the first law of motion. Since we can never eliminate friction completely in our experiments, and since our efforts to compensate for it are imperfect, we must recognize that Newton's first law is an idealization. However, it is an idealization which provided the key for building a consistent and understandable theory of motion. There are, of course, many ways in which this great principle may be enunciated. Another statement is the following:

A body at rest remains at rest, and a body in motion remains in motion with constant velocity along the same straight line unless acted upon by some resultant force.

When a very small force acts on a reasonably massive body for a very short time, the resulting change in the velocity of the body is very small, and the zero-force requirement in Newton's first law is *almost* satisfied. Under these conditions we can snap a card from under a coin (Fig. 6.1) or jerk a tablecloth from under a glass. Newton's first law may also be invoked to explain how we put the head of a hammer onto the handle (Fig. 6.2).

6.2 Inertia

In Newton's first law of motion an important property of matter appears. It is known as inertia—that property of matter by which it maintains a constant velocity in the absence of an unbalanced external force. When an automobile is suddenly stopped, the passengers obey Newton's first law and continue in motion with constant velocity until some external force changes their state of motion. Seat belts in an automobile can provide such an external force—one much preferred to that exerted by the windshield or dashboard. A man running on an icy sidewalk finds it difficult to stop suddenly because friction is inadequate to provide the necessary external force. When a baseball leaves the pitcher's hand, it continues to move with essentially constant velocity until it reaches the catcher's glove. No force is required to keep it moving. Of course, the ball is slowed down slightly by air resistance and is pulled toward the earth by its weight.

If a heavy ball is suspended from a string (Fig. 6.3) and an identical string is fastened below, the upper string breaks under a slowly increasing steady pull from below. But if a sudden jerk is applied to

FIGURE 6.2
Newton's first law also states that a body in motion remains in motion with constant velocity unless acted upon by some resultant force.

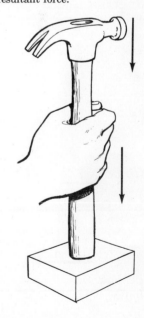

FIGURE 6.3

Inertia is one aspect of mass. A slow continuous increase in the downward force breaks the string above the heavy ball, but a sudden increase breaks the lower string.

the lower string, it breaks. The inertia of the ball is so great that it isolates the upper string from the jerk.

All matter has inertia. The concept of mass was introduced by Newton as a measure of inertia. At any point on the earth the weight of any body is proportional to its mass, but if the body were in interplanetary space where it no longer had observable weight, it would still have inertia. It would still take the same force of toe on ball to give a football a specified acceleration. If the football were filled with mercury, its inertia would be greatly increased. To kick such a football would be just as painful in a rocket ship as on the earth, even though the mercury-filled ball might have little or no weight in interplanetary space.

6.3 Newton's Second Law

If no external unbalanced force acts upon a body, it maintains a constant velocity. What happens if there is an external unbalanced force? To answer this question quantitatively, let us consider a set of idealized experiments.

1. Suppose that we have a perfectly level and frictionless table along which we can accelerate a mass of several kilograms. (We could make the friction very small by using small wheels with roller bearings.) If we now take an accurately calibrated spring balance and exert a force **F** on the mass, a certain acceleration is produced. Let us measure this acceleration. Next, let us exert exactly twice as great a force and again measure the acceleration (Fig. 6.4). We find the acceleration to be exactly double the first acceleration. If we again double the resultant force, the acceleration doubles once more and is thus four times the first acceleration. By measuring the acceleration for a large number of different resultant forces, we find that (within experimental error) the *acceleration* of our chosen mass *is directly proportional to the resultant force* **F,** and its direction is that of the *resultant* force.

2. Next suppose that we choose a resultant force **F** and measure the acceleration it produces on a mass of 1 kg. Then let us keep the force constant but increase the mass accelerated to 2 kg (Fig. 6.5). We find the acceleration is half as great as it was the first time. If we increase the mass accelerated to 3 kg and measure the acceleration, we find it

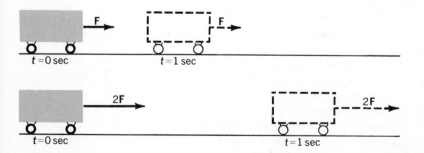

FIGURE 6.4

The acceleration of a body is directly proportional to the resultant force acting on the body.

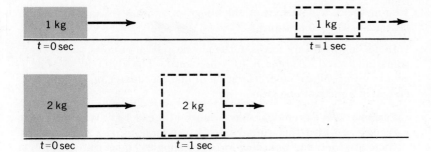

FIGURE 6.5
The acceleration due to a given resultant force is inversely proportional to the mass accelerated.

is one-third as great. If this experiment is performed for a number of different masses, we find that the data are consistent with the idea that *the acceleration* **a** *is inversely proportional to the mass accelerated.*

If we combine the results of these two series of experiments, we conclude that

$$\mathbf{a} = \frac{k\mathbf{F}}{m} \qquad \text{6.1}$$

This equation is a statement (in restricted form) of Newton's second law of motion. *The acceleration of a body is directly proportional to the resultant force acting upon it and is inversely proportional to the mass of the body.*

The proportionality constant k in Eq. (6.1) depends upon the units in which the force, the mass, and the acceleration are measured. By a suitable choice of these units one can make the constant k equal to unity. Such a choice results in convenience in handling the great structure of mechanics which is built around Newton's second law of motion. Unfortunately, many different schemes for making $k = 1$ have been devised. Each has advantages and disadvantages. In our work with Newton's second law and its consequences, we shall use two of the many possible choices—one for working in the metric system and a very different one for the English system.

6.4 The Newton

In the metric system we have defined the fundamental units of mass (the kilogram), length (the meter), and time (the second). In order to write Newton's second law in the form

$$\mathbf{F} = m\mathbf{a} \qquad \text{6.2}$$

we define a new unit of force called the *newton*. *One newton is that force which produces an acceleration of one meter per second per second in a mass of one kilogram.*

The newton is the basic force unit in the mks system of units; its value is about 0.2248 lb. The newton is a so-called "absolute" unit of force because its definition is made without any reference to the earth or its pull. From $\mathbf{F} = m\mathbf{a}$, we see that 1 newton is equivalent to

1 kg-m/sec². The weight of one kilogram at sea level and 45° north latitude is 9.80665 newtons.

<   In dealing with tiny forces in the metric system of units, the dyne is sometimes used (1 dyne = 10^{-5} newton). The dyne is the force required to produce an acceleration of one centimeter per second per second in a mass of one gram.

Example   An automobile has a mass of 1,600 kg. What force is required to give this automobile an acceleration of 1.20 m/sec² if there are frictional retarding forces totaling 200 newtons?

By Newton's second law, the unbalanced force is given by

$F = ma$
   $= 1,600$ kg $\times$ 1.20 m/sec²
   $= 1,920$ newtons

This is the resultant, or unbalanced, force on the automobile. The total force is

1,920 newtons + 200 newtons = 2,120 newtons

6.5 Gravitational Units of Force

For the *British engineering system* of units an entirely different approach is adopted. The constant k in Newton's second law of motion is made equal to unity by choosing not a new unit of force, but a new unit of mass.[1] In this system the basic unit chosen for acceleration is the foot per second per second, and the basic force unit is the pound, which is the gravitational attraction of the earth for a 1-lb mass at a place where the acceleration due to gravity has the value 32.17398 ft/sec². This force unit is known as a *gravitational unit,* since it is defined in terms of the pull of gravity on a standard object. Once we have chosen such a force unit and an acceleration unit, we make k equal to unity by choosing a new unit of mass. This unit, called the *slug* (*slug*gishness = inertia), is defined as follows: *One slug is the mass of a body which experiences an acceleration of one foot per second per second when acted upon by an unbalanced external force of one pound.*

   A force of 1 lb gives a 1-lb mass an acceleration of 32.17 ft/sec² and gives a 1-slug mass an acceleration of 1 ft/sec². Therefore, the slug has a mass slightly more than 32 times that of the standard pound mass. In the British engineering system, forces are measured in pounds, masses in slugs, and accelerations in feet per second per second.

   When the unbalanced force acting on a body is its weight **W,** the resulting acceleration is **g,** the acceleration due to gravity. For this case $\mathbf{F} = m\mathbf{a}$ becomes

$$\mathbf{W} = m\mathbf{g} \qquad\qquad \text{6.3}$$

[1] An alternative giving rise to the British *absolute* system of units is to retain the pound as a unit of mass and to define a new unit of force called the *poundal.* One poundal is that force which produces an acceleration of one foot per second per second in a mass of one pound.

If we divide Eq. (6.2) by Eq. (6.3), we obtain $\mathbf{F}/\mathbf{W} = \mathbf{a}/\mathbf{g}$, or

$$\mathbf{F} = \frac{W}{g}\mathbf{a} \qquad\qquad 6.4$$

a form in which it is often convenient to put Newton's second law, especially when using the British engineering system of units.

Example A 160-lb man stands in an elevator. Find the force exerted on the man by the floor of the elevator (a) when the elevator has an upward acceleration of 4.0 ft/sec², (b) when the elevator has a downward acceleration of 4.0 ft/sec², and (c) when the elevator has a constant downward velocity of 4 ft/sec.

(a)

$$F = ma = \frac{W}{g}a$$

$$= \frac{160 \text{ lb}}{32 \text{ ft/sec}^2} \times 4.0 \text{ ft/sec}^2 = 20 \text{ lb}$$

This is the *unbalanced force* on the man. If E is the force exerted by the elevator, $F = E - W$, $20 = E - 160$, or $E = 180$ lb upward.

(b) The unbalanced force is now 20 lb downward so that E is 20 lb less than W.

$$E = 160 - 20 = 140 \text{ lb}$$

(c) If the velocity is constant, $a = 0$, and the unbalanced force is zero. The elevator exerts a force just equal to the man's weight.

$$E = W = 160 \text{ lb}$$

6.6 Newton's Third Law of Motion

In Sec. 3.2 we introduced Newton's third law in treating a system of bodies at rest. This law is equally valid in dealing with bodies in motion, either uniform or accelerated. The wheels of an automobile in motion push backward on the road, but the road pushes forward on the wheels with an equal force. *Whenever one body exerts a force upon a second body, the second body exerts an equal and opposite force on the first.*

Whenever a force acts upon a body, there is always an equal and opposite force exerted by the body (Figs. 6.6 and 6.7). A train pulls the locomotive back with a force which is exactly as great as the for-

FIGURE 6.6
The action (force exerted on the trailer by the car) is equal to the reaction (force exerted on the car by the trailer).

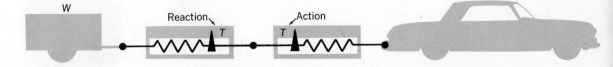

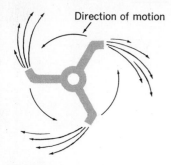

Direction of motion

FIGURE 6.7

The force of the water pushing forward on the nozzle is exactly equal and opposite to the force the nozzle exerts on the water.

FIGURE 6.8

An Atwood's machine.

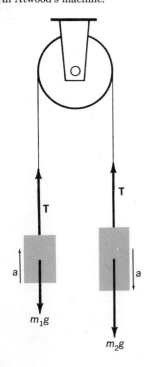

ward force which the locomotive exerts on the train. A helicopter pushes downward on the air with a force equal to that which the air exerts upward on the helicopter. The sun pulls on the earth and the earth pulls on the sun with equal and opposite forces. Newton stated his third law in the form: *To every action there is an equal and contrary reaction.* Here the term "action" is used to imply "force."

6.7 Application of Newton's Second Law

In a problem involving Newton's second law, the first question which we must ask ourselves is: To what body do we wish to apply $\mathbf{F} = m\mathbf{a}$? Once this question is answered, we must find *all the forces* which act on this body and determine their resultant $\mathbf{F}$. In many situations it is desirable to isolate the body and draw a diagram showing every force which acts on the body. Note that $\mathbf{F}$ is the resultant force, while m is the mass accelerated by $\mathbf{F}$.

Newton's second law can be applied to a system of bodies as well as to individual bodies. For example, it applies equally well to a system composed of an elevator, several people, and their luggage as to any one individual in the elevator.

Consider two masses m_1 and m_2 ($m_2 > m_1$) suspended by an inextensible string which passes over a frictionless pulley (Fig. 6.8). Such an arrangement is known as an *Atwood's machine.* We wish to find the tension T in the string and the acceleration a of the system. Since the string is inextensible, the accelerations of both masses have the same magnitude. We now apply Newton's second law to each mass separately. For m_2 there is a downward force m_2g and an upward force T; the resultant force is $m_2g - T$. For m_1, which rises, the unbalanced force is $T - m_1g$. Hence,

For m_2: $\qquad m_2g - T = m_2a$
For m_1: $\qquad T - m_1g = m_1a$

If we add these equations, we obtain

$$m_2g - m_1g = (m_1 + m_2)a$$

which is just what we obtain from applying Newton's second law to the system composed of m_1 plus m_2.

If $m_1 = 1.20$ kg and $m_2 = 1.80$ kg, we have

$(1.80 \text{ kg} \times 9.80 \text{ m/sec}^2) - T = 1.80 \text{ kg} \times a$
$T - (1.20 \text{ kg} \times 9.80 \text{ m/sec}^2) = 1.20 \text{ kg} \times a$

If we add these equations, we obtain

$(17.64 - 11.76) \text{ kg-m/sec}^2 = 3.00 \text{ kg} \times a$
$a = 1.96 \text{ m/sec}^2$

whence

$T = 14.1 \text{ kg-m/sec}^2 = 14.1$ newtons

As a second illustration of the application of Newton's second law of motion, consider a mass M sliding along a smooth horizontal table

(Fig. 6.9) with a second mass m fastened to it by means of a string that passes over a frictionless pulley.

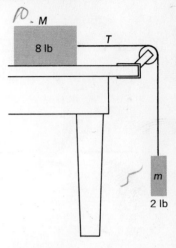

Let T be the tension in the string, and a the acceleration of the system. For m the resultant force is T, since the weight Mg is exactly balanced by the upward force exerted by the table. Applying Newton's second law of motion to each mass separately, we obtain

For M: $\qquad\qquad T = Ma$
For m: $\qquad mg - T = ma$

If M weighs 8.00 lb, and m 2.00 lb, these equations become

$$T = \frac{8.0}{32}\ \text{slug} \times a$$

$$2.0\ \text{lb} - T = \frac{2.0}{32}\ \text{slug} \times a$$

from which $a = 6.4$ ft/sec², and $T = 1.6$ lb.

Next, let us suppose that the coefficient of kinetic friction between M and the table is 0.20. Then there is a frictional force (0.20×8.0) lb acting to the left, and the resultant force on M becomes $T - 1.6$ lb. Applying Newton's second law to the two masses now yields

For M: $\qquad T - 1.6\ \text{lb} = \dfrac{8.0}{32}\ \text{slug} \times a$

For m: $\qquad 2.0\ \text{lb} - T = \dfrac{2.0}{32}\ \text{slug} \times a$

from which $a = 1.3$ ft/sec², and $T = 1.9$ lb.

FIGURE 6.9
Newton's second law of motion applies to the system as a whole and to each of the masses independently.

6.8 Mass: Another Point of View

Ordinarily, when we wish to determine the mass of a body, we do so by comparing its mass with that of standard masses on an equal-arm balance or by some equivalent method. The question may arise: Can we determine the mass of a body by a method which is completely independent of the earth's gravitational pull? We can see that the answer is affirmative by considering an imaginary but fundamentally straightforward experiment.

Consider a space ship located in a region in which there is no observable gravitational pull. In this ship imagine several bodies, one of which we arbitrarily agree is to be our standard mass, to which we assign a value m_s. To determine the mass m_1 of one of the other bodies, we allow it to interact with the standard body in the several different ways suggested by Fig. 6.10. In each case the interaction produces accelerations of magnitudes a_s and a_1 in opposite directions. We measure both these accelerations at the same instant and find that, for any interaction, the ratio a_1/a_s is always the same. We now define the ratio of the masses to be

$$\frac{m_s}{m_1} = \frac{a_1}{a_s} \qquad\qquad\qquad\qquad \textbf{6.5}$$

so that $m_1 = (a_s/a_1)m_s$, or $m_1 a_1 = m_s a_s$, which is just what Newton's second and third laws predict.

(1) Compressed spring

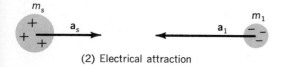

(2) Electrical attraction

FIGURE 6.10
Equal but opposite forces are exerted on m_1 and m_2 by one another when they interact. In the absence of any other net force on either body, $m_1\mathbf{a}_1 = -m_2\mathbf{a}_2$, regardless of the particular way in which the bodies interact.

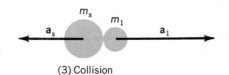

(3) Collision

In a similar way the mass m_2 of a second body can be determined by having it interact with the standard mass m_s. In this case $m_2a_2 = m_s a_s$, where a_2 and a_s are the magnitudes of the accelerations of m_2 and m_s, respectively, when they are interacting only with each other. If m_2 and m_1 interact, we find $m_1a_1 = m_2a_2$. Thus, a consistent set of mass values can be assigned to any number of particles, even in a region in which none of the particles has any weight.

6.9 Momentum and Newton's Second Law

In Sec. 6.3 we introduced Newton's second law in a somewhat restricted form. In order to express this law in a more general form, we introduce linear *momentum*. The linear *momentum of a body is the product of the mass and the linear velocity.* Momentum is a *vector* quantity which has the direction of the velocity.

Example A fullback with a mass of 90 kg is running with a velocity of 8 m/sec due north. Find his momentum.

Momentum = mass × velocity
= 90 kg × 8 m/sec north = 720 kg-m/sec north

A force changes the momentum of a free mass upon which it acts. The rate at which the momentum of the body changes is directly proportional to the force. Indeed, Newton's second law may be written in the form: *The time rate of change of the momentum of a body is proportional to the net force acting upon the body and is in the direction of this resultant force.* As an equation, we may write

$$\mathbf{F} = \frac{\Delta(m\mathbf{v})}{\Delta t}$$

6.6

If we are dealing with a single simple mass and a velocity small compared with that of light, the mass is constant, and we may write Eq. (6.6) as $\mathbf{F} = m\,\Delta\mathbf{v}/\Delta t = m\mathbf{a}$. However, there are several situations in which we must use Newton's second law in its more general form (Eq. 6.6). For example, at a speed approaching the speed of light, the mass of a body increases as the speed increases (Sec. 46.8). Similarly, if a sailor pulls a rope along a deck from a large coil, the mass in motion constantly increases. In rocket propulsion (Sec. 9.3) the mass of the rocket decreases as the hot gases are ejected. In each of these cases the problem of finding the velocity and displacement as functions of time requires the use of Newton's law in the form $\mathbf{F} = \Delta(m\mathbf{v})/\Delta t$.

Questions

1. A book rests on a board which makes an angle of 30° with the horizontal. What forces act on the book? By what bodies are these forces exerted? What are the reactions to these forces, and upon what bodies are they exerted?

2. Aristotle argued that if one stone lies on another, the upper one pushes down on the lower; as a consequence two stones fall faster than one, and a heavy stone falls faster than a light one. What is wrong with this argument?

3. A serious neck injury is sometimes incurred by the driver of a stopped car which is struck from behind. Discuss the underlying physics.

4. Newton's third law says that action and reaction are always equal and opposite. If this is true, why don't they always cancel one another and leave no unbalanced force acting on any body?

5. Discuss the possibility of driving a sailboat by means of a blower which directs a stream of air against the sails. Which way would the boat be most likely to move? Why?

6. If the same retarding force is available to stop a car regardless of its speed, how much is the stopping distance increased by doubling the speed?

7. A man stands on the platform of a large, sensitive scale. Discuss the reading as a function of time if the man tosses a heavy ball upward and catches the ball on its way down. How would things differ if he tossed the ball horizontally to a person standing nearby?

8. One 0.5-kg mass is suspended from a spring balance, and an identical 0.5-kg mass is balanced on one pan of an equal-arm balance. If both masses are in an elevator, what happens in each case when the elevator is given an upward acceleration? 5 m/sec² ?

9. Describe and discuss the motion of a man standing in a bus (*a*) when the brakes are suddenly applied and (*b*) when the bus has a large acceleration.

10. Why is it that a piece of paper slips out from under a glass of water when the paper is jerked suddenly, yet the glass moves with the paper if the paper is pulled slowly?

11. What is the fallacy in the assertion that you cannot throw a baseball because (*a*) by Newton's third law the ball exerts as big a force on you as you can exert on it, (*b*) the sum of these forces is zero, and (*c*) therefore, by Newton's second law, there is no acceleration?

Problems

Use the approximate values $g = 32$ ft/sec^2 = 9.8 m/sec^2 for these problems.

1. What resultant force is required to give an airplane of mass 30,000 kg an acceleration of 2 m/sec^2?   *Ans.* 60,000 newtons

2. What resultant force is required to give a 3,000-lb automobile an acceleration of 8 ft/sec^2?

3. What total force is required to produce an upward acceleration of 2 m/sec^2 in a mass of 5 kg?   *Ans.* 59 newtons

4. A man weighing 176 lb slides down a rope that can sustain only 135 lb. What is the smallest acceleration the man can have without breaking the rope?

5. A man weighing 160 lb slides down a rope that serves as a fire escape. The maximum force that can be applied to the rope without breaking it is 145 lb. Find the least acceleration that the man can have without breaking the rope.   *Ans.* 3 ft/sec^2

6. A football has a mass of 0.42 kg. What unbalanced force is required to give this football an acceleration of 200 m/sec^2?   84 Newtons

7. A baseball has a mass of 0.145 kg. Find the resultant force required to give this baseball an acceleration of 400 m/sec^2.   *Ans.* 58 newtons

8. A string that can sustain a tension of 20 newtons is fastened to a mass of 4 kg lying on a smooth horizontal table. What is the largest acceleration that can be imparted to the mass without breaking the string?

9. A catapult for launching aircraft from a carrier produces an acceleration of 3 g's (96 ft/sec^2) on a 40,000-lb aircraft. Find the unbalanced force required to produce this acceleration. Through what distance must this unbalanced force act to give the plane a speed of 120 ft/sec?   *Ans.* 120,000 lb; 75 ft

10. If the frictional forces on a 3,200-lb automobile add up to 120 lb retarding force, what would be the deceleration of the car coasting to a stop on a level road? How far would it coast from an initial speed of 50 ft/sec? 1.2 ft/sec^2 ; 1090 ft.

11. The brakes of an automobile that weighs 3,600 lb can exert a retarding force of 1,350 lb. Find the distance the car will move before stopping if it is traveling at the rate of 30 mi/hr when the brakes are applied.   *Ans.* 80.7 ft

12. A 10-kg block pulled along a level surface by a horizontal force of 45 newtons has an acceleration of 2 m/sec^2. Find the coefficient of friction. Draw a diagram showing all forces acting on the block.

13. A helicopter weighs 12,800 lb. Find the total force exerted on the helicopter by the air when it has an upward acceleration of 2 ft/sec^2. What is the force when the helicopter has a constant upward velocity of 4 ft/sec?   *Ans.* 13,600 lb; 12,800 lb

14. An 8-kg mass interacts with a 3-kg mass through a light stretched spring. If the 8-kg mass has an acceleration at some instant of 1.2 m/sec^2, find the net force on and the acceleration of the 3-kg mass at that instant. 9.6 NEW ; 3.2 m/sec^2

15. A 2-kg mass is placed on one of two identical carts, initially at rest. The carts are then driven apart by an ideal massless spring and receive velocities of 3 and -7 m/sec. (*a*) Find the mass of the carts. (*b*) An unknown mass is added to the second cart, and the experiment is repeated; the observed velocities are now 4 and -5 m/sec, respectively. What mass was added?   *Ans.* 1.5 kg; 1.3 kg

16. A 20-kg block of ice is given a speed of 10 m/sec on the surface of a pond for which the coefficient of friction is 0.012. How far will the ice go before coming to rest?

17. A block of mass m slides down a plane that is inclined at 35° with the horizontal. If the coefficient of friction between the block and the surface of the incline is 0.2, find the acceleration of the block.   *Ans.* 4 m/sec²

18. What horizontal force is needed to push a 26-kg box up an inclined plane which rises 5.00 m in a distance of 13 m measured along the plane if the coefficient of friction is 0.125? What horizontal force is required to give this box an acceleration of 2.00 m/sec² up the plane? *125.4 NEW*.   *177.4 Newtons*

19. A man stands on a spring scale in an elevator. When the elevator is at rest, the scale reads 176 lb. What does it read when the elevator has an upward acceleration of 6 ft/sec²? A downward acceleration of 6 ft/sec²? What is the acceleration when the scale reads 196 lb?   *Ans.* 209 lb; 143 lb; 3.6 ft/sec² up

20. A 192-lb man stands on a spring balance in an elevator. What does the balance read when the elevator has (*a*) a constant upward speed of 7 ft/sec, (*b*) a constant upward acceleration of 7 ft/sec², and (*c*) a constant downward acceleration of 7 ft/sec²?

21. The car of a frictionless elevator and its contents exert a force of 4 tons on the cables when at rest. How great is the force when an upward acceleration of 5 ft/sec² is being given to the elevator? When the acceleration is numerically the same but downward?   *Ans.* 9,250 lb; 6,750 lb

22. A porter carries a bag weighing 24 lb into an elevator. What force must he exert on the bag in order to hold it when the car is started with an upward acceleration of 4 ft/sec²? When the car has a constant upward velocity of 4 ft/sec?

23. A boy tosses a book on a table. It slides off and lands 3 ft from the edge of the table, which is 4 ft high. (*a*) Find the horizontal velocity of the book as it left the table. (*b*) If the book had a speed of 10 ft/sec when it was sliding 5 ft from the edge of the table, what was the coefficient of kinetic friction between book and table?
                                    Ans. (*a*) 6 ft/sec; (*b*) 0.2

24. A brick with a mass of 2 kg is given an initial velocity of 10 m/sec up an inclined plane which makes an angle of 37° with the horizontal. If the coefficient of sliding friction is 0.2, find (*a*) the frictional retarding force, (*b*) the deceleration of the brick, (*c*) how far the brick moves up the plane, and (*d*) the acceleration of the brick as it slides back down the plane. *3.14 New.; 7.95 m/sec² ; 6.72 hm ; 4.31 m/sec²*

25. An elevator weighs 1,900 lb. A counterweight of 1,900 lb is attached to it, and the cable between the two passes over a pulley. A person weighing 200 lb steps onto the elevator. If all other forces are neglected, what would be the acceleration of the system? The tension in the cables?   *Ans.* 1.6 ft/sec²; 1,995 lb

26. An Atwood's machine (Fig. 6.8) consists in masses of 2 kg and 2.5 kg suspended from a massless, frictionless pulley. When released from rest, how long is required for the larger mass to descend 1 m? What is the tension in the cord during the descent?

27. Two bodies are suspended by means of a flexible string that passes over a weightless pulley. If one body weighs 9 lb and the other 7 lb, what are the acceleration of the system and the tension in the string?   *Ans.* 4 ft/sec²; 7.88 lb

28. A 16,000-lb aircraft lands on a level field at a speed of 120 ft/sec. If the greatest acceleration which its brakes can produce is −6 ft/sec², find the minimum distance in which the aircraft can stop, the time required to stop, and the retarding force available.

29. Each car of a toy train weighs 1.5 lb. The engine weighs 5 lb. In a train containing four cars and the engine, the engine pulls on the first car with a force of 1.6 lb. If the acceleration of the train is 4 ft/sec^2, with what force does the first car pull on the engine? What is the unbalanced force on the first car? What is the total frictional force on the four cars? *Ans.* 1.6 lb; 0.19 lb; 0.85 lb

30. A 32,000-lb airplane starts from rest and has a uniform acceleration of 10 ft/sec^2. If it requires a speed of 120 ft/sec to take off, find (*a*) the minimum run for a takeoff, (*b*) the minimum time from rest to takeoff, and (*c*) the net thrust from the engine available for acceleration.

31. A block of mass 6 kg resting on a horizontal frictionless surface is connected to a hanging 4-kg block by a cord passing over a frictionless pulley. Find the tension in the cord and the acceleration of the blocks. *Ans.* 23.52 newtons; 3.92 m/sec^2

32. A 6-kg block resting on a horizontal surface is connected to a hanging block of 4 kg mass by a cord passing over a light, frictionless pulley. When the system is released, the blocks have an acceleration of 2 m/sec^2. Find the unbalanced force on each mass, the tension in the cord, and the coefficient of friction between the 6-kg block and the horizontal surface.

33. A mass of 10 kg rests on a horizontal table and is attached to a mass of 5 kg by means of a flexible cord passing over a weightless pulley. The 5-kg mass hangs vertically. If the coefficient of friction between the mass and the table is 0.2, what is the acceleration of the system? The tension in the cord? *Ans.* 1.96 m/sec^2; 39.2 newtons

34. A 10-lb block resting on a horizontal surface is connected to a 6-lb hanging weight by a cord passing over a frictionless pulley. The acceleration of the system is 4 ft/sec^2. Find the unbalanced force on the 6-lb body, the tension in the cord, and the coefficient of kinetic friction between the block and the plane.

35. (*a*) If $m_1 = 1$ kg, $M = 10$ kg, and $m_2 = 3$ kg, find the acceleration of the system and the tension in both cords of the accompanying figure, assuming there is no friction and the pulleys are massless. (*b*) If the coefficient of friction between the table and mass M is 0.100, find the acceleration and the tension in both cords.
Ans. (*a*) 1.4 m/sec^2, 11.2 newtons, 25.2 newtons; (*b*) 0.7 m/sec^2, 10.5 newtons, 27.3 newtons

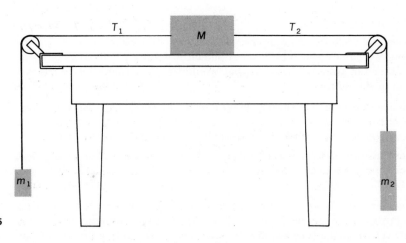

36. Find the acceleration and tension in both cords of the accompanying figure if m_1 is 0.1 slug, m_2 is 0.3 slug, M is 0.6 slug, and the coefficient of friction between M and the table is 0.2.

37. Body A of mass 3 kg and body B of mass 2 kg are connected by a light string (see accompanying figure). If the coefficients of friction for A and B are, respectively, 0.250 and 0.100, find the acceleration of the system and the tension in the string.

Ans. 4.39 m/sec²; 1.41 newton

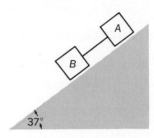

PROB. 37

38. A mass of 3 kg rests on a smooth inclined plane that makes an angle of 30° with the horizontal. It is fastened to a mass of 2 kg by means of a flexible string that runs up parallel to the plane, at the top of which it passes over a weightless pulley. (*a*) Find the acceleration of the system and the tension in the string. (*b*) Find the acceleration and tension if the plane has a coefficient of kinetic friction equal to 0.2.

39. Find the acceleration of the blocks and the tension in the cord of the accompanying figure if A has a mass of 2 kg, B has a mass of 3 kg, θ is 30°, ϕ is 37°, the planes are frictionless, and the pulley is massless. *Ans.* 1.57 m/sec²; 12.9 newtons

40. The planes of the accompanying figure are frictionless, and the pulley is massless. Find the acceleration of the blocks if A weighs 6 lb, B weighs 4 lb, θ is 30°, and ϕ is 37°.

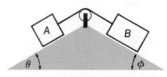

PROBS. 39 AND 40

CHAPTER 7 *Thus far we have discussed the motion of an object in terms of the forces acting upon it. However, in some cases we may not know what the forces are at every point in the path of a particle, for example, a neutron passing close to a uranium nucleus. In such a case we can still make many predictions about the motion by invoking the principle of conservation of energy, one of the great conservation laws of nature. Before we can apply the conservation of energy in any problem, we must learn what energy is and in what forms it appears. This in turn requires that we define and become familiar with* work *as this word is used in physics.*

Work and Energy

7.1 Work

The word *work* is a familiar one, used in many everyday senses. In physics, however, it is used in a highly restricted and carefully defined manner. When a force acts upon a body to produce a displacement, the *work done by the force is defined as the product of the displacement and the component of the force in the direction of the displacement.* If the angle between the displacement vector and the force vector is θ (Fig. 7.1), the component of the force in the direction of the displacement is $F \cos \theta$, and the work $\mathcal{W}$ is defined by the equation:

$$\mathcal{W} = Fs \cos \theta \qquad\qquad 7.1$$

If the force does not produce a displacement, no work is done in the sense in which work is used in physics. A man holding a 10-lb weight at rest does no work on it. A desk or cement post could hold the weight indefinitely without any difficulty. Although the man holding the weight does *no work on it,* the muscles in his arm do stretch and contract, and thus some work is done internally, which may result in fatigue. Similarly, when a man walks at a constant horizontal velocity carrying a suitcase, he does no work *on the suitcase,* since the force **F** he exerts on the suitcase and the displacement **s** are mutually perpendicular.

7.2 Units of Work

Since work is measured by the product of force and displacement, its units involve a unit of force multiplied by a unit of length. In the British engineering system the force is ordinarily measured in

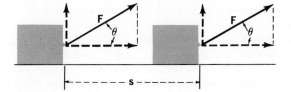

FIGURE 7.1
The work $\mathcal{W}$ done by a force **F** acting at an angle θ to the displacement **s** is $Fs \cos \theta$.

pounds, and the displacement in feet; the resulting unit of work is the *foot-pound. One foot-pound is the work done when a force of one pound acts through a distance of one foot.*

In the metric system the basic units of force and distance are the newton and the meter. Work is measured in newton-meters. This unit has been named the *joule* in honor of James Prescott Joule, a distinguished British physicist whose work on the relation between heat and mechanical work was of great importance. *One joule is the work done when a force of one newton acts through a distance of one meter.*

There are many other units in which work may be measured. For example, large amounts of work are sometimes reported in ton-miles. Small amounts in the metric system are sometimes measured in ergs; 1 erg is equal to 10^{-7} joule.

Example How many joules of work are done by a force in lifting a mass of 2 kg upward a distance of 3 m?

Work in joules = force in newtons $\times$ distance in meters
$$F = mg = 2 \text{ kg} \times 9.8 \text{ m/sec}^2 = 19.6 \text{ newtons}$$
$$\mathcal{W} = 19.6 \text{ newtons} \times 3 \text{ m} = 58.8 \text{ joules}$$

Example A force of 10 lb is used to move a box across a horizontal floor a distance of 5 ft. If the force makes an angle of 30° with the floor, how much work is done?

Work $= Fs \cos \theta$
$$\mathcal{W} = 10 \text{ lb} \times 5 \text{ ft} \times 0.866$$
$$= 43.3 \text{ ft-lb}$$

7.3 Power

In physics, *power is the time rate of doing work.* Thus, power P is equal to work divided by time:

$$P = \frac{\text{work}}{\text{time}} = \frac{\mathcal{W}}{t} \qquad \text{7.2}$$

An engine of high power can do work rapidly.

In the mks system power is measured in joules per second or *watts* (in honor of James Watt, developer of the steam engine). One watt of power is expended when one joule of work is done each second. In the British engineering system power may be expressed in foot-pounds per second, but more often it is given in *horsepower;* 1 hp = 550 ft-lb/ sec = 745.7 watts.

< The origin of the horsepower is of interest. When James Watt tried to sell steam engines to British coal mines, the question arose as to how many horses one of these new engines would replace. Watt found that, on the average, the horses were doing about 550 ft-lb of work per second; he called this unit the horsepower. He measured the rate at which his steam engines could work and thus rated them in "horsepower."

Example A building crane lifts a 1,500-lb steel beam to a height of 44 ft in 10 sec. Find the power developed.

$$P = \frac{\text{work}}{t} = \frac{1,500 \text{ lb} \times 44 \text{ ft}}{10 \text{ sec}} = 6,600 \text{ ft-lb/sec}$$

$$= 6,600 \frac{\text{ft-lb}}{\text{sec}} \times \frac{1 \text{ hp}}{550 \text{ ft-lb/sec}} = 12 \text{ hp}$$

Example An electric motor exerts a force of 400 newtons on a cable and pulls it a distance of 30 m in 1 min. Find the power supplied by the motor.

$$P = \frac{\text{work}}{t} = \frac{400 \text{ newtons} \times 30 \text{ m}}{60 \text{ sec}} = 200 \text{ joules/sec}$$

$$= 200 \text{ watts}$$

When a constant force acts on a body in the direction of the body's motion, the power can be expressed in the form $P = \text{work/time} = Fs/t$. Since $s/t = v$,

$$P = Fv \qquad\qquad\qquad 7.3$$

This equation is useful in resolving such practical questions as how powerful a motor must be provided to lift an elevator at a specified speed or how many diesel units are required to pull a railroad train at a given speed. If one wishes to make the speed of an airplane greater, Eq. (7.3) shows that there are basically two things one can do: increase the power and decrease the retarding forces.

Example An aircraft has four 2,000-hp engines and flies 300 mi/hr (440 ft/sec) when all engines are delivering rated power. Find the drag.

$$P = Fv$$

$$8,000 \text{ hp} \times \frac{550 \text{ ft-lb/sec}}{1 \text{ hp}} = F \times 440 \text{ ft/sec}$$

$$F = 10,000 \text{ lb drag}$$

7.4 Energy and Its Conservation

Energy is defined as the ability or capacity to do work. It occurs in many forms. A swinging hammer can do work by virtue of its motion; energy associated with motion is known as *kinetic energy*. A raised pile driver can do work by virtue of its elevated position; it has what we call *potential energy*. When we buy gasoline, we buy chemical energy. The food we eat provides energy for our living. We purchase electrical energy so our electric motors can do work for us. Energy may exist in the form of electromagnetic radiation; indeed, the earth's primary source of energy lies in the radiation it receives from the sun. Much of physics involves the relationships among the many forms of energy and the transformations from one form to another.

The study of the various forms of energy and of the transformation of one kind of energy into another has led to the statement of a very important principle, known as the *law of conservation of energy*:

Energy cannot be created or destroyed; it may be transformed from one form into another, but the total amount of energy never changes.

This principle is one of the great generalizations of physical science.

As an example of the transformations which energy may undergo, consider radiation coming to the earth from the sun. Some of this energy falls on plants, where it is transformed into chemical energy through photosynthesis. The energy stored in the plant may be converted eventually into coal or oil, or the plant may be eaten by some animal which utilizes the energy to carry on its existence. Part of the radiant energy from the sun goes into evaporating water from the surface of the ocean. The water vapor, lifted high above the earth by solar energy, eventually returns to the earth in the form of rain which may be trapped behind a dam. The water thus stored has potential energy by virtue of its position. The water may be led through a giant turbine where the potential energy is converted into energy of motion, and this kinetic energy of motion in turn converted into electrical energy in a generator. Electrical energy is distributed to houses where it may be converted into heat or light or used to perform work through an electric motor. Throughout all these transformations, the total energy remains constant.

Early in the twentieth century it was found that mass itself could be converted into energy, and we now regard mass as one of the forms of energy. We know that the sun's mass is decreasing because mass energy is converted into radiant energy in the sun. In atomic bombs and nuclear reactors mass is converted into energy. Einstein showed that, whenever mass is converted into another form of energy (or vice versa), the equivalence could be expressed by the equation

$$E = mc^2 \qquad\qquad\qquad \textbf{7.4}$$

where E is the amount of some other form of energy appearing or disappearing, m is the mass disappearing or appearing, and c is the speed of light. If c is expressed in meters per second and m in kilograms, E is in joules.

Example What is the total energy in a gram of matter at rest?

$m = 10^{-3} \text{ kg}$

The velocity of light c is 3×10^8 m/sec, and $c^2 = 9 \times 10^{16}$ m²/sec².

$$E = mc^2 = 9 \times 10^{13} \text{ kg-m}^2/\text{sec}^2 = 9 \times 10^{13} \text{ joules}$$

This energy is sufficient to lift a mass of 1 million kg through a distance of 9,000 km against the action of gravity!

Energy is an important commodity in economics and commerce. It is bought and sold in many forms, for example, as coal, petroleum products, food, and electricity. Energy is used to operate automobiles, refrigerators, stoves, washing machines, and television sets. In the past century the amount of energy consumed per person has undergone a remarkable increase. Primitive man used energy only for his food and warmth; modern man has hundreds of appliances which transform energies for his entertainment, comfort, and convenience.

7.5 Potential and Kinetic Energy

In mechanics it is natural that we should be concerned primarily with the various mechanical forms of energy. It is convenient to distinguish between two types—*potential energy* and *kinetic energy*.

The energy that a body has by virtue of its position or configuration is called potential energy (Fig. 7.2). When a mass is lifted above the surface of the earth, it has energy because of its position. When a spring is compressed or a bow bent, potential energy is stored up. Other examples of potential energy are found in the mainspring of a watch and in a stretched rubber band. In these cases the material of a body is in a state of strain; because of this strain, the body possesses potential energy.

The measure of the potential energy which a body has because of its position is the work done against gravity in lifting the body. The upward force required is equal to the weight of the body W, and the work done in lifting the body through a height h is given by the product Wh; therefore,

Potential energy $= Wh = mgh$ **7.5**

In the English system we ordinarily measure potential energy in foot-pounds, in the metric system in joules (newton-m).

FIGURE 7.2
Examples of potential energy are the taut bow and the elevated weight.

Example   A block weighing 3 lb is lifted 6 ft against gravity.   What potential energy is stored?

Potential energy $= Wh = 3$ lb $\times$ 6 ft
$$= 18 \text{ ft-lb}$$

Example   Find the potential energy given to the 50-kg hammer of a pile driver when it is raised 4 m.

Potential energy $= mgh = 50$ kg $\times$ 9.8 m/sec^2 $\times$ 4 m
$$= 1{,}960 \text{ joules}$$

Kinetic energy is the energy a body possesses by virtue of its motion. Any body in motion can set other bodies in motion by colliding with them.   The moving head of an axe can do work in splitting a log. The bullet leaving the muzzle of a gun has kinetic energy and can do work in penetrating a board.

To find the kinetic energy which a body possesses, we consider the work which must be done on the body in order to give it its speed. When the body is stopped, it gives up this amount of energy.   By definition, this is its kinetic energy.   Consider a mass m, initially at rest, upon which a constant force F is applied through a displacement s in the direction of the force.   The work done on the body is Fs. By Newton's second law, $F = ma$; thus the work is equal to mas.   Since the acceleration of the body is constant, Eq. (5.7) is applicable.   Therefore, $v^2 = 2as$, since $v_0 = 0$.   If we replace as with $v^2/2$ and recall that the work done appears as kinetic energy, we have

Kinetic energy $= \frac{1}{2}mv^2$ **7.6**

In metric units we express the kinetic energy in joules (or the equivalent kg-m^2/sec^2), while in the British system the kinetic energy is given in foot-pounds (or the equivalent slug-ft^2/sec^2).

Example   If an automobile weighing 3 tons is moving with a speed of 30 ft/sec, what is its kinetic energy in foot-pounds?

Kinetic energy $= \frac{1}{2}mv^2 = \dfrac{1}{2}\dfrac{W}{g}v^2$

$$= \frac{6{,}000 \text{ lb} \times (30 \text{ ft/sec})^2}{2 \times 32 \text{ ft/sec}^2} = \frac{3{,}000 \text{ lb} \times 900 \text{ ft}^2/\text{sec}^2}{32 \text{ ft/sec}^2}$$

$$= 84{,}000 \text{ ft-lb}$$

Example   What force is required to stop a bullet that has a mass of 15 g and a velocity of 400 m/sec in a distance of 20 cm?

Force $\times$ distance $=$ change in kinetic energy

$$0.20 \text{ m} \times F = \frac{1}{2}(0.015 \text{ kg})(400 \text{ m/sec})^2$$

$$= 1{,}200 \text{ kg-m}^2/\text{sec}^2 \text{ (or joules)}$$

$$F = \frac{1{,}200 \text{ kg-m}^2/\text{sec}^2}{0.2 \text{ m}}$$

$$= 6{,}000 \text{ kg-m/sec}^2 = 6{,}000 \text{ newtons}$$

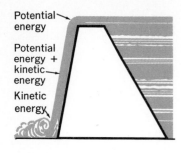

Potential energy

Potential energy + kinetic energy

Kinetic energy

FIGURE 7.3

The potential energy of the water at the top of the dam is converted to kinetic energy at the bottom.

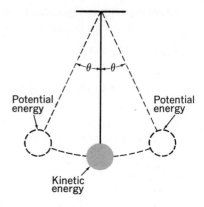

Potential energy

Potential energy

Kinetic energy

FIGURE 7.4

Transformation of potential energy to kinetic energy and then back to potential energy.

FIGURE 7.5

The sum of the potential and kinetic energies remains constant as the mass on the end of the spring rises and falls.

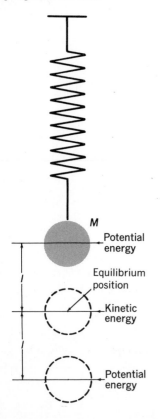

M

Potential energy

Equilibrium position

Kinetic energy

Potential energy

7.6 Transformation of Potential and Kinetic Energy

The potential energy of a body due to its position depends upon its height h, and this in turn depends on what one wishes to call the zero for height. A book on a table has no potential energy relative to the table top, but it does have potential energy relative to the floor and relative to mean sea level. If the book weighs 2 lb and the table top is 3 ft above the floor, the potential energy of the book is 6 ft-lb relative to the floor. Potential energy is always determined *relative* to some level or position which is assigned the value of zero. The choice of this level is at the disposal of the person working the problem.

In many situations we have a simple transformation of potential into kinetic energy with no other forms of energy involved. For example, when a pile driver is lifted into position, it is given potential energy. This potential energy is transformed into kinetic energy before the hammer strikes the pile upon which it is to do work. Similarly, consider water going over a dam (Fig. 7.3). Just above the dam the water has potential energy and, if its velocity is negligible, no significant kinetic energy. As the water falls, its potential energy decreases and its kinetic energy increases. When the water strikes bottom, part of this kinetic energy is transformed into heat.

The swinging of a pendulum illustrates the way in which potential energy may be transformed into kinetic energy and then back to potential energy (Fig. 7.4). When a pendulum is pulled to one side, the mass has no velocity and no kinetic energy, but it does have potential energy. When the mass is released, it swings downward, acquiring kinetic energy and losing potential energy. At the bottom of the swing the pendulum bob has maximum kinetic energy. As it swings upward, this kinetic energy is retransformed into potential energy. A very similar transformation of energy can be traced in the case of a mass on the end of a spring (Fig. 7.5).

Example A pendulum bob is pulled to one side until its center of gravity has been raised 10 cm above its equilibrium position. Find the speed of the bob as it swings through the equilibrium position.

Potential energy at top = kinetic energy at bottom
$$mgh = \tfrac{1}{2}mv^2$$

whence

$$v^2 = 2gh$$
$$= 2 \times 9.8 \text{ m/sec}^2 \times 0.1 \text{ m} = 1.96 \text{ m}^2/\text{sec}^2$$
$$v = 1.4 \text{ m/sec}$$

7.7 Energy in the Human Body

The human body is capable of doing work. The energy necessary for the performance of this work comes from the burning of carbohydrates, fats, and proteins, which also provide energy for maintaining the body temperature and for carrying on its internal vital functions. The pumping of blood through the veins and arteries is an illustration of the internal work performed in the body. This work is done by the heart muscle. For a man at rest the heart normally beats about 70 times per minute and develops a power of about 1.3 watts. An average working man uses about 10 million joules of energy per day, of which about half goes into maintaining temperature and carrying on internal functions. The remainder is available for the performance of external work.

7.8 Simple Machines

To aid us in doing work we frequently make use of simple machines. A machine is a device for overcoming a resisting force at one point by the application of a force at some other point. Consider a specific example: Suppose a man wishes to move a boulder which is too large to shove. He might find a strong stick and use it to move the boulder (Fig. 7.6). If he pulls on one end of the stick with a force F_{in}, a very much larger force F_{out} is exerted on the boulder. When the stick is in equilibrium, the torque condition gives the relation $F_{in}\, a = F_{out}\, b$. If a is 20 times b, F_{out} is 20 times F_{in}. By using this lever, our man can exchange an input force F_{in} for an output force F_{out} 20 times as great.

At first glance it might seem that this violates the principle of conservation of energy, but a little further consideration shows that this is not the case. In order to move the boulder 1 in., the input force must be exerted for a distance a/b in. The work done by the man on the

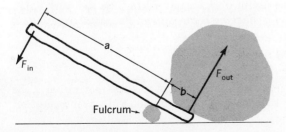

FIGURE 7.6
The lever was one of the first simple machines used by man.

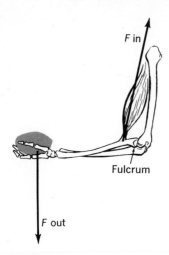

FIGURE 7.7

The human forearm is a lever with mechanical advantage much less than unity.

FIGURE 7.8

In raising the load W, work must be done to lift the lower pulley block and to overcome friction.

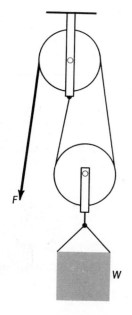

stick is equal to the work done on the boulder by the stick. By the use of a simple machine, *it is possible to exchange a small force acting through a large distance for a large force acting through a small distance,* or vice versa.

There are many kinds of simple machines. Among them are levers, inclined planes, pulleys, gear wheels, screws, wheels and axles, the wedge, and the differential pulley. Complicated machines, such as the automobile or the mechanical cotton picker, are composed of large numbers of interconnected simple machines.

7.9 Mechanical Advantage and Efficiency

As we have seen, a simple machine is a device for providing some output force in return for an input force. *The ratio of the output force F_{out} to the input force F_{in} is the actual mechanical advantage* (AMA) *of the machine:*

$$AMA = \frac{F_{out}}{F_{in}} \qquad\qquad 7.7$$

In defining the actual mechanical advantage of the machine, we concern ourselves only with the magnitudes of the forces, and not with their directions.

In our example of a man moving a boulder, we used a lever which had a large mechanical advantage. It is by no means true that all useful machines have large mechanical advantage. The simple pulley has a mechanical advantage of essentially unity and serves only to change the direction of the force. However, if we are trying to lift some mortar to the top of a building, it is convenient to be able to stand on the ground and pull downward on the rope to lift the mortar. Some of our most useful machines have mechanical advantages of less than 1. In the human forearm (Fig. 7.7) the output force exerted by the hand is very much smaller than the input force exerted by the muscles, so that the mechanical advantage is much less than unity. In such a machine we have a smaller output force moving through a greater distance than does the input force.

In real machines friction opposes the motion, and work must be done to overcome this friction. In addition, it may be necessary to raise some part of the machine which gives no useful work output. For example, in Figure 7.8 the lower pulley block must be raised when we lift the load W. The work done against friction and in lifting parts of the machine does not appear as useful work output. Therefore, in any real machine the useful work output is less than the work input. *The efficiency (Eff) of a machine is the ratio of the useful work output to the work input.*

$$Eff = \frac{work_{out}}{work_{in}} = \frac{\mathcal{W}_{out}}{\mathcal{W}_{in}} \qquad\qquad 7.8$$

For an ideal machine, with no friction and massless moving parts, the efficiency would be 100 per cent. The mechanical advantage of an ideal machine is called the *ideal mechanical advantage* (IMA). Let d_{out} be the distance moved by the output force, and d_{in} the distance moved by the input force. For an ideal machine the efficiency is 100 per cent, and $\mathcal{W}_{out} = \mathcal{W}_{in}$; hence, $F_{out}d_{out} = F_{in}d_{in}$. Therefore, *the mechanical advantage F_{out}/F_{in} for an ideal machine is d_{in}/d_{out}.* This ratio is the *ideal mechanical advantage.*

$$\text{IMA} = \frac{d_{in}}{d_{out}} \qquad\qquad 7.9$$

For any real machine the ideal mechanical advantage is greater than the actual mechanical advantage. Indeed, the efficiency can be seen to be equal to the ratio of the actual mechanical advantage to the ideal mechanical advantage by observing that

$$\text{Eff} = \frac{\mathcal{W}_{out}}{\mathcal{W}_{in}} = \frac{F_{out}}{F_{in}}\frac{d_{out}}{d_{in}} = \frac{\text{AMA}}{\text{IMA}}$$

The concepts of actual mechanical advantage, ideal mechanical advantage, and efficiency may be applied to all types of simple machines.

7.10 Rotating Systems

In the automobile transmission and in other rotating machinery one torque is exchanged for another. For a rotating system the actual mechanical advantage is the torque output divided by the torque input, while the ideal mechanical advantage is given by the angle turned through by the input torque divided by the corresponding angle turned through by the output torque.

When a pulley is being driven by a belt (Fig. 7.9), the tensions in the straight parts of the belt are not equal. They differ by the friction that is exerted between the belt and the pulley. Let T_2 be the tension in that part of the belt which is moving toward the pulley, T_1 the tension in that part which is moving away from the pulley, and V the velocity with which the belt is moving. The net frictional force between the belt and the pulley is $T_1 - T_2$. The power delivered to the pulley is $(T_1 - T_2)V$, provided the belt does not slip over the pulley.

Example The tension on one side of a belt is 350 lb, and that on the other side is 150 lb. The belt is moving at 300 ft/min. Find the horsepower delivered to the pulley.

$$\text{Power} = (350 - 150) \text{ lb} \times (300 \text{ ft/min})$$
$$= \frac{200 \text{ lb} \times 300 \text{ ft/min}}{60 \text{ sec/min}} \times \frac{1 \text{ hp}}{550 \text{ ft-lb/sec}}$$
$$= 1.8 \text{ hp}$$

Engines and motors are rated in terms of the brake horsepower which they develop. This may be measured by using the engine to drive a shaft similar to that of Figure 7.9 while the belt is held sta-

FIGURE 7.9

A belt-and-pulley system. When the belt drives the pulley as shown here, T_1 exceeds T_2; when the pulley drives the belt, T_2 is larger than T_1.

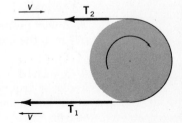

tionary by spring balances which read the tensions in the two sides. Such an arrangement is known as a *Prony brake*. Under these conditions, when the shaft is rotated in the direction shown, T_2 exceeds T_1. The power output, dissipated in heat by friction, is determined by measuring the net frictional force $F = T_2 - T_1$ and the linear speed v of a point on the surface of the shaft and is given by the product Fv.

Questions

1. Discuss the stable, neutral, and unstable equilibria of a body in terms of potential energy.

2. Why does it hurt one's bare hand more to catch a baseball when the hand is held in a fixed position than when the hand moves back as the ball is caught?

3. A stone is thrown from a cliff with an initial speed v_0. How does its speed as it hits a body below depend on the angle at which it is thrown? Explain.

4. A man is swimming against the current in a river. If he remains stationary relative to the ground, does he do any work? Explain.

5. Why does a railroad track often wind up a long hill when a road may go directly up and over?

6. A barrel is rolled up an inclined plane which makes an angle of 30° with the horizontal. If no work is done against friction, what is the mechanical advantage if the applied force is parallel to the plane and acts through the center (and center of gravity) of the barrel? What is the mechanical advantage if the force acts tangentially to the circumference of the barrel? Explain the difference.

7. Show that the efficiency of a jackscrew must be less than 50 per cent if the jack remains set when no force is applied at the handle.

8. Why is a high jumper less likely to be injured if he falls in sawdust or sand rather than on hard clay?

Problems

1. To what height can a piece of structural steel weighing 2 tons be lifted if work amounting to 110,000 ft-lb is done on it? What horsepower is required to do this lifting in 50 sec?

Ans. 27.5 ft; 4 hp

2. A horizontal force of 40 lb is required to pull a 250-lb box along a floor. How much work is required to move the box 50 ft across a level floor in 10 sec? What power is required?

3. A man pushes a lawn mower 50 ft in 5 sec by exerting a force of 30 lb at an angle of 53° with the horizon. Find the work done and the average power expended.

Ans. 900 ft-lb; 0.327 hp

4. A cylindrical standpipe 40 ft high has an internal diameter of 10 ft. How much work would be required to fill the standpipe with water (*a*) if the water were pumped in at the bottom and (*b*) if it were pumped in at the top? One cubic foot of water weighs 62.5 lb.

5. An 80-kg man is lifted by an elevator through a distance of 50 m in 30 sec. What is the increase in his potential energy? What power is expended in raising him?

Ans. 39,200 joules; 1,307 watts

6. A 165-lb man climbs to the fourth floor of a building. If he climbs 50 ft in 20 sec, how much work has he done in increasing his elevation? How much power has he expended?

7. If the net retarding force on a ship is 25,000 lbs when it is traveling 22 ft/sec (15 mph), find the work required to overcome fluid friction in going 1 mile and the power which must be delivered by the screws to overcome this friction.

Ans. 1.32×10^8 ft-lb; 1,000 hp

8. The locomotive of a freight train exerts a force of 30,000 lb on the train as it pulls it along on a level track at a speed of 30 mi/hr (44 ft/sec). Find the power supplied by the engine and the work done on the train in a distance of 1 mile.

9. How much work is required to hoist an elevator and its contents with total mass of 2,500 kg to the top of a building 200 m high? What average power is required if this work is done in 40 sec? *Ans.* 4.9×10^6 joules; 122.5 kW

10. An elevator and its contents have a mass of 1,500 kg. Find the work and power required to lift this system 40 m at a constant speed of 4 m/sec.

11. An escalator is designed to lift 100 people of 75 kg average mass from one floor of a department store to another 10 m higher in 1 min. What power is required, assuming that 80 per cent of the power goes into lifting people? *Ans.* 15.3 kW

12. A jackscrew (see accompanying figure) with a pitch of 0.125 in. has a handle 20 in. long. A force of 15 lb must be applied when a load of 6,000 lb is being lifted. Calculate the ideal mechanical advantage, the actual mechanical advantage, and the efficiency.

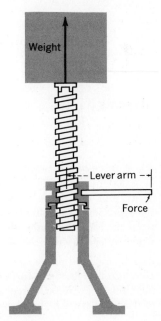

PROB. 12

13. A 3,200-lb automobile requires 60 hp to overcome retarding forces on a level road when traveling at a speed of 110 ft/sec. Find the net retarding force on the automobile. If the power and retarding force remain the same, find the speed of the car on a 3 per cent grade (i.e., one which rises 3 ft in 100 ft of roadway).

Ans. 300 lb; 83 ft/sec

14. A motor drives a hoist which lifts a 2-ton load a distance of 50 ft in 30 sec. The efficiency of the motor is 85 per cent, and that of the hoist is 45 per cent. What power is supplied to the load? To the hoist? To the motor?

15. A water bucket weighing 60 lb is raised by a crank-and-axle arrangement. The axle has a radius of 3 in., and the crank has a radius of 12 in. If a force of 20 lb is required on the crank, find the actual mechanical advantage, the ideal mechanical advantage, and the efficiency. *Ans.* 3; 4; 0.75

16. What is the retarding force on a small plane if 80 hp are required to overcome the drag when the plane is flying level at a constant speed of 120 mi/hr?

17. In the pulley system shown in Figure 7.8 a force of 80 lb is required to lift a 120-lb weight. Find the ideal mechanical advantage, the actual mechanical advantage, and the efficiency. *Ans.* 2; 1.5; 75 per cent

18. Show that for a simple pulley system with two blocks, one fixed and one movable as in Figure 7.8, the ideal mechanical advantage is the number of strands directly supporting the load.

19. An inclined plane (see accompanying figure) 25 ft long is used as a simple machine to pull 1,000-lb boxes up to a height of 7 ft. A force of 500 lb up the plane is required to pull the boxes up. If it takes 50 sec to bring a box to the top, find the actual mechanical advantage of the inclined plane, the ideal mechanical advantage, the efficiency, and the power required. *Ans.* 2; 3.57; 0.56; 0.45 hp

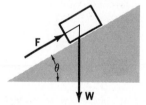

PROB. 19

20. A force of 500 newtons is required on the bar of a capstan to obtain an output force of 4,000 newtons for lifting an anchor. The axle of the capstan has a radius of 5 cm, and the input force is applied 0.6 m from the axis. Find the work done by the input force in lifting the anchor 10 m in a time of 2 min, the actual mechanical advantage, the ideal mechanical advantage, the efficiency of the capstan, and the power provided by the input force.

21. An inclined plane 13 ft long is used to slide a 260-lb box up to a loading platform 5 ft above ground level. A force of 160 lb is required. Find the efficiency of the inclined plane for this job. What force is required to overcome friction? What is the coefficient of friction between the plane and the box? *Ans.* 62.5 per cent; 60 lb; 0.25

$\mu = \dfrac{f}{N}$ 60 lbf

22. Show that the ideal mechanical advantage of a differential pulley (see accompanying figure) is given by $2R/(R-r)$, where R and r are the radii of the larger and smaller sheaves, respectively. Find the ideal mechanical advantage of a differential pulley in which the radius of the larger pulley is 4.5 in. and that of the smaller pulley is 4 in.

23. A boy, starting from rest, slides down a hill 81 ft high on a sled. If friction is negligible, find the speed of the sled at the bottom. If 20 per cent of the energy were dissipated in friction, what would be his speed at the bottom? *Ans.* 72 ft/sec; 64.5 ft/sec

24. A 0.25-lb ball is given an upward velocity of 40 ft/sec. If 10 per cent of its energy is lost owing to air resistance during its rise, how high will the ball go?

25. A boy throws a 0.25-lb stone from the top of a 37.5-ft cliff with a speed of 60 ft/sec. Find its kinetic energy and speed when it lands in a river below.
Ans. 23.4 ft-lb; 77.5 ft/sec

26. A 0.2-kg mass is dropped through 1.6 m so that all its potential energy is changed to kinetic energy. Calculate its final velocity by applying the law of conservation of energy. Verify your result by calculating the velocity of a body that falls freely through 1.6 m.

27. A pendulum bob has a mass of 0.5 kg. It is suspended by a cord 2 m long which is pulled back through an angle of 30°. Find its maximum potential energy relative to its lowest position and its potential energy when the cord makes an angle of 15° with the vertical. Find its maximum speed and its speed when the cord makes the angle of 15° with the vertical. *Ans.* 1.31 joule; 0.33 joule; 2.29 m/sec; 1.98 m/sec

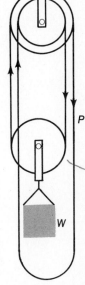

PROB. 22

28. A 64-lb boy on a swing is pulled backward and upward until his center of gravity has been raised 4 ft. What is his potential energy? If the swing is released, what will be his maximum speed?

29. A 2,000-lb car starts from rest and rolls down a hill 100 ft high and 1,000 ft long as measured along the road. At the bottom of the hill the car's speed is 60 ft/sec. How much energy has been dissipated? To what average frictional retarding force does this energy dissipation correspond? *Ans.* 87,500 ft-lb; 87.5 lb

30. A 3,000-lb car starts from rest and coasts down a uniform grade, at the bottom of which it has a speed of 40 ft/sec. If the car has traveled 800 ft and has descended 45 ft, how much energy was dissipated on the way down? To what average frictional retarding force does this energy dissipation correspond?

31. A ski jumper glides down a 37° slope for 50 ft before taking off from a negligibly short horizontal takeoff. If his speed at takeoff is 40 ft/sec, find the coefficient of kinetic friction on the slide. *Ans.* 0.125

32. Three men using a block and tackle are lifting a safe weighing 2,200 lb to a height of 25 ft. Each man develops ¼ hp. How long will it take to raise the safe if only half the work done by each man is useful?

33. The combined mass of a boy and his sled is 30 kg. His father pulls the boy and sled up a slope which rises 14 m in a distance of 50 m measured along the slope. If the frictional force between snow and loaded sled is 40 newtons, find the work done by the father. If the boy slides back down the slope, find his speed at the bottom.
Ans. 6,120 joules; 11.9 m/sec

34. The upper end of an inclined ramp 25 ft long is 7 ft above the lower end. A force of 100 lb is required to push a 250-lb box up the incline. Find the coefficient of friction and the work done against friction. If the box were released at the top of the ramp, would it slide down? If so, what would be its speed at the bottom?

35. If dissipative resisting forces total 100 lb, find the horsepower necessary to give an automobile weighing 3,200 lb an acceleration of 6 ft/sec² when it has a velocity of 30 mi/hr.   *Ans.* 56 hp

36. A mass weighing 100 lb rests on an inclined plane that makes an angle of 30° with the horizontal. If the coefficient of friction between the mass and the plane is 0.2, how much work is done in moving the mass up the plane a distance of 10 ft? If the mass slides back down, what will its speed be when it reaches its original position?

37. A 25,000-kg airplane takes off at a speed of 50 m/sec. Five minutes later it is at an elevation of 2,000 m and has a speed of 100 m/sec. What average power is required during this 5 min if 40 per cent of the power is used in overcoming dissipative forces?

Ans. 3.2×10^6 watts

CHAPTER 8 *In the preceding chapter we learned the principle of conservation of energy and saw how useful such a principle can be. Next we shall make use of Newton's second and third laws of motion (Chap. 6) to derive a second great conservation principle—that of the conservation of momentum. With the aid of conservation of momentum we can treat some problems of motion in which we do not have knowledge of the precise forces acting on an object.*

Momentum

8.1 Momentum and Impulse

The *momentum* of a body is a vector defined as the product of its mass m and its velocity $\mathbf{v}$. Consider an unbalanced force $\mathbf{F}$ acting on a body of mass m for a time Δt. By Newton's second law (Eq. 6.6),

$$\mathbf{F} = \frac{\Delta(m\mathbf{v})}{\Delta t} = \frac{m(\mathbf{v} - \mathbf{v}_0)}{t}$$

from which

$$\mathbf{F}t = m\mathbf{v} - m\mathbf{v}_0 \qquad\qquad\qquad \textbf{8.1}$$

The right side of this equation is just the momentum at time t minus the initial momentum, or the change in momentum of the body. The quantity on the left side of the equation, *the product of the force and the time during which the force acts, is called the impulse.* From Eq. (8.1) we see that *the impulse is equal to the change in the momentum.*

In many types of collisions the force acting on a body is not constant, but varies during the reaction. For example, when a football is kicked off, the toe of the kicker exerts zero force on the ball until it comes in contact, and the force increases rapidly as the ball is distorted (Fig. 8.1). As the ball returns to its initial shape, the force diminishes. A picture of the force as a function of time might be that of Figure 8.2. In this case the impulse is given by the area under the force-as-a-function-of-time curve. Alternatively, we can express the impulse as the product of the average force and the time during which the force acts. The average force is indicated by the dashed line of the figure.

In many situations the force varies so rapidly that it is not practical to know what the force is at any particular instant, but the change in the momentum of the body is equal to the total impulse. If we know how long the impulsive force acts, we can calculate the average value of the force even though we cannot know the instantaneous value, i.e., the exact shape of the force curve. We have impulsive forces in play when a pitched ball is hit by a bat or when two billiard balls collide.

FIGURE 8.1
High-speed X-ray picture of a
football being kicked.

FIGURE 8.2
Force on the football as a
function of time.

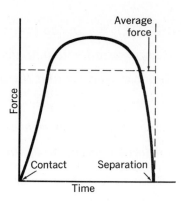

Example A baseball of mass 0.145 kg is thrown by the pitcher with
a speed of 30 m/sec. The bat is in contact with the ball for 0.01 sec
and gives it a speed of 40 m/sec in a direction straight toward the
pitcher. Find the impulse and the average value of the force.

$$\text{Impulse} = \text{change in momentum}$$
$$= 0.145 \text{ kg } [30 - (-40)] \text{ m/sec}$$
$$= 10.1 \text{ kg-m/sec}$$
$$= 10.1 \text{ newton-sec}$$
$$F_{\text{av}} = \frac{\text{impulse}}{\text{time}}$$
$$= \frac{10.1 \text{ newton-sec}}{0.01 \text{ sec}}$$
$$= 1{,}010 \text{ newtons}$$

8.2 The Conservation of Momentum

Consider a freely suspended rifle, cocked and ready to fire (Fig. 8.3).
When the trigger is pulled, a force $\mathbf{F}_b$ is exerted on the bullet. By
Newton's third law, if the gun exerts a force $\mathbf{F}_b$ on the bullet, the bullet exerts an equal and opposite force $\mathbf{F}_g$ on the gun. We therefore
write $\mathbf{F}_b = -\mathbf{F}_g$. By Newton's second law, $\mathbf{F}_b = m_b\mathbf{v}_b/t$, and, similarly,
$\mathbf{F}_g = M_g\mathbf{V}_g/t$, since the initial velocities were both zero. Clearly, the
forces $\mathbf{F}_b$ and $\mathbf{F}_g$ act for exactly the same length of time, and the im-

FIGURE 8.3
The momentum of the system
comprising the bullet and the
rifle is zero both before and after
the bullet is fired. The
momentum given the bullet is
equal and opposite to that given
the rifle.

pulses for the gun and the bullet are equal in magnitude and opposite in direction. Therefore,

$$m_b\mathbf{v}_b = -M_g\mathbf{V}_g \qquad \text{8.2}$$

The momentum gained by the bullet is equal in magnitude and opposite in direction to that received by the gun. Since momentum is a vector quantity, the resultant of the momenta is zero, just as it was before the trigger was pulled. The momentum of the system composed of the gun and the bullet has not changed.

It follows directly from Newton's second and third laws of motion that *if two or more bodies interact, the momentum after the interaction is equal to the momentum before the interaction.*

This important principle is known as the *law of conservation of momentum.* It may be stated in the following form: *The total momentum of any system of bodies is unchanged by any actions which occur among the different members of the system.*

When a battleship fires a broadside, the shells are given a large momentum in one direction. The battleship recoils with an equal momentum in the opposite direction. When two billiard balls collide, momentum is transferred from one ball to the other, but the resultant momentum after the collision is equal to the momentum before the collision. When two football players collide in midair, the law of conservation of momentum determines which way they fall.

Example An 80-kg halfback dives over the line of scrimmage at a velocity of 7 m/sec. He is met in midair by a 100-kg linebacker going 5.4 m/sec in the opposite direction. If they fall together, find the horizontal component of their velocity.

Momentum before = momentum after
$(80 \text{ kg} \times 7 \text{ m/sec}) - (100 \text{ kg} \times 5.4 \text{ m/sec}) = 180 \text{ kg} \times v$
$20 \text{ kg-m/sec} = 180 \text{ kg} \times v$
$v = {}^{20}\!/_{180} = 0.11$ m/sec in direction of halfback's initial velocity

Consider one aircraft chasing another of about the same maximum speed. If the pursuing craft opens fire, the bullets are given forward momentum, and the plane loses an equal momentum. On the other hand, when the pursued craft opens fire, the bullets have momentum toward the rear, and this aircraft gains speed.

8.3 Center of Mass

When a shell traversing the usual parabolic path explodes in midair (Fig. 8.4), fragments are ejected in all directions. However, the resultant momentum of all the fragments of the shell just after the explosion is the same as the momentum of the shell just before the explosion. Indeed, a unique point associated with the system, known as the *center of mass,* continues to move along the same path whether the shell explodes or not. The x coordinate of the center of mass of a system of

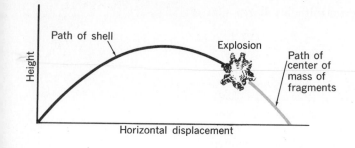

Path of shell

Explosion

Path of center of mass of fragments

Horizontal displacement

FIGURE 8.4

The center of mass of the shell fragments moves along the same trajectory before and after the explosion.

particles with masses $m_1, m_2, \ldots, m_N$ is defined at any instant by the relation

$$x_c = \frac{m_1 x_1 + m_2 x_2 + \cdots + m_N x_N}{m_1 + m_2 + \cdots + m_N} \qquad 8.3$$

where x_1 is the x coordinate of m_1, etc. Similar relations locate the y and z coordinates of the center of mass. The sum of the individual masses in the denominator is simply the total mass M of the system of particles.

If we place the origin of a coordinate system at the point of explosion of our shell and consider the positions of the fragments a time t after the explosion, we may divide Eq. (8.3) by t to obtain

$$\frac{x_c}{t} = \frac{m_1(x_1/t) + m_2(x_2/t) + \cdots + m_N(x_N/t)}{M}$$

or

$$v_{xc} = \frac{m_1 v_{x1} + m_2 v_{x2} + \cdots + m_N v_{xN}}{M} \qquad 8.4$$

where v_{xc} is the x component of the velocity of the center of mass. Similar equations give the y and z components of this velocity, and we see that *the velocity of the center of mass of a system of particles is equal to the resultant momentum of the system divided by the mass of the system.*

The forces of explosion for our shell are forces exerted by one part of the system on other parts of the system. Such *internal* forces do not change the resultant momentum of the system. However, the weight of the shell (and of the fragments) is an *external* force which does change the momentum of the system. *The resultant momentum $M\mathbf{v}_c$ of a system remains constant when no external forces act on the system; if external forces act, the center of mass has an acceleration proportional to the resultant external force and inversely proportional to the mass of the system.*

Figure 8.5 is a multiple-flash photograph of a rotating wrench moving freely in the absence of any external force. The center of mass, indicated by the black cross, moves with constant velocity; other mass elements of the wrench have more complicated motions. If an external force were applied to the wrench, it would produce an acceleration of the center of mass. Whether it would change the rotation about

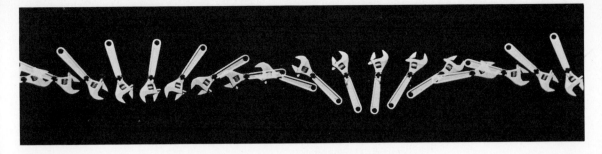

FIGURE 8.5

The constant velocity of a center of mass (marked by the black cross) is demonstrated by a timed-sequence photograph of a thrown wrench. Intervals are $\frac{1}{30}$ sec.

the center of mass depends on the line of action of the force. In general, when the resultant force on a body acts through the center of mass, there is no resultant torque to change the rotational velocity about the center of mass; conversely, if the resultant force does not act through the center of mass, there is a resultant torque, and the rotational motion is changed.

The acceleration due to gravity is essentially the same at all points occupied by a body of reasonable size. Then the center of mass coincides with the center of gravity (Sec. 4.2).

8.4 Rocket Propulsion

Rockets are clearly to be preferred for propelling long-range missiles and for placing satellites in orbit. A jet of hot gases is ejected from the combustion chamber of a rocket (Fig. 8.6). Since the rocket exerts a rearward force on the gases, the gases exert an equal and opposite forward force on the rocket. Let $\mathbf{u}$ be the velocity of the ejected gases relative to the rocket, and Δm the mass of gas ejected at a constant rate in time Δt. Then $\mathbf{u}\ \Delta m/\Delta t$ is the time rate of change of momentum of the exhaust gases, which, by Newton's second law of motion, is the force exerted on the gases by the rocket. This, by Newton's third law, is the reaction force $\mathbf{F}_R$ exerted on the rocket by the gases. Thus the *thrust* $\mathbf{F}_R$ of the rocket motion is

$$\mathbf{F}_R = -\mathbf{u}\frac{\Delta m}{\Delta t}$$

8.5

where the minus sign appears because $\mathbf{F}_R$ is opposite to $\mathbf{u}$.

Ordinarily the rocket has other forces, such as its weight, acting upon it. If the resultant of these external forces is represented by $\mathbf{F}_E$,

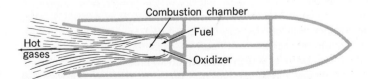

Combustion chamber

Fuel

Hot gases

Oxidizer

FIGURE 8.6

Schematic diagram of a rocket engine.

the net force acting on the rocket is $\mathbf{F}_E + \mathbf{F}_R$. By Newton's second law,

$$\mathbf{F}_E + \mathbf{F}_R = M\mathbf{a} \qquad\qquad\text{8.6}$$

where $\mathbf{a}$ is the acceleration of the rocket relative to some fixed coordinate system, and M is the mass of the rocket. Note that M varies during the flight as fuel is burned or as some portion of the rocket system is jettisoned.

Example   A Thor ballistic missile has a gross weight of roughly 96,000 lb at the beginning of flight. It has a rocket engine which produces 135,000 lb of thrust. If the exhaust velocity of the gases is 6,750 ft/sec, find the rate at which mass is ejected and the acceleration at launch and after 100 sec of operation.

By Eq. (8.5),

$$F_R = u\frac{\Delta m}{\Delta t}$$

$$135{,}000 \text{ lb} = 6{,}750 \text{ ft/sec} \times \frac{\Delta m}{\Delta t}$$

$$\frac{\Delta m}{\Delta t} = 20 \text{ lb-sec/ft} = 20 \text{ slugs/sec}$$

At launch the unbalanced force is the difference between the thrust and the weight. By Newton's second law,

$$135{,}000 \text{ lb} - 96{,}000 \text{ lb} = \frac{96{,}000}{32} \text{ slugs} \times a$$

$$= 3{,}000 \text{ slugs} \times a$$

$$a = 13 \text{ ft/sec}^2 = \frac{13}{32}g$$

After 100 sec of operation 2,000 slugs have been ejected, and the mass of the rocket is 1,000 slugs. If we assume that air friction is negligible but that the rocket is not so high that g is appreciably different from 32 ft/sec², the weight of the rocket is 32,000 lb, and the unbalanced force is 135,000 lb − 32,000 lb, or 103,000 lb. Then

$$103{,}000 \text{ lb} = 1{,}000 \text{ slugs} \times a$$

$$a = 103 \text{ ft/sec}^2 = 3.2\,g$$

8.5 Collision Phenomena

When two bodies collide, the laws of conservation of momentum and of conservation of energy are both always applicable. However, in some collisions part of the kinetic energy of the bodies is transformed into some nonmechanical form of energy such as heat or sound. In this case the application of the law of conservation of energy to the problem becomes exceedingly difficult, because many kinds of energy may be involved, some of which are difficult to measure. If a steel ball is dropped on a steel plate, the ball and plate are distorted during the action of the impulsive forces, but they return to their original shapes, and the ball springs away from the plate.   In this case the bodies are only temporarily deformed, and they regain their original shapes immediately after collision.   Bodies which return to their original shapes after collision are said to be *elastic*.

In a perfectly elastic collision, kinetic energy, as well as momentum, is conserved.   Collisions between atomic nuclei, atoms, molecules, and electrons are often perfectly elastic.   Such an ideal situation is never achieved with large-scale objects; thus we have no perfectly elastic collisions of macroscopic bodies.

Collisions between billiard balls or between a basketball and the floor are *imperfectly elastic*.   Although the bodies spring apart, the kinetic energy of the system after collision is less than it was before. Energy is transformed to heat, sound, or some other form.

If a bullet is fired into a block of wood, the bullet sticks in the block, and the two remain together indefinitely.   Such a collision is called a *perfectly inelastic* one.   The bodies are permanently deformed and never separate.

In every kind of collision *momentum is always conserved*; kinetic energy is conserved only in perfectly elastic collisions.   In the next three sections we consider "head-on" collisions between two bodies of masses m and M (Fig. 8.7) which have initial velocities $\mathbf{v}_i$ and $\mathbf{V}_i$, respectively, before collision, and final velocities $\mathbf{v}_f$ and $\mathbf{V}_f$ after collision.   Velocities are vector quantities; therefore, we shall need to concern ourselves with directions as well as magnitudes.   In the equations which follow we adopt the convention that velocities to the right are positive, and velocities to the left negative.

8.6 Perfectly Inelastic Collisions

In an inelastic collision the two bodies stick together after they have made contact.   As a consequence, they both have the same final velocity.   The law of conservation of momentum alone is adequate to permit us to compute the final velocity if the masses and initial velocities are known:

$$m\mathbf{v}_i + M\mathbf{V}_i = (m + M)\mathbf{V}_f \qquad \textbf{8.7}$$

> **Example**   A 2-g bullet is fired into a 2.398-kg block (Fig. 8.8) of wood suspended from a long cord.   The bullet is embedded in the block, and the two start off together with a speed of 0.700 m/sec. Find the velocity of the bullet before collision.
>
> $$(0.00200 \text{ kg} \times v_i) + (2.398 \text{ kg} \times 0) = 2.4 \text{ kg} \times 0.700 \text{ m/sec}$$
> $$v_i = 840 \text{ m/sec}$$

< An arrangement such as that of Figure 8.8 by which the speed of a moving body is measured by capturing it in a massive pendulum bob is known as a *ballistic pendulum*.   Since the collision is inelastic, Eq. (8.7) is applicable to the collision between body and pendulum bob. The velocity V of the body plus bob immediately after collision is determined by measuring how much the center of gravity of the system

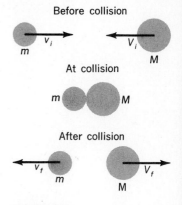

FIGURE 8.7
Head-on collision between two moving spheres.

FIGURE 8.8
The speed of a bullet is determined by firing it into the bob of a ballistic pendulum and measuring how much the center of gravity of the bob is raised at the end of the swing.

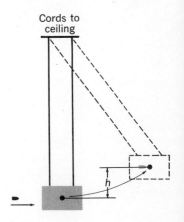

is raised in the upward swing of the pendulum. If the center of gravity is raised a distance h, conservation of energy yields $(m + M)gh = \frac{1}{2}(m + M)V^2$, where m and M are the masses of body and pendulum bob, respectively.

8.7 Perfectly Elastic Collisions

In a perfectly elastic collision both momentum and kinetic energy are conserved. If two bodies collide along the line connecting their centers, we may write

$$mv_i + MV_i = mv_f + MV_f \qquad \text{conservation of momentum} \qquad \textbf{8.8}$$

and

$$\tfrac{1}{2}mv_i{}^2 + \tfrac{1}{2}MV_i{}^2 = \tfrac{1}{2}mv_f{}^2 + \tfrac{1}{2}MV_f{}^2 \qquad \text{conservation of energy} \qquad \textbf{8.9}$$

These equations may be rewritten as

$$m(v_i{}^2 - v_f{}^2) = M(V_f{}^2 - V_i{}^2) \qquad \text{and} \qquad m(v_i - v_f) = M(V_f - V_i)$$

If we divide the first by the second, we obtain $v_i + v_f = V_f + V_i$ or

$$v_i - V_i = V_f - v_f = -(v_f - V_f) \qquad \textbf{8.10}$$

Note that $v_i - V_i$ is the *velocity of approach*, or the velocity of the smaller mass relative to the larger one before the collision, while $v_f - V_f$ is the *velocity of separation*, or the velocity of the smaller mass relative to the larger after the collision. In a perfectly elastic collision the velocity of approach is equal in magnitude to the velocity of separation, but opposite in direction.

Example A 40-g ball traveling east with a speed of 5.0 m/sec has a "head-on" collision with a 60-g ball traveling 3.0 m/sec west (Fig. 8.7). If the collision is elastic, find the velocities after the collision.

Let us choose east as the positive direction, so velocities to the west are negative. By Eq. (8.8),

$$(0.040 \text{ kg} \times 5.0 \text{ m/sec}) + (0.060 \text{ kg} \times -3.0 \text{ m/sec})$$
$$= 0.040 \text{ kg} \times v_f + 0.060 \text{ kg} \times V_f$$
$$v_f + 1.5V_f = 0.50 \text{ m/sec} \qquad \textbf{A}$$

By Eq. (8.10),

$$5.0 \text{ m/sec} - (-3.0 \text{ m/sec}) = V_f - v_f$$
$$-v_f + V_f = 8.0 \text{ m/sec} \qquad \textbf{B}$$

Adding Eqs. (*A*) and (*B*) yields

$$2.5V_f = +8.5 \text{ m/sec}$$
$$V_f = +3.4 \text{ m/sec}$$
$$v_f = -4.6 \text{ m/sec}$$

The minus sign means the 40-g ball is moving westward.

8.8 Imperfectly Elastic Collisions

In a perfectly elastic collision kinetic energy is conserved, and the velocity of approach is equal to the velocity of separation in magnitude but opposite in direction.   In an inelastic collision the velocity of separation is zero, since the two bodies remain together.   Imperfectly elastic collisions lie between these two extremes.   Newton studied collisions between many types of spheres and concluded that in general the velocity of separation was equal to a constant times the velocity of approach;

$$-(v_f - V_f) = e(v_i - V_i) \qquad\qquad 8.11$$

where, for a given pair of materials, e is a constant which lies between zero and 1.   This constant is called the *coefficient of restitution*.   It is zero when the materials stick together and approaches unity for highly elastic materials.   If the coefficient of restitution is known, the use of Eqs. (8.8) and (8.11) is sufficient to find the final velocities of the two bodies.   Figure 8.9 shows imperfectly elastic collisions of a steel ball and a hardened steel plate.   Since the plate is fastened to the earth, M is essentially infinity, and $V_i = V_f = 0$.   Hence, $e = -v_f/v_i$.

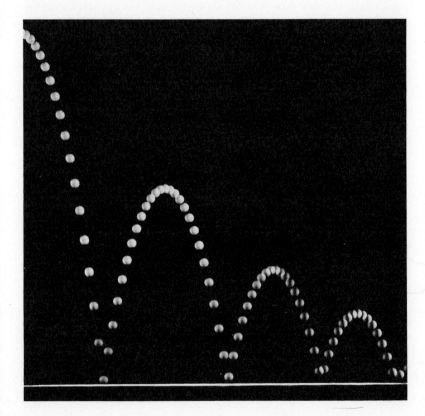

FIGURE 8.9
Imperfectly elastic collisions of
a ball.

Example If the ball of Figure 8.9 is dropped from a height of 40.0 cm, and if the coefficient of restitution is 0.80, find the height attained on the first bounce.

By conservation of energy, $mgh = \frac{1}{2}mv_i^2$, or $v_i^2 = 2gh$. Therefore, the velocity v_i for the first collision is $\sqrt{2 \times 9.8 \times 0.400} = 2.80$ m/sec. By Eq. (8.11), $-v_f = ev_i$, since V_f and V_i are essentially zero.

$$-v_f = 0.80v_i = 2.24 \text{ m/sec}$$

This initial upward speed will carry the ball to a height h_1 such that $v_f^2 = 2gh_1$ or

$$h_1 = \frac{(2.24)^2 \text{ m}}{2 \times 9.8} = 0.256 \text{ m} = 25.6 \text{ cm}$$

8.9 Collisions in Space

Thus far we have considered only collisions in one dimension. Typical collisions between billiard balls involve two dimensions, while collisions between air molecules occur in three dimensions. In every case momentum is conserved. Since momentum is a vector quantity, its conservation requires that the components of the resultant momentum be conserved also. Thus, in a three-dimensional collision each component of the resultant momentum remains the same, and we obtain three equations by application of the conservation of momentum.

Consider a body of mass m, moving with a velocity $\mathbf{v}_i$, which has an elastic collision in two dimensions with a body of mass M initially at rest. After the collision the first body moves off at an angle θ to its original path (Fig. 8.10). Let the x axis be determined by $\mathbf{v}_i$. Applying the conservation of momentum yields

x component: $mv_i + M(0) = mv_f \cos \theta + MV_f \cos \phi$

y component: $0 + 0 = mv_f \sin \theta - MV_f \sin \phi$

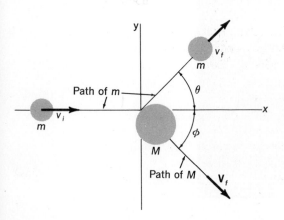

FIGURE 8.10
Glancing elastic collision of a moving sphere with another initially at rest.

Conservation of kinetic energy provides the equation

$$\tfrac{1}{2}mv_i{}^2 = \tfrac{1}{2}mv_f{}^2 + \tfrac{1}{2}MV_f{}^2$$

Thus, if m, M, v_i, and θ are given, we have three equations in three unknowns (v_f, V_f, and ϕ).

Questions

1. A shell explodes in midair. Is its total momentum greater than before the explosion? Is its kinetic energy changed? Explain.

2. Does the center of mass of a solid body necessarily lie within the body? If not, what are some familiar bodies for which the center of mass is not located within the body?

3. Under what conditions does the center of mass of a body *not* coincide with its center of gravity?

4. Discuss what happens when a novice marksman fires a rifle while holding the butt about an inch from his shoulder.

5. Discuss qualitatively what happens when a light sphere collides head on with a more massive sphere initially at rest. How does this compare with what happens if the more massive sphere is in motion and strikes the light sphere head on? What happens if the two spheres have the same mass?

6. Prove that, if a ball makes an elastic collision with a smooth wall, the angle of incidence (between the incident path and a perpendicular to the surface) and the angle of reflection are equal.

7. Eighty per cent of the weight of a certain guided missile is fuel. Assuming that the thrust exerted by the rocket motor is constant, discuss the factors which influence the acceleration of the rocket as it rises vertically to a height of 200 miles.

Problems

1. A 160-lb swimmer dives from a 320-lb rowboat initially at rest. If the swimmer leaves the boat with a horizontal speed of 8 ft/sec, find the recoil speed of the boat, neglecting the transfer of momentum to the water. *Ans.* 4 ft/sec

2. A 50-kg artificial satellite has a velocity of 8,000 m/sec. Find its momentum and its kinetic energy.

3. A pitcher exerts an average resultant force of 8 lb for 0.125 sec on a baseball weighing 0.32 lb. Find the average acceleration, the impulse, the speed of the ball, and the magnitude of the momentum. *Ans.* 800 ft/sec^2; 1 lb-sec; 100 ft/sec; 1 slug-ft/sec

4. A bullet of mass 5 g is projected from a gun of mass 7 kg with a velocity of 350 m/sec. What is the velocity with which the gun recoils?

5. A 2-g bullet is fired from a 2.5-kg rifle with a velocity of 350 m/sec north. Find the momentum of the bullet and the recoil velocity of the rifle, assuming that no other bodies are involved. *Ans.* 0.70 kg-m/sec north; 0.28 m/sec south

6. A 0.32-lb baseball approaches a batter with a speed of 80 ft/sec. The batter lines the ball directly back at the pitcher with a speed of 120 ft/sec. Find the change in momentum and the impulse. If bat and ball were in contact for 0.01 sec, find the average force exerted on the ball during this period.

7. An aircraft with a mass of 10,000 kg catapulted from a carrier has a uniform acceleration of 25 m/sec^2 over a distance of 40.5 m. Find the resultant force required, the time the force acts, the momentum of the aircraft as it leaves the catapult, and the impulse provided to the aircraft.

Ans. 250,000 newtons; 1.8 sec; 450,000 kg-m/sec; 450,000 newton-sec

8. Find the recoil velocity of a rifle weighing 9 lb when it projects a 0.25-oz bullet with a velocity of 2,400 ft/sec.

9. A football of mass 0.42 kg is passed with a velocity of 22 m/sec due south. A defending player lunges at the ball and deflects it so the new velocity is 20 m/sec 37°W of south. Find the magnitude of the impulse. If the player is in contact with the ball for 0.008 sec, what is the magnitude of the average force he exerts?

Ans. 5.6 newton-sec; 700 newtons

10. Three spheres are located with their centers along a straight line as follows: a 2-kg mass is 0.5 m to the right of a 6-kg mass, and an 8-kg mass is 0.75 m to the right of the 2-kg mass. Find the center of mass of the system.

11. Find the distance from the center of the earth to the center of mass of the earth-moon system if the earth-moon separation is 3.8×10^5 km and the mass of the earth is 80 times the mass of the moon. *Ans.* 4,700 km

12. A machine gun fires eight bullets per second into a target. The mass of each bullet is 3 g, and the velocity 600 m/sec. Find the average force required to hold the gun in position. *19.4 Newton*

13. A machine gun fires 90 bullets per minute with a velocity of 800 m/sec. If each bullet has a mass of 0.075 kg, what average force is required to hold the gun against the recoil? What power is delivered to the bullets by the gun?

Ans. 90 newtons; 36 kW

14. A machine gun fires 240 bullets each minute with a velocity of 1,800 ft/sec. If the weight of each bullet is 0.025 lb, what horsepower is developed by the gun? What average force is required to hold the gun in position?

15. A rocket engine ejects 30 kg/sec of hot gases at a speed of 2,000 m/sec. Find the thrust and the vertical acceleration available at launch for a missile of 4,000 kg total mass. *Ans.* 60,000 newtons; 5.2 m/sec^2

16. A small vernier rocket ejects 0.8 kg of gases with a speed of 2,000 m/sec in order to make a small corrective increase in the speed of a missile of 2,000 kg mass. Find the momentum of the exhaust gases and the change in speed of the missile.

17. The Redstone ballistic missile was used by the United States for sending its first astronauts on ballistic trajectories. The Redstone has a rocket engine of 75,000 lb thrust. It weighs 40,000 lb at launch, and its jet exhaust has a speed of 6,000 ft/sec. If the Redstone rises vertically, find its initial acceleration, the rate at which mass is ejected, the acceleration after 30 sec of operation, and the time at which the acceleration becomes 5 *g*'s. *Ans.* 28 ft/sec^2; 12.5 slugs/sec; 53.7 ft/sec^2; 68.8 sec

18. A rocket engine ejects gaseous combustion products at a speed of 2,400 m/sec. If it ejects 5 kg/sec, find the thrust exerted on the rocket by the escaping gases.

19. A 10-lb body moving with a speed of 6 ft/sec strikes a 4-lb body moving in the same direction with a speed of 2 ft/sec. Find the speed after impact, assuming that the masses are perfectly inelastic. *Ans.* 4.86 ft/sec

20. A freight car weighing 60 tons runs into another freight car of the same weight. One car was stationary, and the other was running at the rate of 7.5 mi/hr (11 ft/sec). If the cars move off together after collision, with what speed do they move?

21. A 5-g bullet is fired into a 2.995-kg block of wood which is the bob of a ballistic pendulum. If the bob leaves its equilibrium position with a speed of 1 m/sec, find the speed of the bullet and the height above the equilibrium position reached by the center of gravity of the block. *Ans.* 600 m/sec; 0.051 m

22. A 0.005-kg bullet going 800 m/sec strikes a 1.995-kg wooden block which is the bob of a ballistic pendulum. Find the speed at which block and bullet leave the equilibrium position and the height which the center of gravity of the bullet-block system reaches above the initial position of the center of gravity.

23. A 4-g bullet is fired horizontally with a speed of 1,000 m/sec into a 4-kg block of wood at rest on a table. If the coefficient of friction between the block and the table is 0.25, how far will the block slide? What fraction of the bullet's energy is dissipated in the collision? *Ans.* 20.4 cm; 99.9 per cent

24. A 3-g bullet is fired into a 1.997-kg block suspended by a long cord. The bullet remains in the block, which swings until its center of gravity is raised by 1.6 cm. Find the speed of the block and bullet as they leave the equilibrium position of the block. What was the initial speed of the bullet?

25. A 5-g bullet is fired horizontally into a 2-kg block of wood suspended from a cord 2 m long. The block swings because of the impact, deflecting the cord to a position 20° from the vertical. Find the initial speed of the bullet. *Ans.* 615 m/sec

26. A ball dropped from a height of 9 ft rebounds from a flat surface to a height of 4 ft. Find the speed of the ball just before it strikes and just after it leaves the floor. What is the coefficient of restitution?

27. A tennis ball bounces down a flight of stairs, striking each step in turn and rebounding to the height of the step above. If the height of each step is 20 cm, find the coefficient of restitution. *Ans.* 0.707

28. If the coefficient of restitution for a golf ball dropped on a cement sidewalk is 0.80, find the height to which the ball returns if it is dropped from a height of 4 ft.

29. If the small steel ball in the accompanying figure has a mass of 0.1 kg, and the large one a mass of 0.2 kg, find the recoil velocity of each ball if the larger one is pulled out and released in such a way as to have an elastic collision when it is moving to the left with a speed of 0.5 m/sec. *Ans.* 0.667 and 0.167 m/sec to the left

30. In the accompanying figure the smaller ball has a mass of 0.3 kg, and the larger one a mass of 0.5 kg. If the smaller one is pulled back and released so that it has a velocity of 2 m/sec just before collision, find the velocities of both balls immediately after they have an elastic collision.

31. Two perfectly elastic balls, one weighing 6 lb and the other 4 lb, are moving in opposite directions with velocities of 8 and 10 ft/sec, respectively. Find their velocities after head-on impact. *Ans.* −6.4 ft/sec; 11.6 ft/sec

32. A mass A of 2 kg moving to the right with a speed of 5 m/sec collides head on with a mass B of 4 kg moving in the opposite direction with a speed of 3 m/sec. After the collision A is moving to the left with a speed of 4 m/sec. Find the velocity of B after collision and the coefficient of restitution.

33. A proton of mass 1.66 × 10⁻²⁷ kg collides head on with a helium atom at rest. The helium atom has a mass of 6.64 × 10⁻²⁷ kg, and it recoils with a speed of 8 × 10⁵ m/sec.

PROBS. 29 AND 30

32 ANS   156 f/sec to right ; 0.69

If the collision was elastic, find the initial and final speeds of the proton and the fraction of its initial energy transferred to the helium atom.

Ans. 2×10^6 m/sec; -1.2×10^6 m/sec; 64 per cent

34. Show that when a moving particle of mass m collides head on and elastically with a particle of mass M initially at rest, it transfers to the stationary particle the fraction $4 mM/(m + M)^2$ of its initial kinetic energy.

35. A spherical mass of 2 kg moving along the x axis with a velocity of 5 m/sec collides elastically with a spherical mass of 4 kg initially at rest. After the collision the 2-kg mass moves off at an angle of 37° with the x axis. Find the speed of both masses after the collision and the angle which the path of the 4-kg sphere makes with the x axis. *Ans.* 4.51 m/sec; 1.53 m/sec; 62°

36. A body of mass m and speed V has an elastic head-on collision with a mass M at rest. What must M be (in terms of m) if m and M have equal energies after the collision?

37. Sphere A of mass m and velocity v_i has a perfectly elastic collision with an identical sphere B initially at rest. (*a*) Show that for a head-on collision sphere A is left at rest while sphere B is given a velocity equal to v_i. (*b*) If the collision is not head-on, show that the angle between the velocities of the spheres after collision is 90°.

CHAPTER 9 *In Chap. 5 we studied trajectories of short-range projectiles, assuming that the acceleration **g** is constant both in magnitude and direction. For a long-range projectile or a space capsule or a planet the direction of the acceleration varies along the path, and, unless the orbit is circular, the magnitude changes also. From the accumulated knowledge of the motions of the planets Newton deduced the law of force which predicts the observed accelerations of the planets and in terms of which we can understand the acceleration **g** of freely falling bodies. We now follow some of the reasoning which led to the formulation of Newton's law of universal gravitation and apply this law to such problems as those involving space satellites.*

Uniform Circular Motion and Gravitation

9.1 Ptolemy's Theory of the Universe

When Newton formulated his laws of motion, he was particularly interested in explaining the movements of the moon, the planets, and other heavenly bodies. These motions had fascinated men since the beginning of history. In Greek mythology the daily journey of the sun was attributed to the god Apollo driving a flaming chariot across the sky. In the second century A.D. Ptolemy developed the theory that the stars, the sun, the moon, and the planets all revolved about the earth (Fig. 9.1). He postulated that one might think of the stars as mounted on a great transparent sphere which rotated at a constant rate around the earth at its center. The sun and the moon were mounted on similar, but smaller, spheres which rotated about the earth at rates different from that of the stars. To explain the motions of the planets (*planet* means "wanderer"), which move most of the time in the same direction as the stars but occasionally retrogress, the Ptolemaic theory assumed that each planet moved in a circular path about a center, which in turn followed a much larger circular path about the earth. Small circles superimposed on a large circle were called *epicycles*.

9.2 Copernicus, Galileo, Brahe, and Kepler

In 1543, Nicholas Copernicus, a Polish monk, published the results of some 35 years of patient study in a celebrated book which showed that the need for epicyclic paths of planets and many of the other

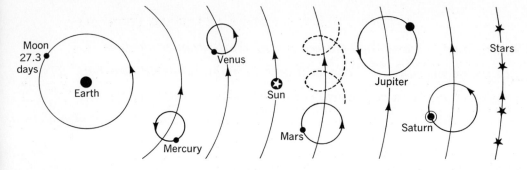

FIGURE 9.1
In the Ptolemaic system, the earth is at the center of the universe.

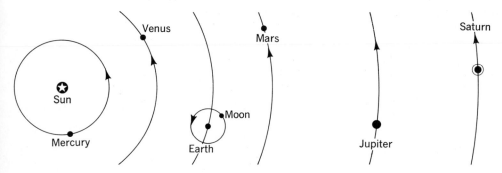

FIGURE 9.2
In the Copernican system, the sun is the center of the solar system.

complications of the Ptolemaic system disappeared if one took the sun as the center of the universe (Fig. 9.2). The idea of a heliocentric (*helios* means "sun") system as opposed to the Ptolemaic geocentric (*geos* means "earth") system was a great stimulus to the field of astrophysics. Supporting evidence for the Copernican theory grew over the next century.

Galileo constructed a telescope shortly after a Dutch spectacle maker discovered in 1608 that he could use two spectacle lenses to form an enlarged image of a distant object. With his telescope Galileo discovered four of Jupiter's moons, that there were mountains on the surface of the moon, that Saturn had rings, and that the sun had dark spots moving across its disk which gave evidence that the sun itself was in rotation. Some of these discoveries were readily explained on the basis of the Copernican theory, but not by the Ptolemaic theory. Galileo became one of the major supporters of Copernicus, but he soon suffered persecution and imprisonment because his views differed from those held by certain high officials of the church.

The Danish astronomer Tycho Brahe (1546–1609) devoted most of his professional life to making accurate measurements of the positions of stars and planets. His data were analyzed by the mathematical physicist Johan Kepler (1571–1630). Kepler found that the motions of the planets did not always agree exactly with those predicted by the Copernican theory of circular paths. After many years of work he was able to show that the motions of the planets could be predicted by use of three generalizations, which we know as *Kepler's laws.*

1. The orbit of each planet is an ellipse with the sun at one focus.

2. The speed of the planet varies in such a way that the line joining the planet and the sun sweeps out equal areas in equal times (Fig. 9.3).

3. The cubes of the semimajor axes of the elliptical orbits are proportional to the squares of the times for the planets to make a complete revolution about the sun.

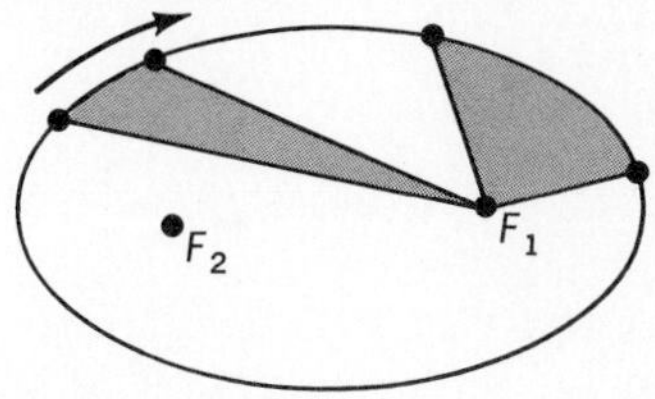

Although the general motions of the planets about the sun occur in elliptic orbits, the motions of the earth and of several of the other planets around the sun can be reasonably well described by circular orbits, as can the motion of the moon around the earth. Since the geometrical complexity of circular motion is substantially less than that of general elliptic motion, and since the physical ideas involved in both types are equivalent, we shall focus our attention on circular motion and leave elliptic motion to more advanced treatments. We observe that the circle may be regarded as a limiting case of the ellipse, namely, that in which the two foci merge into one.

FIGURE 9.3

The line joining a planet and the sun at F_1 sweeps out equal areas in equal time intervals, even though the speed of the planet varies.

9.3 Uniform Circular Motion

When a body moves in a circular path with constant speed, it is said to describe *uniform circular motion.* The magnitude of the velocity is constant, but the direction is always changing. A body describing uniform circular motion has an acceleration, illustrated in Figure 9.4. By the definition of acceleration, $\mathbf{a} = (\mathbf{v} - \mathbf{v}_0)/t$, or $\mathbf{v} - \mathbf{v}_0 = \mathbf{a}t$. In Figure 9.4 the vector difference $\mathbf{v} - \mathbf{v}_0 = \mathbf{a}t$ is shown. Note that the vector $\mathbf{a}t$ is directed roughly toward the center of the circle. Indeed, if we draw a vector diagram similar to that of Figure 9.4 for the case in which the angle θ approaches zero, the acceleration is directed toward the center of the circle. The acceleration is constant in magnitude throughout the circular path, but it varies in direction.

To calculate this acceleration, we proceed as follows: Suppose that the particle passes over the arc AB with constant speed v in time t.

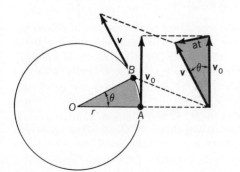

FIGURE 9.4

The magnitude of the velocity remains constant in uniform circular motion, but its direction changes. The acceleration is always toward the center of the circle.

The distance passed over is $AB = vt$. If θ is a small angle, the chord AB is essentially equal in length to the arc AB. In the velocity vector triangle of Figure 9.4, the angle between $\mathbf{v}$ and $\mathbf{v}_0$ is also θ (since the velocity of uniform circular motion is always perpendicular to the radius). Therefore, the gray triangles are similar, from which we conclude that $vt/r = at/v$, and

$$a = \frac{v^2}{r}$$ 9.1

The acceleration of a body describing uniform circular motion is always directed toward the center of the circle and has the magnitude v^2/r.

9.4 Centripetal Force

If a body has an acceleration toward the center of a circle, there is a net force in that direction, by Newton's second law. This force is called the *centripetal force*. To find its magnitude, we recall that $\mathbf{F} = m\mathbf{a}$ and that $a_c = v^2/r$, whence

$$F_c = ma_c = m\frac{v^2}{r}$$ 9.2

Consider a model airplane constrained to move in a horizontal circle by a control wire. The wire pulls on the airplane toward the center of the circle. By Newton's third law, if the wire exerts a force on the airplane toward the center, the airplane must exert an equal force on the wire away from the center. This force, *away* from the center of the circle and *acting on the wire,* is known as the *centrifugal force*.

Note carefully that the force *on the airplane* is *toward the center* of the circle. If this force were suddenly removed and no unbalanced force acted on the airplane, it would move along a tangent to the circular path. No force acts upon the airplane outward along the radius. The airplane does exert a force outward on the restraint, which in this case is the control wire. This outward force on the restraint is the centrifugal force; it is the reaction to the centripetal force which acts inward on the body describing circular motion.

9.5 Newton's Law of Universal Gravitation

Let us now apply these ideas and equations to the motion of the earth about the sun. Imagine for the moment that the sun itself is fixed rigidly in space. If we assume that the path of the earth is circular, the earth has an acceleration toward the sun (the center of the circle) given by $a_c = v^2/r$. To produce this acceleration there must be an unbalanced centripetal force $F_c = mv^2/r$.

The magnitude of the earth's velocity is $2\pi r/T$, where T is the period (1 year = time for one complete revolution). Therefore, the centripetal force is

$$F_c = m\frac{4\pi^2 r^2}{T^2}\frac{1}{r} = \frac{4\pi^2 mr}{T^2}$$ 9.3

For a circular orbit the semimajor axis is equal to the radius r. By Kepler's third law, T^2 is proportional to r^3, or $T^2 = cr^3$, where c is a constant. Substituting this in Eq. (9.3) yields

$$F_c = \frac{4\pi^2 m}{c} \frac{1}{r^2}$$

so the centripetal force F_c is inversely proportional to r^2. Furthermore, if the proportionality constant for all planets is to be the same, F_c must be proportional to the mass of the body describing the orbit, so that the mass cancels out of Eq. (9.3). Otherwise the relationship between the period and the semimajor axis would have to involve the mass of the rotating heavenly body. If the mass of one of the bodies is involved in the attractive force between the two, it seems reasonable that the mass of the central body should be involved in a similar way. After extensive reasoning closely related to the arguments above, Newton proposed his great law of universal gravitation:

Between every two particles in the universe there is a force of gravitational attraction which is proportional to the product of the masses of the two particles and inversely proportional to the square of the distance between them. This force, which acts along the line joining the two particles, is given by

$$F_G = G \frac{m_1 m_2}{r^2} \qquad\qquad \textbf{9.4}$$

where G is the universal gravitational constant. Its value has been measured and is 6.67×10^{-11} newton-m^2/kg^2.

When we deal with the gravitational attraction between large objects whose separation is very large compared to the dimensions of either body, we need not calculate the forces between every particle of one body and every particle of the other. If m_1 and m_2 are the masses of the bodies, and r the distance between their centers of mass, Eq. (9.4) is directly applicable.

The force of attraction between two identical lead spheres of mass 1 kg with centers 1 m apart is only 6.67×10^{-11} newton. The gravitational forces between two ordinary man-sized objects are detectable only under the most favorable of conditions. When the bodies involved are stars or planets, the masses involved are so great that the forces become exceedingly large.

Evidence for the validity of Newton's law of gravitation is obtained from astronomical observations. By application of the law, it is possible to predict with great accuracy the motions of the planets and their satellites many years in advance. Such long-term predictions are a severe test of the law.

9.6 Determination of the Gravitational Constant and the Mass of the Earth

The gravitational constant G was first measured by Cavendish in the eighteenth century. He used a torsion balance (Fig. 9.5) in which two spheres of mass m are fixed to the end of a light rod which is sus-

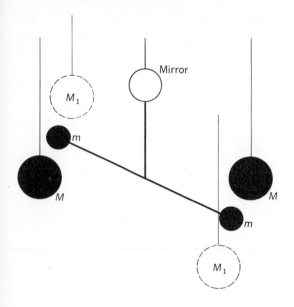

FIGURE 9.5

Schematic diagram of the apparatus with which Cavendish measured the universal gravitational constant. As the small masses were attracted by the large masses, their displacement was determined from the twisting of the suspending cord. A light beam reflected from the mirror to a scale measured the amount of twisting.

FIGURE 9.6

Jolly's method of measuring the universal gravitational constant.

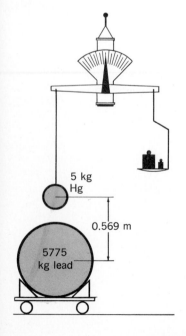

pended by a long, fine wire so that it can turn easily. When two heavy lead balls are placed at the positions marked M, the rod carrying the two small balls turns to a new position. If the lead balls are placed at M_1, the light rod with the small spheres turns in the opposite direction. By measuring the elastic constant of the suspending wire, it is possible to determine the attractive force between the movable spheres and the balls.

A method of measuring G which is simple to understand was developed by Jolly. A spherical vessel containing 5 kg of mercury was attached to one arm of a sensitive balance, and the balance put in equilibrium (Fig. 9.6). Then a lead sphere of mass 5,775 kg (over 6 tons) was rolled beneath the mercury flask with its center about 0.57 m below the center of mass of the mercury. The gravitational attraction between the lead and the mercury was found to be such that a mass of 0.589 mg on the left pan was able to restore equilibrium. All the quantities in Eq. (9.4) were thus known except for G, the value of which was calculated.

Once the value of the gravitational constant is known, it is possible to calculate the mass of the earth m_E. For the moment, consider the earth to be a perfect sphere of radius $r = 6.4 \times 10^6$ m. The force which the earth exerts on a mass of 1 kg at its surface is 1 kg-wt = 9.8 newtons. Therefore, from $F_G = Gmm_E/r^2$,

$$9.8 \text{ newtons} = 6.67 \times 10^{-11} \frac{\text{newton-m}^2}{\text{kg}^2} \frac{1 \text{ kg} \times m_E}{(6.4 \times 10^6 \text{ m})^2}$$

from which $m_E = 6 \times 10^{24}$ kg.

We may also find the mass of the sun M_s. The earth revolves around the sun in an elliptical path which is fairly close to a circle of radius 93,000,000 miles (1.5×10^{11} m). The centripetal force for the earth is provided by the gravitational attraction between the earth and the sun. Thus,

$$F_G = G\frac{M_s m_E}{r^2} = m_E\frac{v_E^2}{r} \qquad\qquad \textbf{9.5}$$

and

$$M_s = \frac{v_E^2 r}{G} = \frac{(2\pi r)^2 r}{T^2 G} = \frac{(2\pi)^2(1.5\times 10^{11})^3}{(365.26\times 86,400)^2\times 6.67\times 10^{-11}} = 2\times 10^{30}\,\text{kg}$$

Table 9.1 gives important data about the solar system.

9.7 Artificial Satellites

Men have long dreamed of "space stations" circling the earth at a height of a few hundred miles. Let us find the velocity required for such a station to remain in circular orbit 600 km above the earth's surface and therefore some 7,000 km from the center of the earth. For this satellite the gravitational attraction of the earth provides the required centripetal force. If m_s is the mass of the satellite,

$$G\frac{m_s m_E}{r^2} = m_s\frac{v^2}{r}$$

or

$$6.67\times 10^{-11}\frac{\text{newton-m}^2}{\text{kg}^2}\frac{6\times 10^{24}\,\text{kg}}{(7\times 10^6\,\text{m})^2} = \frac{v^2}{(7\times 10^6\,\text{m})}$$

$$v = 7,600\,\text{m/sec}$$

or about 17,000 mi/hr.

At this speed the satellite would require a time to encircle the earth of $(2\pi\times 7\times 10^6\,\text{m})/(7,600\,\text{m/sec}) = 5,600\,\text{sec} = 1.6\,\text{hr}$.

TABLE 9.1 *Data on the Solar System*

Body	Mass, kg	Average radius,* km	g at surface, m/sec²	Sidereal period, days	Radius of orbit,† km
Moon	7.35×10^{22}	1,738	1.67	27.3	3.8×10^5
Sun	1.97×10^{30}	695,000	274.4		
Mercury	3.28×10^{23}	2,570	3.92	88	5.8×10^7
Venus	4.82×10^{24}	6,310	8.82	245	1.08×10^8
Earth	5.98×10^{24}	6,370	9.80	365.26	1.50×10^8
Mars	6.37×10^{23}	3,430	3.92	687	2.28×10^8
Jupiter	1.88×10^{27}	71,800	26.46	4,333	7.78×10^8
Saturn	5.62×10^{26}	60,300	11.76	1.08×10^4	1.43×10^9
Uranus	8.62×10^{25}	26,700	9.80	3.07×10^4	2.87×10^9
Neptune	1.0×10^{26}	2,490	9.80	6.02×10^4	4.5×10^9
Pluto				9.09×10^4	5.9×10^9

* Bodies are not exactly spheres.

† Orbits are actually elliptical; the values quoted are mean distances.

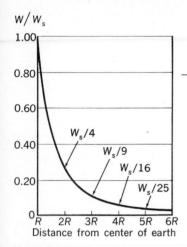

FIGURE 9.7

Weight decreases as an object's distance from the center of the earth increases. W_s is the weight at the earth's surface.

If the only force on the satellite were gravitational, the satellite would encircle the earth indefinitely. Actually air friction and other small forces gradually reduce the speed, so that eventually it approaches the earth and dissipates its energy in the earth's atmosphere.

9.8 Variation of Weight with Position

The weight of an object of mass m is mg, where g is the observed acceleration due to gravity. If the earth were isolated, at rest, and a perfect sphere of radius r, the weight of an object would be the same at all points on its surface. Actually, the earth is somewhat flattened at the poles. Consequently, a body at one of the poles is closer to the center of the earth than an identical body at the equator. This leads to a somewhat greater weight at the poles than at the equator. Another factor which makes the weight of an object less at the equator is the rotation of the earth. At the equator a portion of the gravitational pull is used to supply the centripetal force to keep the body moving with uniform circular motion. Therefore, the force which must be applied to the body to prevent it from falling to the earth is smaller at the equator. The total variation from equator to pole is approximately 0.5 per cent.

The gravitational pull is just adequate to produce the required centripetal acceleration for a body in a space capsule in orbit around the earth. The body is "weightless" in the sense that no force is required to hold it in its position in the capsule. An astronaut can place his camera 2 ft in front of him, and it will "float" in that position. Here we have a special case in which the entire gravitational attraction of the earth is required to produce centripetal acceleration, leaving no *net* force on the camera as viewed from the capsule.

The weight of a body varies not only with latitude but also with altitude. The weight is somewhat less atop Pike's Peak than it is in Death Valley. As we go above the earth, the weight of a body decreases gradually as r increases. Figure 9.7 shows how the weight varies with distance from the center of the earth (neglecting effects arising from rotation or revolution). Table 9.2 shows how g differs from place to place.

TABLE 9.2 *Acceleration of Gravity g at Various Locations*

Place	Elevation, m	g, m/sec²
Equator	0	9.78039
Panama Canal	5	9.78243
Latitude 45° (Standard)	0	9.80665
North Pole	0	9.83201
Boston, Mass.	22	9.80395
Chicago, Ill.	182	9.80277
Denver, Colo.	1,638	9.79608
Pike's Peak, Colo.	4,293	9.78953
San Francisco, Calif.	114	9.79965

In prospecting for oil and for heavy masses of ore below the surface of the earth, very careful measurements of g are commonly made at selected points over a fairly large area. Modern gravimeters are sufficiently sensitive so that a change in g of a few parts in 100 million can be readily detected. The variation in g over a region is plotted on a map, and experts can frequently locate places where drilling for oil or ore is most likely to be successful.

The variations in the acceleration of gravity at different places on the earth's surface are small enough so that they may be neglected in ordinary activities. However, if man develops his rocket ships to the point where travel to the moon or to Mars becomes feasible, he will find that the pull of these objects is very different from that of the earth. On the surface of the moon his weight (force with which the moon would hold him to its surface) would be only one-sixth of that on the earth. Indeed, the gravitational pull on the moon is so small that gas molecules escape readily, and therefore the moon has no atmosphere. On the planet Jupiter a man would be pulled down by a force 2.6 times as great as his weight on the earth. Under these circumstances it would be difficult for him to walk about.

9.9 Gravitational Potential Energy

The potential energy of a body of mass m raised a distance h above the surface of the earth is, by Eq. (7.5), mgh. This relation is valid, however, only if the weight of the body mg does not vary significantly over the range of heights involved. Let us now consider the potential energy when the mass is lifted or projected to a height h of hundreds of miles above the surface of the earth. Let R be the radius of the earth, and r the distance from the center of the earth to a point a distance h above the earth's surface (Fig. 9.8). The potential energy of the mass relative to the earth's surface is the work required to move it from the surface of the earth to h. To calculate this work, we divide the displacement from R to r in many small intervals and calculate the work performed in each of these intervals. From R to r_1 the force on mass m varies from GMm/R^2 to GMm/r_1^2. If R and r_1 are close to one another, the average force in the interval from R to r_1 is GMm/Rr_1, and the work done in this interval is, by Eq. (7.1),

$$\mathcal{W}_1 = \frac{GMm(r_1-R)}{Rr_1} = GMm\left(\frac{1}{R} - \frac{1}{r_1}\right)$$

Similarly the work $\mathcal{W}_2$ required to move the mass from r_1 to r_2 is

$$\mathcal{W}_2 = GMm\left(\frac{1}{r_1} - \frac{1}{r_2}\right)$$

and so forth. The total work done in carrying m from R to r is

$$\mathcal{W} = \mathcal{W}_1 + \mathcal{W}_2 + \cdots = GMm\left(\frac{1}{R} - \frac{1}{r_1} + \frac{1}{r_1} - \frac{1}{r_2}\cdots + \frac{1}{r_n} - \frac{1}{r}\right)$$

$$= GMm\left(\frac{1}{R} - \frac{1}{r}\right) \qquad \textbf{9.6}$$

FIGURE 9.8

The potential energy of a mass at a great height above the earth's surface is determined by dividing the displacement from R to r into many small intervals, calculating the change in potential energy for each interval, and adding the results.

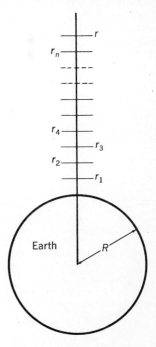

If a projectile is fired straight upward with a speed v, and if air friction is negligible, the projectile rises until its kinetic energy is transformed into potential energy, or

$$\tfrac{1}{2}mv^2 = GMm \left(\frac{1}{R} - \frac{1}{r_{max}} \right)$$

where r_{max} is the maximum radius attained by the projectile.

Example A projectile is fired upward with a speed of 5,000 m/sec. How high will it rise above the earth's surface, if air friction is ignored?

Kinetic energy at launch = potential energy at maximum height

$$\tfrac{1}{2}m \times 2,500 \times 10^4 \frac{m^2}{sec^2} = 6.67 \times 10^{-11} \frac{newton\text{-}m^2}{kg^2}$$
$$\times m\ (5.98 \times 10^{24}\ kg) \left(\frac{1}{6.37 \times 10^6\ m} - \frac{1}{r_{max}} \right)$$

from which $r_{max} = 8.0 \times 10^6$ m, corresponding to a height above the earth's surface of about 1.6×10^6 m.

9.10 The Formation of Tides

One of the familiar and important phenomena which is explained by gravitational attraction is that of the tides. It is easy to see how the moon raises the tide (Fig. 9.9) on side A nearest to it, since water flows readily and is subjected to an extra force due to the gravitational attraction of the moon. To understand why there is a tide on the opposite side of the earth at the same time, one must recall that the moon does not revolve about a fixed earth, but rather both bodies perform essentially uniform circular motion about the center of mass O of the earth-moon system. Since point C is much farther from O than point A, the centripetal force required for a kilogram of water at C is greater than that for a kilogram at A, and consequently g is lower at C (Sec. 9.8). As a result water piles up on this side also. Lunar tides have their greatest heights twice in a period of 1 day and 51 min. The inertia of the water, forces of friction, and other causes produce lags in the motion of the water and otherwise complicate the picture, so that high tide does not coincide with the time when the moon is directly overhead.

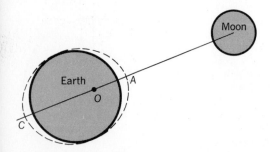

FIGURE 9.9

How the moon forms the earth's tides. Sizes are not to scale.

The sun produces tides too, but solar tides are much smaller. They, of course, have their greatest height twice in the period of 24 hr. The resulting tide is a combination of the large lunar tide and the relatively small solar tide. When the sun, moon, and earth are all in line, unusually large tides are formed.

9.11 Applications of Centripetal Force

When an automobile goes around a curve (Fig. 9.10) on a perfectly level road, friction between the tires and roadway is required to provide the necessary centripetal force mv^2/r. If the road is coated with ice, this frictional force may be too small to provide the necessary centripetal acceleration, and the car may slide off the road. Note that *there is no force pulling the car outward* along the radius. By Newton's first law, the car would continue to move indefinitely with constant velocity in the absence of any force. If there is a force toward the center of the circle which is inadequate to provide the full centripetal force, the car is accelerated toward the center of the curve, but not enough to keep it on the road.

If the road is suitably banked, the car may go around the curve without requiring any frictional force at all. If friction between tires and roadway is absent, the road pushes on the car only in the direction perpendicular to the surface. The vertical component of this normal force (Fig. 9.11) is exactly the weight of the vehicle. If the horizontal component is just mv^2/r, the automobile goes around the curve without skidding. We observe that to satisfy these conditions the angle θ must be such that

$$\tan \theta = \frac{mv^2/r}{mg} = \frac{v^2}{gr} \qquad\qquad \textbf{9.7}$$

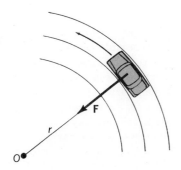

FIGURE 9.10

Centripetal force must be provided when an automobile goes around a curve, either by the friction of the tires or by the banking of the pavement.

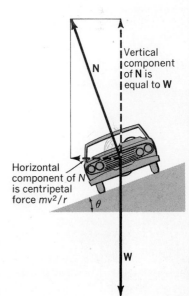

FIGURE 9.11

A curve is perfectly banked for a given speed v when the force exerted by the road perpendicular to its surface has a vertical component equal to the weight of the vehicle $W = mg$, and a horizontal component equal to the centripetal force mv^2/r.

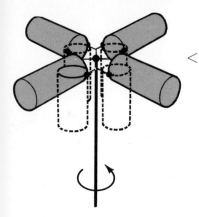

FIGURE 9.12

Centrifuge.

The ideal angle at which the road should be banked depends on the speed of the car, but not on its mass.

The centrifuge, which is widely used in the separation of liquids of unequal densities, depends for its operation on centripetal force. One type of centrifuge (Fig. 9.12) consists in a wheel that rotates in a horizontal plane. To this wheel are attached buckets that are vertical when the wheel is at rest. However, when the wheel is revolving rapidly, the buckets assume a position such that their axes are almost horizontal. If a mixture of liquids of unequal densities is introduced into the buckets and the wheel is rotated rapidly, the liquids separate, the heavy liquids farther from the axis of rotation, and the lighter liquids nearer to it. This means that the heavier liquids are at the bottom of the buckets when the centrifuge is stopped. The cream separator works on the same principle as the centrifuge.

9.12 Centripetal Forces in Aviation

When an aircraft makes a turn in a horizontal plane, it banks in such a way that the vertical component of the forces on the wings is equal to the weight of the aircraft, while the horizontal component provides the necessary centripetal force. Very-high-speed aircraft cannot make exceedingly sharp turns because it is not feasible to provide the necessary centripetal force.

When an aircraft pulls out of a steep dive, large forces must be exerted by the wings. More than one pilot has pulled the wings off his aircraft when he has tried to pull out of a dive too quickly. Consider an aircraft which is descending at the rate of 800 ft/sec and tries to pull out of the dive in a circle of radius 2,000 ft (Fig. 9.13). The centripetal acceleration becomes

$$a_c = \frac{v^2}{r} = \frac{800 \text{ ft/sec} \times 800 \text{ ft/sec}}{2,000 \text{ ft}} = 320 \text{ ft/sec}^2$$

or 10 times the acceleration due to gravity. Thus, the *unbalanced upward force* required on the aircraft is 10 times the weight. At the bottom of the circle the wings must not only provide this centripetal acceleration, but also overcome the pull of the earth as well. They must provide 10×32 ft/sec^2 = 10 *g*'s centripetal acceleration plus 1 *g* to take care of the pull of the earth on the aircraft—a total of 11 *g*'s. The wings of most aircraft are not designed for such heavy loading. A typical fighter aircraft is designed to take accelerations of the order of 8 or 9 *g*'s, while passenger aircraft, bombers, and transports are designed for lower *g* loadings. At the top of the circular path (Fig. 9.13) the pull of gravity helps to provide the centripetal acceleration, and the net force exerted by the wings is $mv^2/r - mg$.

Not only does the aircraft itself have to stand these accelerations, but so do all the objects in the aircraft, including the organs of the pilot's body. Consider a gram of blood in a pilot's brain when the aircraft is performing a 6-*g* turn. The total force on this gram of blood must be six times the ordinary force exerted. The blood may

FIGURE 9.13

Forces exerted by the wings on an airplane at the upper and lower extremities of a circular loop.

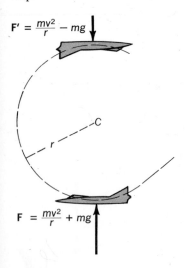

rush out of the pilot's brain, resulting in his "blacking out."   If the heart is unable to pump hard enough to get the blood to the brain, the blood accumulates in the legs and the lower body.   Considerable research has been done to develop techniques which allow pilots to take large g loadings without losing consciousness.

Questions

1. How would the weight of a radio transmitter vary on a rocket trip to the moon? Would its mass also vary?

2. A ball has a mass of 0.1 kg.   If it were taken to the moon, what would be its mass? Would Newton's second law be valid?   Would $m = W/g$ be valid?   Would the weight of the ball be 0.98 newton?

3. The moon falls about 0.28 ft toward the earth each minute, yet it always stays about the same distance away.   Explain how this can be.

4. Explain carefully why an automobile may overturn if it goes around a curve too fast. Which wheels leave the ground first?

5. An airplane makes a complete loop in a vertical plane.   Under what condition does the pilot press upward on the seat at the top of the loop?

6. Does the centripetal force do any work on a body in uniform circular motion?

7. An astronaut in a stable orbit two earth radii from the center of the earth is "weightless" in his space capsule.   How can this statement be reconciled with Figure 9.7, which shows a weight one-fourth that at the earth's surface?

8. Suppose that the moon were to move slowly toward the earth until it came to rest on the earth's surface.   Would the center of mass of the moon coincide with its center of gravity?   Why not?   Which would be closer to the earth?

9. Why is the vector acceleration due to gravity **g** not ordinarily directed toward the center of the earth?   Where on the earth's surface might **g** be expected to point to the center of the earth?

10. An earth satellite which would revolve with the same angular velocity as the earth and would appear stationary to observers on the earth has been proposed as a relay station for television and communications systems.   Could such a station remain on the zenith above Chicago for an extended period?   Why not?   Above what could such a satellite remain stationary to observers on the earth?   (See Prob. 29.)

Problems

1. A 3,000-lb car is going around a curve of 500 ft radius at a speed of 80 ft/sec (54.5 mi/hr).   Find the centripetal acceleration and the centripetal force.

Ans. 12.8 ft/sec^2; 1,200 lb

2. A 2,800-lb automobile traveling 100 ft/sec (68.2 mi/hr) goes around a curve of radius 1,000 ft.   Find the centripetal acceleration and the centripetal force.

3. A 3,200-lb car begins to skid when traveling 90 ft/sec (61 mi/hr) around a level curve of 400 ft radius.   Find the centripetal acceleration and the coefficient of friction between the tires and the road.   *Ans.* 20.25 ft/sec^2; 0.63

4. What is the highest speed at which an automobile can travel around a curve 100 ft in radius, on a level road, if the coefficient of friction between the road and the tires is 0.49?

5. A 160-lb pilot in an aircraft moving at a constant speed of 500 ft/sec pulls out of a vertical dive along an arc of a circle of 2,500 ft radius. Find the centripetal acceleration, the centripetal force, and the total force which the aircraft exerts on the pilot at the bottom of the dive.   *Ans.* 100 ft/sec²; 500 lb; 660 lb

6. A 16,000-lb aircraft with a constant speed of 400 ft/sec (270 mi/hr) pulls out of a vertical dive along an arc of a circle of radius 1,000 ft. Find the centripetal acceleration and the total lift required at the bottom of the dive.

7. What is the smallest speed an airplane may have when it is making a vertical loop with a radius of 1,250 ft so that, at the top of the loop, objects in the plane will not begin to drop?   *Ans.* 200 ft/sec

8. The responses of humans to high accelerations are tested by use of a test chamber at one end of a 20-ft horizontal beam which is rotated about a vertical axis at its other end. How many revolutions per minute must the beam make to provide an acceleration of 10 *g*'s (320 ft/sec²)?

9. A pendulum bob hangs from the roof of a moving van. If the van is traveling 80 ft/sec around a curve of 500 ft radius, find the angle which the cord makes with the vertical when the bob is at rest relative to the van.   *Ans.* 22°

10. A ball is whirled in a vertical circle on the end of a string 3 ft long. At what speed will the tension in the string be zero at the top of the circle?

11. When a sphere of lead is placed 50 cm from another sphere of lead of mass 5 kg, the attraction of one for another is found to be 3×10^{-8} newton. What is the mass of the first sphere?   *Ans.* 22.5 kg

12. Find the gravitational attraction between two identical 50-kg lead spheres with center 0.250 m apart. Compare this force with the earth's gravitational force on one of the spheres.

13. Calculate the attractive force of the earth for the sun. How many times greater is this than the attraction of the earth for the moon?   *Ans.* 3.6×10^{22} newtons; 174

14. From the masses and radii given in Table 9.1 estimate the acceleration due to gravity on the surface of (*a*) the moon, (*b*) the sun, (*c*) Jupiter, and (*d*) Mars. What would be the weight of a 2-kg mass at the surface of each?

15. A rocket is 637 km (0.1 earth radius) above the surface of the earth. What is *g* at this height? Find the weight of a 5-kg mass at this point.
                                           Ans. 8.1 m/sec²; 40.5 newtons

16. Imagine a planet of the same average density as the earth, but with twice the radius. Calculate the acceleration due to gravity at the surface of this planet.

17. Find the centripetal acceleration of an object at the equator due to the rotation of the earth.   *Ans.* 0.034 m/sec²

18. How many revolutions per hour would the earth have to make in order that the weight of a body at the equator may become zero?

19. A body weighs 150 lb on the surface of the earth. Find its weight 2,000 miles above the surface of the earth. Assume the radius of the earth to be 4,000 miles.
                                           Ans. 66.7 lb

20. What is the centripetal acceleration of the moon in its orbit around the earth?

21. A 0.5-kg mass is suspended from a cord 2 m long to form a simple pendulum. If the mass is pulled to one side until it is raised 0.100 m and then released, find the velocity of the mass and the tension in the cord at the bottom of the swing.

Ans. 1.4 m/sec; 5.39 newtons

22. A boy weighing 64 lb is swinging in such a way that he describes an arc of 10 ft radius. If his horizontal speed at the lowest point of the swing is 5 ft/sec, what is the total force which the ropes of the swing must sustain at that instant?

23. With what speed must a 2-kg pendulum bob swing in the circular path of the accompanying figure if the supporting cord is 1.60 m long and θ is 30°? Find the tension in the cord.

Ans. 2.13 m/sec; 22.6 newtons

24. At what distance from the earth along the line joining the earth and the moon are the gravitational pulls of the earth and the moon equal and opposite?

25. A curve of 200 m radius is banked at 15°. At what speed must an automobile go around this curve if no frictional forces are to be used to keep the automobile on its circular path?

Ans. 22.9 m/sec

26. What is the angle at which a circular speedway must be banked for cars running at 120 ft/sec if the radius of the track is 1,000 ft and no frictional force is involved?

27. A small cart on the circular loop-to-loop track of the accompanying figure can be approximated as a mass m sliding on a frictionless track. (*a*) Find the smallest height h in terms of the radius r from which the mass can be released and still remain in contact with the track throughout the path. (*b*) If the cart starts from a height of $4r$, what is its acceleration at the top of the loop? With what force does the track press down on the cart at the top? When the cart starts at $h = 4r$, find the horizontal and vertical components of its acceleration at point A on the end of a horizontal diameter.

Ans. (*a*) 2.5 *r*; (*b*) 4 *g*; 3 *mg*; 6 *g*, *g*

28. At what angle should a curve of 200 ft radius be banked if no frictional forces are to be required for a speed of 60 ft/sec?

29. Find the radius of the orbit of a satellite which revolves about the earth in one sidereal day (86,164 sec). What is its orbital velocity?

Ans. 4.2 × 10⁴ km; 3,060 m/sec

30. If a planet had a circular orbit about our sun with a radius twice that of the earth's orbit, what would be its period of revolution and orbital speed?

31. It is proposed to put a space station in a circular orbit at a distance of one earth's

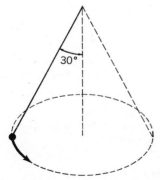

PROB. 23

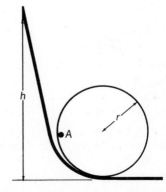

PROB. 27

radius above the earth's surface. What will be the acceleration due to gravity at this station? Find the speed of this station if it is to go around the center of the earth in a circular orbit. How long will it take to make one complete revolution?

Ans. 2.45 m/sec^2; 5,600 m/sec; 1.43 $\times$ 10^4 sec

32. A 50-g mass (see accompanying figure) slides down a smooth (frictionless) hemisphere of 0.25 m radius, starting at the top with a very tiny speed. Find the force exerted on the mass by the hemisphere as a function of the angle θ and the angle at which the mass leaves the surface of the hemisphere.

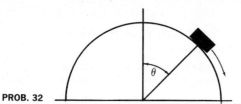

PROB. 32

CHAPTER 10 *In Chap. 4 we found that both the resultant of all forces and the resultant of all torques acting on a body in equilibrium are zero. In the five chapters which followed, we studied the translational motion of a body on which the resultant force is not zero. In this case the body undergoes an acceleration proportional to the force and inversely proportional to its mass. Now we turn to rotational motion, which we develop in terms of several quantities, each of which has an analogue in translational motion.*

Rotational Motion

10.1 Rotational Velocity

Rotational motion is almost as common in our everyday life as translational motion. The flywheel of a stationary engine, the armature of an electric motor, and the spinning top all perform rotational motion. The wheel of a moving automobile describes rotational and translational motions simultaneously. In general, the motion of any moving body may be regarded as a translation of the center of mass and a simultaneous rotation about the center of mass.

Consider the flywheel shown in Figure 10.1, which is rotating about the axis O. A straight line at OA on the flywheel rotates from OA to OB. The rate at which the line rotates is called its *angular velocity*. It is usually expressed in radians per second, although it might also be measured in revolutions per second, revolutions per minute, or degrees per second. If the rate of rotation is constant, the angular velocity is constant and is equal to the angle turned through divided by the corresponding time. If we represent the angular velocity by ω, the angular displacement by θ, and the time by t, we have

$$\omega = \frac{\theta}{t} \qquad\qquad \textbf{10.1}$$

The angular velocity ω is a vector quantity with its direction along the axis of rotation in the sense indicated by the outstretched thumb of the right hand when the fingers point in the direction of rotation.

If we consider the linear velocity of the point A on the flywheel, we observe that θ, the angle swept through in radians, is equal to the length of arc AB divided by the radius r. The distance s traveled by the point is just the arc length AB, and

$$s = \theta r \qquad\qquad \textbf{10.2}$$

FIGURE 10.1
A flywheel rotating through an angle θ about an axis through O carries line OA to OB.

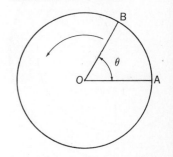

The linear velocity v of the point is given by

$$v = \frac{s}{t} = \frac{\theta r}{t} = \omega r \qquad \text{10.3}$$

For a rigid body the linear velocity of a point increases as the distance from the axis of rotation increases. Note that Eqs. (10.2) and (10.3) are valid *only* if angles are measured in radians.

Example The spoke of a wheel makes 60 rev/min. It is 18 in. in length. Find the linear velocities of a point on its outer end and of a point halfway between the axis and the outer end.

$$v_e = \omega r_e = 2\pi \text{ rad/sec} \times 18 \text{ in.} = 113 \text{ in./sec}$$
$$v_m = \omega r_m = 2\pi \times 9 = 56.5 \text{ in./sec}$$

10.2 Angular Acceleration

In situations in which rotating bodies are speeding up or slowing down, the angular velocity is no longer constant. The *instantaneous angular velocity* ω is then defined by the relation

$$\omega = \lim_{\Delta t \to 0} \frac{\Delta \theta}{\Delta t} \qquad \text{10.1a}$$

The instantaneous angular acceleration α of a rotating object is defined as the rate of change of angular velocity. If the angular acceleration is constant,

$$\alpha = \frac{\Delta \omega}{\Delta t} = \frac{\omega - \omega_0}{t} \qquad \text{10.4}$$

where ω and ω_0 are the angular velocities of the body at the times t and 0.

Any point in a rotationally accelerated body has a linear acceleration a_t tangential to its path and given by

$$a_t = \alpha r$$

if we measure α in radians per second per second. This equation gives only the tangential component of the total linear acceleration of the point. The point is moving in a circle and has also a centripetal acceleration a_c equal to v^2/r.

Example At a certain instant the angular velocity of a wheel is 10 rad/sec. In 20 sec the angular velocity has become 50 rad/sec. What is the angular acceleration?

$$\text{Angular acceleration} = \frac{\text{change in angular velocity}}{\text{time}}$$
$$= \frac{50 \text{ rad/sec} - 10 \text{ rad/sec}}{20 \text{ sec}}$$
$$= 2 \text{ rad/sec}^2$$

Example What are the tangential and total linear accelerations of a particle that is 1.5 ft from the axis of a wheel (Fig. 10.2) when the angular acceleration of the wheel is 3 rad/sec² and ω is 2 rad/sec?

FIGURE 10.2

Linear acceleration **a** is the resultant of tangential acceleration **a**$_t$ and centripetal acceleration **a**$_c$.

$\omega = 2$ rad/sec; $\alpha = 3$ rad/sec²

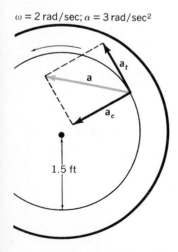

1.5 ft

Tangential linear acceleration $= \alpha r$

$a_t = 3 \text{ rad/sec}^2 \times 1.5 \text{ ft} = 4.5 \text{ ft/sec}^2$

Centripetal linear acceleration $= \dfrac{v^2}{r} = \omega^2 r$

$a_c = (2 \text{ rad/sec})^2 \times 1.5 \text{ ft} = 6.0 \text{ ft/sec}^2$

Total linear acceleration $= \sqrt{a_t{}^2 + a_c{}^2} = 7.5 \text{ ft/sec}^2$

10.3 The Equations of Angular Motion

The equations of angular motion have the same form as the corresponding equations of translational motion. This is true because the angular velocity and angular acceleration are defined analogously to linear velocity and linear acceleration. In the following paragraphs we treat several of the more common special cases.

1. If a body rotates with uniform velocity ω, the angle θ through which it turns in t sec is

$$\theta = \omega t \qquad\qquad\qquad\qquad \text{10.1}b$$

Example An electric motor rotates at a constant angular velocity of 1,800 rev/min. Find the angle turned through in 10 sec.

$\omega = 1{,}800 \text{ rev/min} \times \dfrac{1 \text{ min}}{60 \text{ sec}} = 30 \text{ rev/sec}$

$= 30 \text{ rev/sec} \times 2\pi \text{ rad/rev} = 60\pi \text{ rad/sec}$

$\theta = \omega t = 600\pi = 1{,}885 \text{ radians}$

2. If a body begins to rotate from rest with a uniform angular acceleration α, the angular velocity ω at the end of t sec is αt by Eq. (10.4). During the acceleration the average angular velocity is given by

$$\omega_{av} = \frac{\omega_0 + \omega}{2} = \frac{0 + \alpha t}{2} = \frac{1}{2}\, \alpha t$$

The angle θ swept out in t sec is the average angular velocity times the time, so that

$$\theta = \tfrac{1}{2}\alpha t^2$$

Example A flywheel starts from rest and has a uniform angular acceleration of 4 rad/sec² for a time of 10 sec. Find the final angular velocity, the average angular velocity during the 10 sec acceleration, and the angle turned through in the 10 sec.

$\omega = \alpha t = 4 \text{ rad/sec}^2 \times 10 \text{ sec}$

$= 40 \text{ rad/sec}$

$\omega_{av} = \dfrac{\omega_0 + \omega}{2} = \dfrac{0 + 40}{2} = 20 \text{ rad/sec}$

$\theta = \tfrac{1}{2}\alpha t^2 = \tfrac{1}{2} \times 4 \text{ rad/sec}^2 \times 100 \text{ sec}^2$

$= 200 \text{ radians}$

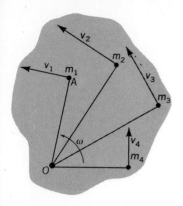

FIGURE 10.3

The kinetic energy of rotation of a body is the sum of the kinetic energies of rotation of all the particles (such as m_1, m_2, m_3, and m_4) of which the body is composed.

3. If a body has an initial angular velocity ω_0 and a uniform angular acceleration α, its velocity at the end of t sec is given by

$$\omega = \omega_0 + \alpha t \qquad \text{10.4}a$$

If the acceleration is uniform, the average angular velocity is

$$\omega_{av} = \frac{\omega_0 + \omega}{2} = \omega_0 + \frac{\alpha t}{2}$$

The angle θ swept out is given by

$$\theta = \omega_{av}t = \omega_0 t + \tfrac{1}{2}\alpha t^2 \qquad \text{10.5}$$

If we eliminate t between Eqs. (10.4) and (10.5), we obtain

$$\omega^2 = \omega_0{}^2 + 2\alpha\theta \qquad \text{10.6}$$

10.4 Kinetic Energy of Rotation

A rotating body has kinetic energy by virtue of the motion of its parts. To find the expression for kinetic energy of rotation, consider Figure 10.3, which represents a body rotating with an angular velocity ω about an axis through O perpendicular to the plane of the paper. For the particle at A having a mass of m_1 and linear velocity v_1, the kinetic energy is $m_1 v_1{}^2/2$. Since $v_1 = \omega r_1$, the kinetic energy of the particle at A becomes

$$\frac{m_1 r_1{}^2 \omega^2}{2} = m_1 r_1{}^2 \frac{\omega^2}{2}$$

For other particles m_2, m_3, m_4, ... moving with velocities v_2, v_3, v_4, ... similar expressions are found. The total kinetic energy is

$$\frac{m_1 r_1{}^2 \omega^2}{2} + \frac{m_2 r_2{}^2 \omega^2}{2} + \cdots = \frac{\omega^2}{2}(m_1 r_1{}^2 + m_2 r_2{}^2 + \cdots)$$

$$= \frac{1}{2}\omega^2 \sum_i m_i r_i{}^2$$

The quantity $\Sigma m_i r_i{}^2$ is called the *moment of inertia* I of the body about the axis through O. The kinetic energy of the rotating body is

Kinetic energy $= \tfrac{1}{2}I\omega^2 \qquad \text{10.7}$

This equation is the rotational analogue of $\tfrac{1}{2}mv^2$ for the kinetic energy of a mass m moving with a translational velocity v. Note that ω must be expressed in radians per second.

10.5 Moment of Inertia

If we wish to obtain the moment of inertia of a rigid body about any axis, we regard the body as composed of a large number of small mass elements. If we multiply the mass of each element by the square of its distance from the axis and add the contributions of all the elements, we obtain the moment of inertia I:

$$I = m_1 r_1{}^2 + m_2 r_2{}^2 + m_3 r_3{}^2 + \cdots = \sum_i m_i r_i{}^2 \qquad \text{10.8}$$

Such a summing process for bodies of most shapes involves detailed numerical calculation or the application of integral calculus. However, we can compute the moment of inertia of a simple ring of mass m and radius r about its central axis by direct application of Eq. (10.8). Since all parts of the ring are essentially at the same distance R from the axis, the moment of inertia is $I = MR^2$. In Figure 10.4 moments of inertia are given for bodies of several simple shapes—in every case for an axis through the center of mass as indicated. The moment of inertia may be expressed in kg-m², slug-ft², or in terms of the product of any mass unit multiplied by the square of a unit of length.

If we know the moment of inertia about an axis through the center of mass, it can be shown that the moment of inertia about any *parallel* axis is given by the relation

$$I = I_0 + MA^2 \qquad\qquad \text{10.9}$$

where M is the mass, I_0 the moment of inertia about an axis through the center of mass, and A the distance from this axis to the *parallel* one about which the moment of inertia is I.

It is sometimes convenient to write the moment of inertia of an extended rigid object in the form $I = Mk^2$, where k is a constant called

FIGURE 10.4
Moments of inertia of common shapes about the indicated axes through the centers of mass.

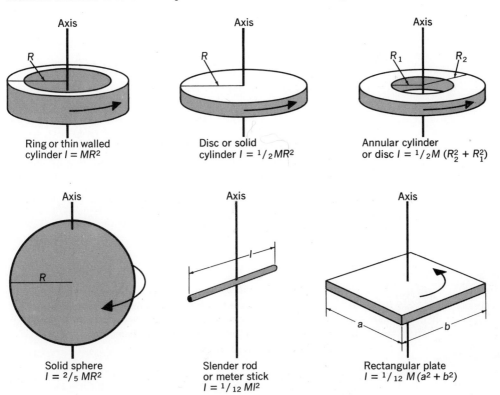

Ring or thin walled
cylinder $I = MR^2$

Disc or solid
cylinder $I = 1/2\,MR^2$

Annular cylinder
or disc $I = 1/2\,M\,(R_2^2 + R_1^2)$

Solid sphere
$I = 2/5\,MR^2$

Slender rod
or meter stick
$I = 1/12\,Ml^2$

Rectangular plate
$I = 1/12\,M\,(a^2 + b^2)$

the *radius of gyration.* Clearly, k corresponds to the radius of a thin circular ring which has the same mass and the same rotational inertia as the rigid body in question.

Example Find the moment of inertia of a thin rod of mass 2 kg and length 1.6 m about an axis through its center. Also find the moment of inertia about an axis at one end.

For an axis through the center of mass,

$$I_0 = \frac{Ml^2}{12} = \frac{2 \text{ kg} \times (1.6 \text{ m})^2}{12}$$
$$= 0.427 \text{ kg-m}^2$$

For an axis at one end,

$$I = I_0 + MA^2 = 0.427 \text{ kg-m}^2 + 2 \text{ kg} \times (0.8 \text{ m})^2 = 1.71 \text{ kg-m}^2$$

Example Find the moment of inertia of a mass of 10 kg and another mass of 15 kg about an axis of rotation which is 0.3 m from the 10-kg mass and 0.4 m from the 15-kg mass. Find the radius of gyration for this system.

$$I = m_1 r_1^2 + m_2 r_2^2$$
$$= 10 \text{ kg} \times (0.3 \text{ m})^2 + 15 \text{ kg} \times (0.4 \text{ m})^2$$
$$= 3.3 \text{ kg-m}^2$$
$$I = mk^2$$
$$3.3 \text{ kg-m}^2 = 25 \text{ kg} \times k^2$$
$$k = 0.36 \text{ m}$$

< 10.6 Combination of Energy of Translation and Energy of Rotation

Consider a solid wood disk and a brass ring which have identical radii R and masses M. If both are placed at the top of an inclined plane (Fig. 10.5), they have identical potential energies Mgh. If the disk and ring are allowed to roll down the plane starting from rest, which will reach the bottom first?

To answer this question, we apply the law of conservation of energy. At the bottom of the inclined plane both the solid cylinder and the ring will have kinetic energy equal to the original potential energy. For each, the kinetic energy is partly associated with the translational velocity of the center of mass and partly with rotation about the center

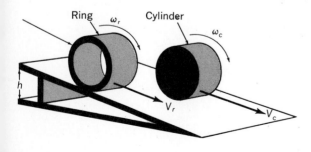

FIGURE 10.5

A solid cylinder rolls down an inclined plane with greater speed than a ring, whether or not they have the same outside diameter.

of mass. Let subscript c represent the cylinder, and subscript r the ring. Then

$$Mgh = \tfrac{1}{2}Mv_c{}^2 + \tfrac{1}{2}I_c\omega_c{}^2$$

and

$$Mgh = \tfrac{1}{2}Mv_r{}^2 + \tfrac{1}{2}I_r\omega_r{}^2$$

For a uniform disk of mass M and radius R, $I = MR^2/2$, while for the ring $I = MR^2$. Further, $\omega^2 = v^2/R^2$. Therefore, for the cylinder,

$$Mgh = \frac{Mv_c{}^2}{2} + \frac{Mv_c{}^2}{4}$$

or

$$v_c{}^2 = \frac{4gh}{3} \qquad\qquad\qquad \textbf{A}$$

For the ring,

$$Mgh = \frac{Mv_r{}^2}{2} + \frac{Mv_r{}^2}{2}$$

or

$$v_r{}^2 = gh \qquad\qquad\qquad \textbf{B}$$

Note that the object with the smaller moment of inertia has the greater linear velocity. Further, neither the mass nor the radius appears in Eqs. (A) and (B). Therefore the restrictions that both disk and ring have the same radius and mass were quite unnecessary; indeed, Eq. (A) is valid for any homogeneous disk or cylinder, and Eq. (B) for any thin ring.

10.7 Newton's Laws for Rotational Motion

Experiments show that the opposition of a body to being set in translation is proportional to the mass of the body and does not depend on the distribution of this mass. We shall now show for one simple situation that the opposition which a body offers to being set in rotational motion about any axis depends on the moment of inertia about that axis. Consider a small mass m fastened by a light rod to point O, about which the mass m is to be set in rotation, as indicated in Figure 10.6. Let us exert on this mass a force F tangential to the circle. The torque L exerted by force F about the axis through O is Fr, and, since $F = ma$, $L = mar$. The linear acceleration a is equal to the angular acceleration α multiplied by the radius r, from which

$$L = mr^2\alpha = I\alpha$$

In general, to change the angular velocity of a rigid rotating body, we must apply an unbalanced torque, just as we must apply an unbalanced force to change the linear velocity of a body. The angular acceleration of a body is directly proportional to the torque applied:

$$L = I\alpha \qquad\qquad\qquad \textbf{10.10}$$

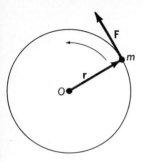

FIGURE 10.6

Angular acceleration is proportional to unbalanced torque.

FIGURE 10.7

Angular velocity or angular acceleration may be represented as a vector along the axis of rotation; its direction may be found by using the right-hand rule.

where L is the unbalanced torque acting, α the angular acceleration, and I the *moment of inertia* (or the *rotary inertia*) of the body. The moment of inertia is the measure of the opposition of the body to being set into rotation. It is analogous to the mass of a body, which is a measure of the opposition of the body to being set into translational motion.

Equation (10.10) expresses Newton's second law for rotary motion, which we have developed from $F = ma$. *If an unbalanced torque acts on a rigid body, an angular acceleration is produced which is proportional to the unbalanced torque and inversely proportional to the moment of inertia of the body.* The angular acceleration is in the direction of the unbalanced torque. As we saw in Chap. 4, the direction of a torque is that in which a right-handed screw moves when acted upon by a torque about its axis. Angular acceleration and angular velocity (but not angular displacement) are vector quantities with directions determined just as for torque (Fig. 10.7).

Example A flywheel has a moment of inertia of 300 kg-m². Find the torque necessary to produce an angular acceleration of 3 rad/sec².

Torque = moment of inertia $\times$ angular acceleration

$$L = 300 \text{ kg-m}^2 \times 3 \text{ rad/sec}^2$$
$$= 900 \text{ newton-m}$$

If we raise the front wheel of a bicycle off the ground and set it spinning, its angular velocity gradually decreases until finally the wheel comes to rest. We recognize that torques due to bearing friction and air friction produce the deceleration. If we reduce the friction, the wheel spins longer. If we could eliminate friction, the wheel would spin indefinitely with constant angular velocity. This is a direct analogue of Newton's first law for translational motion and is known as Newton's first law of rotational motion. *A rigid rotating body continues to revolve about an axis fixed in direction with constant angular velocity unless acted upon by some unbalanced external torque.* The rotation of the earth on its axis is a reasonable example, although the earth is not quite a rigid body and there are some unbalanced frictional torques introduced by tides and other considerations.

Newton's third law of rotational motion states: *For every torque acting on one body there is an equal and opposite torque about the same axis acting upon some other body (or bodies).*

TABLE 10.1 *Linear Quantities and Their Angular Analogues*

Linear		Angular	
Displacement	s	Displacement	θ
Velocity	v	Angular velocity	ω
Acceleration	a	Angular acceleration	α
Force	F	Torque	L
Mass	m	Moment of inertia	I

10.8 The Analogy between Linear and Angular Relationships

We have seen that for many of the equations which govern linear motion, there are analogous equations in rotary motion. *These equations are valid when the angles are expressed in radians.* It is unnecessary to memorize many of the equations of angular motion if use is made of the analogy between linear and rotational motions. Table 10.1 lists quantities which correspond to one another in the two kinds of motion. Knowing a relationship between linear quantities, one can often write the corresponding relationship between angular quantities by simply replacing each linear quantity with the corresponding angular one. For example, in linear motion, work = force × displacement. The corresponding expression for angular motion is work = torque × angular displacement. The angular analogue of $P = Fv$ is $P = L\omega$.

10.9 Angular Momentum

When a body is rotating about an axis, its *angular momentum is defined as the product of moment of inertia I and angular velocity* about this axis. Newton's second law for rotational motion may now be stated in a form more general than that of Sec. 10.7: *The unbalanced torque acting on a body is equal to the time rate of change of angular momentum.* If there is no unbalanced torque, the angular momentum is constant.

In a system of bodies which interact only with each other, Newton's third law for rotational motion tells us that if body A exerts a torque on body B, body B exerts an equal and opposite torque on body A. Therefore the change in angular momentum of body A is equal to and opposite that of body B. Thus *the angular momentum of a system of bodies remains constant in the absence of external torques.* The conservation of angular momentum is one of the key conservation laws of nature, which include conservation of energy and conservation of linear momentum.

Not only is angular momentum conserved, but evidence from atomic and molecular physics shows that it is quantized (comes in small, well-defined chunks) as well. Changes in the angular momentum of an atomic system come in units of size $h/2\pi$, where h is Planck's constant and has the magnitude 6.6×10^{-34} kg-m^2/sec (or joule-sec). This is a tiny angular momentum, utterly insignificant for macroscopic bodies, but of immense importance in systems of atomic size.

< In Figure 10.8 a man stands on a platform mounted on ball bearings. In his hands he holds heavy weights. His moment of inertia is greater when his arms are outstretched than when they are folded. If this man is set in rotation with arms outstretched, he rotates with a constant angular velocity as long as he does not change his moment of inertia. If he folds his arms as indicated in the figure, the moment of inertia I of the system (man plus weights) is decreased. Since the angular momentum $I\omega$ remains constant, the angular velocity ω increases. If he stretches his arms again, his angular velocity is reduced. When a diver performs a somersault from the high board, he doubles up to make his moment of inertia small while he is making his turn, and then he decreases his rotational velocity by increasing his moment of inertia through stretching out to his full length.

10.10 Gyroscopes

There are many kinds of gyroscopes, but all include a body of high moment of inertia which is spinning rapidly about an axis. In the gyroscopic compass this gyro element is mounted in such a way that no significant torques are applied. Under these circumstances the law of conservation of angular momentum requires that the vector angular momentum remain constant. The axis of the gyro element always points in the same direction, regardless of the maneuvers of the aircraft or ship. Thus, it can be made the key element of an automatic pilot.

A gyroscope such as that of Figure 10.9, which is supported at point O only, does not fall to the ground when the gyro wheel is in rapid rotation. Rather, the entire frame rotates about a vertical axis through O at a constant speed. This motion is called *precession*.

The behavior of the gyroscope can be analyzed in terms of angular momentum. Let the angular momentum of the rotating gyro wheel at $t = 0$ be represented by $\mathbf{G}_0$ (Fig. 10.9). The torque due to the weight of the rotor and frame produces an angular acceleration about

Large I
Small ω

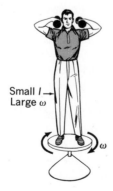

Small I
Large ω

FIGURE 10.8

Conservation of angular momentum about the vertical axis requires that angular velocity increase when the moment of inertia is decreased.

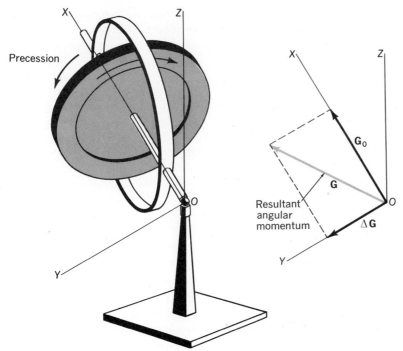

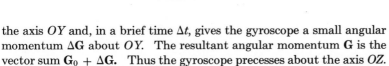

FIGURE 10.9
Precession of a gyroscope.

the axis OY and, in a brief time Δt, gives the gyroscope a small angular momentum ΔG about OY. The resultant angular momentum G is the vector sum $G_0 + \Delta G$. Thus the gyroscope precesses about the axis OZ.

There is an alternative way of looking at the precession of a gyroscope. Suppose that the rotating element of the gyroscope consists in a metal disk in which balls are mounted in slots (Fig. 10.10). When this disk is put into rapid rotation about an axis perpendicular to the plane of the paper, the balls move in the directions indicated in the figure. Now, if a torque is suddenly exerted about a vertical axis, the upper balls continue to move to the left, and the lower ones to the

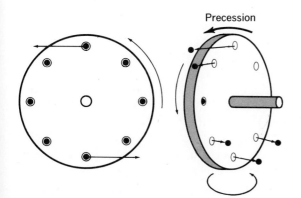

FIGURE 10.10
Precession occurs when the rotating wheel is turned about a vertical axis; the steel balls fly out of their retaining pockets, and the disk tends to tilt.

right. Not only does the inertia of each ball keep it going in the same direction, but so also does the inertia of each particle comprising the disk. Hence, the entire wheel tilts, and the axle precesses upward.

An aircraft moving eastward with a single propeller rotating clockwise tends to nose down when it turns south and to nose up when it turns north, since the rotating propeller acts like a gyroscope. If the airplane is traveling eastward and the propeller is rotating clockwise as viewed by the pilot, at any given instant the top blade of the propeller is traveling southward, and the lower blade northward. If at this instant the airplane is turned toward the north, the upper blade continues to move southward, and the lower one northward. As a result, the airplane noses up.

_____

Questions

1. A solid rod, a solid ball, and a hollow tube roll down an inclined plane together. If all start simultaneously from rest, in what order do they reach the bottom of the incline?

2. A flywheel rotating with constant angular velocity about a fixed axis is in equilibrium. Is every particle in the flywheel in equilibrium? Explain.

3. Why does a typical small helicopter have a small propeller exerting a torque about a vertical axis? Discuss the torques involved in helicopter flight.

4. The flywheel of an automobile rotates counterclockwise when viewed from the rear. Will the rear wheels skid more readily during a right or left turn? Why?

5. Explain how to distinguish between a hard-boiled egg and a raw one by spinning each on a flat table top.

6. What fraction of the kinetic energy of a rolling billiard ball is rotational? Of a rolling solid cylinder? Of a rolling hoop?

7. Why does an airplane tend to yaw (tilt sideways) when pulling out of a dive? Explain with the aid of a vector diagram.

8. Discuss the conservation of angular momentum for a diver performing a 2.5-turn forward somersault from a high board.

9. Why does an automobile nose downward if it is traveling at a high speed when the brakes are applied? (See Prob. 31.)

Problems

1. An electric motor operates at 1,200 rev/min. Find its angular velocity in radians per second. What is the speed of a point 3 cm from the axis of rotation?

Ans. 126 rad/sec; 3.77 m/sec

2. A diver makes 2.5 revolutions in the 1.5 sec he is in the air. Find his average angular velocity.

3. Compute the angular speed, about the axle, of an automobile wheel 14 in. in radius when the car is moving 60 mi/hr (88 ft/sec). What angular acceleration is needed to bring the wheel from rest to this speed in 11 sec? *Ans.* 75.4 rad/sec; 6.85 rad/sec²

4. A small motor starts from rest and attains its rated speed of 1,800 rev/min in 8 sec.

236 rad/sec² 120 Rev

Calculate the angular acceleration, assuming it to be uniform. Through how many revolutions does the motor turn in achieving its rated speed?

5. A grinding wheel starts from rest and has a constant angular acceleration of 10 rad/sec². At $t = 5$ sec find the centripetal and tangential accelerations of a particle 6 cm from the axis, the angular velocity, and the angle turned through.

Ans. 150 m/sec²; 0.6 m/sec²; 50 rad/sec; 125 radians

6. A bicycle wheel initially at rest is accelerated uniformly until it attains an angular speed of 15 rad/sec in 5 sec. Find the angular acceleration and the angle turned through in this time. 3 rad/sec² 37.5 Rad

7. The coefficient of friction between a wooden block and the floor of a merry-go-round is 0.20. If the block is 10 ft from the axis, at what angular speed will it slide off?

Ans. 0.8 rad/sec

8. One method of determining the speed of a bullet is to fire it through two cardboard disks mounted on a long axle and rotated at high angular speed. If the disks are 1.10 m apart and are rotated at 1,800 rev/min, find the speed of a bullet fired parallel to the axis if it makes holes which are 18° apart.

9. A racing car starts from rest and accelerates uniformly along the track with an acceleration of 10 ft/sec². If the track is circular with a radius of 800 ft, at what speed is the centripetal acceleration equal to the tangential acceleration? How long does it take to achieve this speed? *Ans.* 89.4 ft/sec; 8.94 sec

10. The radius of the earth is approximately 4,000 miles, and it rotates about its axis once each sidereal day of 86,164 sec. Find the angular velocity of the earth in radians per second, the linear speed due to the earth's rotation of a point near the equator, and the speed of a point on the earth's surface at 37° latitude.

11. The tip of the propeller of an airplane is 5 ft from the propeller shaft. The moment of inertia of the rotating propeller and associated shaft is 60 slug-ft². If the propeller is making 1,200 rev/min and is given an angular acceleration of 4 rad/sec², how long a time is required to increase the angular speed to 1,500 rev/min? What unbalanced torque acts on the propeller shaft during the acceleration? At what angular velocity will the tip of the propeller have a linear speed equal to the local speed of sound, which is 1,000 ft/sec at the position of the airplane? *Ans.* 7.85 sec; 240 lb-ft; 200 rad/sec

12. The moment of inertia of a body about its axis of rotation is 6 kg-m². A torque of 15 newton-m is applied to it. If the body starts from rest, find the angular acceleration. What are the angular velocity and the kinetic energy at the end of 20 sec?

13. The turbine of a jet engine has a moment of inertia of 500 kg-m². It is to be accelerated uniformly from rest to an angular velocity of 300 rad/sec in 25 sec. Find the angular acceleration, the unbalanced torque required, the angle turned through during the acceleration, and the kinetic energy of the turbine at its final angular velocity.

Ans. 12 rad/sec²; 6,000 newton-m; 3,750 radians; 2.25 × 10⁷ joules

14. Find the torque developed by an airplane engine which rotates a propeller at 1,800 rev/min when supplying 1,200 hp.

15. Find the moment of inertia about an axis through the center of mass and the kinetic energy of a system consisting in two masses of 3 kg and 2 kg, respectively, connected by a rod of negligible mass 1 m long, when the center of mass of the system has a velocity of 20 m/sec and the system rotates about the center of mass with an angular velocity of 60 rad/sec. *Ans.* 1.2 kg-m²; 3,160 joules

16. A circular hoop has a mass of 0.5 kg and a radius of 60 cm. Find its moment of inertia about an axis through the center of the hoop and perpendicular to its plane; about an axis through the circumference of the hoop and parallel to the axis through the center.

17. If a flywheel has a moment of inertia of 5 kg-m², what angular speed does the wheel attain if 100,000 joules of work are done in producing rotational kinetic energy? What torque is required to bring this flywheel to rest in 25 sec?

Ans. 200 rad/sec; 40 newton-m

18. Calculate the moment of inertia of a wheel that has a kinetic energy of 12,000 ft-lb when it is making 600 rev/min. Find the radius of gyration if the mass of the wheel is 20 slugs.

19. A body consists of a solid horizontal cylindrical shaft, weighing 180 lb, with a radius of 2 in. and a solid disk having a mass of 250 lb and a radius of 1.2 ft. The cylinder and the disk are mounted so that they have the same axis. What torque is necessary to give the body an angular speed of 24 rad/sec at the end of 6 sec, starting from rest?

Ans. 22.8 lb-ft

20. A hollow cylinder weighs 40 lb and has a diameter of 3 ft. Its mass is concentrated in the rim. It is rolling with a linear speed of 5 ft/sec. What is its kinetic energy of rotation? Its total kinetic energy?

21. A flywheel has a mass of 500 kg, all concentrated in the rim, and a radius of 1.2 m. It is rotating with an angular velocity of 20 rad/sec. How much work was necessary to give the flywheel this angular velocity? If the wheel is stopped in 1 min by a friction brake, what torque is applied? *Ans.* 1.44×10^5 joules; 240 newton-m

22. A turbogenerator with a moment of inertia of 300,000 slug-ft² rotates at the rate of 40 rev/sec. The power and load are shut off simultaneously, and friction stops the rotation in 3,000 sec. Find the initial kinetic energy of rotation, the initial angular momentum, and the torque due to friction.

23. A hoop weighing 4 lb and having a radius of 0.5 ft rolls down an inclined plane that makes an angle of 30° with the horizontal. Assuming that there is no slipping, what is the linear acceleration of the hoop? The angular acceleration? The speed of the center of mass after the hoop has rolled a distance of 9 ft?

Ans. 8 ft/sec²; 16 rad/sec²; 12 ft/sec

24. What linear velocity is acquired by a solid steel disk that has a radius of 25 cm and a mass of 4 kg when it rolls down an inclined plane which is 2 m long and makes an angle of 10° with the horizontal? What is the acceleration of the disk?

25. A solid sphere having a diameter of 8 in. rolls down an inclined plane that is 12 ft in length. What is the angular velocity of the cylinder at the bottom of the plane if it requires 6 sec for it to reach the bottom? What is the angle of the plane?

Ans. 12 rad/sec; 1.7°

26. A 4-lb ring of radius 6 in. rolls down an inclined plane of which one end is 2 ft above the other. If the ring starts from rest at the top, show that its kinetic energy of rotation is equal to its kinetic energy of translation at the bottom. Find the kinetic energy of rotation at the bottom and the speed of the center of mass at the bottom.

27. A yo-yo has a moment of inertia about its center of mass of 2×10^{-5} kg-m² and a mass of 0.05 kg. If the string is wrapped around a center post of 5 mm radius and the yo-yo is released from rest, find the angular acceleration and the tension in the string.

Ans. 115 rad/sec^2; 0.461 newton

28. What angular acceleration will be imparted to a solid disk that has a radius of 1.5 ft and a weight of 96 lb by a weight of 16 lb hanging from a cord wound around the disk? Find the tension in the cord.

29. A meter stick has a small hole bored at the 10-cm mark so it may be hung from a horizontal nail. If the meter stick is rotated about the nail until it makes an angle of 37° with the vertical and is then released, find its angular velocity as it passes through its equilibrium position, assuming that friction is negligible. *Ans.* 2.54 rad/sec

30. A solid uniform disk with a 5-cm radius starts from rest and rolls down a plane 2 m long and inclined at 30° to the horizontal. What is its linear speed at the bottom? Its angular velocity? How long does it take to reach the bottom?

31. A 3,600-lb automobile has a 9-ft wheelbase, and its center of mass is 4 ft behind the front axle and 2.25 ft above the road. Assuming that the center of mass does not move relative to the wheels, find the vertical force on the front wheels when the car has a uniform deceleration of 16 ft/sec^2. *Hint:* Recall that the retarding forces at the road produce a torque about the center of mass which is balanced by a redistribution of the force on the front and rear wheels. *Ans.* 2,450 lb

32. Show that if a solid cylinder is to roll down an inclined plane without slipping, the coefficient of static friction between cylinder and plane must be at least (tan θ)/3, where θ is the angle between the plane and the horizontal.

CHAPTER 11 *In the preceding chapters we have been concerned with the mechanics of particles and rigid bodies. But solid objects represent only a part of our physical universe. Much of the surface of the earth is covered with water, and we live in a great shell of gas which comprises our atmosphere. In this chapter we consider several mechanical properties of such fluids at rest. By fluid we mean anything which flows; both liquids and gases are fluids. In general, gases are readily compressible, while liquids offer large resistance to efforts to change their volume.*

Fluids at Rest

11.1 Fluids and Pressure

Although a liquid has no shape of its own, but takes the shape of the containing vessel, the liquid does occupy a well-defined volume. A gas, however, occupies completely any enclosed volume in which it is placed. Liquids yield to a continued application of force that tends to deform them or change their shape. They do, however, manifest wide differences in their readiness to yield to distorting force. Water, alcohol, and ether are very mobile liquids; glycerin is less mobile, and tar still less so. There is no sharp line of demarcation between liquids and solids (see Chap. 21).

A fluid contained in a vessel exerts forces against the walls of the vessel. In order to discuss the interaction between the fluid and the walls, it is convenient to introduce the concept of pressure. *Pressure is defined as the ratio of force to the area on which it acts when the area is perpendicular to the force.*

$$p = \frac{F}{A} \qquad\qquad\qquad \textbf{11.1}$$

More precisely, *the pressure at any point is the ratio of the normal force ΔF exerted on a small ΔA surrounding the point to this area.* Pressure may be expressed in pounds per square inch, newtons per square meter, etc.—in general, as any unit of force divided by a unit of area.

11.2 Pressure in a Liquid

If we explore a liquid confined in a vessel with a device for measuring pressure, we find that at a given level in the liquid the magnitude of the force acting on an area is the same regardless of how the area is oriented.   The force is always perpendicular to the area.   Further, we find that the deeper we go, the greater the pressure becomes.   If p_0 represents the pressure at the surface of the liquid, and p the pressure at a depth y, we find that the increase in pressure due to the liquid is directly proportional to the depth y and to the density d of the liquid. Let p_L represent the increase in pressure due to the liquid.   Then

$$p_L = p - p_0 = dgy \qquad \qquad \text{11.2}$$

where g is the acceleration due to gravity.   That this should be true is easy to understand if we consider the force on an area A at the bottom of a container (Fig. 11.1).   This area supports the weight of a column of fluid above it.   The weight is given by $yAdg$.   The contribution of the liquid to the pressure at A is the weight of this column divided by the area A.   Hence $p_L = yAdg/A = dgy$.

In many problems it is convenient to use weight density d_w (weight per unit volume) rather than density (mass per unit volume).   The weight of a given volume is equal to $d_w V$, and the pressure due to the liquid is yd_w.   In the British engineering system we ordinarily use weight density (lb/ft³) rather than mass density (slugs/ft³).   Hence the relation

$$p_L = p - p_0 = d_w y \qquad \qquad \text{11.2a}$$

is frequently more convenient than $p_L = dgy$.   (Note that, since $W = mg$, $d_w = W/V = mg/V = dg$.)

Although we have derived Eqs. (11.2) and (11.2a) only for the bottom of our container, they are applicable at any point in the liquid at rest.   Observe that y is the *vertical* height from the point to the free surface.

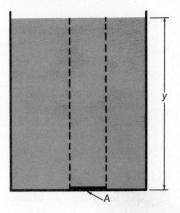

FIGURE 11.1

The pressure due to a liquid at a depth y is proportional to the depth and to the density of the liquid.

Example   The hatch of a submarine is 100 ft under the surface of the ocean.   If the weight density of sea water is 64 lb/ft³, find the pressure at the hatch due to the water and the net force on the hatch if it is a rectangle 2 ft wide and 3 ft long.   The pressure inside the submarine is the same as that at the surface.

$$p_L = p - p_0 = d_w y$$
$$= 64 \text{ lb/ft}^3 \times 100 \text{ ft}$$
$$= 6{,}400 \text{ lb/ft}^2$$

The net force on the hatch is the difference between the inward force pA and the outward force p_0A.   Therefore,

$$F = pA - p_0A = (p_L + p_0)A - p_0A = p_LA$$
$$= 6{,}400 \text{ lb/ft}^2 \times 6 \text{ ft}^2$$
$$= 38{,}400 \text{ lb}$$

11.3   Pressure of the Atmosphere

Just as water is the most widely distributed and most important of liquids, so air is the most important and intimate of gases.   It consists for the most part of nitrogen and oxygen.   In spite of the fact

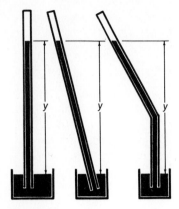

FIGURE 11.2

Torricelli's experiment (left), in which he showed that mercury would rise only 76 cm in a closed glass tube 100 cm long. The height of the mercury is independent of the shape or length of the tube, as shown.

FIGURE 11.3

Variation of atmospheric pressure with height above mean sea level.

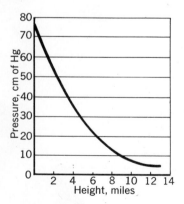

that there is no chemical union between the two, the composition of the air is extraordinarily constant. Up to a height of 7 miles it contains about 21 parts of oxygen to 78 parts of nitrogen by volume. Besides oxygen and nitrogen, the air contains small amounts of other gases, the most important of which are water vapor, argon, and carbon dioxide. A cubic yard of air weighs over 2 lb at sea level, although to an ordinary observer the air seems to have no weight and to offer little resistance to bodies moving through it.

Since it has weight, a column of air exerts pressure, just as does a column of liquid. However, Eq. (11.2) is not directly applicable, because the density of a gas, unlike that of a liquid, depends on the pressure (Sec. 13.8). Though a cubic foot of air weighs little, even at ground level, the height of the atmosphere is large, and the weight of all this air pressing on the earth is great.

About 1644 Torricelli, a pupil of Galileo, measured atmospheric pressure in the following way: A glass tube closed at one end was filled with mercury. A finger was then placed over the open end of the tube, the tube inverted in a basin of mercury, and the finger removed from the open end of the tube under the mercury. The mercury in the tube sank until its level was about 76.0 cm (Fig. 11.2) higher than the level in the basin. The pressure of the atmosphere on the mercury in the basin supported the mercury in the tube. Since the density of mercury is 13,560 kg/m³, the pressure exerted by the atmosphere is given by Eq. (11.2): $p = dgy = 13,560$ kg/m³ $\times$ 9.80 newtons/kg $\times$ 0.760 m $= 1.013 \times 10^5$ newtons/m², or 14.7 lb/in.². Mercury has 13.6 times the density of water; therefore 1 atmosphere (atm) can support a column of water 13.6×0.760 m $= 10.3$ m high. This corresponds to 33.8 ft.

Our atmosphere is a great ocean of air which becomes steadily less dense as we go upward. In 1647 Pascal showed that when a Torricelli tube is carried up a mountain the level of the mercury drops; the greater the height, the greater the decrease in pressure. At 1 mile elevation the mercury column has fallen 15 cm. At 18,000 ft the pressure is half that at sea level. The approximate variation of pressure with altitude is shown in Figure 11.3. Less than one-quarter of the atmosphere remains above a height of 7 miles.

The breathing of animals is an application of atmospheric pressure. A reduction of pressure is caused by a movement of the diaphragm. The greater pressure of the outside air causes a fresh supply to flow into the lungs. Then air is forced out when the internal pressure is made greater than atmospheric. Sucking and drinking animals take advantage of atmospheric pressure to aid them in these operations. They reduce the pressure in the mouth and allow water to be forced into the mouth by the outside atmospheric pressure.

Many types of pressure gauges read the excess of pressure over atmospheric pressure—this is the so-called *gauge pressure*. If a typical gauge reads 24 lb/in.², the pressure is 24.0 lb/in.² greater than atmospheric pressure (14.7 lb/in.²). The absolute pressure p is then 38.7 lb/in.².

Example The gauge pressure of water in the water mains is 35 lb/in.². How much work is required to pump 500,000 ft³ of water at atmospheric pressure into the mains?

$$\text{Work} = \text{net force} \times \text{distance} = \frac{\text{force}}{\text{area}} \times (\text{distance} \times \text{area})$$

$$= \text{net pressure} \times \text{change in volume}$$

$$= 35 \text{ lb/in.}^2 \times 144 \text{ in.}^2/\text{ft}^2 \times 500,000 \text{ ft}^3$$

$$= 25 \times 10^8 \text{ ft-lb}$$

11.4 Liquids in Communicating Vessels

It is a matter of common experience that liquids seek their own level in interconnected vessels. If tubes of various sizes and shapes are connected, liquid poured into one of them (Fig. 11.4) comes to the same level in all the tubes (provided surface-tension effects may be neglected). This result is to be expected from the fact that the pressure in the liquid depends on the depth below the free surface. *At all points at the same level within a liquid at rest, the pressure is the same.* If it were not, the liquid would flow from one point to the other until the pressure became equalized.

In Figure 11.4 the areas of the openings at which vessels A, B, C, and D join the bottom reservoir are the same. The following question may be raised: If the liquid pressure is due to the weight of the fluid above, why is the pressure not greater in vessel D, in which the sides slope outward, than in vessel B, in which the sides slant inward? Certainly vessel D contains a greater weight of water. The answer is: In D the slanting sides exert forces on the liquid which have an upward component. Thus, a portion of the weight of the fluid is actually held up by the sloping sides. On the other hand, in B the force exerted by the slanting sides on the liquid is downward. When the force due to the slanting walls is added to the weight of the fluid, the pressure at the bottom is the same in all four vessels.

Let two liquids that do not react chemically be placed in a bent tube (Fig. 11.5a). When the liquids are at rest, the pressure exerted by the column of lighter liquid is balanced by the pressure due to the column of heavier liquid above the junction level of the liquids. Then

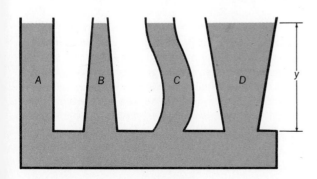

FIGURE 11.4
Pressure is the same at all points on a given level in a liquid at rest, regardless of the shape of the containing vessel.

(a)   (b)

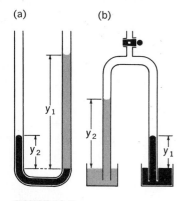

FIGURE 11.5

The pressure produced by liquid 1 at depth y_1 is equal to that produced by liquid 2 at depth y_2, in both (a) and (b).

$d_1gy_1 = d_2gy_2$, from which $h_1/h_2 = d_2/d_1$. *The heights of two liquids above their surface of separation are inversely proportional to their densities.*

If the liquids react chemically, the bent tube may be inverted, and the ends placed in cups containing the liquids (Fig. 11.5b). The air from the upper part of the bent tube is partly removed, and the stopcock closed. The pressure above both liquids is the same, and the atmospheric pressure on the liquids in the open vessels is the same. The difference between the pressure inside the tube and atmospheric pressure is balanced in each case by the rise of the liquid in the tube. These differences in pressure are the same, and again $d_1gy_1 = d_2gy_2$

Example If one of the beakers in Figure 11.5b contains sulfuric acid and the other contains water, and if the height of the column of water is 40 cm when the height of the column of acid is 30 cm, find the density of the sulfuric acid.

$$y_a d_a g = y_w d_w g \qquad d_w = 1{,}000 \text{ kg/m}^3$$
$$\frac{d_a}{d_w} = \frac{y_w}{y_a} = \frac{0.40 \text{ m}}{0.30 \text{ m}}$$
$$d_a = 1{,}330 \text{ kg/m}^3$$

11.5 Pascal's Principle

If we increase the pressure at any one point in a fluid which is completely enclosed (Fig. 11.6), the pressure increases by an equal amount at all other points. For example, if we add a weight of 1 lb to piston A of Figure 11.6, it is found that a weight of 1 lb must be added to pistons B and C in order to keep them from moving. This is a special case of a general law known as *Pascal's principle. If the pressure at any point in an enclosed fluid at rest is changed, the pressure changes by an equal amount at all points in the fluid.* Note that Pascal's principle does *not* say that the pressure is the same everywhere within the enclosed fluid. The pressure continues to be greater at greater depth. Pascal's principle deals with the change in pressure, not with the absolute pressure.

Consider two cylinders which are connected together and filled with water (Fig. 11.7). If each cylinder is fitted with a piston which moves

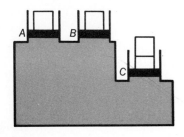

FIGURE 11.6

A pressure change at any point in an enclosed fluid at rest results in an equal pressure change at all other points.

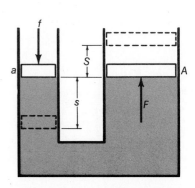

FIGURE 11.7

Multiplication of force by transmitted pressure in a hydraulic press.

without friction, and if the two pistons are at the same level, the pressure at each will be the same. If A is the area of the larger piston, and a the area of the smaller one, the force f on the smaller piston is given by pa, while the force F on the larger piston is given by pA. By applying a force f on the small piston, it is possible to produce a force $F = Af/a$ on the larger piston. When the larger piston is raised a distance S, the smaller moves through a greater distance s, where $s = SA/a$.

If the larger and smaller pistons are not at the same level, the pressures on the two pistons are not the same; they differ by dgy, where y is the difference between the heights of the two pistons. If the pressure is increased 10 lb/in.² on the smaller piston, it also increases 10 lb/in.² at the larger piston, but the pressures are not equal. A direct application of these ideas is found in the hydraulic press.

An important application of Pascal's principle occurs in the hydraulic system of an automobile (Fig. 11.8). If the pressure is increased in the master cylinder by pressing on the brake pedal, the pressure increases by an equal amount at each piston in the hydraulic system. If all the pistons at the brake shoes have the same cross-sectional area, an equal force is applied at all the brake shoes.

Pascal's principle applies to all fluids, gases as well as liquids. A typical application of Pascal's principle to gases is the automobile lift pump. Compressed air exerts pressure on the oil in a reservoir. The oil in turn transmits the pressure to a cylinder which lifts the automobile.

Example Find the minimum gauge pressure which must be supplied to an automobile lift pump with a piston of area 120 in.² to lift an automobile and piston weighing 3,000 lb.

Net force = net gauge pressure × area
    3,000 lb = p × 120 in.²
         p = 25 lb/in.²

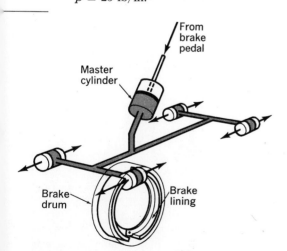

FIGURE 11.8
Pascal's principle as it is applied in the brake system of an automobile.

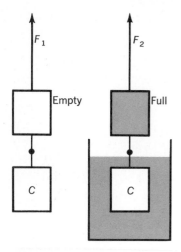

FIGURE 11.9

How cylinder *C* is buoyed up by a force equal to the weight of the fluid it displaces is shown in this experiment. F_1 equals F_2 when displaced liquid is transferred to container above.

FIGURE 11.10

The net upward force on the cylinder is equal to the weight of the displaced fluid.

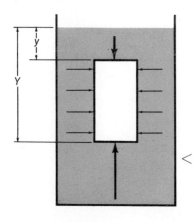

11.6 Archimedes' Principle

It is a matter of common experience that bodies are apparently lighter under water than in air. A fresh egg sinks in pure water, but floats in salty water. A piece of iron sinks in water, but floats in mercury. If a diver picks up a stone under water and brings it to the surface, he finds that the stone is much heavier above the surface. The principle which explains these observations, discovered by the distinguished Greek mathematician and physicist Archimedes, states that:

A body immersed in a fluid is buoyed up by a force equal to the weight of the fluid displaced.

An experimental verification of Archimedes' principle can be obtained by use of the equipment of Figure 11.9. A hollow cylindrical cup and a piece of brass turned so that it will just fill the cavity inside the cup are suspended from one arm of a balance, and the weights necessary to restore equilibrium are added to the other pan. When a vessel of water is brought up in such a way that the cylinder *C* is completely submerged, the side of the balance carrying the cylinder rises, showing that the water is pushing upward on the cylinder. If water is now poured into the cup until it is full, the original equilibrium of the balance is restored. The cylinder is buoyed up by a force equal to the weight of the water displaced.

Archimedes' principle follows directly from the laws of fluid pressure. If a cylindrical block (Fig. 11.10) is immersed in a vessel filled with liquid, the resultant of the forces on the vertical sides is zero. Upon the upper face of the cylinder there is a downward force equal to the pressure at the upper surface multiplied by the cross-sectional area *A* of the cylinder. On the lower face there is an upward force equal to the pressure at the bottom multiplied by the area. The upward force exceeds the downward force, because the pressure is greater at the greater depth. The net upward force is $YdgA - ydgA = (Y - y)Adg = Vdg$, where V is the volume of the cylinder. The net buoyant force is equal to the weight of the fluid displaced. The same sort of reasoning holds for a body of any shape in any liquid. Hence, a body immersed in any fluid is lighter by the weight of fluid which it displaces.

Example An aluminum casting weighs 5.40 lb in air and 3.40 lb when submerged in water. Find the volume of the casting and the weight density of aluminum.

Loss of weight = 5.4 lb − 3.4 lb = 2.00 lb, the weight of water displaced. Since 1 ft³ of water weighs 62.5 lb, 2 lb occupy 2/62.5 = 0.032 ft³.

$$d_w = \frac{W}{V} = \frac{5.40 \text{ lb}}{0.032 \text{ ft}^3} = 169 \text{ lb/ft}^3$$

< Fish are capable of moving toward the surface or into deep water by regulating the quantity of water which they displace and, therefore, the buoyant force. By distending the air bags in their bodies, they can change their volumes and thus change the buoyancy of the water

on them. By contracting its air sacs, a fish diminishes its volume, and it sinks. Similarly, a submarine can submerge by taking water into tanks, thus making the submarine heavier than an equal volume of water. It rises from below the surface by blowing or pumping this water out of the tanks.

11.7 Floating Bodies

When a body floats on a liquid, the buoyant force is equal to its weight. The body sinks until it displaces its own weight (Fig. 11.11) and then remains in equilibrium. This explains why a ship rides lower in the water when loaded than when empty and why it rides higher in salt water than in fresh.

Example   A barge is 30 ft long and 16 ft wide and has vertical sides. When two automobiles are driven on board, the barge sinks 2 in. farther into the water. How much do the automobiles weigh?

Volume of displaced water $= 30$ ft $\times$ 16 ft $\times$ ⅙ ft
$= 80$ ft^3
Weight of water displaced $= 80$ ft$^3 \times 62.5$ lb/ft^3
$= 5,000$ lb
Weight of automobiles $=$ weight of displaced water $= 5,000$ lb

The buoyant force acts through the center of mass of the displaced fluid, known as the *center of buoyancy*. The buoyant effect of all the displaced fluid may be replaced by a single force acting at the center of buoyancy. For a floating body such as a ship to be in stable equilibrium, there must be a torque which restores the body to its stable position whenever it undergoes an angular displacement. This torque is provided by the combined action of the weight W of the body acting downward at the center of gravity G (Fig. 11.12a) and the buoyant

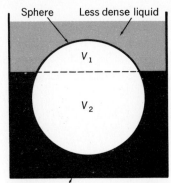

FIGURE 11.11
A sphere floating at the interface between two liquids of different densities. The sphere sinks until the sum of the weight of the first liquid displaced and the weight of the second liquid displaced is equal to the weight of the sphere.

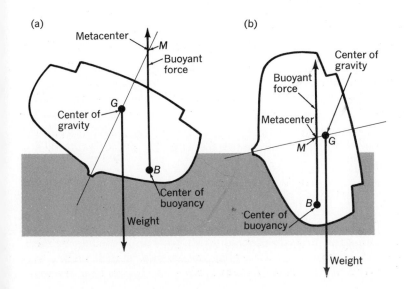

FIGURE 11.12
(*a*) When the center of gravity is below the metacenter *M*, the boat is stable. (*b*) When the center of gravity is above the metacenter, the boat is unstable.

force acting upward through the center of buoyancy. The condition for stability will be realized if the metacenter M lies above the center of gravity of the body. The position of the metacenter is determined by the intersection of two lines, one drawn vertically through the center of buoyancy B and the other drawn vertically through the center of gravity G of the body *before displacement*. If the metacenter lies above the center of gravity, there is a restoring torque, and the body is in stable equilibrium. If, however, the metacenter lies below the center of gravity, the torque that comes into play when the body is displaced from its normal position increases the displacement further. The body is in unstable equilibrium (Fig. 11.12*b*) and turns over.

11.8 Density and Specific Gravity

The density of a body is the ratio of its mass to its volume, while the weight density is the ratio of weight to volume. Table 11.1 lists the densities of a number of common liquids and solids. It is often difficult to compute the volume of a body, especially when it has an irregular shape. In such cases the volume may be determined by application of Archimedes' principle.

When a body is heavier than an equal volume of water (and is insoluble in water), its volume can be determined by finding the loss of weight when it is weighed in water. From the mass and volume the density may be obtained.

TABLE 11.1 *Densities of Solids and Liquids (20°C)*

Substance	Density kg/m^3	Density $lb\ mass/ft^3$	Substance	Density kg/m^3	Density $lb\ mass/ft^3$
Alcohol	789	49.3	Iron (cast)	7,200	450
Aluminum	2,650	164	Iron (wrought)	7,800	480
Balsa wood	160	10	Kerosene	820	51.2
Brass	8,600	535	Lead	11,370	710
Brick	2,100	131	Mercury	13,600	840
Copper	8,930	555	Oak	800	50
Cork	240	15	Pine	500	31.2
Diamond	3,520	220	Silver	10,500	655
Glass (crown)	2,500	156	Turpentine	870	54.3
Glass (flint)	3,700	230	Tin	7,290	455
Gasoline	790	49.4	Water (fresh)	1,000	62.5
Gold	19,320	1,200	Water (sea)	1,030	64.4
Glycerin	1,260	78.7	Zinc	7,150	446.2
Ice (0°C)	917	57.2			

Example A piece of iron has a mass of 0.0780 kg. When submerged in water, it has an apparent weight of 0.666 newton. What is the volume of the iron? What is its density?

$$\text{Weight of iron } (mg) = 0.078 \text{ kg} \times 9.8 \text{ m/sec}^2$$
$$= 0.764 \text{ newton}$$
$$\text{Weight of water displaced} = 0.764 \text{ newton} - 0.666 \text{ newton}$$
$$= 0.098 \text{ newton}$$
$$\text{Mass of water displaced} \left(\frac{W}{g}\right) = \frac{0.098 \text{ newton}}{9.8 \text{ m/sec}^2}$$
$$= 0.010 \text{ kg or } 10 \text{ g}$$
$$\text{Volume of water displaced} \left(\frac{m}{d}\right) = \frac{0.010 \text{ kg}}{1{,}000 \text{ kg/m}^3}$$
$$= 10^{-5} \text{ m}^3 \text{ or } 10 \text{ cm}^3$$
$$\text{Volume of iron} = 10^{-5} \text{ m}^3 \text{ or } 10 \text{ cm}^3$$
$$\text{Density of iron} \left(\frac{m}{V}\right) = \frac{0.078 \text{ kg}}{10^{-5} \text{ m}^3} = 7{,}800 \text{ kg/m}^3$$

If the object is lighter than water (and insoluble), its volume may still be determined by this method by fastening to the body a sinker large enough to pull it below the surface of the water. In this case (Fig. 11.13) the combined weight of the body and the sinker is first determined when the sinker is immersed in water and the body is above the surface of the water. The body is then also submerged, and the combined weight redetermined. The reduction in weight is equal to the weight of water displaced by the body.

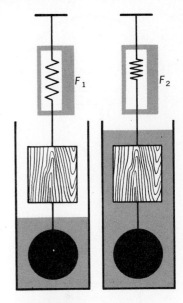

FIGURE 11.13

The buoyant force on the block of wood, which would float if there were no sinker, is the difference between F_1 and F_2.

Example A piece of cork has a mass of 0.025 kg. When it is fastened to a sinker and the sinker alone immersed in water, the combined apparent weight of sinker and cork is 1.960 newton. When both sinker and cork are immersed, they weigh 0.735 newton. What is the density of the cork?

$$\text{Loss of weight due to submerging body} = (1.960 - 0.735) \text{ newton}$$
$$= 1.225 \text{ newton}$$
$$\text{Mass of water displaced by cork} = \frac{1.225 \text{ newton}}{9.8 \text{ m/sec}^2}$$
$$= 0.125 \text{ kg}$$
$$\text{Volume of water displaced} = \frac{0.125 \text{ kg}}{1{,}000 \text{ kg/m}^3}$$
$$= 1.25 \times 10^{-4} \text{ m}^3$$
$$\text{Density of cork} = \frac{\text{mass of cork}}{\text{volume}}$$
$$= \frac{0.025 \text{ kg}}{1.25 \times 10^{-4} \text{ m}^3}$$
$$= 200 \frac{\text{kg}}{\text{m}^3}$$

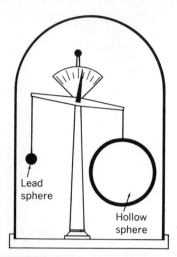

FIGURE 11.14

A body immersed in air is buoyed up by a force equal to the weight of the air it displaces. The two spheres balance one another at normal air pressure, but when air is evacuated from the jar, the larger sphere sinks.

The specific gravity of a body is the ratio of its density to the density of water. If the specific gravity of a body is equal to 5, the body weighs 5 times as much as an equal volume of water.

11.9 Buoyant Effect of the Air

Archimedes' principle applies to all fluids. In general, the densities of gases are much smaller than those of liquids, and the buoyant effects are correspondingly reduced. Nevertheless there are many examples of situations in which the buoyant effects of gases—in particular of air—are of considerable importance. The density of air is 1.293 kg/m³ at 0°C and one standard atmosphere pressure.

A simple demonstration of the buoyant effect of air may be made by suspending a lead ball (Fig. 11.14) from one side of a small balance and a large hollow brass sphere from the other side. The hollow sphere is just heavy enough to balance the lead ball when both are in air. If the balance, together with the suspended spheres, is placed under a bell jar and nearly all the air removed by means of a pump, the lead ball no longer balances the hollow sphere. This is because the buoyancy of the air on the hollow brass sphere is greater than on the lead ball; when this lift has been removed, the true weights of the spheres become evident, and the hollow sphere weighs more than the lead sphere.

The gross lifting capacity of a balloon is equal to the weight of the air that it displaces. The pressure and density of the air become less at higher elevations. However, as the pressure outside the balloon decreases, the lighter gas inside the balloon expands, thus displacing a larger volume of the less dense air. In manned balloons ballast is carried along and thrown overboard when it is desired to make the balloon rise higher. By allowing some of the gas in the balloon to escape, the balloon can be made to descend.

Example A balloon has a volume equal to that of a sphere 15 yd in radius. What is the gross weight which it will lift when the weight density of the air is 2 lb/yd³?

$$\text{Volume of balloon} = \tfrac{4}{3}\pi(15)^3 = 14{,}000 \text{ yd}^3$$
$$\text{Weight of air displaced by balloon} = \text{volume} \times \text{weight density}$$
$$= 14{,}000 \text{ yd}^3 \times 2 \text{ lb/yd}^3$$
$$= 28{,}000 \text{ lb}$$

Questions

1. Does the force exerted on a dam by an artificial lake depend on how far the water has been backed up? Upon what factors does it depend?

2. Why is the radius of the stem of a sensitive hydrometer (Prob. 31) much smaller than the radius of the submerged bulb?

3. An iron ball floats in a beaker half filled with mercury. If water is poured over the mercury until the beaker is filled, will the level at which the ball floats change?

4. What physics underlies the filling of a fountain pen?

5. An athlete stands on the platform of a sensitive scale. When he takes a deep breath, will his weight as read by the scale change?

6. What determines the height to which a balloon rises?

7. Explain why a balloon can remain in stable equilibrium at a given height in the atmosphere while a submarine cannot remain in stable equilibrium at a given depth in the ocean.

8. A beaker partly filled with water rests on the pan of a spring balance. A small boat filled with lead balls floats on the water. If the boat is tipped over so that it and its contents sink to the bottom, does the water level in the beaker change? Does the balance reading change?

Problems

1. A man of 80 kg mass is skating on ice. Find the pressure exerted by one skate when the other is not touching the ice if the length of blade in contact with the ice is 0.15 m and the runners are 0.006 m wide. *Ans.* 8.7×10^5 newtons/m²

2. What is the average pressure due to the weight of a 180-lb person if the effective area of each foot is 20 in.² and the person is standing on both feet? On just one foot?

3. The pressure in an automobile tire is 26 lb/in.² greater than atmospheric pressure. If the wheel on which the tire is mounted supports 900 lb, what area of the tire is in contact with the ground? (Neglect the mechanical strength of the casing.)
Ans. 34.6 in.²

4. What is the weight of the air in a living room of dimensions 24 by 15 by 8 ft? The weight density of air is 0.081 lb/ft³.

5. Assuming an average weight density of 62.4 lb/ft³ for the human body, find the volume occupied by a 180-lb swimmer. What pressure due to the water does the swimmer experience at a depth of 8 ft in fresh water? *Ans.* 2.89 ft³; 500 lb/ft²

6. A submarine is designed to withstand a maximum water pressure of 26,000 lb/ft². If 1 ft³ of sea water weighs 65 lb, find the maximum depth to which the submarine can be taken without exceeding the design pressure. Find the net force on a rectangular hatch of dimensions 3 by 2 ft at this depth.

7. The water level in a reservoir standpipe is 300 ft above the lowest part of a town. What is the maximum water pressure in pounds per square inch available due to this head of water? *Ans.* 130 lb/in.²

8. A submarine is at a depth of 50 ft in sea water which has a density of 2 slugs/ft³. Find the pressure due to the water and the resulting force on a hatch of dimensions 3 by 2 ft.

9. Water and oil are standing in opposite legs of a U tube open at both ends. Water fills the bottom and stands 19 cm above the oil-water interface. How high does the oil stand above the interface if its density is 800 kg/m³? *Ans.* 23.8 cm

10. The apparatus of Figure 11.5*b* contains kerosene in one arm and distilled water in the other. When the level of the water is at 26.2 cm, the kerosene level is at 32 cm. Find the density of kerosene in both metric and British engineering units.

11. Find the force on the glass side of an aquarium containing salt water with a density of 1,030 kg/m³ if the glass is 0.8 m wide and the water behind it is 50 cm deep.
Ans. 1,010 newtons

12. A lock gate is 25 ft wide and 30 ft high. The height of water on one side is 25 ft, and on the other side is 12 ft. What is the net horizontal force on the gate due to water pressure?

13. A man carries a barometer from the bottom to the top of a building that is 200 m high. At the bottom of the building the barometer reads 76 cm Hg, and at the top it reads 74.15 cm Hg. Find the average density of the air between these heights.

Ans. 1.26 kg/m³

14. What is the reading of a barometer on the top of a building that is 100 m high when the barometer at the base of the building reads 74 cm Hg if the average density of air between these heights is 1.25 kg/m³?

15. A liquid-filled reservoir is connected to two cylinders with closely-fitting pistons which are at the same level. One cylinder has a diameter of 0.5 in., while the other has a diameter of 6 in. If a force of 3 lb is exerted on the smaller piston, find the increase in pressure on the larger piston. How large a force is required on the larger piston to keep it at rest if frictional forces are negligible? *Ans.* 15.3 lb/in.²; 432 lb

16. One end of a closed hydraulic system is 5 m above the other end. The system is filled with oil of density 800 kg/m³. At the higher end, a force of 200 newtons is applied on an area of 10 cm². What is the net force on a piston with an area of 15 cm² at the lower end?

17. A barge with vertical sides is used to transport automobiles down the Mississippi River. Twenty cars weighing 3,000 lb apiece are driven on the barge, which is 60 ft long and 30 ft wide. Find the additional volume of water which the barge must displace. How much deeper does the barge ride in the water? *Ans.* 960 ft³; 0.53 ft

18. A truck loaded to a total weight of 5 tons drives onto a ferryboat, causing the latter to sink ¼ in. deeper into the water. What is the area of the horizontal section of the boat at the water line?

19. A piece of aluminum is "weighed" with an equal-arm laboratory balance. When the aluminum is in air, the balancing mass is 108 g. When it is immersed in water and in kerosene, the balancing masses are 68 and 76 g, respectively. Find the densities of aluminum and kerosene. *Ans.* 2,700 kg/m³; 800 kg/m³

20. A body was "weighed" in water, in oil, and in alcohol. Its loss of weight in water was 1.50 newton, in oil 0.98 newton, and in alcohol 1.20 newton. What is the specific gravity of the oil? Of the alcohol?

21. Find the volume and the mass of a specimen of copper that has an apparent weight of 2.5 newtons when under water. *Ans.* 3.22 × 10⁻⁵ m³; 0.288 kg

22. A piece of glass with a mass of 341 g is "weighed" when immersed in various liquids. It weighs 247 g in water and 225 g in glycerin. Find the density of the glass and the specific gravity of the glycerin.

23. A piece of wood with a weight of 1.64 newtons is immersed in water by use of a sinker that weighs 0.85 newton in water. The combined weight of the wood and the sinker when both are immersed is 0.56 newton. Find the density of the wood.

Ans. 850 kg/m³

24. A piece of cork weighs 0.6 lb. A 2-lb sinker is attached to it. With only the sinker in water, the cork and sinker weigh 2.3 lb. With the sinker and cork both in water, they weigh 0.1 lb. What is the density of the cork? What is its specific gravity? What is the density of the sinker?

25. The volume of the gas bag of an airship is 140,000 m³. The density of air at 0°C and at atmospheric pressure is 1.29 kg/m³, and that of the hydrogen with which the gas bags are filled is 0.092 kg/m³. If the mass of the airship and its necessary equipment is 80,000 kg, what is the maximum net lift available for a useful load?

Ans. 8.6 × 10⁵ newtons

26. A balloon with a volume of 1.5×10^7 ft³ is filled with helium of weight density 0.011 lb/ft³. The weight density of air is 0.081 lb/ft³. What is the net buoyant force on the balloon?

27. A 2-kg mass of wrought iron floats in a beaker of mercury. What fraction of the iron is submerged? If sufficient water is poured into the beaker to cover the iron completely, what fraction of the iron is submerged in the mercury?   Ans. 0.57; 0.54

28. A 250-g plastic sphere has a density of 900 kg/m³. It floats at a water-kerosene interface (Fig. 11.11). What volume V_2 lies beneath the interface?

29. Find the volume of cork that must be employed in a life preserver if it is designed to support one-fifth of a man's body out of fresh water, assuming the man weighs 175 lb, has a specific gravity of 1.00, and that all the cork is submerged.   Ans. 0.74 ft³

30. A diver with his suit weighs 300 lb. Blocks of lead with a volume totaling 50 in.³ attached to his shoes just cause him to sink. How many cubic feet of water are displaced by the suit?

31. A hydrometer (see accompanying figure) has a mass of 110 g. The graduated stem BA is 30 cm long and has a cross-sectional area of 0.5 cm², while the bulb below B has a volume of 107.5 cm³. What fraction of the stem BA will be submerged when the hydrometer floats in water? What is the lowest density the hydrometer can read? What is the specific gravity of a liquid in which the hydrometer floats with the liquid level at B?

Ans. 1/6; 0.90; 1.023

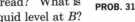

PROB. 31

32. A rectangular block of wood has a cross-sectional area of 120 cm² and a height of 40 cm. It floats vertically in water because to its lower edge is fastened a weight of 600 g of lead. How much of the wood projects out of the water? (Take the density of wood to be 450 kg/m³.)

CHAPTER 12   *We have been considering the physics of fluids at rest.   But fluids also move, and in moving they exert forces on the bodies past which they flow.   Fluids also exert forces on bodies which move through them.   Indeed, the forces depend only on the relative motion of body and fluid.   Hence the forces on an airplane wing at rest in a wind tunnel are identical with those on the same wing moving through air at rest.   In this chapter we examine some of the phenomena associated with moving fluids.*

Fluids in Motion

12.1 Viscosity

When a liquid or a gas is in motion, the shape as well as the position of a given mass of the fluid may be changing.   Because different layers move with different speeds, the internal friction between the various layers must be considered.   For example, the velocity of the water in a river is greater in midstream than it is near the bank, and the velocity of the wind increases as we go above the surface of the earth.   Water flowing through a circular pipe moves with increasing velocity as we go from the pipe surface to its center.   Each layer of water is pulled forward by the layer of water moving over it, and backward by the layer of water over which it moves.   The internal friction between fluid layers is known as *viscosity*.

If two beakers, one containing heavy oil and the other water, are tilted from side to side, the mobility of the water is greater than that of the oil; oil is more viscous than water.   Gases have lower viscosity than liquids because of the increased distance between the molecules.

Suppose that liquid flows over a horizontal surface *SS′* (Fig. 12.1).   The layer of liquid in contact with the surface remains stationary because of adhesion, but each successive layer of liquid moves with respect to the layer directly below it.   The speed of each layer increases with the distance of the layer from the surface *SS′*.   A slowly moving layer retards the motion of an adjacent layer which is moving faster.   Each horizontal layer is acted upon by the layer above with a tangential force in the direction of the motion, and by the layer below with a retarding force.   These forces arise from momentum transfer between the particles of the liquid.   The dotted figures *abcd* and *efgh* (Fig. 12.1) show the distortion of the liquid as it moves.   The upper layer *fg* travels faster than the lower layer *eh*.   Consider an imaginary cube represented by *abcd* which becomes *efgh* a short time later.   Let *F* be the tangential force on the plane which cuts the page in *bc* (and

FIGURE 12.1

Displacement of layers of a moving liquid relative to a surface at rest.

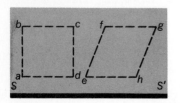

TABLE 12.1   *Viscosities of Fluids*

Liquids	η, newton-sec/m^2	Gases	η, newton-sec/m^2
Ethyl alcohol at 20°C	0.0012	Air at 20°C	18×10^{-6}
Glycerin at 20°C	1.48	Argon at 20°C	22×10^{-6}
Mercury at 20°C	0.0015	Hydrogen at 20°C	9×10^{-6}
Oil		Oxygen at 20°C	20×10^{-6}
SAE 10 at 55°C	0.16–0.22		
SAE 20 at 55°C	0.23–0.30		
Water at 20°C	0.001		

later in *fg*). Let A be the area of this surface of the cube, l be the distance ab, and v represent the speed of bc relative to ad. When v is not too great, F/A is proportional to v/l, or

$$\frac{F}{A} = \eta \frac{v}{l} \qquad\qquad \textbf{12.1}$$

where η is a constant called the *coefficient of viscosity*. It is equal to the force per unit area necessary to maintain unit difference of velocity between two parallel planes when the planes are unit distance apart.

The viscosities of several fluids are listed in Table 12.1. The coefficient of viscosity of a typical liquid changes with both temperature (Fig. 12.2*a*) and pressure (Fig. 12.2*b*). From Eq. (12.1) it is clear that η may have the dimensions newton-seconds per square meter. In many handbooks viscosities are given in poises; 1 poise = 0.1 newton-sec/m^2.

12.2 Fluid Friction

When an object is dropped from a slow-moving airplane, the force of gravity at first exceeds the retarding force due to air friction. As the velocity of the body increases, these frictional forces also increase,

(a)

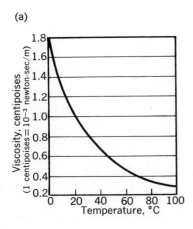

(b)

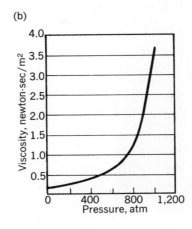

FIGURE 12.2

Viscosity changes. (*a*) Viscosity of water decreases as temperature rises. (*b*) Viscosity of a typical oil increases as pressure rises.

while the force of gravity remains essentially constant. Eventually the frictional force becomes equal to the weight, and there is no further increase in velocity. The *terminal velocity* depends on the shape and mass of the falling body as well as on the air density. A pilot who bails out of a plane at 20,000 ft may achieve a velocity of about 150 mi/hr, which then decreases as the air becomes more dense. On the other hand, a streamlined bomb may have a terminal velocity well over 700 mi/hr at the earth.

<   The increase of air friction with the velocity of the moving body is one reason for the excessive cost of operation when automobiles or trains are run at high speeds. At moderate speeds fluid friction increases directly with the speed. At higher velocities it varies with the square or even a higher power of the speed. Meteorites move through the air with such high velocities that they become incandescent and rapidly vaporize (Fig. 12.3). In a flash flood, fluid friction is sometimes large enough to transplant large boulders.

The interaction between a fluid and an object depends on the relative velocities. It makes no difference whether the fluid is moving past a body at rest or the body is moving through the fluid at rest. Thus the characteristics of an airfoil or a projectile can be studied by blowing air past it in a wind tunnel, and predictions made of its behavior hold when it moves through still air. Figures 12.4 and 12.5 show how the direction of flow is changed by inserting objects of different forms into the path of a fluid. When the flow is steady and

FIGURE 12.3
Meteor trail. Air resistance is large at such high speeds.

FIGURE 12.4
Two-dimensional flow around a plane.

every particle passing a given point follows the same path as did all preceding particles which passed that point, we say the flow is *streamlined*. Streamlines (or lines of flow) are clearly evident in the figures. When the flow is erratic and swirling eddies are created, the flow is said to be *turbulent*. Note how much more turbulence is evident behind the plane of Figure 12.4 than behind the cylinder of Figure 12.5. The energy required to produce eddy currents comes from work done against the fluid drag.

"Streamlining" in airplanes and in automobiles (to some extent) is an attempt to reduce frictional drag by the air. By reducing eddy currents to a minimum, the power necessary to drive the airplane or automobile at a given speed is decreased.

12.3 Pressure in a Moving Fluid: Bernoulli's Theorem

Consider a liquid flowing through a pipe of varying cross section (Fig. 12.6). Because the cross section of the pipe is smaller at b than it is at a, the velocity of the liquid must be greater at b than at a in order that the flow of the liquid through each cross section of the pipe may be the same. Consequently, the momentum of the liquid per unit volume increases in going from a to b. According to Newton's second law, a force is necessary to produce a change of momentum. In this case, the force results from a difference in pressure between a and b. The pressure at a is greater than the pressure at b, thereby producing

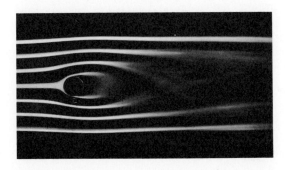

FIGURE 12.5
Flow around a cylinder.

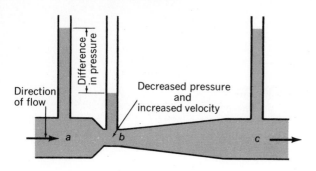

Direction of flow

Decreased pressure and increased velocity

a   *b*   *c*

FIGURE 12.6
Flow velocity is greater, and pressure less, in regions of reduced cross-sectional area in a horizontal tube of varying cross section.

a positive acceleration of the liquid and an increase in its momentum per unit volume. *The pressure in the fluid is smaller where the velocity is greater.*

The change in pressure can be measured by observing the heights of the liquid in transverse manometers at *a*, *b*, and *c*. If the liquid is *incompressible*, the amount passing through every cross section of the tube per second is the same. Let v_a, v_b, and v_c represent the velocities and A_a, A_b, and A_c represent the cross-sectional areas at *a*, *b*, and *c*, respectively. Then

$$v_a A_a = v_b A_b = v_c A_c \qquad\qquad \textbf{12.2}$$

For steady flow the velocity is inversely proportional to the cross section of the tube.

Example   The cross section of the tube at *a* is 10 in.², and at *b* is 2 in.². If the velocity of the stream at *a* is 12 ft/sec, what is it at *b*?

$$\text{Velocity at } b = \text{velocity at } a \times \frac{\text{area at } a}{\text{area at } b}$$

$$= 12 \text{ ft/sec} \times \frac{10 \text{ in.}^2}{2 \text{ in.}^2} = 60 \text{ ft/sec}$$

Consider the case in which all parts of a tube of varying cross section (Fig. 12.7) are not at the same height. Let us assume that (1) the liquid is incompressible, (2) the flow is streamlined, and (3) there is no fluid friction (no viscosity). Under these conditions we can use the conservation of energy to derive a relationship between the pressure, velocity, and height at any one point and pressure, velocity, and height at some other point. Let volume V of liquid be forced from *a* to *c*. The work done *on* the system in forcing the liquid past *a* is $F_a S_a = p_a A_a (V/A_a) = p_a V$, where the subscript *a* represents the value at point *a*. The work done *by* the system when the volume V is forced past point *c* is $F_c S_c = p_c A_c (V/A_c) = p_c V$. The *net* work done *on* the system is $(p_a - p_c)V$. Since there are no energy losses, we have

Work done on system = energy of volume V at c — energy of V at a
$$(p_a - p_c)V = [\tfrac{1}{2}(dV)v_c{}^2 + dVgy_c] - [\tfrac{1}{2}(dV)v_a{}^2 + dVgy_a] \quad \textbf{A}$$

where d is the density of the liquid, and dV the mass of the volume V.

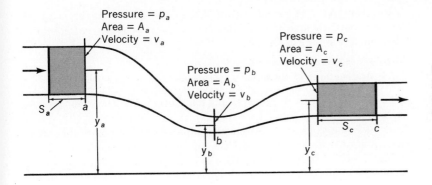

Pressure = p_a
Area = A_a
Velocity = v_a

Pressure = p_c
Area = A_c
Velocity = v_c

Pressure = p_b
Area = A_b
Velocity = v_b

S_a a y_a b y_b y_c S_c c

FIGURE 12.7

Flow of a liquid through a tube of variable cross section at different heights.

If we divide both sides of Eq. (*A*) by V and rearrange the terms, we obtain Bernoulli's theorem,

$$p_a + \tfrac{1}{2}dv_a{}^2 + dgy_a = p_c + \tfrac{1}{2}dv_c{}^2 + dgy_c = \text{constant} \qquad \textbf{12.3}$$

The sum of the pressure, the kinetic energy per unit volume, and the potential energy per unit volume is the same at all points along the same streamline in the case of streamlined flow for a nonviscous, incompressible fluid.

Example Salt water of weight density 64 lb/ft³ is passing through the tube of Figure 12.7. The cross-sectional area at a is twice that at b. At a, $v = 20.0$ ft/sec, $y_a = 30$ ft, and $p_a = 20$ lb/in.². If $y_b = 25$ ft, find the velocity and pressure at b.

Since the area at a is twice that at b, the speed at b must be twice that at a by Eq. (12.2); hence

$$v_b = 40 \text{ ft/sec} \qquad p_a = 20 \text{ lb/in.}^2 = 2{,}880 \text{ lb/ft}^2$$

$$d = \frac{64 \text{ lb/ft}^3}{32 \text{ lb/slug}} = 2.0 \text{ slug/ft}^3$$

By Eq. (12.3),

$$2{,}880 \,\frac{\text{lb}}{\text{ft}^2} + \tfrac{1}{2}\!\left(2.0 \,\frac{\text{slug}}{\text{ft}^3} \times 400 \,\frac{\text{ft}^2}{\text{sec}^2}\right) + \left(64 \,\frac{\text{lb}}{\text{ft}^3} \times 30 \text{ ft}\right)$$

$$= p_b + \tfrac{1}{2}\!\left(2.0 \,\frac{\text{slug}}{\text{ft}^3} \times 1{,}600 \,\frac{\text{ft}^2}{\text{sec}^2}\right) + \left(64 \,\frac{\text{lb}}{\text{ft}^3} \times 25 \text{ ft}\right)$$

$$5{,}200 \text{ lb/ft}^2 = p_b + 3{,}200 \text{ lb/ft}^2$$

$$p_b = 2{,}000 \text{ lb/ft}^2 \text{ or about } 13.9 \text{ lb/in.}^2$$

If frictional forces are acting, some energy is lost, and the sum of the three terms of Eq. (12.3) decreases as we move in the direction of fluid velocity. When water flows through a horizontal tube of uniform cross section, the pressure drops along the tube if there is an energy loss due to viscosity.

Although we have derived Bernoulli's theorem for an incompressible fluid, Eq. (12.3) is approximately true for air so long as the speed is well

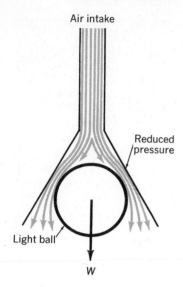

Air intake

Reduced pressure

Light ball

W

FIGURE 12.8

A light ball can be supported in an inverted funnel by the Bernoulli pressure reduction.

below the speed of sound (about 330 m/sec or 740 mi/hr). In advanced treatises equations are developed which take into consideration the compressibility of the air.

12.4 Applications of Bernoulli's Theorem

Among the common applications of Bernoulli's theorem are the following:

A Ball in an Air Jet. A light ball can be held in position in an air jet, as shown in Fig. 12.8. In the space between the surface of the funnel and the surface of the ball the pressure is less than atmospheric pressure. This difference in pressure gives rise to a force which supports the ball.

The Sprayer. The forward stroke of the piston (Fig. 12.9) produces a stream of air past the end of the tube *D*. The other end of this tube is immersed in the liquid to be sprayed. The stream of air flowing past the open end of the tube reduces the pressure on the liquid in the tube. Atmospheric pressure acting on the surface of the liquid in *A* forces liquid into the tube *D* from which it is carried away by the stream of air. A spray results from this mixture of air with the fine particles of liquid.

Flow of Liquid through an Orifice. In Figure 12.10 liquid is flowing out of an orifice. Both at the top of the liquid and at the orifice the pressure is atmospheric. At the top of the container the liquid has potential energy and no kinetic energy. If we pick the opening as our position of zero height, the escaping liquid has kinetic energy, but no potential energy. If we apply Bernoulli's theorem to points at the top of the fluid and at the orifice, we have

$$p_{\text{atm}} + 0 + dgy = p_{\text{atm}} + \tfrac{1}{2}dv^2 + 0$$

where p_{atm} represents atmospheric pressure, d the density of the fluid, and v the escape velocity.

$$dgy = \tfrac{1}{2}dv^2 \qquad \text{or} \qquad v = \sqrt{2gy}$$

Figure 12.11 shows streamlines associated with flow through a sharp-edged orifice. In this case the fluid is still being accelerated as it passes the sharp edges at the opening. As the fluid gains speed, the area of flow decreases in accordance with Eq. (12.2). The flow lines converge to give a *vena contracta,* with the effective area a little less than two-thirds the actual area for a sharp circular orifice. A well-

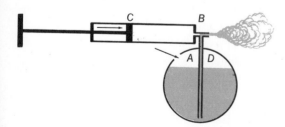

C   B

A   D

FIGURE 12.9

A sprayer in which reduction of pressure at *B* causes liquid to rise in tube *D*.

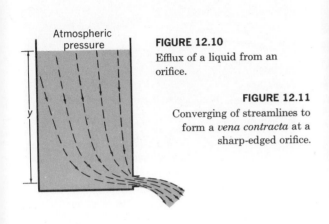

FIGURE 12.10
Efflux of a liquid from an
orifice.

FIGURE 12.11
Converging of streamlines to
form a *vena contracta* at a
sharp-edged orifice.

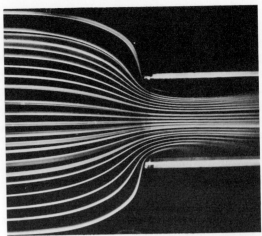

designed nozzle gives a flow which utilizes the actual opening far more
effectively.

The Curving Ball. It is well known that a ball follows a curved path
if it is hit or thrown in such a way that it has both a high speed and a
large amount of spin. This is readily understood in terms of
Bernoulli's theorem. If we consider the center of the ball as the origin
of a coordinate system, the air is rushing past the ball as shown in
Figure 12.12. Because of friction, a thin layer of air is pulled around
by the rotating ball. At B this layer is moving in the direction of the
passing air, and the resultant velocity is the sum of the velocities due
to the rotation and to the linear motion. At A the velocity due to

(a)

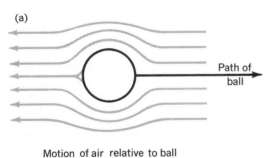

Path of
ball

Motion of air relative to ball

(b)

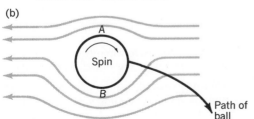

Path of
ball

FIGURE 12.12
The motion of air past a ball (*a*) when it is not spinning,
and (*b*) when it is spinning.

(a)

(b)

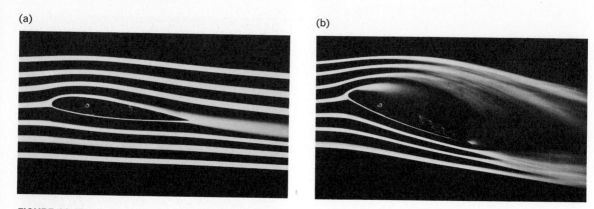

FIGURE 12.13

Flow around a tapered airfoil. (*a*) A lifting airfoil. (*b*) A stalled airfoil. The increased flow speed and reduced pressure above an airfoil result in a net lift.

rotation is opposite that due to translation, and the net velocity is lower. Therefore, the pressure is greater at *A*, and the ball curves in the direction shown.

Lift on an Airfoil. In a well-designed aircraft wing the velocity of the air above the wing relative to the aircraft is greater than the velocity below the wing (Fig. 12.13). As a consequence, the pressure is less above the wing than below. This pressure difference gives rise to a net lift. Often the speed of the air below the wing is less than the speed of free air some distance from the plane, so the pressure beneath the wing is greater than that in the free air.

When a stream of air strikes a surface inclined to the flow lines, there is a net force directed upward and backward which arises from the rate of change of momentum of the air. The upward component contributes to the lift, the backward component to the drag. The lift due to the Bernoulli effect is enough to support many aircraft in normal flight, so that no lift by impact is needed, and the lower wing surfaces may be horizontal. When a plane is taking off, part of the lift is usually contributed by the impact of air on the lower wing surfaces. To enhance these forces, the angle of attack is increased, and the wing flaps are lowered. This increases drag as well as lift. The lift due to the Bernoulli effect may be very simply demonstrated by blowing over a sheet of paper held at adjacent corners; lift due to impact can be shown by blowing under the sheet.

Questions

1. Why does the speed of a liquid increase and pressure decrease when the liquid passes a constriction in a pipe?

2. When there is a steady, streamlined flow of liquid through a pipe of varying cross section, does a small volume element of the fluid remain in equilibrium as it moves through the pipe?

3. A tennis ball travels southward, rotating counterclockwise as viewed from above. Which way does it curve?

4. Discuss the operation of a siphon and a paint sprayer.

5. When an object is dropped from a balloon at high altitude, its velocity may increase for a while and then decrease as it nears the earth. Why does this occur?

6. By applying Bernoulli's theorem to the siphon (Prob. 2), show that the velocity of efflux is given by $v = \sqrt{2gy}$. What limits the height h over which the siphon can operate? If h is less than this limit, will v depend at all on h? If so, why doesn't h appear in the formula for v?

7. Why is the maximum height over which a siphon can successfully operate reduced when the velocity of efflux is increased? Explain quantitatively by applying Bernoulli's theorem.

Problems

1. Find the velocity of efflux of water from a hole in the side of a tank when the water in the tank is 16 ft above the hole. If the area of the hole is 0.75 in.², how many cubic feet will be discharged each minute? (Neglect the contraction of the streamlines as they emerge from the hole.)   *Ans.* 32 ft/sec; 10 ft³

2. A siphon (see accompanying figure) has a tube with a cross-sectional area of 0.4 cm². Find the velocity of efflux and the quantity of water transferred per minute if $y = 10$ cm.

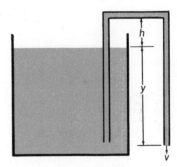

PROB. 2

3. In a paper machine, paper is formed on a Fourdrinier wire screen, which moves at a speed of 15 ft/sec, by ejecting a mixture of paper fibers and water from a slit orifice onto the screen. What gauge pressure is required at the orifice to match the horizontal speed of efflux to the speed of the wire screen moving just below the slit orifice? Take the density of the mixture (known as *stuff*) to be 2.4 slugs/ft³.   *Ans.* 270 lb/ft²

4. With what speed will water discharge from the bottom of a tank 4 ft deep through an orifice? If the orifice has a diameter of 0.5 in., what weight of water will be discharged each second?

5. Water flows at the rate of 2 liters/min from a hole at the bottom of a tank in which the water is 0.9 m deep. Find the effective area of the hole. Find the rate at which the water would escape if an additional pressure of 10⁵ newtons/m² were applied to the surface of the water.   *Ans.* 0.08 cm²; 7 liters/min

6. Find the velocity with which water in an enclosed tank will be forced through an orifice in the side of the tank if the orifice is 1 ft below the surface of the water in the tank and there is a gauge pressure of 167.5 lb/ft² on the surface of the water in the tank.

7. A stream of water projected horizontally from a hose 2.5 m above the ground strikes the ground 6 m away. Find the velocity of efflux and the fluid pressure in the nozzle.
Ans. 8.4 m/sec; 3.53 × 10⁴ newton/m²

8. A reservoir is filled with mercury. In its side there is an opening 2 mm in diameter. If the opening is 0.4 m below the surface, how many grams of mercury will escape per second?

9. Water flowing from an orifice in the side of a tank situated at a height of 6.4 m from the ground strikes the ground 8 m from the foot of the tank. Compute the escape velocity of the water and the gauge pressure in the tank at the level from which the water is squirting.
Ans. 7 m/sec; 2.45 × 10⁴ newtons/m²

10. A Pitot head (see accompanying figure), much used to measure the air speeds of planes, consists of a *Pitot tube* open in the direction of flight and a *static tube* with holes drilled in the sides to permit its pressure to be the same as that of the surrounding air. When the Pitot head moves through the air, the pressure in the Pitot line builds up to a value above that of the static line. Show that if Δp is the difference in pressure between the Pitot and the static tubes, the speed is given by

$$v = \sqrt{\frac{2\Delta p}{d}}$$

where d is the local density of the air.

11. A plane is flying at a speed of 200 m/sec at an altitude at which the density of the air is 0.8 kg/m³. Find the difference in pressure Δp between the Pitot tube and the static tube (see accompanying figure). To how many millimeters of Hg does this correspond?
Ans. 16,000 newtons/m²; 120 mm

12. The level of the water in the manometer at a (Fig. 12.6) reads 30 cm, and the cross section at a is 15 cm². The cross section of the constriction at b is 2 cm². Find the height of the water column at the constriction b, where the velocity is 60 cm/sec.

13. Air is streaming past a horizontal airplane wing such that the speed is 400 ft/sec over the upper surface and 300 ft/sec at the lower surface. If the air density is 0.001 slug/ft³, find the difference in pressure between the top and bottom of the wing. If the wing is 30 ft long and has an average width of 6 ft, calculate the gross lift of the wing.
Ans. 35 lb/ft²; 6,300 lb

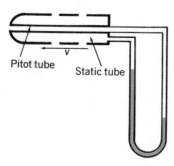

Pitot tube   Static tube

14. Water is flowing through the pipe (Fig. 12.6), which has an area of 0.75 ft² at a and an area of 0.5 ft² at b. The pressure at cross section a is 20 lb/in.², and that at b is 15 lb/in.². Find the velocity in each of the cross sections.

15. A viscosimeter consists of two concentric cylinders of large diameter with a thin annular space between them. The cylinders have a mean radius of 5 cm and a length of 15 cm. The thickness of the annular ring is 2 mm. If the outer cylinder is rotated at 50 rev/min while the inner one is held fixed, find the torque on the inner cylinder when the viscosimeter contains oil of viscosity 0.15 newton-sec/m². *Ans.* 0.0463 newton-m

16. If the viscosimeter of Prob. 15 is filled with a different kind of oil and a torque of 0.08 newton-m is required to rotate the outer cylinder at 40 rev/min when the inner one is fixed, find the viscosity of the oil.

17. Water in streamline flow is moving with a speed of 5 m/sec through a pipe with a cross-sectional area of 4 cm². If the water gradually descends 10 m and the pipe increases in area to 8 cm², find the pressure and speed of flow at the lower level if the pressure is 1.50×10^5 newtons/m² at the higher level.

Ans. 2.57×10^5 newtons/m²; 2.5 m/sec

18. A constriction in a pipe line similar to that of Figure 12.6, with the associated pressure gauges, can be used to measure the rate of flow through the line. When so used, it is called a *Venturi meter*. Show that the volume Q of fluid flowing through the pipe each second is given by

$$Q = A_a A_b \sqrt{\frac{2(p_a - p_b)}{d(A_a{}^2 - A_b{}^2)}}$$

19. Water is flowing through a horizontal pipe of varying cross section. The pressure is 8,000 lb/ft² where the cross-sectional area is 4 in.², and 3,000 lb/ft² where the area is 2 in.². What is the rate of flow of water in cubic feet per second? *Ans.* 1.15 ft³/sec

CHAPTER 13   *Thus far we have considered rigid bodies, which ideally do not change their shapes under the influence of forces, and fluids, which have no well-defined shape.   Actually, all real solid bodies undergo changes in shape or size when subjected to a system of forces.   If the forces applied to a solid body are not too great, it returns to its original condition when they are removed.   The elastic properties of solid bodies such as cables, springs, and beams are of great engineering importance.   Fluids, too, have elastic properties upon which the propagation of waves through the fluid depends.   We turn now to some fundamental characteristics of elastic bodies.*

Elastic Properties of Matter

13.1 Molecular Composition of Matter

In this chapter we consider certain facets of the molecular nature of matter.   Here we deal with particles too small to be seen in the most powerful microscope and of mass too minute to be detected by the most sensitive analytical balance.

In the fifth century B.C. Greek philosophers, the most prominent of whom was Democritus, advanced the theory that all matter was composed of tiny particles called atoms (*atom* means "uncut," or "indivisible").   About 1800, the English chemist Dalton introduced experimental evidence for the existence of atoms and laid the groundwork for modern chemistry.   Although we now know that the atom itself is composed of still smaller particles, we need not consider this fact in discussing the properties of interest here, and we defer discussion of the structure of atoms to Chap. 48.

One or more atoms may be bound together to form a chemical compound.   The smallest unit into which a substance can be divided without chemical decomposition is known as a *molecule*.   In gases such as helium and neon the molecule consists of a single atom. In other gases, such as hydrogen and oxygen, two atoms form a molecule.   Molecules of carbon dioxide and of water vapor contain three atoms.   In the gaseous state the molecules are usually separated by distances which are large compared with the molecular dimensions. The molecules at room temperature move with high velocities and have frequent collisions.   The gas entirely fills the space of the containing vessel and exerts on it a pressure which results from the change in momentum of the molecules in colliding with the walls (Chap. 20).

In general, the forces between molecules in a gas are small; for an "ideal" gas they are zero. When the forces between the molecules of a gas are sufficiently great and the molecular speeds are reduced by lowering the temperature, the molecules stick together to form a liquid. In the liquid, molecules cling together but are free to move with respect to each other. Liquids do not resist forces tending to change their shape, but they strongly resist forces tending to change their volume. Because the molecules of the liquid can easily be displaced with respect to each other, layers flow relatively freely over each other, and the liquid assumes the shape of the vessel in which it is placed. In the liquid two or more molecules may stick to one another and move about as a unit.

In a solid, atoms cling strongly together and tend to keep the same relative positions. Solids resist any tendency to change their shape or size. They preserve their original form, unless acted upon by large external forces. The true solid is crystalline in nature; the atoms of the crystal are arranged in a regular and repetitive way (Fig. 13.1) by interatomic forces which are reasonably idealized in terms of relatively stiff springs connecting nearest neighbors and weaker springs connecting next nearest neighbors. The interatomic forces are such that once a crystalline array is established, it is no longer meaningful to say that a particular atom belongs to a particular molecule. In the crystalline solid the molecule is no longer a separate entity; rather, there is an array of atoms, and any one atom is bound to many others.

Under suitable conditions it is possible to change a given material from the solid to the liquid phase, and from the liquid to the gaseous phase. Water can be frozen to form ice and evaporated to form steam. The change from one phase to another is discussed in Chap. 21.

13.2 Elasticity

When a body or a substance is subjected to external forces, it ordinarily undergoes changes in size or shape or both. These changes, which depend on the physical properties of the substance, reveal significant and often useful information concerning the internal forces which act among the constituent molecules of the substance.

If we hang a weight from a spring, the spring stretches. If we increase the weight, the spring stretches still more. If we remove the weight, the spring returns to its original length. When a diver stands at the end of a diving board, the board is distorted, but when he leaves the board, it returns to its original position. When an archer prepares to shoot an arrow, he bends the bow, which springs back to its original form when the arrow is released. The spring, the diving board, and the bow are examples of elastic objects. *Elasticity is that property of a body by which it experiences a change in shape or volume when a deforming force acts upon it and by which it returns to its original size or shape when the deforming force is removed* (Fig. 13.2).

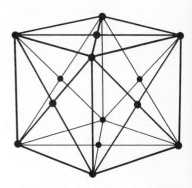

FIGURE 13.1
In a crystal each atom is bound to many others by elastic forces.

FIGURE 13.2
Elastic deformation of a golf ball.

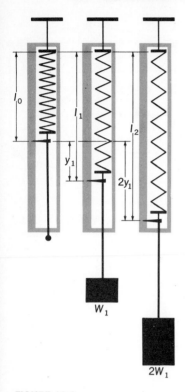

FIGURE 13.3

Elongation of a linear spring is proportional to stretching force.

Materials which do not resume their original shape after being distorted are said to be *inelastic*. Mud, putty, and dough are inelastic materials. Lead and solder are relatively inelastic, since it is easy to distort them permanently.

13.3 Hooke's Law

Consider the spring of Figure 13.3. Let its length when there is no load applied be l_0. If we add a load W_1, we find a new length l_1 for the spring. The change in length $(l_1 - l_0)$ we denote by y_1; in general, we shall represent the extension of the spring by y. If we now double the load on the spring, we find that y is twice as great. The fact that the change in length is proportional to the applied force was first reported by the English physicist Robert Hooke about the middle of the seventeenth century in the words "Ut tensio, sic vis" (as the extension, so the force). We extend Hooke's law and state: *The deformation of an elastic body is directly proportional to the magnitude of the applied force.*

Before applying Hooke's law to other situations we shall calculate the amount of work required to stretch a spring a given distance. When the extension is zero, the force is zero. As we increase the displacement y, the force F required increases proportionally. We may write Hooke's law

$$F = ky \tag{13.1}$$

where k is known as the *force constant* of the spring. The average force producing the displacement y is just equal to $(0 + ky)/2 = ky/2$. The work done is equal to the product of the average force and the displacement:

$$\text{Work} = \frac{ky}{2}\, y = \frac{1}{2}\, ky^2 \tag{13.2}$$

The work required to stretch the spring is equal to the potential energy in the spring.

13.4 Stress and Strain: Young's Modulus

In order to treat problems in elasticity in a convenient and consistent way, we introduce two new terms, *stress* and *strain*. When we apply a force to distort a body, internal forces are set up within the body to resist the distortion. For example, if we try to stretch a light bar (Fig. 13.4), the material at the left of some plane PP' exerts a force **F** to the left on the material at the right of PP'. Since the bar is in equilibrium, the material at the right of PP' exerts an equal and opposite force on the material at the left. The material is said to be under stress. For our bar *the stress is the ratio of the internal force to the area over which the force is distributed.* (When the stress varies from point to point in a material, we must take the limit of this ratio as the area chosen approaches zero to obtain the stress at a point.) We shall

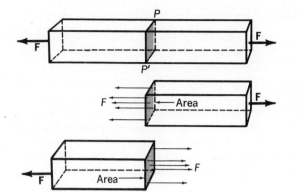

FIGURE 13.4
The stretching stress in a bar is the ratio of the internal tensile force to the cross-sectional area over which the force is distributed.

consider only situations in which the stress is uniform over the area in question. In this case

$$\text{Stress} = \frac{\text{force}}{\text{area}}$$

As a result of the applied stress, some change in the shape or size of the elastic body is produced. The term *strain* is applied to the relative change occurring in the dimensions or shape of a body when it is subjected to a stress. We shall define three particular types of strain later in this chapter. For all these types of strain Hooke's law states that *the stress applied is directly proportional to the strain produced.*

When a steel cable supports an elevator or a suspension bridge, it is stretched by the load. How much its length changes depends on the load, on the cross-sectional area of the cable, on its original length, and on the material of which it is made. The bigger the load, the larger the stretch expected; the greater the cross-sectional area of the cable, the smaller the stretch. The stress in the cable is the force applied divided by this area. *The stretching strain produced is the ratio of the change in length to the original length.*

$$\text{Stretching (or longitudinal) strain} = \frac{\text{change in length}}{\text{original length}} = \frac{\Delta l}{l}$$

For any elastic material the stretching stress is directly proportional to the longitudinal strain. *The ratio of the stretching stress to the longitudinal strain is known as Young's modulus* (or sometimes as the *longitudinal* modulus or *stretch* modulus) of elasticity. We denote it by Y.

$$\frac{F}{A} = Y\frac{\Delta l}{l} \qquad\qquad \textbf{13.3}$$

Example A wire 120 in. long with a cross section of 0.125 in.^{2} hangs vertically. When a load of 450 lb is applied to the wire, it stretches 0.015 in. Find Young's modulus of elasticity.

$$\text{Young's modulus} = \frac{\text{stress}}{\text{strain}} = \frac{F/A}{\Delta l/l} = \frac{450 \text{ lb}/0.125 \text{ in.}^2}{0.015 \text{ in.}/120 \text{ in.}}$$
$$= 2.88 \times 10^7 \text{ lb/in.}^2$$

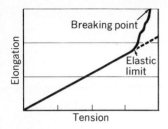

FIGURE 13.5
The relation between tension and elongation of a wire is approximately linear until the elastic limit is reached, after which Hooke's law no longer applies.

13.5 Limit of Elasticity

A body that has been deformed and then released will return to its original size and shape unless the stress has exceeded a certain limit. In this case the body does not recover its original shape; it has acquired a *permanent set*. The maximum stress from which the substance will completely recover its original size and shape is called the *elastic limit*. It differs widely for different substances, being high for steel and low for lead. Figure 13.5 shows the typical relation between tension and elongation for a wire both above and below the elastic limit. The greatest stress which can be applied to the wire is the *ultimate tensile stress*. Table 13.1 lists some typical elastic constants.

When a metal rod is stretched beyond its elastic limit and the stress is increased still further, a stage is reached at which the rod begins to stretch rapidly, even though the stress is somewhat decreased. The stress at which this begins is called the *yield point*. Even though the metal is cold, it behaves as if it were in a semifluid state. Once a metal is strained beyond the elastic limit, the strain becomes a function of the time which has elapsed after application of the load. Under such conditions there is a viscous flow which depends both on temperature and on the applied load.

13.6 Stiffness and Strength of Beams

It is important in many engineering applications to be able to calculate the amount of bending that will be produced in a beam by a given load (Fig. 13.6). Experiments on beams of different sizes and shapes have shown that the deflection for a given load depends on the length of the beam, on its breadth, and on its depth.

$$\text{Deflection} = \frac{\text{load} \times (\text{length})^3}{4 \times \text{Young's modulus} \times \text{breadth} \times (\text{depth})^3}$$

The stiffer of two beams is not necessarily the stronger. The mere fact that the one beam bends more than the other does not mean that it will hold less. The strength depends on the same dimensions as the stiffness, but it depends on them in a different way: the strength is proportional to the breadth and to the square of the depth and inversely proportional to the length.

TABLE 13.1 *Typical Elastic Constants*

Material	Young's modulus lb/in.²	Young's modulus newtons/m²	Bulk modulus, lb/in.²	Shear modulus, lb/in.²	Elastic limit, lb/in.²	Ultimate tensile stress, lb/in.²
Aluminum	10×10^6	6.9×10^{10}	10×10^6	3.8×10^6	19,000	21,000
Brass	14	9.8	8.5	5.1	55,000	65,000
Copper	17	12	17	6.0	22,000	49,000
Medium steel	30	21	24	12	37,000	70,000

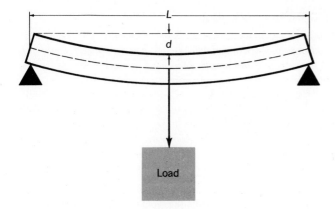

FIGURE 13.6
Bending of a beam under load.

In the bending of a beam the top layer is shortened since it resists compression, while the lower layer is lengthened and must resist tension. A central layer of the beam remains the same length. Therefore, to make a beam as strong or as stiff as possible for a given amount of material, most of the material is put in the upper and lower layers, and relatively little in the middle. For this reason steel beams are usually manufactured in shapes similar to that of the letter **I**. They are called I beams and have great strength and stiffness for a given amount of steel.

13.7 Volume Elasticity

When a solid body such as a piece of iron is immersed in a liquid so that a uniform pressure is applied to its surface, a change in the volume of the solid occurs. By definition,

$$\text{Volume (or bulk) strain} = \frac{\text{change in volume}}{\text{original volume}} = \frac{\Delta V}{V}$$

The corresponding stress (force/area) is taken as $-\Delta p$, with the minus sign appearing because an increase in pressure produces a decrease in volume. The ratio of volume stress to volume strain is called the *bulk modulus* (or *volume modulus*). We denote it by B.

$$B = \frac{\text{volume stress}}{\text{volume strain}} = -\frac{\Delta p}{\Delta V/V} \qquad \text{13.4}$$

Since an increase in pressure always gives rise to a decrease in volume, the bulk modulus B is inherently positive.

Example A sphere of copper having a volume of 100 in.³ is subjected to a pressure of 1,000 lb/in.². Find the change in volume that takes place.

$$-\Delta p = B\frac{\Delta V}{V} \qquad \text{13.4}a$$

$$-1{,}000 \text{ lb/in.}^2 = 17 \times 10^6 \text{ lb/in.}^2 \frac{\Delta V}{100 \text{ in.}^3}$$

$$\Delta V = -0.0059 \text{ in.}^3$$

TABLE 13.2 *Compressibility of Liquids*

Substance	Temperature, °C	Compressibility per atmosphere
Ethyl alcohol	14	0.0000987
Ethyl ether	0	0.000143
Kerosene	20	0.0000543
Mercury	20	0.0000039
Turpentine	20	0.000075
Water	20	0.000048

Not only solids, but also liquids and gases exhibit volume elasticity and have bulk moduli defined by Eq. (13.4). The reciprocal of the bulk modulus is called the *compressibility k*. Thus $k = 1/B$. It is customary to list compressibilities rather than bulk moduli for liquids (Table 13.2).

13.8 Compressibility of Gases: Boyle's Law

When one attempts to decrease the volume of a liquid by the application of pressure, an enormous pressure is required to achieve an appreciable change in volume. The behavior of gases in this respect is quite different. It is relatively easy to compress a gas so that it occupies only one-third of its original volume.

The relationship between the volume of any mass of gas and the pressure exerted by the gas upon the walls of the containing vessel was investigated by Robert Boyle. Boyle's law states that *the product of the pressure and the volume of a given mass of gas is constant if the temperature is not changed.* Thus, if V_0 and p_0 denote the original volume and pressure, while V and p are the final volume and pressure,

$$p_0 V_0 = pV = \text{constant} \qquad \text{13.5}$$

The mass m of gas is the product of the volume V and the density d of the gas. Clearly, the mass does not change as the pressure is varied, so Eq. (13.5) can be written

$$\frac{p_0 m}{d_0} = \frac{p_1 m}{d_1} \qquad \text{or} \qquad \frac{p_0}{d_0} = \frac{p_1}{d_1} \qquad \text{13.6}$$

Thus, *when the temperature is constant, the ratio of pressure to density remains constant.* In other words the density is proportional to the pressure. In applying Boyle's law and its corollary Eq. (13.6), it is necessary to use *absolute* pressures; gauge pressures will not do.

Consider a mass of gas initially occupying a volume V at pressure p. Let us keep the temperature constant and change the pressure by a very small amount Δp, giving us a new volume $V + \Delta V$, where ΔV is also very small. Application of Boyle's law yields

$$pV = (p + \Delta p)(V + \Delta V) = pV + p\,\Delta V + V\,\Delta p + \Delta p\,\Delta V$$

Since Δp and ΔV are both small, we may neglect their product in comparison with $p\,\Delta V$ and $V\,\Delta p$. Therefore $p\,\Delta V = -V\,\Delta p$. Comparison with Eq. (13.4) reveals that $p = B$. Thus the *isothermal* (constant temperature) *bulk modulus of a gas is the initial pressure when the change in pressure is small.*

13.9 Elasticity of Shape: Shear Modulus

If one cover of a thick book is held firmly on the table, and a force parallel to the top of the table is applied to the other cover, the shape of the book is changed while its thickness and volume remain the same. Such a deformation in shape is called a *shear*. The *shearing stress* is defined as the tangential force per unit area of the surface, and the shearing strain is the angle θ of Figure 13.7 in radians ($\theta = CC'/BC$). The ratio of the shearing stress to shearing strain is called the *shear modulus S* of the material. (It is also known as the *torsion modulus* or *modulus of rigidity*.)

$$\frac{F}{A} = S\theta \qquad\qquad 13.7$$

The shear modulus is the elastic constant involved when one twists a rod or a tube in an application such as that of the drive shaft of an automobile. Clearly, this elasticity of shape is characteristic of solids only. It is not exhibited by liquids or gases, although liquids do give evidence of short-range forces between molecules which give rise to interesting surface phenomena.

13.10 Cohesion and Adhesion

In liquids the molecules move freely with respect to each other but are held together by attractive forces. Not only do the molecules of a liquid cling to each other, but they also cling to the molecules of other substances, as may be seen when a piece of glass is dipped into a vessel of water. The molecules of water adhere to the glass and form a thin film over its surface. *The attraction of like molecules for one another is called cohesion; the attraction of unlike molecules for one another is called adhesion.* It is *cohesive* forces which hold together so firmly the molecules of iron, copper, and other solid substances.

If the molecules of a liquid have less attraction for each other than for the molecules of the solid with which they are in contact, the

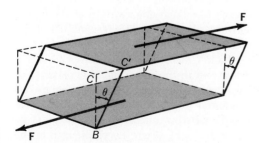

FIGURE 13.7

The shearing stress is the ratio of the force F to one of the shaded areas; the shearing strain is the angle $\theta = CC'/BC$.

liquid adheres to the solid and wets it. Here *adhesive forces are greater than cohesive.* When the cohesive forces are greater than the adhesive, the solid is not wet by the liquid. Such is the case when mercury is in contact with glass. If a drop of mercury and a drop of distilled water are placed on a clean glass surface, the water spreads over the glass in a thin layer, while the mercury forms a distorted ball.

The attractive forces between molecules are large only when the molecules are very close together. If molecules are much further apart than a few millionths of a centimeter, the attractive forces are not appreciably great. Intermolecular forces have short ranges. It takes a moderate force to break a piece of chalk, but after it is broken, the pieces do not adhere if they are pressed back together. Because of the irregular surfaces, not enough molecules are able to exert appreciable attractive forces.

Molecules of water adhere to glass, forming a thin layer over its surface. If we place a little water between two sheets of glass and are careful to see that there is no air trapped between the plates, it requires a significantly greater force to separate the glass plates than it would if they were dry. The water is acting as an adhesive. Glues and cements act as much superior adhesives. Once a glue has set, it may be stronger than the materials which it is binding together. If a thin layer of gold foil is placed over a layer of metal and carefully pressed into place, the molecular attraction between the gold and the base metal is strong enough to keep the gold foil in place without the use of a cement. If a gold foil is pounded into a cavity in a tooth, the cohesive forces between gold molecules and adhesive forces between gold molecules and tooth material are sufficiently great so that a strong permanent filling is created.

13.11 Surface Energy and Surface Tension

If a needle is greased and gently placed on the surface of water, it floats, although the density of the needle is greater than that of the water. Some insects can walk on the surface of a lake or stream, which behaves as though it were covered with a thin elastic film. It requires a force to break this film, the amount of force depending on the nature of the liquid. The apparent surface film is due to molecular attraction in the liquid.

A molecule inside a mass of liquid is attracted equally in all directions by neighboring molecules. But a molecule on the top surface of the liquid is not attracted by molecules on the side away from the liquid, although it is attracted downward. Because of this, a molecule at the surface is pulled toward the interior of the liquid.

Consider Figure 13.8, in which *CEHD* is a bent wire and *AB* is a straight wire which may be moved in the direction of the arrow. If we dip this system in a soap solution, we may have the area *AEHB* covered by a soap film. In order to prevent the soap film from contracting and pulling the side *AB* toward *EH*, a force *F* must be applied. This force is given by $F = 2Tl$, where l is the length of the

FIGURE 13.8

A force *2Tl* is required to hold the movable wire *AB* in equilibrium against surface tension.

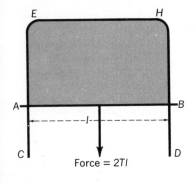

Force = 2Tl

TABLE 13.3   *Surface Tension*

Substance	Temperature, °C	Surface tension, newtons/m
Acetic acid	20	0.0234
Alcohol (ethyl)	20	0.0216
Ether (ethyl)	20	0.0169
Glycerin	18	0.0632
Mercury	18	0.545
Turpentine	20	0.0289
Petroleum	20	0.0259
Water	20	0.0728

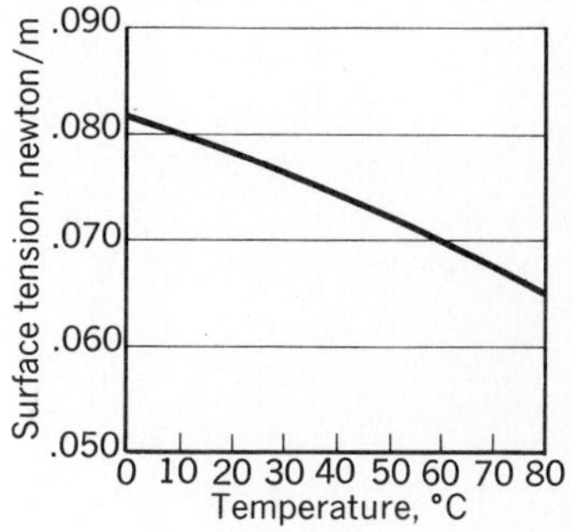

FIGURE 13.9
How the surface tension of water varies with temperature.

wire AB, and T is the force per unit length.   The factor 2 is introduced because the film has two sides.   *The force per unit length which must be applied to overcome molecular forces is the surface tension.*

If the wire AB is drawn down a distance s, the work done is

$$\mathcal{W} = Fs = T(2ls) = T\,\Delta A \qquad\qquad 13.8$$

where $\Delta A = 2ls$, the increase in area counting *both* sides of the film. Thus, T is the ratio of the work required to increase the area against the surface molecular forces to the change in area.

The surface tension of a liquid depends on the temperature, as Figure 13.9 shows for water.   The values of the surface tension for several liquids are listed in Table 13.3.

One of the standard ways of measuring surface tension is to measure the force required to pull a platinum ring through the surface of a liquid.   The total length of liquid surface which must be broken is twice the circumference of the ring.   Thus the force required to break the surface is $T \times 4\pi r$, where r is the radius of the ring.

The splashes formed (Fig. 13.10) when drops of milk fall on a surface of milk give an illustration of the effects produced by surface tension.

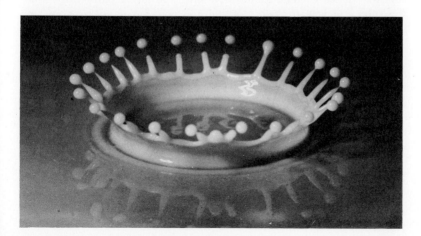

FIGURE 13.10
Surface tension creates splash patterns on the surface of milk.

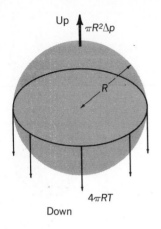

FIGURE 13.11

Excess pressure Δp inside a soap bubble produces a net upward force $\pi R^2 \, \Delta p$ on the top hemisphere of the bubble; this force is balanced by the downward force $2(2\pi R)T$ due to surface tension.

If a drop of oil is placed in a mixture of water and alcohol of the same density, the oil droplet does not rise or fall. Under the action of molecular forces it assumes a spherical form. Lead pellets for a shotgun can be produced by allowing liquid lead to fall from an opening of suitable size. Because of surface forces the freely falling lead drops assume a spherical shape in which they solidify before they strike anything.

Surface tension plays a vital role in the formation of bubbles. The pressure p inside a bubble in equilibrium is greater than the external pressure p_0 because of surface tension. The forces across the equatorial plane of a stable soap bubble (Fig. 13.11) are balanced; hence, $\pi R^2 (p - p_0) = 4\pi RT$. The excess pressure in the soap bubble is then

$$\Delta p = p - p_0 = \frac{4T}{R} \qquad \text{13.9}$$

The surface force is $4\pi RT$ for the soap bubble because there are two surfaces to the bubble. A bubble in a carbonated liquid or a bubble of steam in boiling water has only a single surface. In these cases the excess pressure is only half that given by Eq. (13.9), or $2T/R$.

13.12 Capillarity

If a piece of glass tubing of very small bore is thoroughly cleaned and then dipped into water (Fig. 13.12a), the water wets the inside of the tube and rises in it. If the liquid does not wet the tube (Fig. 13.12b) as in the case of mercury in a glass tube, the liquid is depressed. The smaller the bore of the tube, the greater the height to which the liquid rises, or the greater the amount which it is depressed. This rise or depression of liquids in tubes of small bore is known as *capillarity*. It is caused by the molecular forces that are responsible for surface energy. The molecules of the liquid have an attraction for each other and for the molecules on the surface of the wall of the tube. If the cohesive forces between molecules of the liquid are greater than the adhesive forces between liquid and wall, the liquid pulls away from the tube and is depressed. If the adhesive forces are greater, the liquid wets the capillary tube and rises.

When a glass tube is thrust into water, the molecules in the surface of the wall just above the water pull up on the molecules of water lying nearest to them and raise them above the level of the water in the vessel. This carries upward a column of water, which is supported by the surface forces. The net upward force available is the vertical component of the surface-tension forces if we are dealing with a vertical cylindrical tube. The angle of contact θ (Fig. 13.12) between the surface of the liquid and the tube depends on the liquid, the gas above, and the kind of tube involved. The upward force per unit length is $T \cos \theta$, and the total upward force is $T \cos \theta$ multiplied by the length of liquid in contact with the tube, which is the circumference. Thus, the net upward force is $2\pi r T \cos \theta$. The liquid rises until the

FIGURE 13.12

(a) Water wets glass, and the angle of contact θ approaches zero. (b) Mercury does not wet glass; the angle of contact θ is 140°.

(a)   (b)

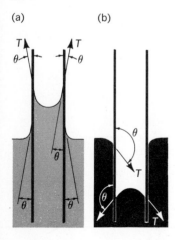

weight of liquid supported, $\pi r^2 hdg$, is equal to this force. Hence, for equilibrium

$$2\pi rT \cos \theta = \pi r^2 hdg \qquad\qquad 13.10$$

or

$$h = \frac{2T \cos \theta}{rdg}$$

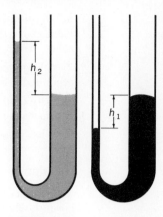

FIGURE 13.13
Unequal heights of water and mercury in connecting glass tubes of different radii.

For water in clean glass the angle θ is zero, and $\cos \theta$ becomes unity. Whenever a liquid wets a tube thoroughly, θ is zero. When cohesive forces exceed adhesive, θ is greater than $90°$, the liquid is depressed in the capillary, and h is negative. For water on paraffin θ is $107°$. Water does not wet paraffin. For mercury the angle of contact is approximately $140°$. Figure 13.13 shows how mercury and water behave when placed in glass containers with tubes of unequal radii.

Example The liquid in a capillary tube rises to the height of 7 cm. The radius of the tube is 0.1 mm, and the density of the liquid 800 kg/m³. If the angle between the liquid and the surface of the tube is zero, find the surface tension of the liquid.

$$2\pi rT \cos \theta = \pi r^2 hdg$$
$$2T \times 1 = 10^{-4} \text{ m} \times 0.07 \text{ m} \times 800 \text{ kg/m}^3 \times 9.8 \text{ newtons/kg}$$
$$T = 0.0274 \text{ newton/m}$$

< In recent years the chemical industry has developed a number of *waterproofing* agents which prevent water from wetting a fabric. For these compounds θ is greater than $90°$. Similarly, a number of *wetting agents,* or *detergents,* have been developed. These agents change θ to a smaller angle. The addition of a suitable detergent can make water wet paraffin.

There are many illustrations of capillary action in nature. The oil in a lamp rises in the wick by capillary action. Ink spreads in a blotter, and water in a lump of sugar, by this same action. If one end of a towel dips into a bucket of water and the other end hangs over the bucket, the towel soon becomes wet throughout.

Questions

1. If two springs of different stiffnesses but the same length are stretched by the same force, is more work done on the stiffer or the softer spring? Explain.

2. If a body such as a bow is distorted until Hooke's law is no longer applicable, does it necessarily follow that the elastic limit has been exceeded? Explain.

3. Should steel reinforcing rods in a concrete beam be embedded near the upper or near the lower side of the beam? Explain why.

4. Why does the flame polishing of a piece of glass by putting it in a bunsen flame round off sharp edges?

5. A razor blade can be made to float on water. What forces act on this blade? Is Archimedes' principle applicable?

6. Water rises to a height of 5 cm in a certain capillary tube. If the tube is broken off 2 cm above the level of the liquid in the main vessel, will water run out the top of the tube? Why not?

7. A large soap bubble is formed at one end of a capillary tube, and a small one at the other end. Which will grow at the expense of the other?

8. Why does the pressure inside a soap bubble decrease as it is blown up? How does a rubber balloon behave in this respect? Explain.

9. Why do carbonated beverages often foam when a bottle or can is opened?

Problems

1. A force of 50 newtons stretches a spring 75 cm. What is the force constant of the spring? How much force is required to stretch the spring an additional 15 cm? What is the potential energy of the spring when it is stretched 90 cm?

Ans. 66.7 newtons/m; 60 newtons; 27 joules

2. A mass of 0.5 kg suspended from a vertical spring produces an elongation of 2 cm. Find the force constant of the spring. What elongation would a force of 20 newtons produce? What is the potential energy of the spring when the elongation is 2 cm?

3. A spring balance reads forces in newtons. The scale is 20 cm long and reads from 0 to 200 newtons. Find the potential energy of the spring (*a*) when it reads 150 newtons, (*b*) when it is stretched 20 cm, and (*c*) when a mass of 10 kg is suspended from the spring. *Ans.* 11.25 joules; 20 joules; 4.8 joules

4. A brass wire with a cross section of 1.2 mm² is 1.8 m long when supporting a load of 2 kg. How much longer will it be when the load is increased to 5 kg?

5. A wire made of medium steel is 20 ft long and has an area of 0.01 in.². What is the maximum load which this wire can support? What is the greatest load which can be supported without exceeding the elastic limit? If the wire is fastened at its upper end, how far can it be stretched without exceeding the elastic limit?

Ans. 700 lb; 370 lb; 0.296 in.

6. An elevator weighing 12,000 lb is supported by two steel cables, each 1 in.² in cross section. Find the elongation produced in the cables if the elevator is 200 ft from the supporting cylinder.

7. A wire 3 m long, with a diameter of 0.8 mm, is elongated 0.6 mm when a 4-kg mass is hung on it. What is Young's modulus for the material? *Ans.* 3.9×10^{11} newtons/m²

8. A vertical steel column carries a load of 50 tons. The area of its cross section is 8 in.², and its length is 25 ft. Find the decrease in length produced by this load.

9. Find how many cables of 0.8 in.² cross section should be used to support an elevator which weighs 12,800 lb if the elevator will have a maximum acceleration of 10 ft/sec² and the stress is not to exceed one-fifth of the elastic limit of the cable steel, which is 40,000 lb/in.². *Ans.* 3

10. How much will a copper wire 3 m long stretch when a mass of 2 kg is suspended from one end, if the cross-sectional area is 0.03 cm²?

11. Find the depth in a lake at which the density of the water is 0.5 per cent greater than at the surface. Ignore temperature differences. *Ans.* 3,500 ft

12. The shearing stress on an aluminum rivet is not to exceed one-tenth of the elastic limit of 19,000 lb/in.^{2}. How many rivets, each 0.2 in.^{2} in cross-sectional area, are needed to hold two parts of an airplane wing together if each rivet carries the same fraction of the load and the total force on the rivets is 20,000 lb?

13. A hydraulic press contains 0.2 m^3 of oil of compressibility 2×10^{-5} per atmosphere. Calculate the decrease in volume of the oil if it is subjected to a pressure of 150 atm. Find the bulk modulus of the oil in newtons/m^2.

Ans. 6×10^{-4} m^3; 5.07×10^9 newtons/m^2

14. Find the increase in pressure required to increase the density of medium steel by 0.01 per cent.

15. A tire pressure gauge reads 10 lb/in.^{2} when a tube has been partially inflated. Weights are placed on the tube so that all the air occupies one-half its former volume. Neglecting any added forces caused by the tube, what does the gauge read?

Ans. 34.7 lb/in.^{2}

16. Compute the compressibilities of aluminum and medium steel in (atmospheres)$^{-1}$. How do they compare with that of water?

17. An air bubble released at the bottom of a pond expands to twice its original volume by the time it reaches the surface. How deep is the pond if atmospheric pressure is 10^5 newtons/m^2?

Ans. 10.2 m

18. If a bubble of air has a volume of 0.2 in.^{3} at 80 ft depth, find its volume at the surface if atmospheric pressure is 2,000 lb/ft^2.

19. A cylindrical diving bell, open at the bottom, has a volume of 250 ft^3 and a cross-sectional area of 20 ft^2. How high will the water rise in the bell when it is immersed to a depth of 40 ft if atmospheric pressure is 2,000 lb/ft^2 and no air leaves the bell?

Ans. 6.94 ft

20. A thin sheet of metal is bent in the form of a hollow square, and the open square end is dipped into a soap solution whose surface tension is 0.025 newton/m. The length of each side of the square is 4 cm. With what force does the surface tension pull the metal into the solution?

21. A capillary tube whose inside radius is 0.5 mm is dipped in water. What is the weight of the water raised by capillary action above the normal water level? To what height is the water raised?

Ans. 2.3×10^{-4} newton; 0.0298 m

22. A solid glass rod is immersed in water such that its axis is perpendicular to the surface of the water. The rod has a circular cross section and a diameter of 0.8 cm. Find the force exerted on the rod by surface tension.

23. A capillary tube whose inside diameter is 0.75 mm is dipped in glycerin. The glycerin rises 2.72 cm in the tube. If the density of glycerin is 1.26 g/cm^3, what is its surface tension? Assume the angle of contact is zero.

Ans. 0.063 newton/m

24. How much will the surface of mercury stand below the normal level when a glass tube that is 0.5 mm in diameter is put into a beaker filled with mercury? (The angle of contact is 140°.)

25. One limb of a U tube (Fig. 13.13) is 1 cm in diameter, and the other is 1 mm in diameter. What will be the difference in surface levels in the two tubes when mercury is poured into them? Take the angle of contact as 140° for mercury.

Ans. 11.3 mm

26. A tube is bent in the form of a U (Fig. 13.13). The diameter of the larger arm is 5 mm, and that of the smaller arm is 0.5 mm. Find the difference in levels when the U tube contains water.

27. Find the work that must be done to increase the total surface area of a soap film by 300 cm^2 if the surface tension of soap solution is 0.026 newton/m. *Ans.* 7.8×10^{-4} joule

28. Find the work which must be done to increase the outside surface area of a soap bubble by 300 cm^2 if the surface tension of soap film is 0.030 newton/m.

29. What is the excess pressure inside a soap bubble that is 5 cm in diameter, assuming 0.026 newton/m as the surface tension of the soap solution? *Ans.* 4.16 newtons/m^2

30. What is the diameter of a soap bubble when the excess pressure inside is 5 newtons/m^2 and the surface tension of the soap solution is 0.026 newton/m?

31. A spring of neutral length 0.4 m and force constant 100 newtons/m is suspended from a second spring of neutral length 0.3 m and spring constant 200 newtons/m, which hangs from a hook. If the bottom of the first spring is pulled down until the combined length of the two springs is 1.5 m, find the individual lengths of the two springs and the stretching force required. *Ans.* 0.933 m; 0.567 m; 53.3 newtons

CHAPTER 14 *When the applied forces distorting an elastic body are suddenly removed, internal forces accelerate the molecules toward their original equilibrium positions. In many cases the molecules have kinetic energy when they reach positions and overshoot, thereby introducing strains in the opposite direction. As a consequence the molecules may oscillate about their equilibrium positions. Such oscillatory motions are at the heart of the wave motions which we treat in Chap. 16 and which are of great importance in mechanics. In this chapter we focus our attention on the oscillatory motion of a single particle.*

Harmonic Motion

14.1 Vibrations

If a mass on the end of a spring is pulled down and then released, it moves back and forth with a *vibratory* or *harmonic* motion (Fig. 14.1). Such periodic motions are very common. They occur in all sorts of mechanical structures (such as automobiles, bridges, and buildings), in sound sources, in waves, and in electric oscillations. When the pendulum of a clock is displaced and then released, a vibratory motion is established. A further illustration of harmonic motion is afforded by clamping one end of a strip of steel (Fig. 14.2) in a vise and displacing the other end. When released, the strip vibrates back and forth a period which depends on the characteristics of the strip of steel. Other examples of harmonic motion are those of a piston in a steam engine or an automobile and the vibration of a tree limb in a breeze.

Elastic forces lead to these periodic motions. In the case of a mass on the end of a spring, the restoring force is upward when the mass is displaced downward. The mass is pulled toward its equilibrium position, but when it reaches this position, it has a velocity and continues upward by virtue of Newton's first law. Thus, it overshoots the equilibrium position until there is a displacement in the opposite direction. The mass on the end of the spring moves back and forth until its energy is gradually dissipated in friction of various kinds.

14.2 Simple Harmonic Motion

Of the many kinds of vibratory motion, we shall consider quantitatively only the simplest type, which is called *simple harmonic motion. Simple harmonic motion is motion in which the acceleration is propor-*

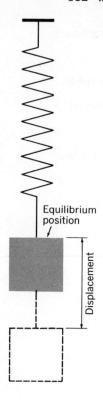

FIGURE 14.1
Oscillatory displacement of a mass suspended
from a stretched spring.

FIGURE 14.2
Harmonic vibrations of a strip of steel.

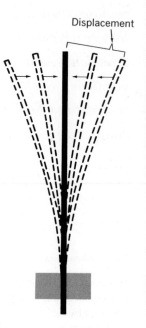

*tional to the displacement from the equilibrium position and in the
opposite direction.*

In discussing simple harmonic motion, there are several terms which
must be defined. They are as follows:

1. The *displacement* is the distance of a body from its equilibrium
position.

2. The *amplitude* is the maximum value of the displacement, or the
distance from the equilibrium position to the end of the vibrating
path.

3. The *period T* is the time necessary for one complete vibration.

4. The *frequency ν* is the number of complete vibrations made
in unit time. Clearly, the frequency is the reciprocal of the period;
$\nu = 1/T$.

To develop equations relating the displacement, the amplitude, the
frequency, and the acceleration in simple harmonic motion, we make
use of the fact that the shadow of a body which is performing uniform
circular motion describes simple harmonic motion. Consider an object
moving around a circle (Fig. 14.3) with uniform speed. Imagine the
shadow of this body being projected on the wall at the right by means
of a beam of light coming from the left. The shadow moves up
and down as the particle moves around the circle with constant speed.
Let R be the radius of the circle, which we call the *circle of reference,*
and θ the angle between the radius vector to the particle and the

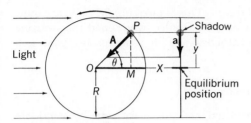

FIGURE 14.3
The shadow of a body moving with uniform circular motion oscillates with simple harmonic motion.

reference line OX. The displacement of the shadow from the "equilibrium position" is

$$y = R \sin \theta \tag{14.1}$$

Let A represent the acceleration of the particle P toward the center of the circle, and a the acceleration of the shadow on the wall. A is given by V^2/R, where V is the speed of the particle; a is the vertical component of A, which is $A \sin \theta$. Since a is directed downward when y is upward, and vice versa,

$$a = -A \frac{y}{R} = -\frac{V^2}{R^2} y$$

Since neither V nor R changes in magnitude during the motion, V^2/R^2 is a constant. We observe that the acceleration of the shadow is proportional to the displacement and in the opposite direction. This establishes the fact that the shadow describes simple harmonic motion.

14.3 The Period of a Simple Harmonic Motion

Of all the characteristics of a harmonic motion, the period is one of the easiest to measure; therefore, let us rewrite our expression for the acceleration in terms of this quantity. To do so, we make use of the fact that the period T is the time for the body to make one revolution on the circle of reference. Hence, $T = 2\pi R/V$, and $V^2/R^2 = 4\pi^2/T^2$. Therefore,

$$a = -\frac{4\pi^2}{T^2} y \tag{14.2}$$

If ν represents the frequency, we may rewrite Eq. (14.2) as

$$a = -4\pi^2\nu^2 y \tag{14.2a}$$

When Eq. (14.2) is solved for T, it yields

$$T = 2\pi \sqrt{\frac{-y}{a}} = 2\pi \sqrt{-\frac{\text{displacement}}{\text{acceleration}}} \tag{14.2b}$$

The quantity under the square-root sign is always positive since the displacement and acceleration are of opposite sign. *The period of a simple harmonic motion is independent of the amplitude.* If the amplitude is small, the body does not move far, but it moves slowly, so that the time required to execute one complete vibration is the same

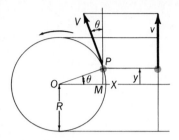

FIGURE 14.4

The speed v of the shadow is $V \cos \theta$ where V is the speed of the body on the circle of reference.

as when the amplitude is larger. This interesting fact about simple harmonic motion was discovered by Galileo, who timed the swinging of a great chandelier in the cathedral at Pisa, using his own pulse as a clock.

14.4 Velocity in Simple Harmonic Motion

The displacement, the acceleration, and the velocity of a body describing simple harmonic motion are all constantly changing. As we have seen, the shadow of uniform circular motion on a wall (or its projection on a diameter of the circle) describes simple harmonic motion. From Figure 14.4 we see that the velocity v of a body describing simple harmonic motion is given by

$$v = V \cos \theta = V \frac{\sqrt{R^2 - y^2}}{R}$$

or

$$v = \frac{2\pi}{T} \sqrt{R^2 - y^2} = 2\pi\nu \sqrt{R^2 - y^2} \qquad \textbf{14.3}$$

If we start a clock at the instant the body of Figures 14.3 and 14.4 passes the line OX on its upward path, the angle θ is given by $\theta = \omega t = 2\pi t/T = 2\pi\nu t$. Hence, by Eqs. (14.1), (14.3), and (14.2a),

$$y = R \sin 2\pi\nu t \qquad \textbf{14.4}$$
$$v = V \cos \theta = 2\pi\nu R \cos 2\pi\nu t = 2\pi\nu R \sin (2\pi\nu t + \pi/2) \qquad \textbf{14.5}$$
$$a = -4\pi^2\nu^2 R \sin 2\pi\nu t = 4\pi^2\nu^2 R \sin (2\pi\nu t + \pi) \qquad \textbf{14.6}$$

Thus we see (Fig. 14.5) that the velocity reaches its maximum 90° ($\pi/2$ radians) ahead of the displacement. Similarly, it passes through its zeros and reaches its minimum value one-fourth of a period ahead of the displacement. We say that the velocity *leads* the displacement by 90° or ¼ period. Similarly, the acceleration leads the velocity by 90° and the displacement by 180°. The displacement, velocity, and acceleration can all be represented by sine (or cosine) waves of the same frequency, but differing in *phase*. Two variables described by sine waves are said to be *in phase* if they reach their maxima, zeros, and minima at the same instant.

Example A body describes simple harmonic motion with an amplitude of 5 cm and a period of 0.25 sec. Find the acceleration and speed of the body when the displacement is 5 cm, 3 cm, and 0 cm.

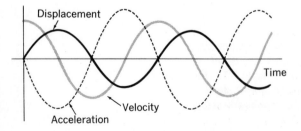

FIGURE 14.5

How displacement, velocity, and acceleration vary with time in simple harmonic motion.

By Eq. (14.2),

$$a = -\frac{4\pi^2}{T^2} y$$

and by Eq. (14.3)

$$v = \frac{2\pi}{T} \sqrt{R^2 - y^2}$$

The amplitude $R = 5$ cm. When $y = 5$ cm,

$$a = -\frac{4\pi^2 \times 0.05 \text{ m}}{(0.25 \text{ sec})^2} = -31.6 \text{ m/sec}^2$$

$$v = \frac{2\pi}{(0.25 \text{ sec})} \sqrt{(0.05 \text{ m})^2 - (0.05 \text{ m})^2} = 0$$

When $y = 3$ cm,

$$a = -\frac{4\pi^2 \times 0.03 \text{ m}}{(0.25 \text{ sec})^2} = -19 \text{ m/sec}^2$$

$$v = \frac{2\pi}{(0.25 \text{ sec})} \sqrt{(0.05 \text{ m})^2 - (0.03 \text{ m})^2} = \pm 1.0 \text{ m/sec}$$

When $y = 0$ cm,

$$a = 0$$

$$v = \frac{2\pi}{(0.25 \text{ sec})} (0.05 \text{ m}) = \pm 1.26 \text{ m/sec}$$

14.5 Force and Energy Relations

When a shadow describes simple harmonic motion, of course no force need act on the shadow. However, if a mass such as the bob of a pendulum describes simple harmonic motion, there must be an unbalanced force F_r to produce the acceleration. By Newton's second law,

$$F_r = ma = -4\pi^2 v^2 m y \qquad\qquad \textbf{14.7}$$

where y is the displacement.

For a mass on the end of a spring, a displacement y brings into play a restoring force $F_r = -ky$, precisely that required to produce simple harmonic motion when the mass is released. If we replace F_r with $-ky$ in Eq. (14.7) and solve for $1/v$, we obtain

$$\frac{1}{v} = T = 2\pi \sqrt{\frac{m}{k}} \qquad\qquad \textbf{14.8}$$

When the mass has a displacement y, its potential energy is $\frac{1}{2}ky^2$, the work (Eq. 13.2) required to produce this displacement from the equilibrium position. The kinetic energy of the mass is $\frac{1}{2}mv^2$, or $2\pi^2 v^2 (R^2 - y^2)m$ if we make use of the fact that $v = 2\pi v \sqrt{R^2 - y^2}$ (Eq. 14.3). The total energy, the sum of the kinetic and potential energies, remains constant in simple harmonic motion. At the ends of the motion the kinetic energy is zero and the total energy is $\frac{1}{2} kR^2$, while at the equilibrium position the potential energy is zero and the kinetic energy is $2\pi^2\nu^2R^2m$. Thus,

$$\text{Total energy} = \tfrac{1}{2}kR^2 = 2\pi^2\nu^2R^2m = \tfrac{1}{2}ky^2 + 2\pi^2\nu^2(R^2 - y^2)m \qquad \textbf{14.9}$$

The total energy of a body performing simple harmonic motion is proportional to the square of the frequency and to the square of the amplitude.

> **Example** A mass of 0.500 kg stretches a spring 20.0 cm. Find the force constant of the spring. If the mass is pulled down an additional 5.00 cm and then released, find the initial restoring force, the period, and the total energy of the resulting simple harmonic motion.
>
> In this case $F = mg = 0.500$ kg $\times$ 9.80 newtons/kg = 4.90 newtons, and $y = 0.200$ m. By Eq. (13.1),
>
> $$F = ky$$
> $$4.90 \text{ newtons} = k \times 0.200 \text{ m}$$
> $$k = 24.5 \text{ newtons/m}$$
>
> By Eq. (14.8),
>
> $$T = 2\pi \sqrt{\frac{m}{k}} = 2\pi \sqrt{\frac{0.500 \text{ kg}}{24.5 \text{ newtons/m}}} = 0.090 \text{ sec}$$
>
> The amplitude $R = 5.00$ cm or 0.0500 m, since that is the maximum displacement. By Eq. (14.9),
>
> $$\text{Total energy} = \tfrac{1}{2}kR^2$$
> $$= \tfrac{1}{2}(24.5 \text{ newtons/m})(0.0500 \text{ m})^2$$
> $$= 0.0306 \text{ joule}$$

FIGURE 14.6

A simple pendulum moves with approximately simple harmonic motion.

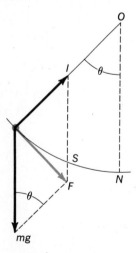

14.6 The Simple Pendulum

A simple pendulum affords an illustration of simple harmonic motion. When the pendulum is displaced from its position of equilibrium (Fig. 14.6), the restoring force is $F = mg \sin \theta$. Since $F = ma$, the acceleration which this force produces is $a = -g \sin \theta$. The displacement of the pendulum bob from its position of equilibrium N is $S = l\theta$. Hence,

$$\frac{\text{Displacement}}{\text{Acceleration}} = \frac{S}{a} = \frac{l\theta}{-g \sin \theta}$$

For small angles, $\sin \theta = \theta$ when the angle is measured in radians, and for small displacements of the pendulum,

$$\frac{\text{Displacement}}{\text{Acceleration}} = -\frac{l}{g} = \text{constant}$$

Consequently, the pendulum moves with nearly simple harmonic motion for small angles of swing; it deviates from simple harmonic motion for large angular amplitudes. Its period is, by Eq. (14.2b),

$$T = 2\pi \sqrt{\frac{l}{g}} \qquad \textbf{14.10}$$

The longer the pendulum, the greater is its period; the greater the acceleration of gravity, the shorter the period of the pendulum.

14.7 Angular Harmonic Motion

When a heavy disk is suspended by a wire (Fig. 14.7) and rotated through an angle θ from its equilibrium position, there is a restoring torque L_r which is proportional to the angular displacement:

$$L_r = -K\theta \qquad\qquad 14.11$$

where K is the *torsion constant* of the wire. By Eq. (10.10), $L = I\alpha$. Consequently, for this *torsion pendulum,*

$$I\alpha = -K\theta$$

the angular acceleration is proportional to the angular displacement, and angular simple harmonic motion is produced. Equations (14.2) through (14.6) and (14.9) are applicable to angular harmonic motion if angular displacement, angular amplitude, angular velocity, and angular acceleration are substituted for the corresponding linear quantities.

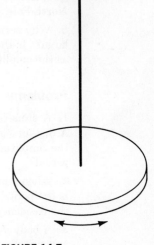

FIGURE 14.7
A torsion pendulum describes angular harmonic motion.

14.8 Damped Vibrations

If a particle is oscillating in a viscous medium, it does work on the medium, and the energy of vibration is correspondingly reduced. For this reason the amplitude diminishes with time (Fig. 14.8). Such vibrations are said to be *damped.*

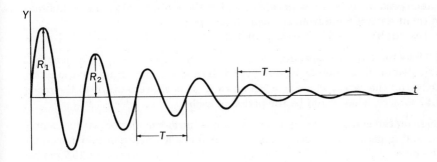

FIGURE 14.8
In a damped vibration, the amplitude decreases with time.

Questions

1. If a hole could be bored through the earth and a body dropped into the hole, it would describe simple harmonic motion with an amplitude equal to the earth's radius. At the center of the earth would the body have any (*a*) weight, (*b*) mass, (*c*) acceleration, or (*d*) momentum?

2. How does the period of a simple pendulum with a 200-g steel bob compare with that of a pendulum of the same length but with a 25-g wood bob?

3. Why are precisely simple harmonic motions rare while approximately simple harmonic motions are common?

4. Qualitatively, what is the effect on the period of a pendulum of taking it (*a*) to the North Pole, (*b*) to the equator, and (*c*) to the top of Mount Whitney?

5. Why is the motion of a simple pendulum *not* simple harmonic when the amplitude is large? Is the restoring force too big or too small? Does the period increase or decrease as the amplitude becomes larger?

Problems

1. A stone is swinging in a horizontal circle 30 in. in diameter, making 15 rev/min. A distant light causes a shadow of the stone to be formed on a nearby wall. What is the amplitude of the motion of the shadow? What is the frequency? What is the period?   *Ans.* 15 in.; 0.25 cycles/sec; 4 sec

2. When a mass of 200 g is suspended from a spring, the spring stretches 10.8 cm. What is the period of oscillation of the mass when it is given a small displacement? What is the frequency?

3. A body describing simple harmonic motion has a maximum acceleration of 8π m/sec^2 and a maximum speed of 2 m/sec. Find T and R.   *Ans.* 0.50 sec; 0.16 m

4. The mass on the end of a spring describes simple harmonic motion with a period of 1.5 sec. Find the acceleration when the displacement is 4 cm.

5. Find the length of a pendulum (in meters) which has a period of 2.5 sec.

Ans. 1.55 m

6. A pendulum has a length of 3 m and executes 20 complete vibrations in 70 sec. Find the acceleration of gravity at the location of the pendulum.

7. A ball moves in a circular path of 20 cm diameter with a constant angular speed of 5 rev/sec. Its shadow performs simple harmonic motion on the wall behind it. Find the acceleration and speed of the shadow (*a*) at the end of the motion, (*b*) at the equilibrium position, and (*c*) at a point 6 cm from the equilibrium position.
      Ans. (*a*) 98.7 m/sec^2, 0 m/sec; (*b*) 0, 3.14 m/sec; (*c*) 59.2 m/sec^2, 2.51 m/sec

8. Identical 0.8-kg masses are suspended from a spring and from a cord. The length of the cord is adjusted until the simple pendulum and the mass on the spring have identical periods of 0.5 sec on the earth, where $g = 9.8$ m/sec^2. If both were taken to the moon, where $g = 1.67$ m/sec^2, what would be the period of each?

9. A 100-g mass on the end of a spring describes simple harmonic motion with an amplitude of 5 cm and a period of 2 sec. Find the maximum acceleration and maximum velocity of the mass.   *Ans.* 49.4 cm/sec^2; 15.7 cm/sec

10. A simple harmonic motion has a period of 0.06 sec and an amplitude of 0.8 cm. What is the acceleration at maximum displacement? What is the acceleration 0.005 sec later?

11. A 200-g mass is suspended from a spring. If the mass is pulled downward 4 cm by an additional force of 0.2 newton and then released, find the period of the motion and the maximum speed.   *Ans.* 1.26 sec; 0.2 m/sec

12. A 0.5-kg mass on the end of a spring has a period of 3 sec and an amplitude of 0.1 m as it describes simple harmonic motion. Find the frequency of the motion, the acceleration of the mass at an end point of its motion, and the maximum velocity attained by the mass.

13. A 0.4-kg mass is suspended from a spring. If the spring is pulled downward with a force of 0.25 newton, it stretches an additional 10 cm. If the spring is released, the mass describes simple harmonic motion with an amplitude of 10 cm. Find the period of the motion and the velocity and acceleration of the mass when the displacement is 8 cm. Find the maximum values of the potential energy and kinetic energy of the vibrating mass, taking the equilibrium position for the zero of potential energy.
Ans. 2.52 sec; 0.15 m/sec; 0.5 m/sec²; 0.0125 joule

14. A 0.1-kg mass suspended from a spring performs simple harmonic motion with a frequency of 2 vib/sec and an amplitude of 0.05 m. Find the maximum acceleration of the mass, the maximum velocity, the acceleration at the instant the displacement is 0.03 m, and the force needed to stretch the spring 0.05 m.

15. A 5-kg mass hangs in equilibrium from a spring of spring constant 80 newtons/m. How far must the spring be stretched to give the mass an acceleration of 4 m/sec² upward when released? What is the period of the motion? Find the speed of the mass 0.1 sec after it passes the equilibrium position.   *Ans.* 0.25 m; 1.57 sec; 0.92 m/sec

16. In a gasoline engine the motion of a piston is approximately simple harmonic. A piston has a mass of 2 kg and a stroke (twice the amplitude) of 10 cm. Find the maximum acceleration and the maximum unbalanced force on the piston if it is making 50 complete vibrations each minute.

17. A particle moves with simple harmonic motion along a line between two points that are 16 cm apart. If the frequency is 2 vib/sec, what is the acceleration of the particle at maximum displacement? What is the speed of the particle as it passes the mid-point? If the displacement is maximum when $t = 0$, write the equations for the displacement and velocity as functions of time.
Ans. 12.6 m/sec²; 1.01 m/sec; $y = 0.08 \cos 4\pi t$ m; $v = -0.32\pi \sin 4\pi t$ m/sec

18. A mass of 40 g is moving with simple harmonic motion with 6 cm amplitude and a period of 2 sec. What is the acceleration of the mass one-sixth of a period after it has passed the mid-point? What is the force acting on the mass? What is the speed?

19. A particle describing simple harmonic motion has a period of 3 sec. If the speed of the particle is 0.6 m/sec when it has a displacement equal to half the amplitude, how long will it take the particle to reach the equilibrium position if it is moving (a) toward the equilibrium position and (b) away from the equilibrium position? What is the maximum speed of the particle?   *Ans.* (a) 0.25 sec; (b) 1.25 sec; 0.69 m/sec

20. To be acceptable, a 16-lb airplane radio receiver must pass a shake test in which it is forced to describe simple harmonic oscillations at 100 vib/sec with a maximum acceleration of 10 g's ($g = 32$ ft/sec²). Find the maximum displacement, unbalanced force, and velocity.

21. A spring of constant k_1 is suspended from a hook. A second spring of constant k_2 hangs from the bottom of the first spring and supports a mass m from its lower extremity. Show that when m is displaced from its equilibrium position it describes simple harmonic motion with a frequency given by

$$\nu = \frac{1}{2\pi} \sqrt{\frac{k_1 k_2}{(k_1 + k_2)m}}$$

22. Prove that if a particle is simultaneously subjected to simple harmonic motions in both the x and y directions, the resultant motion of the particle is a circle, provided the amplitudes and frequencies of the two harmonic motions are the same and they are 90° out of phase (i.e., the displacement in one direction is maximum when the other displacement passes through zero).

23. Show that l meters of liquid in a uniform U tube will, if disturbed, perform simple harmonic motion with a period $T = \pi\sqrt{2l/g}$, provided friction is negligible.

PART II WAVE MOTION AND SOUND

CHAPTER 15   *We have studied several types of motion, starting with that of a particle moving with constant velocity, then extending our knowledge to include motion with constant acceleration and uniform circular motion, and in Chap. 14 taking up the simple harmonic motion of an individual particle.   We now turn to wave motion, in which we have a large number of particles describing simple harmonic motion about their equilibrium positions, with phases varying along the wave.   Wave motion is a highly organized, cooperative synthesis of the simple harmonic motions of innumerable particles through which energy is transmitted from one place to another although the participating particles only vibrate about their equilibrium positions.*

Wave Motion

15.1 Waves

One of the most important phenomena in nature is the transmission of energy from one point to another by wave motion.   Our sense of hearing responds to sound waves, our vision to the electromagnetic waves we know as light.   Other electromagnetic waves transmit our radio and television programs.   All these waves have common characteristics, some of which we consider in this chapter.

There are many kinds of wave motions, one of which is the familiar water wave.   When a stone is dropped into a pool of still water, the surface is covered with circular wavelets which widen out from the point at which the stone entered the water.   The water does not itself move outward from this central point; rather it rises and falls.   That such is the case may be seen by observing a floating cork.   It moves up and down and back and forth in a roughly elliptical path.   The water on which the cork rests goes through this same kind of motion.

In wave motion a disturbance of some kind propagates through a medium.   An individual particle of the medium oscillates up and down or back and forth, but it does not progress with the wave.   Energy is transferred through the medium, although the particles themselves are not transmitted.   In a typical wave motion a vibrating center produces motion in particles of the medium immediately in contact with it; these particles in turn impart their motion to their neighbors.

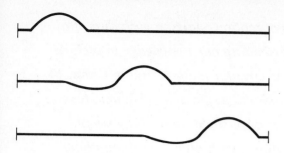

FIGURE 15.1
Wave pulse moving along a stretched string.

15.2 Transverse and Longitudinal Waves

It is convenient to classify waves in terms of the way in which the motion of the individual particles of the medium is related to the movement of the wave itself. In waves produced in a stretched rope (Fig. 15.1) the individual particles move up and down at right angles to the direction in which the wave itself propagates. A wave of this kind is known as a *transverse wave*, because the particles in the medium move perpendicular (*trans* means "across") to the direction of the wave motion. In the simplest form of transverse wave each particle vibrates in simple harmonic motion with its displacement at right angles to the propagation direction. Light and other forms of electromagnetic radiation, as well as waves in stretched strings, are illustrations of transverse waves. *A transverse wave is one in which the vibrations take place at right angles to the direction in which the wave travels.*

If a series of equal masses are joined together by springs (Fig. 15.2) and particle A is moved toward particle B, a wave is propagated down the system. The motion of A toward B compresses the spring between them. B is accelerated toward C, which in turn moves toward D. A compressional wave is produced. Similarly, when mass A is pulled away from B, the spring between them is stretched, and B is accelerated toward A. If A is moved back and forth with simple harmonic motion, a wave motion is propagated along the system with each particle describing simple harmonic motion along the axis of the system. The various masses do not all vibrate in phase. *A wave motion in which the individual particles vibrate back and forth along the direction in which the wave travels is called a compressional or a longitudinal wave.* Sound waves are an important example.

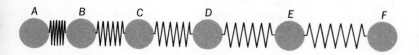

FIGURE 15.2
A series of masses joined by springs can transmit a longitudinal wave if the particles move along the line connecting the masses.

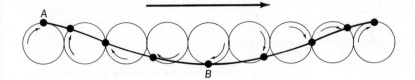

FIGURE 15.3
The particles in a water wave describe circles or ellipses.

15.3 Other Kinds of Waves

In many kinds of wave motion individual particles do not move back and forth along a single line. For example, in water waves, water molecules move forward and back as well as up and down. When a particle is on a crest A (Fig. 15.3), it moves in the direction in which the wave is moving. In a trough B a particle is moving in the opposite direction. The paths are ellipses or circles. We have in this case a mixed wave, neither longitudinal nor transverse. We can, of course, resolve the motion of the particle into components perpendicular to and parallel to the propagation direction and treat the mixed wave as a combination of a longitudinal and a transverse wave.

There are many other kinds of waves besides those in material mediums in which the disturbances arise out of the displacement of particles. If the temperature of one end of a metal rod is first raised gradually, then lowered, raised again, etc., there is set up a succession of changes in the temperature of the rod. These changes travel forward in the rod as a wave of temperature. The daily heating and cooling of the surface of the earth, as it is turned toward and away from the sun, produce waves of temperature that go down into the earth a short distance.

If one end of an ocean cable or telephone wire is suddenly joined to a battery, the change in potential thus produced in the wire is gradually felt along the conductor. If the potential is varied systematically, an electric wave is transmitted along the conductor.

FIGURE 15.4
Wave fronts from a point source S generated at intervals of 1 sec.

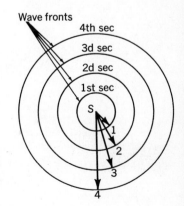

15.4 Wavelength, Frequency, and Velocity

When waves spread out from the center of a disturbance, a surface marking the points which the disturbance has reached is called a *wave front* (Fig. 15.4). When a drop of water falls on the surface of a pond, the wave front is a circle that expands continuously. When a small balloon bursts in the air, the wave front of the sound produced is a sphere with the balloon as the center. The waves of light from a distant star have spherical wave fronts of such large radius that small portions of them may be considered plane.

In waves passing across the surface of water, the distance from crest to crest (or trough to trough) is called the *wavelength* (Fig. 15.5a). In general, *the wavelength is the distance in the propagation direction between two successive points which are in the same phase of vibration.*

(a)

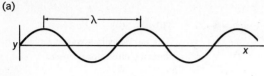

(b)

FIGURE 15.5

Displacement of particles at a particular instant as a function of the distance from the source for (*a*) a plane wave for which the amplitude is constant, and (*b*) a spherical wave in which amplitude decreases with distance.

Let ν be the frequency of the wave, or the number of complete vibrations made by each particle in 1 sec. If each wave is of length λ, the total distance traversed by the disturbance in 1 sec is just the number of vibrations per second multiplied by the wavelength, or

$$V = \nu\lambda \qquad\qquad 15.1$$

where V is the velocity of the wave motion. This relation is applicable to all types of wave motion and is one of the most widely used relationships in physics.

Example If the velocity of a disturbance in a steel rod is 5,000 m/sec and the frequency of the vibrations is 2,500/sec, find the wavelength.

$$\lambda = \frac{V}{\nu} = \frac{5{,}000 \text{ m/sec}}{2{,}500 \text{ vib/sec}} = 2.000 \text{ m}$$

15.5 Representation of Waves

If each particle of a medium through which a wave is traveling describes simple harmonic motion, a simple way of representing the wave graphically is to choose two axes (Fig. 15.5) and to plot on the vertical axis the displacement of a particle at a given instant and on the horizontal axis the distance of that particle from the source of the disturbance. Such a curve gives the displacement at any instant for all the particles in the medium along the direction in which the wave is traveling. In Figure 15.5*a*, the wave is constant in intensity as we go away from the source, since the amplitude of vibration remains constant. In Figure 15.5*b* the amplitude is decreasing as we go away from the source.

If the wave motion is complex, and if a number of frequencies are involved, it is always possible to consider the complex motion of any particle to be composed of a number of simple harmonic ones. Thus, a very complex motion may be treated as the sum of a number of simple ones. Although many waves have a far more complicated picture than that of Figure 15.5*b*, Fourier has shown that all waves can be represented in terms of sine waves similar to that of Figure 15.5*a*. A Fourier analysis of a complex wave into simple harmonic (or sine) waves is beyond the scope of this book, but the fact that this can be done means that the arguments and developments which we base on simple sinusoidal curves can be extended to complex wave forms.

When a wave passes through a medium, the individual particles describe simple harmonic motion. The displacement of a particle moving with this type of motion can be represented by

$$y = R \sin 2\pi\nu t \qquad\qquad 14.4$$

where y is the displacement, R the amplitude, ν the frequency, and t the time. The displacement of any particle in the medium through which a simple wave is passing depends on both the time and the distance of the particle from the origin. Each successive particle is a little later in phase than the adjacent particle nearer the source. The wave reaches point b, one-fourth wavelength from the origin (Fig. 15.6), one-fourth of a period later than it arrives at a. It reaches point c one-half period later. The wave reaches point d, which is a distance x from point a, a time x/V sec later than it passes a. Let the displacement of a be given by Eq. (15.2). To obtain the displacement at d, we must deduct from t the time x/V. The displacement at a point which is any distance x from point a is given by

$$y = R \sin 2\pi\nu \left(t - \frac{x}{V} \right) \qquad\qquad 15.2$$

Although in our plot of displacement as a function of position we obtain a sine curve which suggests a transverse wave motion, this same curve represents equally well a longitudinal wave motion, since the displacement y obeys exactly the same equations. The only difference is that the displacement for longitudinal wave motion is in the direction of propagation, while for a transverse wave motion it is perpendicular to the propagation direction.

15.6 The Flow of Energy in a Medium

When a wave passes, energy is propagated through the medium, although the individual particles describe simple harmonic motion and have no net displacement. The energy transmitted in unit time through a unit area perpendicular to the direction of propagation is called the *intensity* of the wave motion. *The intensity is proportional*

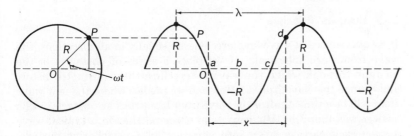

Direction of wave motion ⟶

FIGURE 15.6

Instantaneous displacement depends on both time and distance from the origin.

to the square of the frequency and to the square of the amplitude of the vibrations of the oscillating particles, as is shown below.

For a particle describing simple harmonic motion, the energy is transformed from kinetic energy to potential and back to kinetic energy. The energy of the particle is $\frac{1}{2}mv_{max}^2 = 2\pi^2\nu^2R^2m$ by Eq. (14.9). If we consider a wave propagated in the x direction (Fig. 15.7), the wave front sets in motion every particle which it passes. The intensity of the wave is then given by the total energy supplied to all the particles included in a cylinder having a base of unit area and a length equal to the distance traversed by the wave in unit time. The number of particles included in this tube is equal to nV, where n is the number of particles per unit volume, and V is the velocity of the wave. Each particle receives energy $2\pi^2\nu^2R^2m$, and the total power transmitted per unit area is the intensity, given by

$$I = 2\pi^2\nu^2R^2mnV \qquad \text{15.3}$$

If a disturbance produces waves which are sent out equally in all directions, the wave fronts are spheres with the source as center (Fig. 15.4). If we assume that there is no transformation of the wave energy, the total energy per unit time which passes through any one sphere surrounding the source is exactly equal to the energy per unit time which passes through any other sphere. The energy per unit time passing through a sphere is just the product of the area of the sphere and the intensity I. Therefore, $4\pi R_1^2 \times I_1 = 4\pi R_2^2 \times I_2$, where I_1 and I_2 are the intensities at the spheres of radii R_1 and R_2, respectively, and

$$R_1^2 I_1 = R_2^2 I_2 \qquad \text{15.4}$$

For a spherical wave the intensity varies inversely as the square of the distance from the source.

When the energy cannot spread out freely in all directions, the intensity does not vary inversely as the square of the distance. A cheerleader's megaphone is designed to reflect sound waves toward his cheering section. In this case the intensities at equal distances from the source depend strongly on direction. If there is absorption between the source and a receiver, the intensity falls off more rapidly with distance than the inverse-square law suggests, even though the energy may be radiated equally in all directions.

15.7 Huygens' Principle

If a point source of waves radiates energy equally in all directions, the wave fronts are spherical. If we place a series of obstacles in the medium through which the wave is traveling, these obstacles distort and change the wave fronts. How can we predict where the new wave front will be a time Δt after the wave front has struck an obstacle? The answer was found by Huygens, who observed that in a typical wave motion each particle is set into vibration by a neighboring particle. This led him to postulate that *every point on a wave front acts as a new source sending out secondary wavelets.*

FIGURE 15.7

The energy transmitted in 1 sec across the plane zOy, of unit area, occupies a volume of unit cross-sectional area and of length numerically equal to the speed of the wave motion.

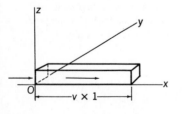

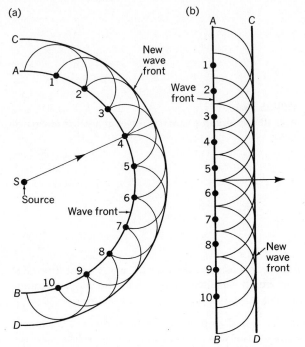

(a)

(b)

FIGURE 15.8

Huygens' principle applied to (*a*) a spherical wave front, and (*b*) a plane wave front.

Consider a spherical wave front (Fig. 15.8*a*). Let us, following Huygens, assume that each point on this wave front is a source of secondary spherical wavelets and ask where the wave front corresponding to *AB* will be a time Δt later. About each point 1, 2, 3, 4, ... on the initial wave front we draw little spheres of radius $V \Delta t$, where V is the velocity of the waves. To find the position of the new wave front, we find the surface which is tangent to all the secondary wavelets. This is the surface *CD* in Fig. 15.8*a*. If we have a plane wave passing through a medium, we may find the new wave front by applying Huygens' method. The new wave front is again plane, as shown by Fig. 15.8*b*.

Huygens' principle may be summarized as follows: *Every point on the wave front by any wave motion may be regarded as a secondary source of "Huygens" wavelets which spread out with the velocity of the primary wave. To find the wave front at any time Δt later, we find the forward surface which is tangent to all these secondary wave fronts. This surface gives the new position of the primary wave front.*

At a considerable distance from a point source the waves are almost plane. If these waves fall on a small aperture (Fig. 15.9) in a partition, the aperture acts as a source which sends out almost circular waves in accordance with Huygens' principle. Clearly the waves spread out once more after they leave the aperture, thus bending into the region shadowed by the partition. The bending of waves into the shadow region of obstacles is called *diffraction*. The Huygens wavelets traveling to each side from a point source are canceled by those from neigh-

FIGURE 15.9
A small aperture in a partition serves as a source of circular waves.

boring sources, moving oppositely, unless the point is at the edge of the wave front, in which case it contributes to the wave spreading into the shadow region.

< The question may be raised as to why there is not also a backward wave if every particle on the wave front sends out wavelets with the same amplitude in all directions. The absence of this backward wave is explained by the fact that the amplitude of the Huygens wavelets varies according to the *obliquity factor* $(1 + \cos \theta)/2$, being greatest in the forward ($\theta = 0$) direction and diminishing to zero in the backward ($\theta = \pi$) direction.

15.8 The Reflection of Waves

One of the important applications of Huygens' principle is to the reflection of waves by an obstacle. Figure 15.10 shows the reflection of a spherical sound wave by a plane surface. When the spherical wave strikes the surface, it is reflected, and the curvature of the wave is reversed. That a spherical wave should be reflected in this way can be shown by application of Huygens' principle.

Consider a plane wave (Fig. 15.11) falling upon a plane reflecting surface. Let A_1B_1, A_2B_2, and A_3B_3 be consecutive positions of the plane wave front. Let us apply Huygens' construction to the wave front A_3B_3 to find the position of the new wave front. We choose the instant at which the end B_3 of the wave front reaches the plane surface as the time at which we wish to locate the new wave front. Let Δt be the interval required for the wave to move from B_3 to the surface. We observe from the figure that the new wave front is given by RS. Since $V\Delta t$ is perpendicular to the wave front, and since the distance A_3S is the same for the triangles A_3SR and A_3B_3S, the two triangles are similar and equal. Therefore, the angle of reflection r is equal to the angle of incidence i.

FIGURE 15.10
Reflection and diffraction of sound waves can be studied by photographing the wave fronts created by an electric spark. In this case the spark wave originated from a point on the stage (below) of Royce Hall at the University of California at Los Angeles.

In dealing with the reflection of waves, it is often more convenient to follow the path of a ray which moves in the direction of propagation of the wave than to observe the wave front. For isotropic mediums the ray is perpendicular to the wave front. If N represents a normal to the surface (Fig. 15.11), the angle of incidence is the angle between the incident ray and N, while the angle of reflection is the angle between the reflected ray and N. Also, the incident ray, the reflected ray, and the normal all lie in the same plane. This leads us to the two laws of reflection:

1. *The angle of incidence is equal to the angle of reflection.*
2. *The incident ray, the normal, and the reflected ray lie in the same plane.*

15.9 Refraction of Waves

When waves pass from one medium in which they have a speed V_1 to a second in which their speed is V_2, the directions of the wavefronts and rays change at the boundary between the two media. This phenomenon is known as *refraction*. Figure 15.12 shows the refraction of waves as they pass from one region to another in which their speed is decreased.

Refraction at the interface between two media is readily explained by use of Huygens' principle. In Figure 15.12 a plane wave front ABC is just reaching the interface between two media. Let V_1 be the speed of the waves in the medium in which the waves are incident, and V_2 their speed in the second medium. While the wave front goes from BC to EF in the first medium, the wavelets from A travel only as far as D in medium 2. When the wavelets from F reach J, the wave front is entirely in the second medium, as is represented by GHJ. If Δt is

FIGURE 15.11
Huygens' construction for a plane wave reflected from a plane surface.

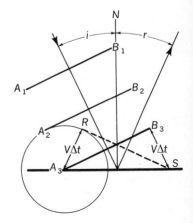

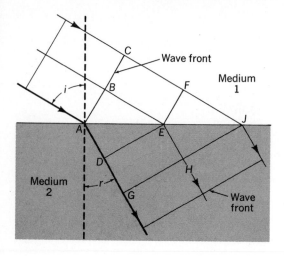

FIGURE 15.12
Refraction at a plane surface.

the time required for the wave front to travel from A to G in medium 2, we have $AG = V_2 \, \Delta t$ and $CJ = V_1 \, \Delta t$. Now $\sin i = CJ/AJ$, and $\sin r = AG/AJ$, where i is the angle of incidence, and r the angle of refraction. Therefore $\sin i/\sin r = V_1 \, \Delta t/V_2 \, \Delta t = V_1/V_2$. The ratio $\sin i/\sin r$ is called the *index of refraction of medium 2 relative to medium 1*; we represent it by n. Thus

$$n = \frac{\sin i}{\sin r} = \frac{V_1}{V_2} \qquad\qquad \textbf{15.5}$$

For refraction:

1. *The ratio of the sine of the angle of incidence to the sine of the angle of refraction is a constant n, known as the index of refraction.*

2. *The incident ray, the normal, and the refracted ray lie in the same plane.*

Water waves become slower as the water becomes shallower. In this case there is no sharp bending, but rather the wave fronts bend continuously as the speed changes. On a sloping beach the waves bend so that the wave fronts are almost parallel to the shore regardless of the direction from which they came. In general, a ray bends toward the normal to an interface as a wave goes from a region of higher speed to one of lower speed.

15.10 Superposition and Interference

It is common to have sound waves from different sources moving through a room at the same time. *If two or more wave motions pass a given point at the same instant, the displacement is the resultant of the displacements which would be produced by each of the waves if it acted separately.* This is a statement of a very important law of nature, sometimes called the *principle of superposition.* It is valid not only for sound, but for all other kinds of waves, provided the amplitudes are not too great.

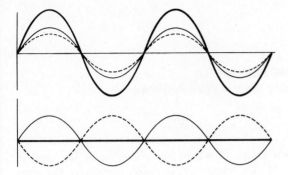

FIGURE 15.13
Constructive and destructive interference.

We shall at the moment apply the principle of superposition to the particular case in which two waves are traveling in the same direction at the same time with the same amplitude and the same frequency. If the waves arrive in such a way that crests meet crests and troughs meet troughs (Fig. 15.13), the displacements due to the two waves add, and the resultant is a wave of double the original amplitude. These two waves show *constructive interference*. On the other hand, if the two waves arrive at the same point in such a way that crest meets trough and trough meets crest, they cancel one another, and we have *destructive interference*.

If the two waves do not have equal amplitudes, they may still interfere; the resulting amplitude is the resultant of the individual amplitudes. Interference is a fundamental property of wave motions. Indeed, if there is a question as to whether some phenomenon has wave properties, the test which resolves the question in favor of the wave position is one which produces interference between two "rays."

15.11 Standing Waves

A particular type of interference which is of great importance in connection with musical instruments is interference between two waves which are traveling in opposite directions. Consider a long elastic cord which is fixed at one end (Fig. 15.14) while the other end is held in the hand. If the cord is stretched tight and the free end is moved up and down with simple harmonic motion, waves are set up in the cord which travel to the fixed end, where they suffer reflection and travel back to the hand. A crest is reflected as a trough and a trough as a crest at a fixed end.

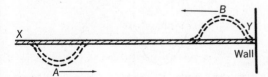

FIGURE 15.14
When a wave in a stretched string is reflected at a wall, a trough is reflected as a crest, and a crest is reflected as a trough.

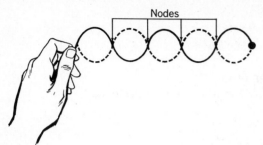

FIGURE 15.15
Standing waves in a stretched string.

At any instant two trains of waves are traveling in the cord in opposite directions. If the frequency is chosen properly, the cord ceases to have the appearance of being traversed by trains of waves, but instead vibrates transversely in one or more segments (Fig. 15.15). The behavior of the cord can be explained by consideration of Figures 15.16 and 15.17. The dotted line represents a wave traveling from right to left, while the broken line represents a similar wave of the same frequency and amplitude traveling from left to right. The resultant disturbance, which arises from the combination of these two trains of waves, is represented by the continuous lines. The resultant at any instant has the form of a wave, but the wave pattern does not move.

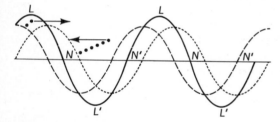

FIGURE 15.16
Standing waves result when two wave trains of identical amplitude and frequency travel in opposite directions, interfering constructively at some points and destructively at others.

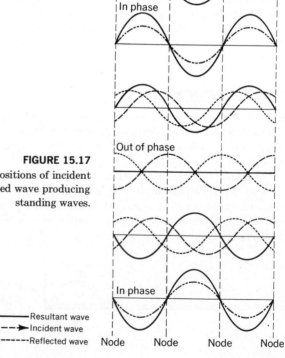

FIGURE 15.17
Successive positions of incident and reflected wave producing standing waves.

In phase

Out of phase

In phase

———— Resultant wave
–––––▸ Incident wave
◂–––––– Reflected wave

Node   Node   Node   Node

Each particle vibrates, but the amplitude of vibration varies along the cord. When the frequency is high, all the eye sees is a characteristic blur that appears to remain motionless. This appearance has given rise to the name *standing waves*. At L (Fig. 15.16), the crests of two component waves are approaching each other. When the two crests coincide, the resulting displacement is maximum. One-quarter of a period later the two components neutralize each other. The crest of one wave meets the trough of the other. At this instant the cord is straight. As the waves travel farther in opposite directions, the portion of the string $N'LN$ is depressed below the horizontal, and after another quarter of a period it has its maximum displacement in the negative direction. At the points N and N' there is never any displacement. At these points, called *nodes,* the two waves traveling in opposite directions always interfere destructively. All the particles of the cord between two adjacent nodes are moving in the same direction at any given instant, but two adjacent segments of the cord are always displaced in opposite directions. The length of the segment between two consecutive nodes is one-half wavelength. The point midway between the nodes at which maximum displacement occurs is called an *antinode* (or *loop*).

Standing waves may result from any kind of wave motion. It is only essential for their production that two waves of the same frequency and amplitude travel in opposite directions in the medium. Figure 15.18 represents standing waves in a column of air. The short vertical lines represent layers of air displaced as shown. At each place marked N there is a node in the displacement; here the air is alternately compressed and rarefied.

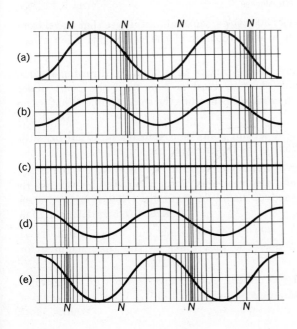

FIGURE 15.18
Different stages of standing sound waves.

Questions

1. As water waves spread out over the surface of a lake, how does the amplitude vary with distance from the source if essentially no energy is dissipated? How does the intensity vary?

2. What happens to a wave when it comes to an interface between two media?

3. What general properties must a body have to be able to transmit longitudinal waves? Transverse waves? Explain why liquids and gases do not transmit transverse vibrations.

4. What points remain stationary in a standing wave? Why don't they move?

5. What conditions must be satisfied to establish a standing-wave pattern?

6. Two sources produce waves of identical frequency, but one produces waves of three times the amplitude of the other. What is the ratio of the two intensities? If the frequency of a wave motion is doubled while the amplitude is kept constant, how does the intensity of the new wave compare with that of the old?

Problems

Unless otherwise stated, take the speed of sound in air to be 1,100 ft/sec or 340 m/sec.

1. A violin string emits a sound with a frequency of 850 vib/sec. What is the wavelength of the disturbance that passes through the air? What is the period of the vibration?   *Ans.* 40 cm; 0.00118 sec

2. Waves travel with a speed of 800 ft/sec through a medium. If 50 waves pass a given point each second, find the wavelength and the period.

3. It is 16 m from crest to crest in a system of waves. If 20 waves pass a given point each minute, find the speed of the waves.   *Ans.* 5.3 m/sec

4. A sounding source with a frequency of 300 cycles/sec sends out waves that travel from air into water. Find the wavelength in each medium if the velocity is 1,450 m/sec in water.

5. A set of circular ripples is produced on the surface of a pond by throwing a stone into the water. At a certain instant, the first crest is 4 m from the point where the stone hit the water, and the fourth crest is 70 cm from the same point. What is the wavelength of the disturbance?   *Ans.* 1.1 m

6. Water waves are observed passing a certain point at a velocity of 15 mi/hr, with a distance of 33 ft between crests. What is the frequency of the waves?

7. When a sound wave is transferred from one medium to another, its frequency does not change. If the wavelength of a disturbance is 17 cm in air, find its wavelength in water, steel, and brass if the speed of sound in water is 1,450 m/sec, in steel 5,000 m/sec, and in brass 3,500 m/sec.   *Ans.* 0.725 m; 2.5 m; 1.75 m

8. A tuning fork with a frequency of 900 cycles/sec sends out waves which travel 1,080 ft/sec. How many vibrations does the fork make in the time required for the sound to travel 600 ft?

9. The speed of sound in water is 1,500 m/sec. A sound wave from an underwater explosion approaches the surface at an angle of incidence of 60°. What is the angle of refraction in air?   *Ans.* 11.3°

10. Compressional waves with a frequency of 1,200 vib/sec are propagated through the air in a tube, the far end of which is closed by a piston. Standing waves are produced. The reflected wave reinforces the source at two successive positions of the piston differing by 6.6 in. What is the velocity of the waves in the tube?

11. Standing waves are produced in a stretched rope. If the distance between successive nodes is 0.4 m, what is the wavelength? If the waves travel with a speed of 84 m/sec, what is the frequency? *Ans.* 0.8 m; 105 per second

12. If a certain particle has a displacement given by $2 \sin 2\pi\nu t$, where $\nu = \frac{1}{12}$ per sec, find the displacement at times $1, 2, 3, \ldots, 9, 10$ sec. Plot the displacement as a function of time.

13. The displacement of a particle in centimeters is given by $y = 8 \sin 2\pi\nu t$. If $\nu = 20$ per second, find the displacement and velocity of the particle at times t of 0.01 sec and 0.07 sec. *Ans.* 7.61 cm, 3.11 m/sec; 4.70 cm, -8.13 m/sec

14. If the displacement along a wave is given by the relation $y = 5 \sin 3(t - 6x)$, where x and y are in centimeters and t in seconds, what are the amplitude, frequency, wavelength, and speed of the wave motion?

15. If the displacement along a wave is given by $y = 0.05 \sin (20\pi t - 0.1\pi x)$, where distances are in meters and times in seconds, what are the amplitude, frequency, wavelength, and speed of the wave motion? *Ans.* 0.05 m; 10 sec^{-1}; 20 m; 200 m/sec

16. A transverse wave in a stretched wire is described by the equation

$$y = 0.03 \sin (50\pi t - 0.2\pi x)$$

where x and y are in meters, and t is in seconds. What are the frequency, amplitude, period, wavelength, and velocity of the wave? Is the wave standing or traveling?

CHAPTER 16 *In the preceding chapter we discussed many of the general characteristics of wave motions and introduced the vocabulary of waves with words such as wavelength, frequency, amplitude, refraction, reflection, and interference. In the two chapters which follow we treat sound waves and their properties. In this chapter we are concerned with the speed of acoustic waves, the relationships between the physical and the psychophysical properties of the waves, the mechanical aspects of hearing, and the acoustic properties of rooms.*

Sound Waves

16.1 The Nature of Sound

Sound has its source in vibrating bodies. Consider the tuning fork of Figure 16.1. As the tine A swings toward the right, it pushes air molecules and produces a region in which the molecules are crowded together. Such a region is called a *compression* or *condensation*. When the tine swings to the left, a region of reduced pressure called a *rarefaction* is produced. The next swing to the right produces another compression, and so forth. Thus, the sound wave consists of a series of alternate compressions and rarefactions. The molecules move back and forth along the line of propagation, which establishes the *longitudinal* nature of the waves. When the condensations and rarefactions reach the eardrum of a listener, they produce small inward and outward motions of the eardrum, and this starts the physiological processes of hearing.

16.2 The Velocity of Sound

The velocity of sound in a medium depends upon the density of the medium and upon its elastic properties; the greater the elasticity and the less the density, the greater the velocity. In a wire or rod of a solid material the velocity of sound waves is given by

$$V = \sqrt{\frac{Y}{d}} \qquad\qquad 16.1$$

where Y is Young's modulus, and d the density. In fluids the velocity is given by

$$V = \sqrt{\frac{B}{d}} \qquad\qquad 16.2$$

where B is the bulk modulus. For a gas the appropriate elastic modulus

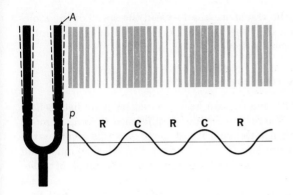

FIGURE 16.1
Sound waves from a tuning fork consist of alternate compressions and rarefactions. The waves shown are at some distance from the tuning fork where the wavefronts, essentially spherical about the fork, are almost plane over small arc lengths.

is the *adiabatic bulk modulus* given by γp, where p is the pressure, and γ is the ratio of two specific heats for the gas (Sec. 20.6). It is 1.67 for monatomic gases, 1.40 for diatomic gases, and 1.28 for triatomic gases. For air,

$$V = \sqrt{\frac{1.4p}{d}} \qquad \qquad 16.3$$

The speed of sound in air at 0°C is 331.4 m/sec or 1,087 ft/sec. In hydrogen, which has a low molecular weight and therefore low density, the speed of sound at 0°C is about 1,270 m/sec.

According to Boyle's law, the ratio of the pressure to the density of a gas is constant if the temperature of the gas remains unchanged. Since the velocity depends only on the *ratio* of pressure to density, it is constant for a given gas so long as the temperature is constant. However, if the temperature is changed, the density varies with the temperature according to the relation $d_t = d_0/(1 + t/273)$, where d_t is the density at temperature $t°\mathrm{C}$, and d_0 the density at 0°C. Consequently, the velocity of sound in a gas increases with the temperature according to the equation

$$V_t = V_0 \sqrt{1 + \frac{t}{273}} \qquad \qquad 16.4$$

If we introduce the absolute temperature $T = 273 + t$ (Sec. 18.5), we may rewrite this equation in the form

$$V_t = V_0 \sqrt{\frac{T}{273}} \qquad \qquad 16.4a$$

Example   Find the velocity of sound in dry air at a 100°C.

$$V_{100} = V_0 \sqrt{1 + \frac{t}{273}} = 331 \sqrt{\frac{373}{273}}$$

$$= 386 \text{ m/sec}$$

The reason the speed of sound in a gas increases with temperature is that the velocity of the molecules increases. We have seen that in a sound wave the energy is transferred from one molecule to the next;

in a gas the speed of the transfer cannot exceed the speed of the molecules. Indeed, we find that the speed of sound is about 70 per cent of the average speed of the molecules.

16.3 Frequencies and Wavelengths of Audible Sounds

A reasonably typical human ear can hear frequencies lying between 20 and 20,000 vib/sec. There is substantial difference in range among various individuals. Since the velocity of sound waves is given by the product of the frequency and the wavelength, and since sounds of all different frequencies have the same velocity in air, the range of wavelengths we hear runs from about 55 ft to 0.6 in. That all frequencies travel with essentially the same speed is clearly shown by the fact that the sounds from all instruments of an orchestra reach a listener at the same time. If the velocity depended on the frequency, the music would sound very different indeed to a person far from an orchestra than to one close by.

Sound waves of higher frequency than the human ear can hear, known as *ultrasonic* sounds, are readily produced and are emitted by many animals. Ultrasonic frequencies can be heard by dogs, birds, and many other species; indeed, the bat locates obstacles and finds its way about by emitting ultrasonic frequencies which it detects as they are reflected from various obstacles.

16.4 Pitch, Loudness, and Quality

The word *sound* is used with two related but separate and distinct meanings. Sometimes we use the word to mean the *sensation due to the stimulation of the auditory nerve centers,* and at other times to mean the *longitudinal waves transmitted through elastic mediums.* To the psychologist "sound" is usually used in connection with hearing, whereas much of the time in physics "sound" is a type of wave motion, even though it may not be heard. For example, if we oscillate a wire at a frequency of 30,000 vib/sec, human ears cannot hear the waves produced. In the sense that longitudinal waves exist in the air there is a sound, but from the point of view of hearing there is none.

To a listener sound is ordinarily characterized by the psychophysical properties *pitch, loudness,* and *quality.* These subjective characteristics are, of course, related to physical properties of the waves, namely, the frequencies present, their amplitudes, and their phase relations.

In general, the pitch of a sound depends upon the frequency of the *fundamental,* or the lowest frequency present in the sound wave. As the fundamental frequency of a sound source is increased, the pitch is raised. A simple experiment which shows there is a direct relation between pitch and frequency can be performed with the aid of a siren which consists of a disk with a number of holes uniformly spaced on concentric circles. If a jet of air is directed against the holes while the disk is in rotation, a puff goes through each hole as it passes the jet. When the number of puffs per second is increased, either by increasing the speed of the disk or by directing the stream of air to more holes, the pitch becomes higher. Although the pitch of a sound is determined primarily by the frequency, it depends to some extent on the loudness and quality as well.

Loudness describes the magnitude of the auditory sensation produced by a sound. In addition to depending on the intensity and the physical composition of the sound, it also depends on the auditory acuity and experience of the individual listener. For a given frequency the loudness of a sound is closely related to the intensity; it increases roughly as the logarithm of the intensity. For a given intensity the loudness depends rather sensitively on the frequency, as we shall see in Sec. 16.5.

Sounds which have the same loudness and pitch may have very different *qualities*. For example, if a piano and a trumpet play the same note at the same loudness, it is easy to distinguish between them. The reason is that neither sound source produces a single frequency; each sends out a group of frequencies. As we have seen, the lowest frequency is called the *fundamental;* it is this frequency which primarily determines the pitch. In addition to the fundamental there are present higher frequencies, called *overtones*. When two notes differ in quality, they differ in the frequencies and relative intensities of the various overtones. Figure 16.2 shows how the characteristics of the sound emitted by a trumpet change according to the way the musician blows it.

16.5 The Ear

The process of hearing begins when sound waves impinge upon an ear. The human ear (Fig. 16.3) may be divided into three distinct parts: the external ear, the middle ear, and the inner ear. The external ear collects the sound waves and directs them along the auditory canal to the *eardrum,* which is caused to vibrate. These vibrations are carried across the middle ear by three small bones, called the *hammer,* the *anvil,* and the *stirrup* because of their shapes. Vibrations of the eardrum are passed from hammer to anvil to stirrup, which in turn is attached to the "oval window" separating the middle ear from the inner ear. The principal parts of the inner ear are the *cochlea* and

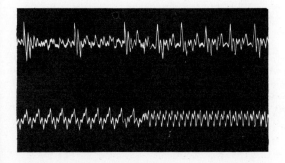

FIGURE 16.2
Sound waves emitted by a trumpet blown in different ways.

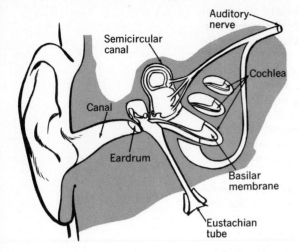

FIGURE 16.3
Anatomical structure of the human ear.

three *semicircular canals*. The cochlea, shaped somewhat like the shell of a snail, serves as a funnel leading to the nerve endings which are sensitive to sound. The cochlea is filled with fluid which is set into vibration by the movement of the oval window. Inside the cochlea are about 2.5 turns of the basilar membrane, to which are connected the roughly 30,000 nerve endings which initiate signals to the brain. Figure 16.4 indicates the location of the nerve endings which show maximum response to a pure tone of 700 cycles/sec and moderate loudness. The semicircular canals are not part of the hearing mechanism, but are vital in keeping one's balance.

The human ear is a remarkably sensitive detector of sound waves. At 3,000 vib/sec the faintest sound the ear can hear has pressure variations of about 2×10^{-5} newton/m², which corresponds to a displacement amplitude of less than 10^{-11} m, or about one-tenth the diameter of a molecule! Yet it can also hear sounds with pressure variations a million times this great.

The loudness of a sound, as judged by the ear, is approximately proportional to the logarithm of the intensity. This fact has led physicists to measure the intensity levels of sounds on an arbitrary

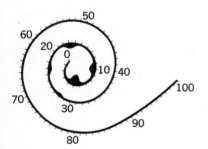

FIGURE 16.4
Parts of the cochlea where maximum response occurs for a pure tone of frequency 700 cycles/sec at moderate loudness.

logarithmic scale. The intensity level n of a sound wave *in decibels* (dB) is defined by the equation

$$n = 10 \log_{10} \frac{I}{I_0} \qquad \text{16.5}$$

where I_0 is a reference level, taken as 10^{-12} watt/m², which is roughly that of the weakest sound which can be heard. For a sound which has an intensity level $n = 60$ dB, the logarithm of I/I_0 is 6, so $I = 10^6\, I_0$. In other words a 60-dB sound level corresponds to an intensity one million times that of the reference level. For ordinary speech, n ranges from 30 to 70 dB, while for loud music it may reach 100.

The lowest sound level which can produce an audible sound depends on the frequency. The range of intensity levels and frequencies which can be heard by a typical ear is shown in Figure 16.5. A sound more intense than that corresponding to the upper curve produces pain rather than hearing.

16.6 Refraction of Sound

When sound waves pass from one medium to another, there is usually a change in velocity. As a consequence, the direction of propagation of the wave in the second medium is changed, provided the incident waves meet the surface of separation obliquely (Sec. 15.9).

Since the speed of sound in warm air is greater than it is in cold air, the direction of propagation of the sound changes continuously as it passes from air at one temperature to air at a different temperature. If the air is at rest and the temperature and density are uniform, a wave front from a point source on the surface of the earth is spherical, and the sound travels in straight lines. If the air at the ground is warmer than it is at higher altitudes, the speed of the sound is greater at the surface of the earth, and a wave front is no longer spherical. Since the direction of propagation is perpendicular

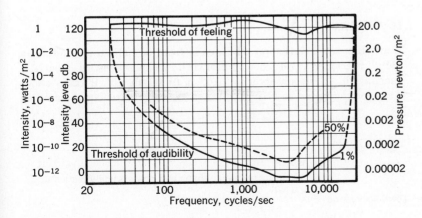

FIGURE 16.5

Chart of intensity levels showing threshold of audibility and threshold of feeling.

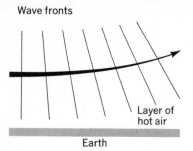

Wave fronts

Layer of
hot air

Earth

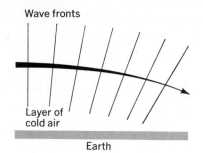

Wave fronts

Layer of
cold air

Earth

FIGURE 16.6
Wave fronts are deflected
upward when air at the ground
is warmer than air higher up
and downward when air at the
ground is cooler.

to the wave front, the sound is deflected upward (Fig. 16.6), and it cannot be heard for as great distances as it could if this distortion did not take place. When air at the ground is colder than it is at higher altitudes, the sound travels more slowly near the ground. The sound is deflected downward, and the distance at which the sound can be heard is increased. This sometimes happens over a lake at the end of a hot day.

When the wind is blowing, the speed of the sound with respect to the earth is decreased in the direction from which the wind comes, and increased in the direction toward which the wind is blowing. Near the earth, the higher the altitude, the greater the velocity of the wind and the greater the change in the speed of the sound with respect to the earth. This unequal change in the speed of the sound waves causes a distortion in the wave front. On the windward side of the source the speed of the sound is greater at the ground than at points above the ground (Fig. 16.7). This inequality of speed causes the wave front near the ground to be inclined to the vertical, and the line of propagation to be directed upward from the earth. On the side of the source toward which the wind is blowing, the speed near the ground is less than at higher altitudes. In this case, the direction of propagation is bent toward the ground, making it possible for the sound to be heard at greater distances.

16.7 Reflection of Sound

If an observer stands some distance in front of a cliff and produces a sound, the sound is returned to him with its characteristics essentially unchanged. If the observer is 1,100 ft from the cliff, it takes about 2 sec for the sound to return to him. We call the reflected sound an

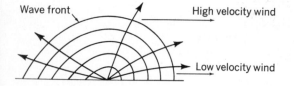

Wave front

High velocity wind

Low velocity wind

FIGURE 16.7
Wave fronts change shape and propagation direction in a wind.

echo. The roll of thunder is due to the reflection of the original sound by clouds at different distances from the observer. These reflections reach the observer at different times and produce the rolling continuation of the sound.

When an orchestra is to play out of doors, a large reflecting shell is often provided behind it so that sound waves are reflected toward the audience, thus greatly increasing the loudness.

Sound waves are reflected when they reach the walls of a speaking tube, which thereby prevents them from spreading out. Consequently, the intensity of the sound does not decrease appreciably as the wave advances, and the sound may be heard with only slightly diminished intensity at the other end of the tube many yards from the speaker. In an ear trumpet the waves entering the wide end are gradually diminished in area by reflections in the wall until, at the small end, the entire energy of the incident waves is concentrated over a small area. As a consequence, the intensity is greatly increased.

16.8 Architectural Acoustics

When sound waves are produced in a room, they spread out until they strike the walls, ceiling, or floor. Here they are partly reflected, partly absorbed, and partly transmitted. A hard smooth wall reflects most of the sound; it transmits and absorbs little. On the other hand, a porous, soft material absorbs most of the sound energy and reflects little.

If a steady sound source is maintained for some time in a room, the sound level in the room builds up, as shown in Figure 16.8. After a short time a state of equilibrium is reached in which the energy lost each second through absorption is equal to the sound power provided by the source. When the source is shut off, the intensity of the sound dies down, as indicated in the second half of the curve in Figure 16.8.

The echoing and reechoing of sounds in a room because of repeated reflections is known as *reverberation*. *The reverberation time of a room is defined as the time required for the sound level to fall 60 dB after the sound source is shut off.* A drop of 60 dB means that the intensity falls to one-millionth of its original value. If the reverberation

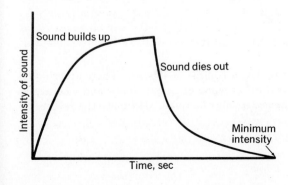

FIGURE 16.8
Rise and decay of sound in a room.

time of a room is too long, the sound waves bounce back and forth many times; a speaker's words become blurred because these reflected waves blend with the new sound waves. Such a blending effect is familiar to anyone who has sung in a hard-walled shower room that has a long reverberation time. On the other hand, if the reverberation time is too short, sounds are thin and weak; we say the room is "dead." In general, a somewhat longer reverberation time is desirable for music than for speech. Reverberation times of about 1 sec for a small room and 1.5 to 2 sec for a larger one are desirable for ordinary uses. For making phonograph recordings, a very dead room with virtually no reverberation is used because the desired reverberation properties are supplied by the room in which the listener sits.

The reverberation time of a classroom or auditorium may be estimated by the use of a formula due to Sabine, a pioneer in the field of architectural acoustics. He found that the reverberation time t_R in seconds for a typical room was given by

$$t_R = 0.16 \frac{V}{A} \qquad\qquad \textbf{16.6}$$

where V is the volume of the room in cubic meters, and A is the total absorbing power of the room and its contents. The total absorbing power of the room is found by adding the contributions of all sound-absorbing surfaces, the contribution of each surface being the product of the exposed area in square meters and the appropriate absorption coefficient. The absorption coefficient, in turn, is the fraction of the incident sound wave energy removed either by absorption or transmission. It is 1.00 for an open window because all the incident energy goes on through and is thus removed from the room. The absorption coefficients of a number of typical materials are listed in Table 16.1.

Example A shower room has the dimensions 5 by 4 by 3 m. All the walls are of tile, and the door has the same absorption coefficient as tile. Find the approximate reverberation time if one man is showering and singing in this room.

$A = (20 + 20 + 12 + 12 + 15 + 15) \times 0.03 +$ the absorbing power of the naked man, which we shall take to be equivalent to 0.25 m² of open window (at least half the absorption of a person is associated with his clothing).

$A = 2.82 + 0.25 = 3.07$

$t_R = 0.16 \dfrac{V}{A} = 0.16 \times \dfrac{60}{3.07} = 3.1$ sec

Example A classroom has a volume of 400 m³. There are exposed 600 m² of tile and 500 m² of wood in chairs, doors, and woodwork. There are 30 persons occupying the room. Estimate the reverberation time.

$A = (600 \times 0.03) + (500 \times 0.05) + (30 \times 0.5 \times 1)$
$\quad = 18 + 25 + 15 = 58$
$t_R = 0.16 \times {}^{400}\!/_{58} = 1.1$ sec

TABLE 16.1 *Sound-absorption Coefficients*

Open window*	1.00	Hair felt	0.40
Brick wall	0.02	Heavy curtains	0.50
Clay tile	0.03	Perforated acoustic ceiling	0.60
Concrete	0.02	Plaster	0.03
Glass	0.03	Wood	0.05

* Absorbing power of typical person is 0.5 m² of open window.

16.9 Interference of Sound Waves

When two trains of waves pass the same point, the displacement of a particle at this point is the resultant of the displacements which each of the two wave trains would produce if it acted alone. If the two trains have the same wavelength and direction, the resultant amplitude depends on the amplitude of the two waves and on the phases of the two component disturbances. If the two arrive at the same phase, they reinforce one another, and we have constructive interference; if they arrive one-half wavelength out of phase, the resultant amplitude is the difference between the individual amplitudes. If these amplitudes are equal, the waves cancel one another, and we have total destructive interference.

The interference of sound waves can be demonstrated with the apparatus of Figure 16.9. Sound waves from a source O travel to point D by separate paths ACD and ABD. If the lengths of the two paths are exactly equal, the waves arrive at the ear in phase, and we have constructive interference. If the path ABD is increased in length, the waves travel different distances, and the resultant amplitude is less than when the interference was constructive. When path ABD is one-half wavelength longer than path ACD, the waves are one-half wavelength out of phase, and destructive interference results. As the path ABD is increased still more, the amplitude of the resultant disturbance increases, and we have constructive interference once more when path ABD is one wavelength greater than ACD. In general, there is destructive interference when path ABD exceeds ACD by an odd number of half wavelengths, and constructive interference when the paths differ by an integral number of wavelengths.

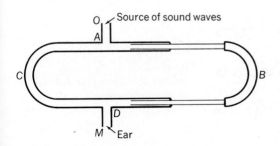

FIGURE 16.9

Apparatus for showing the interference of two sound waves which have traveled paths of different lengths.

16.10 Beats

If two steady sound sources of the same frequency are activated together, the intensity of the sound at a given listening point remains constant. If the frequencies are slightly different, however, the intensity of the sound fluctuates. There are bursts of louder sound with comparative silence between them. Each burst occurs when the disturbances from the two sources reinforce one another, while the periods of relative silence occur when the two waves interfere destructively. The fluctuations in intensity when two sound sources of slightly different frequency are activated simultaneously are called *beats*.

The origin of beats is as follows: Suppose that at a certain instant compressions from both sound sources arrive simultaneously (*A* of Figure 16.10). The amplitude of the resultant disturbance is large, and the intensity relatively high. A short time later the more rapidly vibrating source is one-half vibration ahead of the other, and a compression from one source arrives at the same time as a rarefaction from the other (*B* of Figure 16.10). The two disturbances interfere destructively, and a minimum intensity results. A little later the more rapidly vibrating source has picked up a full vibration, and once again an intensity maximum is observed.

When two sound sources have almost identical frequencies, the number of beats observed each second is small. As the difference in frequencies increases, the number of beats increases. If the sounds differ in frequency by one vibration per second, they reinforce once each second, and we observe one beat per second. In general, the number of beats observed per second is equal to the difference between the frequencies of the two sound sources:

Number of beats per second $= N = \nu_1 - \nu_2$ **16.7**

where ν_1 and ν_2 are the frequencies of the two sources.

$<$ Beats are of great service in tuning string instruments. As two strings are brought more and more nearly into unison, the number of beats per second becomes less; when no beats are observed, the strings have the same frequency.

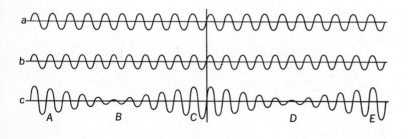

FIGURE 16.10

Beats arise from the superposition of sound waves differing slightly in frequency.

Questions

1. Why is thunder often so prolonged when the single lightning flash which produced it is almost instantaneous?

2. Upon what properties of a transmitting medium does the speed of sound depend? Explain qualitatively why these properties affect the speed.

3. Beats are sometimes called *difference tones*. Why is that term used?

4. Why is the speed of sound in a gas a little less than the average speed of the molecules?

5. How can the position of a gun be determined by using three listening posts and measuring the times of arrival at each post with accuracy?

6. What evidence is available from everyday life to support the assertion that the speed of audible sounds is independent of frequency?

7. Why is it often true that sounds can be heard for particularly great distances at night or after a rain?

8. Draperies and furniture often improve the acoustics of a room. Why? On what factors do the acoustics of the room depend?

9. What is meant by the statement that the sound level in a room is 40 dB?

Problems

Take the speed of sound in air to be 1,100 ft/sec or 340 m/sec.

1. An air-driven turbine breaks up the stream of air into 36 pulses per revolution. What frequency of sound will be heard when the turbine is rotating at the rate of 5,400 rev/min? What is the wavelength of the sound waves generated?

Ans. 3,240 per second; 0.105 m

2. A timer sets his watch by the report of a gun 100 m away. What is the error due to the time required for the sound to travel from the gun to his ear?

3. What is the velocity of a compressional sound wave in a steel rod for which Young's modulus of elasticity is 24×10^{10} newtons/m^2 and the density is 7,800 kg/m^3?

Ans. 5,550 m/sec

4. Sound travels in water at the rate of 1,450 m/sec. What is the bulk modulus of elasticity of water?

5. What is the speed of sound in hydrogen at 0°C and 1 atm pressure? Two grams of hydrogen under standard conditions occupy a volume of 22.4 liters. *Ans.* 1,260 m/sec

6. At what temperature would the speed of sound in air be 500 m/sec if it is 331.5 m/sec at 0°C?

7. A workman strikes the steel rail of a railroad track with a hammer. The sound thus produced reaches an observer through the rail and through the surrounding air. The difference in time is 2 sec. If the speed of sound in steel is 16,300 ft/sec, how far is the observer away from the workman? *Ans.* 2,360 ft

8. A worker, in pounding a spike, strikes a steel railroad track. A person 0.5 mile along the track hears two reports due to the pounding. One travels through air, and one through the rail. What time interval separates the reports if the speed of sound in steel is 16,300 ft/sec?

9. A ship sends signals to a neighboring ship. The sound waves travel by two paths, one in air, and the other in sea water. The signals are heard on the neighboring ship at intervals 5 sec apart. How far is it from one ship to the other if the speed of sound in sea water is 1,450 m/sec? *Ans.* 2,220 m

10. The vertical walls of a canyon are 8,800 ft apart. A man in the canyon fires a gun and hears the echo from the farther wall 5 sec after the echo from the nearer wall. How far is he from the nearer wall?

11. What is the intensity level of a sound of intensity 10^{-7} watt/m² relative to the reference level of 10^{-12} watt/m²? *Ans.* 50 dB

12. Acoustic treatment of certain surfaces in a foundry reduced the sound level by 30 dB. How many times greater was the intensity before the treatment than after?

13. The threshold of pain involves an intensity level of roughly 120 dB. What is the corresponding intensity in watts per square meter? *Ans.* 1 watt/m²

14. If the intensity due to six violins is six times that due to a single violin, how many decibels is the sound level raised by having six violins playing rather than a single one?

15. If a loudspeaker is regarded as a point source radiating equally in all directions, what acoustic power must it develop to produce a sound level of 50 dB at a distance of 100 m? *Ans.* 0.0126 watt

16. Two strings A and B originally produced the same frequency. The tension of B was released slightly, thereby reducing the frequency, and the strings then produced 8 beats per second when sounded together. If the frequency of A is 285 cycles/sec, what is the frequency of B?

17. An auditorium is essentially a rectangle 40 by 30 by 10 m. It has a perforated acoustic ceiling, concrete floor, and plaster walls. It contains 800 seats, each of which is equivalent to 1 m² of wood. Find the approximate reverberation time of the auditorium when empty and when full. *Ans.* 2.3 sec; 1.6 sec

18. A lecture room has a volume of 15,000 m³. If it has 1,000 m² of acoustic ceiling, 2,000 m² of plaster, 1,000 m² of concrete, and 4,000 m² of wood, find the reverberation time when the room is empty and when it holds 300 people.

19. Both loudspeakers of a stereo hi-fi system are sending out, in phase, a pure frequency of 500 vib/sec. A listener, originally equidistant from the speakers, moves to one side until the note fades to a minimum loudness. If he is then 9.00 ft from the closer speaker, how far is he from the farther one? *Ans.* 10.1 ft

20. An oscillator emits a sound with a wavelength of 0.25 m which is divided into two parts in the apparatus of Figure 16.9. The two parts travel the same distances, so that constructive interference is experienced. In order to eliminate the sound, one path is lengthened. What is the shortest distance this path may be lengthened to satisfy this condition? If it is lengthened still further, the intensity increases and then decreases. What total change in path is necessary to obtain the second case of destructive interference? What total change in path is necessary to obtain the third case of destructive interference?

21. A sound wave travels through two branches of a tube which are 1 m long and 1.7 m long, respectively. List the three lowest frequencies which would suffer destructive interference if the waves were recombined after traveling through the branches. *Ans.* 243, 729, and 1,214 cycles/sec

CHAPTER 17 *We have been considering the propagation and detection of sound waves, but we have not examined precisely how these acoustic waves are produced. We turn now to a discussion of how various kinds of sound sources produce the periodic changes in pressure we hear as sound. For some of the simpler sound sources we can predict both the fundamental frequency and the prominent overtones from the length of the source.*

Sound Sources

17.1 Sounding Bodies

Ordinary sound waves are set up by vibrating bodies. A typical source in vibration sends out a series of alternate compressions and rarefactions which are transmitted through the air. Most sound sources do not send out a single frequency, but rather a combination of many frequencies. The lowest prominent frequency is the *fundamental;* the higher frequencies are called *overtones*. In vibrating strings and in organ pipes the overtones are usually integral multiples of the fundamental and are called *harmonics*. *A harmonic is an overtone which has a frequency that is an integral multiple of the fundamental frequency.* Thus, the frequency of the third harmonic is three times that of the fundamental.

Most of the overtones of bells, drums, and vibrating plates are not harmonically related to the fundamental. A few sound sources are especially designed to produce as nearly as possible a single frequency, or a *pure tone*. A tuning fork is an example of such a source. It is essentially a rod bent in the form of a U with the central region reinforced to suppress overtones; even so, careful observation often reveals the presence of undesired frequencies.

In most musical sounds, the same frequency is emitted for an appreciable period of time during which the amplitude does not decrease rapidly. In a noise, on the other hand, we usually have a sudden burst of a wide range of frequencies with no regularity and a marked drop in intensity during the emission of a single vibration. Of course, the distinction between noises and musical sounds is not sharp and definite. What is music for one person may be noise to another.

17.2 Waves in Wires and Strings

Many musical instruments make use of stretched strings as sound sources. These strings may be set into vibration by striking, plucking, bowing, or strumming. When the string is displaced at some point and then released, the disturbance is passed from one element of the string to the next, and transverse waves proceeding in both directions in the string are produced. These waves are reflected at the fixed ends of the string, return in the opposite direction, and go on to the other ends, where they are again reflected. Of the many frequencies of which the initial wave is composed, only those frequencies which are suitable for establishing standing waves in the string are maintained for any length of time.

The velocity V of a transverse wave along a flexible stretched string depends on the tension T and on the mass per unit length m_l of the string. It is shown below that

$$V = \sqrt{\frac{T}{m_l}}$$ 17.1

< Consider a wave traveling toward the right in the cord AE of Figure 17.1. Assume that while the pulse, or wave, is moving toward the right with a velocity V, the cord is made to move toward the left with an equal velocity. As a result of these superposed velocities, the wave pulse remains at rest. For simplicity, assume that the small arc $BD = \Delta s$ is circular in form. The component of the tension T along the radius CO is $T \sin \Delta\theta$, so the net force on Δs toward O is $F = 2T \sin \Delta\theta = 2T \Delta\theta$ (approximately). Since $2 \Delta\theta = \Delta s/R$, $F = T \Delta s/R$. This force provides the centripetal acceleration required if the mass $m_l \Delta s$ is to traverse the circular arc BD. By Eq. (6.2),

$$m_l \Delta s \frac{V^2}{R} = F = T \frac{\Delta s}{R}$$

from which $V = \sqrt{T/m_l}$.

Of the standing waves established in the stretched string, the one with the longest wavelength is that for which the string vibrates as a single segment (Fig. 17.2). The longest wavelength corresponds to the lowest frequency and therefore to the *fundamental* of the string. The standing wave of next longest wavelength is that for which the string vibrates in two segments. In this case the length of the string is equal

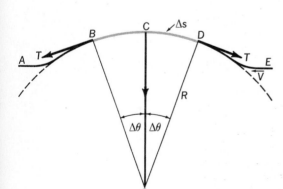

FIGURE 17.1
Transverse wave pulse on a stretched cord.

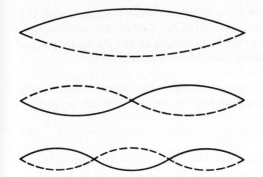

FIGURE 17.2
Vibrations in a stretched string fixed at both ends, showing the fundamental mode and the first two overtones.

to the wavelength. The third longest standing wave which can exist in the stretched string occurs when the string vibrates in three segments, the next in four segments, etc.

The allowed modes of vibration for a stretched string are easy to determine if one remembers that both ends of the string are fastened. These ends cannot move and must therefore behave as nodes for any possible standing wave. We are dealing with a situation in which we impose a condition on the ends of the strings, namely, that they remain at rest. Such conditions are known as *boundary conditions,* and they play a very important role in determining the types of vibrations which are allowed in various kinds of systems. Once we have established the boundary conditions that there be nodes at the ends of the stretched strings, we can readily find the fundamental by finding the longest wave that we can produce which has nodes at both ends. The first overtone corresponds to the next longest possibility, and so on.

If the string is plucked at random, it may vibrate in such a way that both the fundamental and overtones are present. For the string the overtones are all harmonics, and the note from a string consists of the fundamental together with several harmonics.

17.3 Harmonics of a String

Let L be the length of the string. Then, for the fundamental, the wavelength is $2L$ (Fig. 17.2). Since for any wave motion $V = \nu\lambda$, we have, for the fundamental frequency ν_1,

$$\nu_1 = \frac{1}{2L} \sqrt{\frac{T}{m_l}}$$ 17.2

The frequency of the fundamental depends on length, tension, and mass per unit length. A musical instrument such as the piano affords an illustration of how these factors apply. The strings which play the bass notes are ordinarily heavy, thus having large m_l, and they are also long. Strings for the high notes are short, light, and tightly stretched. In tuning a piano, the tension is varied. In instruments such as the violin in which there are only four strings, the strings are of the same length, but they have different masses per unit length and different tensions. When the violinist wishes to play different frequencies on the same string, he varies the length of the string by placing his finger at the point at which he wishes to create a node.

The first overtone for the vibrating string occurs when $\lambda = L$ (Fig. 17.2), and therefore the frequency of the first overtone is given by

$$\nu_2 = \frac{1}{L} \sqrt{\frac{T}{m_l}}$$

17.3

The first overtone has a frequency twice that of the fundamental and is therefore the second harmonic. For the second overtone $\lambda = 2L/3$, and the frequency is

$$\nu_3 = \frac{3}{2L} \sqrt{\frac{T}{m_l}}$$

17.3a

(Second overtone = third harmonic)

In general, the allowed overtones of stretched strings consist of all harmonics.

$<$ Most harmonics blend well with the fundamental to produce pleasing tones. The seventh harmonic is an exception. In order to suppress the seventh harmonic, piano strings are struck at a point where the seventh harmonic would have a node. This assures that there cannot be a perfect node at this point. Violins are often bowed in the vicinity of a node for the seventh harmonic in order to suppress this relatively unpleasant overtone. The superior tonal quality of an expert violinist is associated with his ability to produce not only the desired fundamental, but also a combination of overtones which are pleasing. The relative intensities of overtones can be varied over substantial ranges by an expert.

17.4 Closed Organ Pipes

In an organ pipe the vibrating body is a column of air. At one end of a pipe, the column of air is set into vibration by sending a narrow jet of air toward a thin edge or lip (Fig. 17.3). This end of the pipe is always open so that sound waves can be transmitted from the pipe into the surrounding air. In a closed pipe the other end is blocked off. Thus, a closed organ pipe is closed at one end and open at the other. When air first strikes the lip, a condensation starts down the pipe, is reflected at the closed end, and returns to the lip as a condensation. When it reaches the lip, it pushes the air stream outside the lip, and

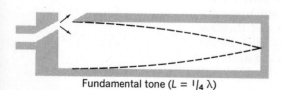

Fundamental tone ($L = \frac{1}{4}\lambda$)

FIGURE 17.3
Displacement pattern (dashed line) for the fundamental in a closed organ pipe.

this starts a rarefaction down the tube. The rarefaction is reflected at the closed end, returns to the lip as a rarefaction, and draws the stream into the pipe again, thereby starting a new compression. Thus the air stream is made to move back and forth across the lip with its period determined by the time required for a compression to travel up and back and a rarefaction to travel up and back. The period is four times the time required for sound to traverse the length of the tube.

An alternative approach to determining the fundamental frequency involves the application of boundary conditions. At the closed end of the pipe an air particle is unable to move forward when a compression comes down the tube. We have a *displacement node at the closed end of an organ pipe.* On the other hand, a particle at the open end is not restrained, and the amplitude of the vibration of a particle is a maximum there. There is always an *antinode at the open end of a pipe;* the displacement there is maximum. The possible standing waves which can be set up in a closed organ pipe are those which have a node at the closed end and an antinode at the open end. The longest wavelength which can fit into the organ pipe is indicated in Figure 17.3. In this case the wavelength is four times the length L of the pipe. The frequency ν_1 of the fundamental is given by the ratio of the velocity V of the wave motion, which in this case is the velocity of sound in the gas in the organ pipe, to the wavelength λ. Therefore,

$$\nu_1 = \frac{V}{4L} \qquad\qquad \textbf{17.4}$$

There are other possible modes of vibration for this column of air which have a node at the closed end and an antinode at the open end. The next longest frequency which can be emitted involves the vibration in which there is one additional node in the pipe (Fig. 17.4). For this case the wavelength is $4L/3$; the *first overtone is the third harmonic,* which has a frequency

$$\nu_3 = \frac{3V}{4L} \qquad\qquad \textbf{17.5}$$

The second overtone is also shown in Figure 17.4. Its frequency, $\nu_5 = 5V/4L$, is that of the fifth harmonic. The closed pipe can emit any frequency which is an odd integer times the fundamental frequency.

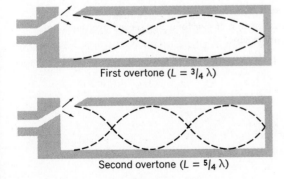

First overtone ($L = {}^3/_4\,\lambda$)

Second overtone ($L = {}^5/_4\,\lambda$)

FIGURE 17.4
First overtone and second overtone in a closed organ pipe.

Harmonics which have frequencies 2, 4, 6, . . . times the fundamental frequency cannot be sustained in a closed organ pipe. *Closed organ pipes emit only odd harmonics.*

The fundamental frequency depends on the velocity of sound in the gas in the tube. If hydrogen is placed in the tube instead of air, the fundamental frequency is almost quadrupled. For any gas in the tube, the fundamental frequency depends upon the temperature, since the velocity of sound is a function of temperature. As the temperature is raised, the frequencies emitted go up.

17.5 Open Pipes

The boundary condition for an open end requires that the oscillation amplitude be maximum. Since both ends of an open pipe are open, there is an antinode at each end. The wavelength of the longest possible standing wave is twice the length of the pipe, as shown in Figure 17.5. Since $V = \nu\lambda$, the frequency ν_1 of the fundamental is

$$\nu_1 = \frac{V}{2L}$$

17.6

We observe that the fundamental of an open pipe has twice the frequency of a closed pipe of the same length. The next possible mode of vibration (Fig. 17.5) is that in which the pipe has a length equal to one wavelength. This gives rise to the first overtone (second harmonic), with a frequency

$$\nu_2 = \frac{V}{L}$$

17.7

For the second overtone, $\nu_3 = 3V/2L$, which is the third harmonic. The frequencies of the harmonics of the open pipe are in the ratio of

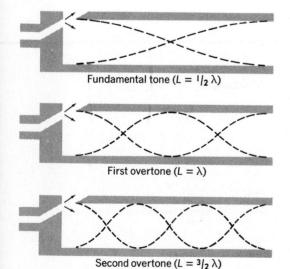

Fundamental tone ($L = \frac{1}{2}\lambda$)

First overtone ($L = \lambda$)

Second overtone ($L = \frac{3}{2}\lambda$)

FIGURE 17.5
Fundamental, first overtone, and second overtone of an open organ pipe.

the integers 1, 2, 3, 4, ... In an open pipe it is possible to have all harmonics; in a closed pipe only the odd harmonics are present.

Throughout this discussion we have assumed that an antinode occurs exactly at the open end of the pipe. Actually the antinode lies outside this open end by an amount which depends on the diameter of the pipe if round and on its shape and size if it is not round. The length must be corrected slightly for exact calculation of the frequencies.

17.6 Musical Scales

Some combinations of sounds are pleasing to the ear; others are not. What is pleasing depends in no small measure on the training of the listener. As long ago as 530 B.C. Pythagoras experimented with stretched strings and found that simultaneous notes from strings were harmonious when the ratios of the frequencies were the ratios of two small whole numbers. When one frequency is double another, we say they differ by one *octave;* this ratio of 2 to 1 is a pleasing one. On the other hand, ratios such as 100 to 81 are ordinarily displeasing, at least in part because of the existence of unpleasant beat notes. Modern occidental music is written with scales which consist of notes with frequencies related by fairly simple ratios. We call the ratio of the frequencies of two sounds the *musical interval* of the two notes. The diatonic C major scale is an example of a typical scale which is rather commonly used. The relationships among the notes in this scale are shown in Table 17.1.

A piano can be tuned to play a diatonic scale in any one key, but then the frequencies are not satisfactory for other keys. In order that a piano be able to play in a number of different keys, it is customary to make certain compromises in which the piano is not tuned perfectly for any key. The compromise usually adopted is known as the *equal-tempered scale.* In one octave of this scale there are 13 notes and 12 intervals; there is a constant ratio between the frequencies of adjacent notes. This ratio is the twelfth root of 2, or 1.05946. The standard frequency of this scale is A = 440 per second, so that this note agrees with that on the diatonic C major scale in Table 17.1. No other note in the octave has exactly the same frequency on the two scales.

TABLE 17.1 *Diatonic C Major Scale (Based on A = 440/sec)*

Major scale note	C	D	E	F	G	A	B	C′
Name	Do	Re	Mi	Fa	Sol	La	Ti	Do
Frequency	264	297	330	352	396	440	495	528
Interval relative to C	1	$9/8$	$5/4$	$4/3$	$3/2$	$5/3$	$15/8$	2
Musical interval		$9/8$	$10/9$	$16/15$	$9/8$	$10/9$	$9/8$	$16/15$
Musician's interval		Major tone	Minor tone	Semi tone	Major tone	Minor tone	Major tone	Semi tone

The physics of music and musical instruments has many fascinating sides. Persons interested in these topics can find a delightful presentation in A. H. Benade, "Horns, Strings, and Harmony" (Anchor Books, Doubleday & Company, Inc., Garden City, N.Y., 1960).

17.7 Resonance

If two identical tuning forks are placed a few feet apart and one of them is set into vibration, the second fork also begins to vibrate (Fig. 17.6). This can be shown by stopping the vibrations of the first fork by grasping the tines. Energy has been transferred through the air from the first fork to the second. Because the second fork has the same frequency as the first, the compressions set out by the first fork arrive at just the right time to build up the amplitude of vibration in the second fork. The two forks are said to be in *resonance*. When two bodies are in resonance, a substantial amount of energy can be transferred to one of the bodies through a series of very small, but perfectly timed, impulses from the other. The amplitude is built up just as the amplitude of a child's swing can be built up by small, well-timed pushes.

$<$ When marching men cross a bridge, they are often commanded to break step because, if a bridge structure happened to be resonant to the frequency of the steps, large and perhaps destructive vibrations could be set up. In automobiles very annoying noises are sometimes produced at certain speeds when some loose object happens to be resonant to a small impulse which is received with the proper timing. The designers of aircraft must be careful to avoid flutters and oscillations which may build up to intolerable levels by virtue of resonance.

On the other hand, resonances are sometimes very desirable. If we want a tuning fork to produce a louder sound, we may hold it over a tube which we gradually fill with water until the air column is resonant to the frequency emitted by the tuning fork. This occurs when the air column, closed at one end by the water, satisfies Eq. (17.4).

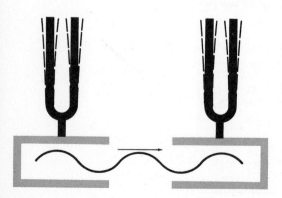

FIGURE 17.6
Resonance occurs when the vibrations of one tuning fork induce sympathetic vibrations of the same frequency in another fork.

17.8 The Human Voice

When we speak, the lungs, by their bellows action, force a stream of air between the vocal cords, two tightly stretched membranes in the throat, thereby setting them into vibration. The frequency of vibration can be changed by varying the tension in the vocal cords. The vibrations start a train of sound waves through the vocal passages. The tongue, the lips, and the cavities of the chest, nose, and throat interact with this wave train. To prove that the quality of the sound is affected by resonant columns in the head, one need only hold one's nose closed while speaking.

The differentiation of speech sounds is nearly all accomplished by the mouth and by positioning the lips. The *voiced sounds* include all the vowel and consonant sounds except *p, t, ch, k, f, s, th* (thin), and *sh*. The vocal cords do not enter into the production of these latter speech sounds, which arise from vibrations set up in the mouth itself.

Vocal sounds are transmitted through the air by exceedingly complex pressure waves. The amplitudes and frequencies of the various components present in speech sounds vary from one voice to another, but average speech includes frequencies from about 60 to 6,000 vib/sec. Most of the speech energy is carried by the vowel sounds. The power output of the normal human voice is only about 10^{-5} watt.

17.9 The Doppler Effect

When an automobile, traveling at high speed and sounding its horn, passes a pedestrian, the pitch heard by the pedestrian drops sharply as the car passes. When a source of sound is moving toward an observer, or an observer toward a sound source, the pitch of the sound heard is higher than the normal pitch. When the sound source moves away from the observer, or the observer from the source, the pitch is lowered.

Consider first the case in which the observer approaches a sound source which is at rest relative to surrounding air. In this case the observer passes more waves each second than he would if he were at rest (Fig. 17.7). Let V represent the speed of sound, and v_L the velocity of the listener toward the sound source. In 1 sec the source sends out v waves. In this same time the observer passes all the waves included in a distance $(V + v_L)$. The frequency v_L heard by the listener is the number of waves he passes each second; thus $v_L = (V + v_L)/\lambda$, where λ is the wavelength. Since $v = V/\lambda$,

$$\frac{v_L}{V + v_L} = \frac{v}{V} \qquad\qquad 17.8$$

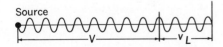

FIGURE 17.7
A listener moving with velocity v_L toward a sound source passes, in 1 sec, all the waves included in the distance numerically equal to $V + v_L$, where V is the speed of the sound.

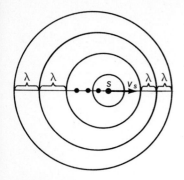

FIGURE 17.8

When a sound source is moving, the wavelength is smaller in the direction of motion and larger in the opposite direction.

If the observer is moving away from the source, v_L is negative, and the observed frequency ν_L is lower than ν.

If the source is moving (relative to the surrounding air) toward a stationary listener (Fig. 17.8), the wavelength of the sound waves in the air is different in different directions. Let ν be the frequency of the waves passing a point in the air, and ν_S the frequency emitted by the source. In 1 sec the sound waves moving to the right go a distance $V - v_S$ relative to the source, which has emitted ν_S waves in this second. Therefore the wavelength in air is $(V - v_S)/\nu_S = V/\nu$, and

$$\frac{\nu_S}{V - v_S} = \frac{\nu}{V} = \frac{\nu_L}{V} \qquad 17.9$$

since the listener hears the frequency of the waves passing in the air. When the source is moving away from the listener, v_S is negative, and the pitch heard is reduced. If both source and observer are moving relative to the air, we may write

$$\lambda_{\text{air}} = \frac{V}{\nu} = \frac{V - v_S}{\nu_S} = \frac{V + v_L}{\nu_L} \qquad 17.10$$

or

$$\frac{\nu_L}{V + v_L} = \frac{\nu_S}{V - v_S} \qquad 17.10a$$

Note that both v_S and v_L are measured *relative to the air; both are positive when the source is moving toward the observer and the observer toward the source.*

17.10 Supersonic Velocities and Shock Waves

When a body travels with a speed greater than that of sound, it is said to be *supersonic*. Figure 17.9 shows a source moving faster than the speed of sound. We observe that the object is beyond the spherical sound waves which it sent out a short time before. However, there exists a surface tangent to all these sound waves which, by Huygens'

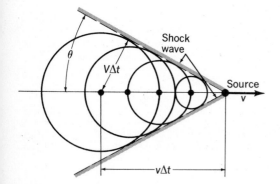

FIGURE 17.9

Wave fronts produced by a source moving faster than sound.

principle, gives us the position of a compressional wave. This wave accompanying a body traveling at a speed in excess of the speed of sound is called a *shock wave*. Figure 17.10 shows a shock wave accompanying a bullet traveling at supersonic speed. Whenever a body travels through a medium at a speed greater than that with which the resulting disturbance is propagated, a similar wave is observed. A common example is the bow wave from a speedboat.

The angle between the direction of motion of the source and the shock wave permits us to compute the velocity of the source, provided the velocity of sound in the medium is known. From Figure 17.9 we see that $\sin \theta = V/v$, where v is velocity of the source, and V the speed of the shock wave.

When a body is moving through the air at subsonic speeds, a compressional wave precedes it, and some of the air particles are moved out of the way. At supersonic speeds the body is traveling faster than the compressional wave. Consequently, there is no preparation in the medium for the oncoming body, and the region of sudden compression which we have called the *shock wave* is produced. A great deal of energy may be associated with this shock wave—energy which comes from the object passing through the air. Sometimes when an aircraft dives at supersonic speeds, it builds up a substantial shock wave which continues on toward the ground after the plane has pulled out of its dive. When the shock wave reaches the earth, it may break windows and cause other damage.

Because of the buildup of a shock wave as an aircraft reaches the speed of sound, the drag on the aircraft increases markedly in this region. In discussing the drag under these conditions, it is customary to compare the speed of the aircraft with the local speed of sound. The latter depends, of course, on the temperature and is substantially

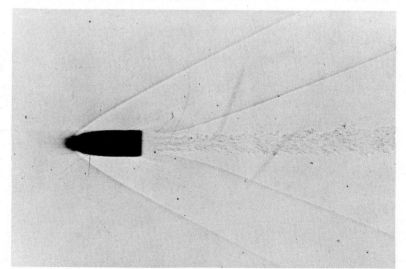

FIGURE 17.10
Compressional shock wave
traveling with a bullet.

lower at high altitudes, where the temperature is low. The ratio of the velocity of the body to the local velocity of sound is called the *Mach number.* Mach 5 means 5 times the velocity of sound. The speeds of missiles and high-velocity aircraft are often quoted in Mach numbers.

If a missile or aircraft is passing through the air, the frictional drag force D may be written

$$D = c_D S(\tfrac{1}{2} d v^2)$$

where S is the cross-sectional area normal to the air stream, d the density of the air, v the velocity of the object, and c_D is an empirical factor called the *drag coefficient.* A typical plot of drag coefficient as a function of Mach number for a missile is shown in Figure 17.11. The drag coefficient depends on the velocity of the moving body and on its size, shape, and smoothness. At low Mach numbers c_D decreases as v increases, because the actual drag is more nearly proportional to v than to v^2. However, as one approaches Mach 1, the drag increases rapidly and much faster than v^2. This region of rapid increase in drag coefficient is called the *transonic region,* because it occurs where the speed passes from below to above sonic velocity. The drag coefficient decreases above Mach 1.5, which indicates that once again the drag force is increasing less rapidly than v^2.

When an atomic bomb is exploded in the air, a tremendously strong shock wave is set up. The shock front represents a moving wall of highly compressed air which may blow down buildings and produce other damage. It has been reported that at a distance of 1,500 ft from the detonation point of a nominal atomic bomb similar to that used at Nagasaki, the pressure of the shock wave is about 50 lb/in.² greater than atmospheric, and the speed of the shock wave is about 2,000 ft/sec. The tremendous compressional shock wave is followed by a rarefaction or *suction phase,* which lasts much longer than the pressure phase.

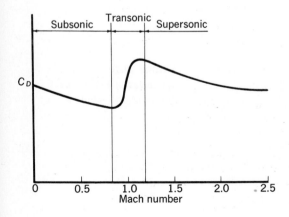

FIGURE 17.11
The drag coefficient of a particular missile as a function of missile speed in Mach numbers.

Questions

1. A violin and an organ are tuned together; what happens if the temperature of the room rises from 20°C to 25°C?

2. If the wave in an organ pipe is a sound wave, how does the sound get from within the organ pipe to your ear?

3. What is required to observe resonance between two mechanical systems?

4. What sound sources have overtones which are not harmonics?

5. How are different frequencies produced in a bugle, which is an open air column of constant length?

6. What are the advantages and disadvantages of the equal-tempered scale?

7. If two sounds are an octave apart, how are their frequencies related?

8. Why do marching men break step when crossing a light bridge?

9. Why are the bass strings of a piano wrapped with a close helical winding of other wire?

10. How may beats be used in tuning a musical instrument such as a piano or a harp?

11. Does wind velocity play any role in the Doppler effect? Explain quantitatively.

12. Can an airplane designed to fly at supersonic speed get its thrust from a propeller? Explain.

Problems

Take the speed of sound in air to be 1,100 ft/sec or 340 m/sec.

1. What is the velocity of a transverse wave in a string 150 cm long with a mass of 5 g and subject to a tension of 1,200 newtons? What is the fundamental frequency of this string? *Ans.* 600 m/sec; 200/sec

2. A steel wire has a mass per unit length of 0.005 kg/m and is 1.2 m long. It is stretched by a force of 98 newtons. Find the speed of transverse waves in this wire. What is the frequency of its fundamental vibration?

3. A stretched wire 5.5 ft long has a fundamental frequency of 250 cycles/sec. What is the velocity of the wave in the wire? What is the wavelength of the fundamental vibration? What is the frequency of the first overtone? What is the frequency of the third overtone? What is the frequency of the third harmonic? *Ans.* 2,750 ft/sec; 11 ft; 500 cycles/sec; 1,000 cycles/sec; 750 cycles/sec

4. A string with a mass per unit length of 0.008 kg/m is stretched by the application of 320 newtons. What length of string will be required to produce a fundamental frequency of 450 cycles/sec? What tension is required to give this string a fundamental frequency of 600 cycles/sec?

5. A stretched string made of steel is vibrating at its fundamental frequency of 1,500 cycles/sec. What is the fundamental frequency of a second string made from the same steel, but which has a diameter twice that of the original and a length twice that of the original and which is stretched by twice the force of the original? *Ans.* 530 cycles/sec

6. A steel piano wire is 1 m long and has a fundamental frequency of 250 cycles/sec. If the mass per unit length is 0.01 kg/m, find the tension in the wire. What is the speed of transverse waves in the wire? If the amplitude at the center of the wire is 0.6 mm, find the maximum acceleration at the mid-point.

7. An open organ pipe is 2.75 ft long. What is the wavelength of its fundamental vibration? What is the frequency of its fundamental vibration? What is the frequency of the first overtone? What is the frequency of the third overtone? What is the frequency of the third harmonic?

Ans. 5.5 ft; 200 cycles/sec; 400 cycles/sec; 800 cycles/sec; 600 cycles/sec

8. Calculate the lengths in meters of open and closed pipes for a fundamental frequency of 680 cycles/sec.

9. Repeat Prob. 7 for a closed organ pipe which is 2.75 ft long.

Ans. 11 ft; 100 cycles/sec; 300 cycles/sec; 700 cycles/sec; 300 cycles/sec

10. The whistle of a steamer is in the form of a closed pipe 1.7 m long. Calculate the frequencies of the fundamental and the first three overtones.

11. An open organ pipe is 2 ft long. Find the frequency of the fundamental and the wavelength of the first overtone. If this pipe is now closed at one end, find the frequency of the fundamental and the wavelength of the first overtone.

Ans. 275/sec; 2 ft; 137.5/sec; 2.67 ft

12. Find the frequencies of the fundamental and first two overtones of an open pipe 1 ft long.

13. Two closed organ pipes of lengths 0.5 m and 0.525 m are sounded together and produce 6 beats per second. What is the velocity of sound in the medium with which the organ pipes are filled? *Ans.* 252 m/sec

14. Two open organ pipes of lengths 68 and 72 cm are sounded simultaneously. How many beats per second are produced?

15. Water is poured into a long glass tube closed at one end. What length of air column must be left above the water level if the column is to reinforce and resonate at a frequency of 440 vib/sec? *Ans.* 0.625 ft

16. A sounding tuning fork is held over a vertical glass tube into which water is poured slowly. The remainder of the tube is filled with air. What is the frequency of the tuning fork when the shortest column of air for resonance is 20 cm?

17. A glass tube open at both ends is so placed that one end is under water. The tube is adjusted until there is resonance when a sounding tuning fork is held above the open end. If the tuning fork makes 680 vib/sec, what is the shortest length of the tube for resonance? *Ans.* 12.5 cm

18. Find the notes of a major diatonic scale based on C = 256 cycles/sec.

19. A major diatonic scale is based on F = 360 cycles/sec. Find the frequencies of the other seven notes. Show that for this scale the intervals D/C = 10/9 and E/D = 9/8. How do these intervals compare with those for the C major scale of Table 17.1? In view of the fact that the intervals for the key of C and for the key of F are different, how does one make a piano which can play reasonably well in both keys?

Ans. 405, 450, 480, 540, 600, 675, and 720 cycles/sec

20. Find the frequency heard by a listener at rest when a sound source emitting a frequency of 1,000 cycles/sec approaches at a speed of 85 m/sec.

21. Two automobile horns emit the same note of frequency 250 cycles/sec. If one of these horns is on a car approaching an observer at 30 mi/hr and the other is on a car moving away from the observer at 30 mi/hr, calculate the frequency heard by the observer in each case.   *Ans.* 260 cycles/sec; 240 cycles/sec

22. What is the apparent frequency heard by an observer at rest toward whom a police car is approaching at 60 mi/hr with its siren emitting a frequency of 500 vib/sec?

23. A man on a train which is running at 34 m/sec listens to a siren which has a frequency of 360 vib/sec. What is the apparent frequency of the sound when the train is approaching the siren?   *Ans.* 396 vib/sec

24. A passenger standing on the rear platform of a train notes that a warning bell at a grade crossing rings with an apparent frequency of 360 cycles/sec. The observation is made after the train has passed the crossing and while it is moving at 45 mi/hr (66 ft/sec). What is the true frequency of the bell?

25. A sounding object emits a sound of frequency 440 cycles/sec. An observer hears it at a frequency of 400 cycles/sec. (*a*) If the source is moving, what is its speed? (*b*) If the observer is moving, what is his speed?   *Ans.* 110 ft/sec; 100 ft/sec

26. At what speed in meters per second must a source of sound approach an observer in order that the pitch of each note is raised by a half tone, i.e., to 16/15 of the original frequency?

27. A train approaching a tunnel in a vertical cliff perpendicular to the tracks sounds its horn, which has a frequency of 250 cycles/sec. If the speed of the train is 110 ft/sec, what is the frequency reflected by the cliff? What frequency does the engineer hear reflected?   *Ans.* 277.8 cycles/sec; 305.6 cycles/sec

28. Estimate the angle θ in Figure 17.10, and calculate the approximate speed of the bullet.

29. Find the angle between the shock wave and the path of a bullet which has a speed of 550 m/sec.   *Ans.* 38.2°

CHAPTER 18 *In mechanics we studied the translational and rotational motions of solid objects, and in sound we considered the organized, coherent vibrations of innumerable molecules which result in sound waves. Now we take up the random, incoherent motions of the molecules of a substance. We shall relate these disorganized motions to the temperature of the substance. In the six chapters which follow we learn that changing the temperature, and consequently the internal energy, of a material results in changes in dimensions and sometimes in changes of phase. We examine how differences in temperature lead to the transfer of heat energy from one region to another, and we discuss how, in heat engines, part of the random internal energy of a hot substance can be transformed into useful work. In this chapter we lay the foundation for these studies by defining the key terms* temperature, internal energy, *and* heat *and by introducing the units in which we measure heat quantities.*

Temperature and Heat

18.1 Temperature

Our first ideas about temperature come from our physiological senses. By touching a body we may determine whether it is hot or cold. For some purposes our senses give us an adequate description of temperature, but often sensory impressions are unreliable. For example, a room may feel hot to a person who has been outdoors in snow, while it may feel cold to a person entering it from a steam bath. Indeed, sensory impressions of temperature depend greatly on the environment during the recent past.

There is a second situation in which the senses give an unreliable comparison of temperature. If one removes a cardboard container and a metal ice tray from the freezing compartment of a refrigerator, both objects are at the same temperature. Nevertheless, the tray feels much colder to the hand than does the cardboard container. The sense of touch is not always able to distinguish between a very hot object and a very cold one. In view of the uncertainties associated with our sensations of temperature it is not surprising that scientists have developed objective and reproducible methods for measuring the relative "hotness" of bodies under various conditions.

FIGURE 18.1

Galilean thermometer using air inside the bulb as the working substance.

The first recorded effort to make an instrument for measuring temperature was that of Galileo about 1593. He took a glass bulb with a long stem and submerged the end of the stem in water (Fig. 18.1). By heating the bulb, he drove some of the air out; as the bulb cooled, water rose in the stem. A change in the temperature of the bulb gave rise to a change in the water level in the stem. Such thermometers were used for many years by physicians and others. The Galilean thermometer has several serious handicaps, the most serious of which is that changes in atmospheric pressure also affect the height of the water in the stem.

In the seventeenth century thermometers using water or alcohol sealed in glass tubes were developed. Alcohol is still widely used in inexpensive thermometers. Early in the eighteenth century Fahrenheit introduced thermometers which used mercury as the thermometric substance. These thermometers rapidly won wide acceptance among scientific workers because they were consistent with each other over the whole length of scale and they were convenient, reliable, and reasonably cheap.

18.2 The Fahrenheit and Celsius Temperature Scales

Fahrenheit elected to call zero on his thermometer "the most intense cold obtained artificially in a mixture of water, of ice, and of sal ammoniac." The temperature of the human armpit he called 96°. The choice of these two "fixed points" established the Fahrenheit temperature scale.

The *Celsius,* or *centigrade,* temperature scale, proposed by the Swedish astronomer Celsius about 1742, takes as its zero the temperature of a mixture of ice and water under standard pressure. The temperature at which water boils under standard atmospheric pressure is 100°C.

$<$ To determine the first of the Celsius fixed points for a thermometer, the bulb is surrounded with finely divided ice and water. When the mercury in the bulb reaches the temperature of the ice, the height of the mercury remains constant. The point at which the mercury stands is marked 0°C. Then the bulb, and as much as possible of the stem of the thermometer, is placed in steam rising from water boiling at standard atmospheric pressure. The mercury expands and assumes a new position in the stem. This position, which does not change after the temperature of the thermometer has reached the temperature of the steam, is marked 100° on the scale. The interval between the marks is divided into 100 equal degrees.

It was soon found that the fixed points of the Celsius (or centigrade) scale could be reproduced easily and with far greater accuracy than could the original fixed points of the Fahrenheit scale. The melting point of ice was approximately 32° on the Fahrenheit scale, and the boiling point of water 212°F. Eventually it became standard practice to use the ice point and the boiling point as the fixed points for the Fahrenheit scale.

It is frequently desirable to convert a Celsius temperature to Fahrenheit, and vice versa. This can be done readily if one recalls the fixed points of the two temperature scales. Let F be the temperature on the Fahrenheit scale, and C the temperature on the Celsius scale (Fig. 18.2). The number of Fahrenheit degrees above the freezing point is related to the total temperature difference between the boiling point and the freezing point on the Fahrenheit scale (180°) as the number of Celsius degrees above the freezing point is to 100°C. This proportion may be written

$$\frac{F - 32}{180} = \frac{C}{100} \qquad\qquad \textbf{18.1}$$

18.3 Heat as a Form of Energy

If we wish to raise the temperature of some water, we "heat" the water. What is the nature of the process? This question was speculated upon and argued over for centuries before the answer began to evolve at the end of the eighteenth century. One idea which held wide support for many years was that a fluid called *caloric* entered a body when it was heated and leaked away as the body cooled. When measurements of the mass of a body showed no increase when the body was heated, the proponents of the caloric theory argued that the fluid was massless. As a rival of the caloric theory, there gradually evolved the modern point of view that heat is a form of energy. More specifically, *heat is energy which is transferred between a substance and its surroundings or between one part of the substance and another as a result of temperature differences only.*

One of the decisive experiments which supported the theory that heat is a form of energy rather than caloric was performed by Count Rumford in 1798. Rumford observed that when cannon were bored a large increase in temperature resulted, although there was no flame or other source of caloric. When the drill was dull, the rise in temperature was exceedingly great and was related to the amount of mechanical work done in the drilling. Thus, adding energy to the cannon by doing work against friction led to the same temperature behavior as heating it in a furnace.

18.4 Internal Energy

The basic particles of all kinds of matter are in constant motion. Atoms in solids vibrate back and forth in complex motions about their equilibrium positions. Molecules in a liquid wander around among the other molecules, having frequent collisions with them and thus exchanging energy. In gases the molecules travel about at high speeds and have frequent elastic collisions with their neighbors. *The sum of the kinetic and potential energies associated with the random motion of the atoms of a substance is the internal energy of the substance.*

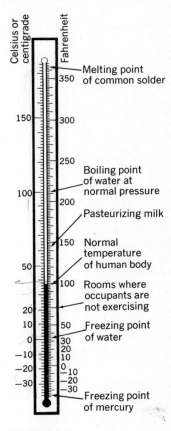

FIGURE 18.2

Comparison of the Celsius (centigrade) and Fahrenheit temperature scales.

When we heat a substance, the random motion and the energy associated with it are increased.

If we pound a nail with a hammer, the nail becomes hot. When the hammer hits, it has kinetic energy associated with the movement of all its particles toward the nail. As the hammer is stopped, the atoms in the nail are given energy which shows up in the form of increased internal energy. After the hammer has struck, the atoms vibrate with greater amplitudes about their equilibrium positions. When a chisel is ground on an emery wheel, its thermal energy and its temperature are increased. When a moving automobile is stopped, its kinetic energy is transferred to internal energy in the brake drums, tires, and road. In all such cases work is done against friction with a resulting increase in the internal energy of the bodies involved.

When we add heat to any substance, we also transfer energy of random motion to its atoms and molecules. Thus we may increase the internal energy of a substance either by adding heat to it or by performing work on it in such a way as to increase the random motion of the atoms. We can raise the temperature of the air in a bicycle pump either by heating the barrel of the pump in a flame or by doing work on the gas by vigorous pumping.

When we put a thermometer in a beaker of water, the random motions of water molecules produce collisions with the molecules of the glass in the thermometer. In turn, the glass molecules exchange energy with the mercury molecules until eventually the "level" of this random motion is the same for the water molecules, the glass molecules, and the mercury molecules. When this occurs, the position of the mercury in the thermometer becomes stationary, and we say the thermometer has come to the same temperature as the water. *Temperature is a measure of the level of internal energy*.

If we put a thermometer in water which is at a higher temperature, heat flows from the water to the thermometer until the temperatures are equal. If the thermometer is at the higher temperature, the molecules of the thermometer lose heat to the water molecules. In general, whenever two bodies are placed in contact, heat is transferred from the one at higher temperature to the one at lower temperature, just as when two bodies of water are connected, water flows through the connection from the higher surface to the lower one. When two bodies are placed in contact and neither gains heat from the other, the two bodies are at the same temperature by definition, and the levels of internal energy are the same for both. When this condition is satisfied, the bodies are in *thermal equilibrium*.

18.5 Absolute Temperature Scales

If the temperature of a body is a measure of the level of internal energy for the body, there must be a lower limit or an *absolute zero* of temperature. If we remove from the atoms and molecules all their available energy of random motion, we can properly assign them a temperature of absolute zero, since temperature measures the level of the energy of random motion. We shall see that there is substantial evidence for the existence of such an absolute zero of temperature, which turns out to be at $-273.15°$C.

Lord Kelvin established an absolute temperature scale based on thermodynamic reasoning (Chap. 23) which uses degrees of the same size as the Celsius degree. In addition to absolute zero, this scale uses as a fixed point the *triple point of water* (Sec. 21.13), which was taken by international agreement in 1954 to be exactly $273.16°$K. The triple point (the temperature at which ice, water, and water vapor are all in equilibrium) is chosen because it is highly reproducible. On the Kelvin absolute thermodynamic scale the ice point is $273.1500°$K, and the steam point $373.15°$K. We shall henceforth use T to indicate absolute temperature, t to represent Celsius or Fahrenheit temperature, and the approximation

$$T(°\text{K}) = t(°\text{C}) + 273 \qquad\qquad \textbf{18.2}$$

The Scotch engineer Rankine devised an absolute scale based on the Fahrenheit degree. Absolute zero on the Rankine scale ($0°$R) corresponds to $-460°$F, and $T(°\text{R}) = t(°\text{F}) + 460$.

18.6 Heat Units

Although heat is a form of energy and can be measured in the units of mechanics (e.g., joules), long before this was known heat units based on temperature increases in a known mass of water became well established. In the mks system *the kilocalorie is the quantity of heat required to raise the temperature of one kilogram of water from* 14.5 *to* 15.5°*C.* In terms of mechanical-energy units 1 kcal = 4,186 joules.

The heat required to raise the temperature of 1 kg of water 1 C° depends only slightly on the temperature (Fig. 18.3). It takes almost exactly 100 kcal to raise the temperature of 1 kg of water from 0°C to 100°C, and in our problems we shall assume that 1 kcal will raise the temperature of 1 kg of water 1 C° at any temperature in this range.

As used by physical scientists, the *calorie* is 0.001 kcal, the heat required to raise the temperature of one gram of water one Celsius degree. In the biological sciences, the kilocalorie is referred to as the *Calorie* (sometimes not capitalized). Thus, if a book on diet suggests that an apple has 100 "calories" of food value, the calories referred to are kilocalories.

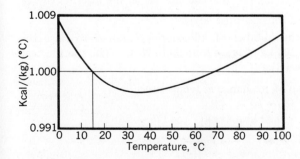

FIGURE 18.3
Specific heat of water as a function of temperature.

In the English system heat is measured in British thermal units (Btu). *One British thermal unit is the heat required to raise the temperature of a one-pound mass of water from 58.5 to 59.5° F.* Since one pound-mass is equal to 0.4536 kg, and 1 F° corresponds to ⅝ C°, it follows that 1 Btu is equal to 0.252 kcal. In mechanical units 1 Btu = 778 ft-lb.

The number of units of mechanical energy necessary to produce the same increase in internal energy as one unit of heat energy is called the *mechanical equivalent of heat.* It is represented by J in honor of Joule, who was a pioneer in studying the relationship between work and heat.

$$J = 4,186 \text{ joules/kcal} = 778 \text{ ft-lb/Btu}$$

One of several experiments devised by Joule to determine J utilizes a well-insulated vessel containing a known mass of water. Within the vessel there is a series of paddle wheels which are rotated to churn the water. The paddle wheels are driven by weights which are hung over pulleys. When the weights descend, the paddle wheels do work on the water in the vessel (calorimeter), causing the water to increase in temperature. From the weights and the distance through which they descend, the work done on the water can be calculated. From the mass of the water, the mass of the container, and the increase in temperature, the heat corresponding to this amount of mechanical energy can be computed.

18.7 Specific Heat

If we add equal amounts of heat to 1 kg of water and to 1 kg of copper, the temperature of the copper goes up far more than the temperature of the water. It takes 0.093 kcal to raise the temperature of 1 kg of copper 1 C°. *The heat required to change the temperature of a unit mass of a substance one degree is the specific heat of the substance.* This definition is worded in such a way that it is applicable to both the metric and the British system of units.

Let Q denote the quantity of heat added to a mass m, and let t_1 and t_2 be the initial and final temperatures, respectively. If c is the specific heat of the material,

$$Q = mc(t_2 - t_1) = mc \, \Delta t \qquad \text{18.3}$$

The quantity $mc \, \Delta t$ of Eq. (18.3) is the increase in the internal energy of the mass.

Example Find the number of kilocalories required to raise the temperature of 0.100 kg of brass from 25 to 75°C. The specific heat of brass is 0.09 kcal/(kg)(C°).

Heat = mass × sp ht × change in temperature
$$= m \times c \times (t_2 - t_1)$$
$$= 0.100 \text{ kg} \times 0.09 \text{ kcal/(kg)(C°)} \times (75 - 25)\text{C°}$$
$$= 0.45 \text{ kcal}$$

TABLE 18.1   *Specific Heats of Solid Elements*

Element	Atomic weight	Specific heat, kcal/(kg)(C°)	Specific heat × atomic weight, kcal/(kg atomic wt)(C°)
Aluminum	27	0.22	5.9
Titanium	47.9	0.14	6.7
Iron	55.8	0.11	6.1
Copper	63.5	0.093	5.9
Tin	118.7	0.054	6.4
Lead	207.2	0.031	6.4

The specific heats of a number of solids and liquids are listed in Tables of Data 1 and 2 in the Appendix. The specific heats of a few elements are shown in Table 18.1. The lightest element listed, aluminum, has the largest specific heat, while the heaviest element has the lowest specific heat. If we multiply the specific heat of each element by its atomic weight, we obtain the number in the last column of the table. *The product of the specific heat of an element and its atomic weight is approximately* 6 kcal/(C°)(kg-atomic wt) *for most solid elements.* This is known as the *law of Dulong and Petit.* The physical meaning of this law is readily seen if we remember that 1 kg-atomic wt of any element contains 6×10^{26} atoms. It requires an average of about 10^{-26} kcal per atom to raise the temperature of most solid elements 1 C°.

There are a few solid elements which are notable exceptions to the law of Dulong and Petit. For example, carbon in the diamond form has a specific heat of only 1.46 kcal/(kg-atomic wt)(C°) at room temperature. However, the value approaches 6 as the temperature is raised (Fig. 18.4). For all elements the specific heat is small at low temperature, approaching zero as the temperature approaches 0°K. Modern quantum theory gives us an understanding of the reasons for the discrepancies between observed specific heats and the law of Dulong and Petit.

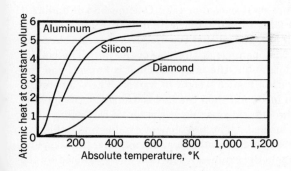

FIGURE 18.4

Atomic heat, the product of specific heat and atomic weight, as a function of temperature for carbon, silicon, and aluminum.

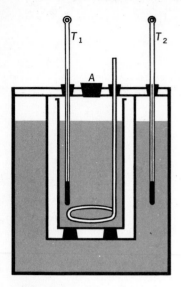

FIGURE 18.5
Calorimeter for measuring the heat transferred to the water in the inner container from a heated mass introduced through the opening closed by plug A. The outer container serves as an insulator for the inner one.

18.8 Calorimetry

One of the most familiar methods of measuring a quantity of heat is by imparting this heat to a known mass of water and observing the change that it produces in the temperature of the water. Experiments of this kind are carried on with the aid of a vessel known as a *calorimeter* (Fig. 18.5) which is carefully insulated so that it neither gains heat from nor loses heat to its surroundings during the experiment. The basic principle underlying all calorimetry experiments is the law of conservation of energy which, for calorimetry, takes the form: *The heat gained by those bodies which gain heat is equal to the heat lost by those bodies which lose heat.*

Example A 0.450-kg cylinder of lead is heated to 100°C and then dropped into a 50-g copper calorimeter containing 0.100 kg of water at 10°C. The water is stirred until equilibrium is established, at which time the temperature of the whole system is 21.1°C. Find the specific heat of lead.

Heat gained = heat lost

$$0.100 \times 1(21.1 - 10) + 0.050 \times 0.093(21.1 - 10) = 0.450c(100 - 21.1)$$
$$1.16 = 35.5c$$
$$c = 0.033 \text{ kcal/(kg)(C°)}$$

When a body such as a calorimeter is used over and over again in heat experiments, it is often convenient to compute its thermal capacity. *The thermal capacity of a body is defined as the heat required to raise the temperature of the entire body one degree.* This quantity is sometimes known as the *water equivalent*. To find the thermal capacity, it is necessary only to multiply the mass m of the body by the specific heat c.

Thermal capacity of body = mc **18.4**

In the example above, the thermal capacity of the calorimeter is $0.050 \text{ kg} \times 0.093 \text{ kcal/(kg)(C°)} = 0.0047 \text{ kcal/C°}$.

18.9 Heat of Combustion

The heat of combustion is the heat liberated by burning a unit mass or unit volume of a fuel such as coal or gas. One method of finding it for a solid or liquid fuel is to place a measured quantity in a crucible inside a bell jar which is closed so that the products of combustion can escape only through the openings at the base of the jar. The bell jar is placed inside a calorimeter, the mass of which is known, and this vessel is then filled with a known weight of water. The temperature of the water is determined, and then the fuel is oxidized. A supply of oxygen is admitted through the opening at the top of the bell jar until all the fuel has been burned. The products of combustion bubble up through the water. When the combustion is complete, the temperature of the water is again determined. The heat energy gained by the water and the calorimeter is equal to the chemical energy released in the oxidation.

Example A sample of coal weighing 0.15 lb was burned in a calorimeter like that described above. The water weighed 100 lb, and its temperature at the beginning of the experiment was 60°F; the final temperature was 80°F. Find the heat of combustion of the coal. The vessel forming the calorimeter has a water equivalent of 5 lb.

Energy released = heat gained
(0.15 lb)(heat of combustion)
$$= [100 \times (80 - 60) \times 1 + 5 \times (80 - 60) \times 1] \text{ Btu}$$
$$= 2100 \text{ Btu}$$

Heat of combustion $= \dfrac{2100 \text{ Btu}}{0.15 \text{ lb}} = 14{,}000 \text{ Btu/lb}$

The heat of combustion of a gas can be measured by oxidizing the gas in a burner inside a special calorimeter. The products of combustion pass out through a series of pipes. Around these pipes there is a continuous flow of water. This water enters the calorimeter at a constant temperature that is measured by a thermometer. The water leaves by an outlet, its temperature being determined just before it leaves the calorimeter. The temperature of the water as it leaves is, of course, higher than when it enters. By weighing the water and measuring the quantity of gas that has been burned, it is possible to calculate the quantity of heat generated per unit volume of gas. If the rate of generation of heat is constant, the difference between the temperatures of the ingoing and outgoing water remains constant.

Example In determining the heat of combustion of natural gas, it was found that 2.40 kg of water flowed through the calorimeter while 3 liters of gas were being burned. The temperature of the ingoing water was 20.0°C, and that of the outgoing water was 30.0°C. Find the number of calories generated by the combustion of 1 liter of gas.

Heat of combustion $= \dfrac{\text{mass of water} \times \text{temperature change} \times \text{sp ht}}{\text{volume of gas}}$

$$= \frac{2.40(30 - 20) \times 1}{3} = 8.0 \text{ kcal/liter}$$

Questions

1. What are the advantages and disadvantages of mercury as a thermometric material?

2. What types of thermometers do you know about? What kind could be used to measure 4°K? 1400°K?

3. What is the distinction between temperature and heat? How are they related?

4. Why are specific heats numerically the same in both British and metric units?

5. What justification do we have for believing that 50°C should be halfway between 0°C and 100°C on a good mercury thermometer?

6. What is the temperature (98.6°F) of the normal human body on the Celsius scale?

Problems

1. A Fahrenheit thermometer shaded from the sun on a hot day reads 104°. What is the temperature on the Celsius scale? *Ans.* 40°C

2. The boiling point of pure ethyl alcohol is 78.5°C. Find the corresponding temperature on the Fahrenheit scale and on the Kelvin scale.

3. A thermostat is set to maintain the temperature at 25°C. What is the corresponding temperature on the Fahrenheit scale? On the Kelvin scale? *Ans.* 77°F; 298°K

4. What is the temperature on the Celsius scale when a Fahrenheit thermometer indicates −50°? 0°? 80°?

5. The temperature at which mercury boils is 675°F, and that at which it freezes is −40°F. Find the corresponding temperatures on the Celsius scale.
Ans. 357°C; −40°C

6. Solid carbon dioxide (dry ice) turns to the gaseous phase at −80°C. Find the corresponding temperature on the Fahrenheit scale.

7. The Reaumur temperature scale has been widely used in France. On this scale the ice point is 0°R and the steam point 80°R. Extend the relationship

$$\frac{C}{100} = \frac{F - 32}{180}$$

to include a term for the Reaumur scale. Find the Celsius and Fahrenheit temperatures corresponding to 24°R. *Ans.* 30°C; 86°F

8. A man of mass 80 kg daily consumes food with a fuel value of about 3,200 kcal. If this energy were used to heat 80 kg of water, how many degrees would the temperature be raised?

9. Upper Yosemite Falls is 436 m high. If all the potential energy lost in this fall is converted into heat, how much is the temperature of the water raised? *Ans.* 1.02 C°

10. One cubic meter of water falls from the top to the bottom of Niagara Falls, a distance of 49 m. If all the potential energy lost in the fall is transformed into heat, how much is the temperature of the water raised?

11. A truck and its load together weigh 8 tons. The brakes are used to bring it to rest from a speed of 60 mi/hr. How much heat is developed? *Ans.* 2490 Btu

12. A hiker with his equipment weighs 900 newtons. If he climbs 1,000 m up a mountain, and if 20 per cent of the energy of the food he consumes goes into potential energy, how many eggs at 80 kcal each would he have to eat to supply himself with food energy for the climb?

13. A lead bullet that has a velocity of 500 m/sec strikes a target. If 90 per cent of the kinetic energy of the bullet is absorbed by the target and the other 10 per cent is retained by the bullet as heat, what is the increase in temperature of the bullet?
Ans. 96 C°

14. How much heat is generated in stopping a flywheel that is making 20 rev/sec about an axis through its center? The flywheel has a moment of inertia of 2 kg-m².

15. A 400-g piece of lead heated to 100°C is dropped into 200 cm³ of water at 4.4°C. The final temperature is 9.9°C. Compute the specific heat of lead.

Ans. 0.031 kcal/(kg)(C°)

16. A piece af aluminum with a mass of 31 g is heated in a steam jacket to a temperature of 98°C and then plunged into 120 g of water at 9°C, causing the temperature to rise to 13.5°C. What is the specific heat of aluminum, assuming that no heat was lost or gained during the experiment?

17. If 200 g of copper at 250°C are dropped into 300 g of water at 10°C contained in a 100-g copper calorimeter, find the resulting equilibrium temperature. *Ans.* 23.6°C

18. To find the temperature of a furnace, a 200-g piece of platinum was placed inside until temperature equilibrium was reached. The platinum was then dropped into a 200-g copper calorimeter containing 500 g of water at 6°C. If the final temperature of the water was 14°C, find the temperature of the furnace.

19. The atomic weights of selenium and ruthenium are 79 and 101, respectively. Estimate their specific heats by use of the law of Dulong and Petit.

Ans. 0.076 and 0.06 kcal/(kg)(C°)

20. Estimate by use of the law of Dulong and Petit the room-temperature specific heats of calcium 40, cadmium 112, lanthanum 139, and rhenium 186.

21. The heat of combustion of natural gas is 1500 Btu/ft³. How many cubic feet of gas are needed to heat 15 ft³ of water from 40 to 180°F in a hot-water heater, assuming that 75 per cent of the energy released is absorbed by the water. *Ans.* 117 ft³

22. Natural gas from the mains, with a heat of combustion of 1500 Btu/ft³, is used to heat water. Assuming that half the available heat is wasted, how much gas will be required to heat 500 lb of water from 42°F to the boiling point?

23. A sample of methyl alcohol of 20 g mass was burned in a fuel calorimeter containing 9 kg of water. The water equivalent of the calorimeter was 800 g. The initial temperature was 11.2°C, and the final temperature was 22.1°C. Calculate the heat of combustion of the methyl alcohol. *Ans.* 5350 kcal/kg

24. A specimen of coal with a mass of 2 g was burned in a copper calorimeter having a mass of 1.1 kg. The mass of the water in the calorimeter was 1.6 kg, and the initial temperature was 14.6°C. The final temperature of the water was 23.9°C. Find the heat of combustion.

25. Into a 100-g copper calorimeter containing 170 g of water at 10°C there are dropped simultaneously 60 g of silver at 100°C, 60 g of iron at 80°C, and 15 g of platinum at 90°C. What is the resulting equilibrium temperature? *Ans.* 14.2°C

26. A sample of coal weighing 0.5 oz with a heat of combustion of 12,000 Btu/lb was burned in a crucible in a calorimeter. The calorimeter contained 12 lb of water, and it had an initial temperature of 48°F. The parts of the calorimeter weighed 6.2 lb and had an average specific heat of 0.18 Btu/(lb)(F°). To what temperature was the water raised?

CHAPTER 19 *In the preceding chapter we saw that increasing the temperature increases the internal energy of random motion of the molecules. For most materials an increase in the internal energy results in an increase in volume, and for solids an increase in length. Such increases are of great practical importance, and in this chapter we introduce quantitative expressions by which we can calculate the expansion produced by a given change in temperature.*

Thermal Expansion

19.1 Expansion of Solids

Most substances expand when heated (Fig. 19.1). This is not surprising if we remember that heating a solid increases the amplitude of vibration of the atoms and has the effect of moving the atoms somewhat farther apart. If the vibrations were simple harmonic, the average position of each atom would not change, and there would be no expansion. However, the forces which restore an atom to its equilibrium position are greater when the atom approaches too close to a neighbor than when the atom moves an equal distance too far away; the forces are *anharmonic*. As the amplitudes of the vibrations increase, the average distance between atoms becomes slightly larger. The change of length of a typical solid is small—only a few parts in ten thousand for an ordinary daily range of outside temperature—but the forces associated with such expansion can be tremendous and must be allowed for in many structures. The amount of expansion depends on the nature of the substance and on the change in temperature. On railroads small distances are usually left between rails to permit expansion without having the tracks bow. In concrete roads and sidewalks, expansion joints filled with tar are provided. Care is taken in selecting types of glass and of metal when one wishes to bring conductors through glass walls into vacuum tubes and light bulbs.

When we heat a solid, the change in length ΔL depends on the material, on the original length L, and on the change in temperature Δt. For most materials we may write the approximate equality

$$\Delta L = \alpha L \, \Delta t \tag{19.1}$$

where α is known as the *coefficient of linear expansion* of the material. From Eq. (19.1) we see that the *coefficient of linear expansion α is the change in length per unit length for a one-degree rise in temperature.* Clearly, α is independent of the units in which the length is measured, but it does depend on the temperature unit. A change of one

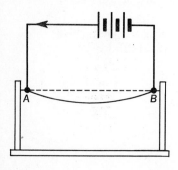

FIGURE 19.1
The length of an iron wire increases when its temperature is raised, in this case by the introduction of electric current.

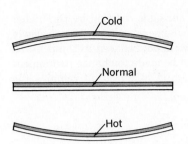

FIGURE 19.2
Unequal expansions of metals in a bimetallic strip. The gray material (iron) has the lower coefficient of linear expansion.

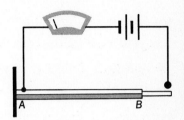

FIGURE 19.3
A bimetallic strip AB closes an electric circuit when it bends upward with a temperature change.

Fahrenheit degree corresponds to a change of only ⅝ Celsius degree. Therefore, α per F° is only ⅝ of α per C°. The coefficient of linear expansion varies with the temperature, usually slowly near room temperature but rapidly at very low temperature. The room-temperature coefficients of linear expansion of many solids are listed in Table of Data 1 in the Appendix.

Example The main cable of a suspension bridge is 5,000 ft in length at 0°C. If the cable is made of steel, find its length on a hot summer day when the temperature is 35°C.

$$\Delta L = \alpha L \, \Delta t$$
$$= 1.2 \times 10^{-5} \times 5,000 \times 35$$
$$= 2.1 \text{ ft}$$

Thus the length is 5,002.1 ft at 35°C.

In the construction of a bridge, or indeed in almost any structure, provision must be made for expansion and contraction. One possible arrangement for a small bridge is to mount one end on a roller. As the length of the bridge increases or decreases, this end of the bridge moves forward or back without injuring the piers.

19.2 Differential Expansion

Consider a strip of brass and a strip of iron welded together (Fig. 19.2) to form a composite bar. If this bar is heated, it bends because of the unequal expansion of the metals. The brass expands more rapidly than the iron, so that the brass is on the outside of the curve when it is heated. Devices of this kind, called *bimetallic strips,* have found many uses. One of the most familiar is in the thermostat, which may be made to open and close electric circuits as the movable end of the bimetallic strip changes its position (Fig. 19.3). Bimetallic strips are used in a common type of thermometer.

In a watch, the balance wheel (Fig. 19.4) is made of bimetallic strips. As the temperature increases, the ends A and B are carried inward, making the moment of inertia of the wheel less; at the same time the expansion of the radius carries the rim of the wheel farther from the center, thereby producing an increase in the moment of inertia.

FIGURE 19.4
Balance wheel of a watch.

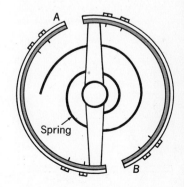

Meanwhile, the elasticity of the hair spring is reduced by the higher temperature. This would make the balance wheel move more slowly if the moment of inertia of the wheel were not reduced to compensate. By proper design the balance wheel can be made to change its moment of inertia just enough so that the period of vibration remains the same at all temperatures.

19.3 Expansion in Area

Consider a square of material with sides of length L. The area is L^2. If we raise the temperature by Δt, the length of each side becomes $L + \Delta L$, and the area becomes

$$(L + \Delta L)^2 = L^2 + 2L \, \Delta L + (\Delta L)^2$$

Since ΔL is very small compared with L, we may neglect $(\Delta L)^2$ in comparison with the other terms and write the new area as $L^2 + 2L \, \Delta L$. The change in area ΔA is then given by

$$\Delta A = 2L \, \Delta L = 2\alpha L^2 \, \Delta t = 2\alpha A \, \Delta t \qquad \textbf{19.2}$$

From Eq. (19.2) we see that *the coefficient of area expansion is twice the coefficient of linear expansion.*

The area of a hole in a sheet of material expands exactly as though it were filled with the material in question, regardless of the shape of the hole or the sheet. The pioneers made use of this fact in putting iron tires on the wooden wheels of their wagons. The iron tire was made slightly smaller than the wooden wheel upon which it was to be placed. Then the tire was heated red hot, and, thanks to its expansion, it could be slipped over the wood. As the iron cooled, it shrank around the wood. In modern manufacturing, when one cylinder is to fit inside and be fastened to another cylinder, the two are often "sweated" together. In this process the inner cylinder is made slightly larger than the hole in the outer cylinder. Then the outer cylinder is heated, and the inner one cooled. Because of expansion of the outer cylinder and contraction of the inner one, the outer cylinder may be slipped over the inner. When the two come to the same temperature, they are held together by extremely strong frictional forces.

19.4 Volume Expansion

Most materials, fluids as well as solids, expand when heated. The change in volume ΔV depends on the substance, the change in temperature Δt, and the original volume V according to the relation

$$\Delta V = \beta V \, \Delta t \qquad \textbf{19.3}$$

where β is *the coefficient of volume expansion* of the substance. *The coefficient of volume expansion is the change in volume divided by the product of the original volume and the change in temperature.*

For most substances β varies somewhat with temperature. *For solids the coefficient of volume expansion β is three times the coeffi-*

cient of linear expansion α, as the following reasoning indicates. Consider a solid cube of length L on each side. When the temperature is raised an amount Δt, the length of each side becomes $L + \Delta L$. The volume is then $(L + \Delta L)^3 = L^3 + 3L^2\,\Delta L + 3L(\Delta L)^2 + (\Delta L)^3$. Since ΔL is very small compared with L, we may neglect the last two terms in comparison with the first two. The initial volume was L^3, and the change in volume is then

$$\Delta V = 3L^2\,\Delta L = 3\alpha L^3\,\Delta t = 3\alpha V\,\Delta t \qquad\qquad \textbf{19.3}a$$

Liquids such as alcohol and kerosene expand when heated. Coefficients of volume expansion for several liquids are listed in Table of Data 2 in the Appendix. However, the most familiar liquid, water, does not behave in so simple a fashion. When warmed from 0 to 4°C, it contracts. As the temperature is raised above 4°, the water expands (Fig. 19.5). Thus a given mass of water has its minimum volume and its maximum density at 4°C. For this reason the temperature of the water at the bottom of a deep northern lake is 4°C the year around. In the winter the surface may freeze over, but the water at great depths remains at 4°C. In the summer the upper layers of the lake are warmed, but very deep layers ordinarily do not increase appreciably in temperature.

19.5 The Expansion of Gases

Gases as well as liquids and solids expand when heated and contract when cooled. If we keep the pressure on the gas constant, we find that a plot of the volume as a function of temperature gives a straight line (Fig. 19.6). The coefficient of volume expansion for the gas is given by $\beta = \Delta V / V\,\Delta t$. Let us agree to use 0°C as our reference temperature. Let V_0 be the volume of the gas at 0°C, and V_t the volume at some temperature t. For 0°C,

$$\beta_0 = \frac{\Delta V}{V_0\,\Delta t} = \frac{V - V_0}{V_0\,\Delta t}$$

or

$$V = V_0(1 + \beta_0 t) \qquad\qquad \textbf{19.4}$$

This relation is known as *Charles' law.* By careful experiments Charles found that the coefficient of volume expansion of all noncondensing gases at constant pressure and 0°C is equal to 0.00367, or ½₇₃. *The coefficient of volume expansion is the same at a given temperature for all gases.* If we extrapolate (Fig. 19.6) a plot of the volume as a function of temperature of any gas to the x axis, the intercept is -273°C, regardless of the original volume of gas taken, of the gas chosen, and of the pressure. The fact that this intercept of -273°C is the same for different gases, different original volumes, and different pressures suggests this temperature has a very special significance. It was the first indication of an absolute zero for temperature. Of course, it should not be concluded that if the temperature of the gas

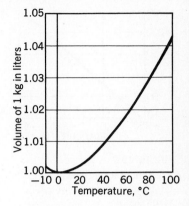

FIGURE 19.5
The volume of 1 kg of water in liters as a function of temperature. The specific volume is minimal at 3.98°C.

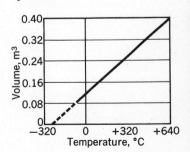

FIGURE 19.6
The volume of a gas as a function of temperature at constant pressure.

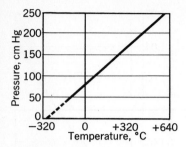

FIGURE 19.7

Pressure as a function of temperature for a gas at constant volume.

were actually lowered to $-273°C$, it would follow the extrapolated line of Figure 19.6 and occupy zero volume. Before any such low temperature is reached, the gas liquefies. On the basis of our absolute temperature scale we may rewrite Eq. (19.4) as

$$V = V_0 \left(1 + \frac{t}{273} \right) = V_0 \frac{273 + t}{273} = V_0 \frac{T}{273} \qquad \text{19.4a}$$

The volume of a gas at constant pressure is proportional to the absolute temperature. In general $V_1/V_2 = T_1/T_2$, where V_1 and V_2 are the volumes occupied by the gas at temperatures T_1 and T_2, respectively, when the pressure is kept constant. From this relation it follows immediately that *the coefficient of volume expansion of a gas is given by the reciprocal of the absolute temperature,* as can be shown by letting T_2 be $T_1 + \Delta T$, and V_2 be $V_1 + \Delta V$.

19.6 Heating a Gas at Constant Volume

If a gas is heated and its volume is kept constant, the pressure varies, increasing ½₇₃ of its value at $0°C$ for every rise of 1 C°. If p_0 represents the pressure at $0°C$, and p_t the pressure at $t°C$,

$$p_t = p_0 \left(1 + \frac{t}{273} \right) = p_0 \frac{T}{273} \qquad \text{19.5}$$

Figure 19.7 shows the relation between the pressure and temperature of a gas at constant volume. Note that once again the intercept on the temperature axis is $-273°C$ (or more exactly $-273.15°C$).

19.7 The General Gas Law

From Boyle's law we know that the product of the pressure and the volume of a gas remains constant if the temperature is held fixed. From Charles' law we know that the volume of a gas is proportional to the absolute temperature if the pressure is constant. If the volume is kept constant, the pressure is proportional to the absolute temperature. If we combine these relations, we may write, for any given mass of gas,

$$pV = bT \qquad \text{19.6}$$

where b is a constant for the particular mass of gas in question. If subscript 1 represents one particular set of conditions for the gas, and subscript 2 another set of conditions, we may write

$$\frac{p_1 V_1}{T_1} = \frac{p_2 V_2}{T_2} \qquad \text{19.7}$$

In both chemistry and physics it is often convenient to measure quantities of substances in moles. *One mole of any gas is that amount of the gas which has a mass in grams equal to the molecular weight.* For example, the molecular weight of gaseous oxygen is 32.0, and hence 480 g of oxygen represent 15.0 moles. A kilomole is 1,000 moles or the amount of the gas which has a mass in kilograms equal to the molecular weight. Thus, since the molecular weight of hydrogen is 2.02, 10 kmole of hydrogen has a mass of 20.2 kg.

It is well known that 1 kmole of any gas occupies the same volume as 1 kmole of any other gas at the same temperature and pressure. At 0°C and one standard atmosphere (76 cm Hg) pressure, 1 kmole of any gas occupies a volume of 22.414 m³; thus 1 mole has a volume of 22.4 liters. The constant b in Eq. (19.6) is the same for 1 kmole of any gas. Let us represent this constant with R. Then for n kmole of any gas,

$$pV = nRT \qquad \text{19.8}$$

The constant R is called the *universal gas constant*. It has the value

$$R = \frac{1.0133 \times 10^5 \text{ newtons/m}^2 \times 22.414 \text{ m}^3}{273.15°\text{K}} = 8{,}314 \frac{\text{joules}}{(\text{kmole})(\text{K}°)}$$

$$= 1.987 \text{ kcal/(kmole)(K}°)$$

The relation expressed by Eq. (19.8) is the *equation of state* for an ideal gas. It is an excellent approximation for real gases so long as the temperature is far above the boiling point and the pressure is not extremely high.

Questions

1. An iron rod lies along the diameter of a circular iron hoop and connects opposite sides of the hoop. If the temperature of the whole system is increased, will the hoop remain circular?

2. What is unique about the thermal expansion of water? What are some of the important consequences? Why wouldn't water in glass make a good thermometer?

3. Does the coefficient of linear expansion depend on what thermometer scale is used? On what units of length are used? Explain.

4. How is thermal expansion allowed for in (a) cement pavements, (b) steel bridges, and (c) ordinary light bulbs?

5. When a mercury-in-glass thermometer is thrust into boiling water, the mercury first descends and then rises. Why?

6. A stretched rubber hose contracts when its temperature is increased. What does this mean about the coefficient of linear expansion? Can you explain why rubber and some other materials contract with increasing temperature?

Problems

1. The steel supporting cables of a suspension bridge have a total length of 550 m at 0°C. Find the length at 30°C.　　　　　　　　　　　　　　　*Ans.* 550.2 m

2. The channel span of the steel Ohio River bridge in Cincinnati is 354 m in length. Calculate the maximum change in its length if it is subject to extreme temperatures of 0°F and 100°F.

3. A bar of copper at 25°C is 80 cm long. At what temperature will it be 0.5 mm shorter?

Ans. −12.5°C

4. If 50-ft steel railroad rails are laid at 10°C, what space should be left between them if they are just to touch at 40°C?

5. Steel rails in 60-ft lengths are laid in winter at 5°C. How much space must be allowed between consecutive rails to permit expansion in summer at a temperature of 45°C?

Ans. 0.35 in.

6. A brass cap is to be "sweated" on a brass cylinder. The inner diameter of the cap is machined to 0.500 in., while the cylinder has an outer diameter of 0.501 in. How hot must the cap be before it can be slipped over the cylinder if the cylinder is at 15°C?

7. A steel ring which is 2.000 ft in diameter at room temperature (20°C) is to be shrunk on a pulley which is 2.004 ft in diameter. Find the temperature to which the ring must be raised so that it will just slip over the pulley.

Ans. 187°C

8. A steam locomotive had driving wheels 70 in. in diameter before the tires were shrunk on. If the diameter of the tire was 69.950 in. at 20°C, find the temperature to which it had to be heated to make its diameter 70.050 in. so it could be slipped over the wheel.

9. Find the coefficient of areal expansion per F° for aluminum. An aluminum panel for an aircraft wing has an area of 450.00 in.² at 50°F. What is its area at 110°F?

Ans. 2.83 × 10⁻⁵ per F°; 450.77 in.²

10. A sheet of brass has an area of 150 cm² at 10°C. What will be its area at a temperature of 90°C?

11. A glass flask holds exactly 500 cm³. It is filled with ethyl alcohol at 0°C and then heated to 40°C. How much ethyl alcohol runs out?

Ans. 21.5 cm³

12. A glass flask holds exactly 500 cm³ of mercury at 70°F. If it is heated to 160°F, how many grams of mercury will run out?

13. A rod of steel and one of brass have exactly the same length, 1 m, at 0°C. The rods are heated together until they differ in length by 0.5 mm. What is the temperature of the rods?

Ans. 69°C

14. A long U tube is filled with ethyl alcohol. One arm of the tube is kept at 5°C, and the other at 35°C. Find the length of the column in the tube at the higher temperature if the length of the column in the tube at the lower temperature is 50 cm.

15. In the early morning, when the temperature is 7°C, the gauge pressure in an automobile tire is 26 lb/in.². In the afternoon, after hard driving, the temperature of the tire is 62°C. If atmospheric pressure has remained constant at 14 lb/in.², find the new gauge pressure.

Ans. 34 lb/in.²

16. A flask with negligible expansion coefficient contains air at a temperature of 27°C and a pressure of 75 cm Hg. Find the pressure in the flask after it is sealed and cooled to −53°C.

17. A stratosphere balloon has a partially filled gas bag containing 200,000 ft³ of helium when the barometer reads 75 cm Hg and the temperature is 17°C. Find its volume when the balloon has risen to such a height that the atmospheric pressure is 15 cm Hg and the temperature is −23°C.

Ans. 8.6 × 10⁵ ft³

18. A sample of gas occupies 300 cm³ at 0°C and 76 cm Hg pressure. What would be its volume if it were heated to 80°C and the pressure increased to 90 cm Hg?

19. Illuminating gas is stored in a tank designed so that the volume may change but the pressure remains constant. If the tank contains 84,000 ft³ under standard pressure, how much does the volume change when the temperature rises from 7 to 27°C? *Ans.* 6,000 ft³

20. The bag of a partially inflated balloon contains 5,000 ft³ of hydrogen at 76 cm Hg pressure and 27°C. The balloon rises to a height of 5 miles, where the temperature is −23°C and the pressure is 27 cm Hg. Find the volume of the hydrogen under these circumstances.

21. An air bubble has a volume of 3 cm³ at the surface of a lake, where the temperature is 27°C. What was its volume at a depth of 90 m, where the temperature was 7°C? *Ans.* 0.29 cm³

22. Air pumped into a tank has a temperature of 100°F, and the pump stops when a pressure of 150 lb/in.² in excess of atmospheric pressure (14.7 lb/in.²) is reached. If the volume of the tank does not change, what will be the gauge pressure in the tank after the air has cooled to 70°F?

23. A brass pendulum is adjusted to beat seconds (i.e., has a period of 2 sec) at 20°C. What will be the gain or loss per day if the temperature of the clock drops to 10°C? *Ans.* Gains 8.3 sec

24. A clock which has a steel pendulum beats seconds correctly when the temperature of the room is 22°C. How many seconds per day will it gain or lose when the temperature of the room is 30°C?

25. What pressure is required to prevent an aluminum block from expanding when its temperature is increased from 15°C to 55°C? *Ans.* 3.1 × 10⁴ lb/in.²

26. A steel rod 15 cm long has a cross section of 2 cm². What force would be required to extend the bar the same amount as the expansion produced by heating it 20 C°?

27. A bimetallic strip is made by soldering a strip of brass to a strip of steel. The strips are each 0.2 mm thick and 10 cm long. If one end is held fast, find how far the other end moves if the strip is heated 100 C°. (Assume the strips were initially straight and that after the temperature rise the brass and steel form arcs of concentric circles 0.2 mm apart.) *Ans.* 1.8 cm

CHAPTER 20 *In Chap. 19 we found that the product of the pressure and the volume of a gas is directly proportional to the absolute temperature; in Chap. 18 we saw that the temperature is a measure of the random kinetic energy of the molecules of a substance. The first of these statements is an experimental fact; if the second is true, it should be possible to develop the form of the general gas law, assuming the validity of our assertion and some reasonable model of a gas. This we now proceed to do.*

Kinetic Theory

20.1 Brownian Motion

The molecular nature of matter is well established by chemical and physical evidence. For developing a theory of gases we shall assume that a gas is composed of a large number of molecules which are in constant motion, and we shall attribute the pressure exerted by the gas to the transfer of momentum to the wall by molecules which are bouncing off. Although we have previously advanced the idea that molecules are in constant motion, we have not yet discussed experimental evidence for this point of view.

Perhaps the simplest and the most direct evidence for the motion of molecules was noted by an English botanist, Robert Brown. With a microscope he observed that very fine particles held in suspension in water were constantly in motion. The smaller the particles, the more freely they moved. The motion is caused by the incessant bombardment of the particles by the molecules of the liquid in which they are suspended. Because of the minute size of the particles, the bombardment on one side is not always equal to the bombardment on the other. Hence, the particles are driven hither and thither. An approximate picture of the behavior of such small particles is obtained by projecting on a screen the shadows of finely divided glass particles that are set in motion by rapidly boiling mercury.

20.2 Kinetic Theory of Gas Pressure

In many respects the behavior of gases is simpler than that of liquids or solids. To explain the physical properties of gases, we make the following assumptions:

1. A gas consists of a very large number of rapidly moving molecules which are so small that the volume of the molecules themselves is negligible compared with the volume of the gas. One justification for

this assumption is the fact that the gas can be compressed so that it occupies a small fraction of its normal volume at atmospheric pressure. When 1 cm³ of water at 100°C is converted to steam at 100°C, it occupies a volume of about 1,670 cm³. The distance between molecules in the steam is $\sqrt[3]{1,670}$ (roughly 12) times the distance between molecules in the liquid.

2. When the rapidly moving molecules collide with one another or with the walls of the container, the collisions are elastic.

3. For an *ideal* gas the attractive forces between molecules are negligible.

Let us now calculate the pressure exerted by a gas on the walls of a container as the molecules strike against them. We begin with a single molecule of mass m moving with velocity v_x parallel to the x axis in a cubical box of length L (Fig. 20.1) and compute the average force which this molecule exerts against one of the faces parallel to the YZ plane. As the molecule approaches the wall, the x component of its momentum is mv_x. After the collision the x component of the velocity is reversed, since the collision is elastic. The change of momentum is $2mv_x$. Some time later, the molecule strikes the opposite wall and eventually returns to the first wall. Between successive collisions at this wall the molecule travels a distance $2L$. Therefore, the time between collisions at the same place is $2L/v_x$. The number of collisions per second is $v_x/2L$. Since at each collision the change of momentum is $2mv_x$, the change in momentum per second at one wall for one molecule is

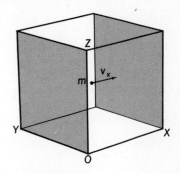

FIGURE 20.1

A single molecule of mass m moving parallel to the x axis with velocity v_x will bounce off the shaded walls.

$$2mv_x \frac{v_x}{2L} = \frac{mv_x{}^2}{L}$$

Let there be n kilomoles of identical molecules in the box. The number N of molecules in each kilomole, known as *Avogadro's number*, is 6.023×10^{26}. The number of molecules in the box is then $6.023 \times 10^{26}n$ or Nn. To find the total change in momentum per second at the wall in question, we add the contributions of all these molecules and obtain

$$\text{Change in momentum per second} = \frac{m}{L}\left(v_{x1}^2 + v_{x2}^2 + \cdots + v_{xNn}^2\right)$$

$$= \frac{nNm}{L}\frac{\left(v_{x1}^2 + v_{x2}^2 + \cdots + v_{xNn}^2\right)}{Nn}$$

$$= \frac{nNm}{L}\overline{v_x{}^2}$$

where $\overline{v_x{}^2}$ represents the average value of the square of v_x for all the molecules in the box.

By Newton's second law of motion the change in momentum per second is equal to the average force. Therefore,

$$F = \frac{nNm\overline{v_x{}^2}}{L} = pL^2$$

since the pressure p is the ratio of the force to the area. Hence,

$$pL^3 = nNm\overline{v_x^2}$$

Now L^3 is just the volume V of the box, so

$$pV = nNm\overline{v_x^2}$$

For a wall of the box parallel to the XZ plane, $pV = nNm\overline{v_y^2}$, and for a wall parallel to the XY plane, $pV = nNm\overline{v_z^2}$. We know from experience that the pressure due to the molecular bombardment is the same on all walls (we assume pressure due to the weight of the gas is negligible); thus we expect that $\overline{v_x^2} = \overline{v_y^2} = \overline{v_z^2}$. By the extension of the pythagorean theorem to three dimensions, $\overline{v_x^2} + \overline{v_y^2} + \overline{v_z^2} = \overline{v^2}$, so that $\overline{v_x^2} = \overline{v^2}/3$, and we may write

$$pV = \frac{nNm\overline{v^2}}{3} = \frac{2nN}{3}\left(\frac{1}{2} m\overline{v^2}\right) \qquad \textbf{20.1}$$

The product of the pressure and the volume is given by two-thirds of the number of molecules multiplied by the average kinetic energy of translation of the molecules.

By the general gas law [Eq. (19.8)], $pV = nRT$. Consequently, $nRT = (2nN/3)(m\overline{v^2}/2)$ or

$$\frac{1}{2} m\overline{v^2} = \frac{3}{2}\frac{R}{N} T = \frac{3}{2} kT \qquad \textbf{20.2}$$

where R is the universal gas constant [8,314 joules/(kmole)(K°)], and N is Avogadro's number. The ratio $R/N = k$ is known as *Boltzmann's constant*. The expression on the left of Eq. (20.2) is the average kinetic energy of translation for the gas molecules, and it is directly proportional to the absolute temperature. Thus, *the absolute temperature is a measure of the average translational kinetic energy of the molecules in a gas.* If we double the absolute temperature, we double this kinetic energy. If we wish to double the average velocity of the molecules in a gas sample, we must increase the absolute temperature by a factor of 4.

The average kinetic energy of a molecule of any gas at temperature T is $\frac{3}{2}kT$, where $k = R/N = 1.38 \times 10^{-23}$ joule/K°. At $27°C$ ($300°$ K), the average kinetic energy of a gas molecule is $\frac{3}{2} \times (1.38 \times 10^{-23}$ joule/K°$) \times 300$ K° $= 6.21 \times 10^{-21}$ joule.

$<$ Let us now calculate the effective velocity of nitrogen molecules at $27°C$. By the "effective velocity" we mean the velocity of a molecule which has the average energy, so $v_{\text{eff}}^2 = \overline{v^2}$. One kilomole of nitrogen has a mass of 28.0 kg, and one molecule a mass of $(28.0/N)$ kg $= 28.0$ kg/$6.025 \times 10^{26} = 4.65 \times 10^{-26}$ kg. Hence, by Eq. (20.2),

$$\tfrac{1}{2}m\overline{v^2} = \tfrac{1}{2}mv_{\text{eff}}^2 = \tfrac{3}{2}kT$$

$$\tfrac{1}{2}(4.65 \times 10^{-26} \text{ kg}) v_{\text{eff}}^2 = \tfrac{3}{2}(1.38 \times 10^{-23} \text{ joule/K°})(300 \text{ K°})$$

$$v_{\text{eff}}^2 = 26.7 \times 10^4 \text{ m}^2/\text{sec}^2$$

$$v_{\text{eff}} = 517 \text{ m/sec}$$

20.3 Dalton's Law of Partial Pressures

We have derived the equations for the pressure exerted by a gas for the case in which the gas contains only molecules of one kind. If the gas contains several different kinds of molecules, each kind rebounds from the walls and contributes to the pressure. The total pressure is the sum of the pressures which each of the various kinds would exert if it occupied the volume alone. We may write

$$p_t = p_1 + p_2 + p_3 + \cdots \qquad\qquad \textbf{20.3}$$

where p_t is the total pressure exerted by all the molecules, and $p_1, p_2, p_3, \ldots$ are the pressures which molecules of type 1, 2, 3, ... would exert if each filled the volume alone. This is known as *Dalton's law of partial pressures.*

Air is a mixture of gases, with nitrogen, oxygen, water vapor, carbon dioxide, argon, hydrogen, and many other kinds of molecules present. The atmospheric pressure is the pressure exerted by the nitrogen plus that due to oxygen, plus that due to each of the other atmospheric constituents. Equation (20.2) shows that the average kinetic energy is the same for each kind of molecule. If we apply this fact to compare the effective velocities of hydrogen and oxygen molecules at a given temperature, we have

$$\frac{3}{2}\frac{R}{N}T = \frac{1}{2}m_h v_h{}^2 = \frac{1}{2}m_0 v_0{}^2$$

where m_h and v_h are the mass and effective velocity of hydrogen molecules, and m_0 and v_0 the corresponding quantities for oxygen molecules. Since $m_0 = 16m_h$, $v_h = 4v_0$. Thus, the effective speed of hydrogen molecules in the atmosphere is four times that of oxygen molecules.

20.4 Distribution of Molecular Velocities in Gases

In writing the expression for the pressure exerted by the ideal gas, we have assumed that a given molecule travels back and forth striking the walls, without taking into account the effects of collisions with other molecules. Although molecules collide frequently with other molecules (Fig. 20.2), these collisions are *elastic.* Therefore, the kinetic energies and momenta of two molecules after collisions add to the same value as before the collision. Although the velocity of any individual molecule undergoes sharp changes and is different one time from another, the average kinetic energy of the molecules is the same at a given temperature. Some molecules are moving rapidly, and some slowly. Figure 20.3 shows the distribution of speeds for gas molecules.

The distance a given molecule travels between collisions differs considerably from collision to collision, but its average value is again well defined. The average length of the path over a large number of colli-

FIGURE 20.2

The path of a molecule colliding with other molecules and with the walls of the container.

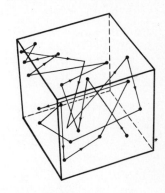

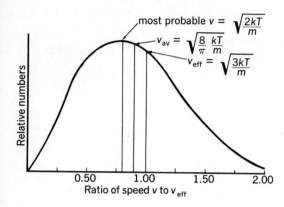

most probable $v = \sqrt{\dfrac{2kT}{m}}$

$v_{av} = \sqrt{\dfrac{8}{\pi}\dfrac{kT}{m}}$

$v_{eff} = \sqrt{\dfrac{3kT}{m}}$

FIGURE 20.3

Maxwellian distribution of speeds for gas molecules. Plotted on the ordinate is the relative number of molecules in each 1 m/sec speed range, and on the abscissa the ratio of the speed v to the effective (or root mean square) speed v_{eff}.

sions is called the *mean free path*. For molecules of the air it is of the order of ten millionths of a centimeter. Table 20.1 lists some of the important molecular quantities for oxygen and hydrogen molecules.

20.5 Work Done by an Expanding Gas

When a gas expands at constant pressure, work must be done to increase the volume. For example, if the gas expands in a cylinder, one end of which is a moving piston (Fig. 20.4) by means of which the pressure is held constant, the work $\mathcal{W}$ done against the piston in moving it from a to b is $p\,\Delta V$, where p is the pressure, and ΔV the change in volume. This may be seen as follows:

$$\mathcal{W} = Fs = pAs$$

where F is the force, s the distance through which the piston moves, and A the area of the piston. The product $As = V_2 - V_1$ is the increase in volume ΔV of the gas during expansion. Therefore,

$$\mathcal{W} = p\,\Delta V \qquad\qquad \textbf{20.4}$$

TABLE 20.1 *Molecular Quantities at 0°C and 76 cm Hg*

Quantity	Hydrogen	Oxygen
Number of molecules per cubic centimeter	2.69×10^{19}	2.69×10^{19}
Diameter of each molecule	2.4×10^{-10} m	3.2×10^{-10} m
Mass of each molecule	3.34×10^{-27} kg	5.3×10^{-26} kg
Mean free path	1.8×10^{-7} m	1.0×10^{-7} m
Number of collisions per second	1.00×10^{10}	4.6×10^{9}
Effective speed	1,840 m/sec	461 m/sec
Average speed	1,700 m/sec	425 m/sec
Most probable speed	1,500 m/sec	376 m/sec
Mass per cubic meter	0.0899 kg	1.43 kg
Volume per gram	1.11×10^{4} cm³	699 cm³
Number of molecules in 1 kmole	6.023×10^{26}	6.023×10^{26}

This work is represented by the shaded area on the pV diagram of Figure 20.4.

Consider the work done when 1 kmole of gas is heated 1 K° under constant pressure. By the general gas law, $pV = RT$. If we raise the temperature 1° at constant pressure, we have

$$p(V + \Delta V) = R(T + 1)$$

Therefore, $p\,\Delta V = R$. Thus, the external work done by 1 kmole of gas when its temperature is raised one Kelvin degree is numerically equal to R.

20.6 Specific Heats of Gases

The specific heat of any substance is defined as the heat required to change the temperature of a unit mass of the substance one degree. For gases the specific heat depends on how the heating is carried out. It takes more heat to raise the temperature of a unit mass of gas 1° if we keep the pressure constant than it does if we keep the volume constant, because of the external work done by the gas when it expands.

Specific Heat at Constant Volume. From Eq. (20.2) we know that $m\overline{v^2}/2 = 3RT/2N$. The total kinetic energy of translation of all the molecules in 1 kmole is $Nm\overline{v^2}/2 = 3RT/2$. To increase the temperature by 1 K°, we must increase the total kinetic energy of translation to $3R(T + 1)/2$, or by $3R/2$. Hence, for any gas in which all the thermal energy is associated with translational motion, the specific heat is $3R/2M$, where $M (=Nm)$ is the mass in kilograms of 1 kmole. This is the case for any monatomic gas for which

$$c_V = \frac{3R}{2M} \qquad\qquad \textbf{20.5}$$

Since $R = 1.987$ kcal/(kmole)(K°), we have the following specific heats for selected monatomic gases: for helium, $M = 4$ kg/kmole, and $c_V = 0.745$ kcal/(kg)(K°); for argon, $M = 39.95$ kg/kmole, and $c_V = 0.075$ kcal/(kg)(K°).

For diatomic and triatomic gases at room temperature the specific heat is greater than the value $3R/2M$ because the molecule has kinetic energy of rotation as well as of translation. We may think of a diatomic molecule as a dumbbell which is rotating as it moves about (Fig. 20.5). When we raise the temperature, the kinetic energy of rotation increases, as well as the kinetic energy of translation. This is why the specific heat at constant volume for diatomic gases is greater than that predicted by Eq. (20.5). At room temperature the specific heat at constant volume for most diatomic gases is given by $5R/2M$. At higher temperatures it becomes still greater; the additional energy goes into exciting vibrations of the two atoms along the line connecting their centers of mass. For triatomic gases near room temperature, the specific heat is $3R/M$ or more, depending on how much energy is associated with vibration.

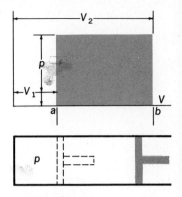

FIGURE 20.4
The work done by a gas expanding at constant pressure is equal to the product of the pressure and the change in volume.

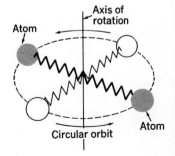

FIGURE 20.5
A diatomic molecule may have kinetic energy of rotation and vibration as well as kinetic energy of translation.

Specific Heat at Constant Pressure. When a gas is kept at constant pressure, the heat required to increase the internal energy of the molecules is the same as when the gas is kept at constant volume. In addition, however, it is necessary to supply heat energy *to do the external work required to expand the gas.* As we saw in Sec. 20.5, the work done in expansion when we increase the temperature of 1 kmole 1 K° at constant pressure is $p \, \Delta V = R$, and the energy which must be added per unit mass of gas is R/M. Therefore, the specific heat of the gas at constant pressure is R/M greater than the specific heat at constant volume:

$$c_p = c_V + \frac{R}{M} \qquad\qquad \textbf{20.6}$$

The ratio of the specific heat of the gas at constant pressure to the specific heat at constant volume is ordinarily represented by γ. For a monatomic gas c_V is $3R/2M$, and $c_p = 5R/2M$. Therefore,

$$\gamma = \frac{c_p}{c_V} = \frac{5R/2M}{3R/2M} = \frac{5}{3}$$

for a *monatomic* gas.

For diatomic gases at room temperature,

$$c_V = \frac{5R}{2M} \qquad \text{and} \qquad \gamma = \frac{7R/2M}{5R/2M} = 1.4$$

20.7 Deviations from the General Gas Law

In our discussions of gases we have made two important assumptions which are not always justified. We have assumed (1) that the volume of the molecules themselves is negligible in comparison with the total space occupied by the gas and (2) that the attractive forces between gas molecules are negligible. For experiments with gases such as oxygen and hydrogen at room temperature and ordinary pressures, these assumptions are justified. However, if they were true under all circumstances, we would never have molecules sticking together to form liquids or solids. Indeed, substances composed of molecules in which the attractive forces are relatively great are already liquid or solid at room temperature.

<   Let us keep the temperature of a given mass of a *real* gas constant and study the behavior of the pressure and volume. If Boyle's law held rigorously, the product pV would be constant for all pressures and volumes so long as the temperature was kept constant. But accurate observations show that the product is not constant when the pressure is varied over a large range. At exceedingly high pressures, the molecules are close together, and the space occupied by the molecules themselves is no longer negligible. Therefore an increase in the pressure of the gas results in too small a decrease in volume, so that pV increases with p instead of remaining constant according to Boyle's law. At exceedingly low pressure the product pV decreases somewhat as p is increased.

Van der Waals has shown that the intermolecular attraction and the space occupied by the molecules themselves can be simply taken into account by a modification of the general gas law. According to Van der Waals, for 1 mole of gas,

$$\left(p + \frac{a}{V^2}\right)(V - b) = RT \qquad\qquad 20.7$$

where a and b are constants characteristic of a given gas but independent of temperature, pressure, and volume. The constant b is a correction to take account of the fact that the molecules themselves occupy a finite amount of space. A detailed analysis shows that b is four times the actual volume of the molecules in the mole of gas. The term a/V^2 takes account of the attractive forces between the molecules which have the effect of reducing the volume just as does the pressure.

20.8 Diffusion

Evidence supporting the idea that molecules are in constant motion is found in the manner in which an odor penetrates to all parts of a room when a bottle of ammonia is opened. The spread of the odor can be explained on the assumption that the ammonia molecules escape from the bottle and wander about among the air molecules. They are buffeted back and forth, gradually spreading throughout the room. The process by which molecules of one kind penetrate and intermix with molecules of another kind is called *diffusion*.

If a porous jar (Fig. 20.6) is surrounded by another vessel into which hydrogen is introduced, hydrogen diffuses through the porous jar and increases the gas pressure inside it, causing gas to bubble up from the water into which the end of the tube leading from the porous jar is dipped. Molecules diffuse out of the porous walls as well as in, but the heavier air molecules diffuse outward far more slowly than the hydrogen molecules diffuse inward. The reason is the greater speeds of the hydrogen molecules; as we saw in Sec. 20.2, the effective speed of a gas molecule is inversely proportional to the square root of its mass. It is diffusion which keeps the air in such a state of uniform mixture and which accounts for the rapid disappearance of the fumes when a bottle of ether is broken out of doors.

In liquids as well as in gases, the molecules are free to move about. If a little sulfuric acid is placed in a bottle of water, it diffuses to form a uniform concentration. When a lump of sugar is placed in a cup of coffee, the contents of the whole cup are sweetened by the distribution of the sugar molecules throughout the coffee; stirring promotes the rapid mixing of the molecules.

If stirring and convection currents are avoided, it can be shown that diffusion in liquids occurs very slowly. This may be demonstrated by use of a tall glass jar filled with water into which, by means of a thistle tube extending to the bottom of the jar, a solution of copper sulfate is carefully poured until the bottom of the jar is filled to a

FIGURE 20.6

The pressure within the porous jar increases because hydrogen diffuses through its walls faster than the heavier air molecules diffuse out.

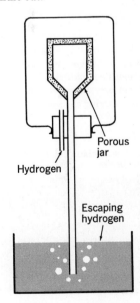

Porous jar

Hydrogen

Escaping hydrogen

height of a centimeter or two. If the jar is allowed to stand for some days without being disturbed, the upward diffusion of the copper sulfate can be observed. Gravity tends to keep the copper sulfate on the bottom, but diffusion occurs, and the copper sulfate gradually rises in the jar.

If two metals such as copper and nickel are placed in contact, atoms of each gradually diffuse into the other. If the specimens are cut into sections after they have been in contact for some time, the concentrations of the two metals at different distances from the contact plane can be determined. The rate of diffusion depends on the temperature, but in any case it is very slow for solids.

20.9 Osmosis

When the pores of a membrane are large enough to pass small molecules, but not big enough to pass larger ones, the membrane is said to be *semipermeable*. The process of preferential diffusion through a semipermeable membrane is called *osmosis*. For example, if a carrot is hollowed out, and a thick sugar syrup placed in the cavity, there is a net flow of water into the carrot when it is placed in water. If a glass tube is sealed to the cavity, the water may rise to a height of several feet. The carrot serves as a semipermeable membrane (Fig. 20.7) having a great number of small holes through which water molecules may pass either in or out. Sugar molecules, on the other hand, are too large to pass through. The fact that the water level rises in the tube means that more water flows in than flows out. The large sugar molecules act somewhat as valves for many of the openings. A water molecule moving inward may slightly displace the large sugar molecule at A in Figure 20.7 and get into the idealized carrot, but a water molecule coming from the other side can only push the sugar molecule more tightly against the hole. There are many holes through which water molecules pass in either direction, but there are more holes through which water molecules enter than there are by which they leave. As water rises in the tube, the pressure inside increases, eventually becoming great enough so that there is no longer a net inflow. The pressure that just prevents further flow of the solvent is called the *osmotic pressure* of the solution. In dilute solutions in which the molecules are not dissociated, the osmotic pressure is proportional to the concentration of the dissolved substance. In a solution of given concentration, the osmotic pressure increases as the temperature is increased, the rate of increase being the same for all solutions because the increase in average kinetic energy is the same for all kinds of molecules.

When dried fruits such as prunes and raisins are cooked, they swell and burst if the pressure inside becomes sufficiently large. The swelling is due to the fact that the vegetable sacs surrounding the fruit are semipermeable membranes through which there is a net diffusion of water from outside to inside. If marine animals such as oysters are

FIGURE 20.7

Sugar molecules prevent water molecules from leaving through many of the holes in a semipermeable membrane, but they do not prevent water molecules from entering the solution.

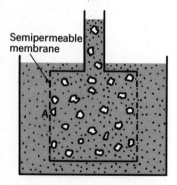

Semipermeable membrane

transferred from salt water to fresh water, more water flows into than out of the animal through the membrane that serves as its covering. Dilation and death of the animal result.

Questions

1. On the basis of what happens to individual molecules, explain why the temperature of a gas rises when the gas is compressed.

2. How would you expect the specific heat of hydrogen at constant volume to compare with that of oxygen? Why?

3. Why does the product pV increase slightly as the pressure is raised when pressure and density are very high, even though the temperature remains constant?

4. Why, at very low pressure and density, does pV decrease slightly as p is increased at constant temperature?

5. Why is the specific heat of a diatomic gas ordinarily greater than the corresponding specific heat of a monatomic gas?

Problems

1. The specific heats of air at constant pressure and at constant volume are 0.24 and 0.17 kcal/(kg)(C°), respectively. If 2 kg of air are heated from 0 to 40°C at constant pressure, find (a) how much external work is done and (b) how much the kinetic energy of the air molecules is increased. *Ans.* (a) 5.6 kcal; (b) 13.6 kcal

2. The specific heat at constant volume of argon, a monatomic gas, is 0.075 kcal/(kg)(C°). One kilogram of argon is heated from 27 to 127°C. How many kilocalories are required if the heating is done at constant volume? At constant pressure?

3. If the average speed of a hydrogen molecule is 1 mi/sec at 27°C and 76 cm Hg pressure, find (a) the average speed of an oxygen molecule under the same conditions, (b) the average speed of a hydrogen molecule at 27°C and 100 cm Hg pressure, and (c) the temperature at which the average speed of a hydrogen molecule is 2 mi/sec. *Ans.* (a) 0.25 mi/sec; (b) 1 mi/sec; (c) 927°C

4. Compute the effective speed of an oxygen molecule under standard conditions, making use of the fact that one molecular weight (32 g) occupies 22.4 liters under these conditions.

5. Calculate the effective speed of molecules of carbon dioxide under standard conditions if the molecular weight is 44. *Ans.* 394 m/sec

6. Find the temperature at which the effective (rms) speed of oxygen molecules is equal to the effective (rms) speed of nitrogen molecules at 27°C.

7. A McLeod gauge indicates pressures as low as 10^{-5} mm Hg (or 10^{-5} Torr). How many molecules per cubic centimeter would be required to produce this pressure at 0°C? *Ans.* $3.54 \times 10^{11}/cm^3$

8. How many molecules of air remain in each cubic centimeter of a radio tube at 27°C in which the pressure has been reduced to 10^{-8} mm Hg?

9. A vessel having a capacity of 2 liters contains nitrogen under a pressure of 4 atm. It is connected to a vessel of capacity 1 liter containing oxygen at a pressure of 2 atm. If the temperature remains constant, what will be the pressure when the gases have mixed?   *Ans.* 3.33 atm

10. Pure oxygen at 0°C is enclosed in a cylinder having a volume of 15 liters. If the pressure in the cylinder is 2,500 cm Hg, what is the mass of the enclosed gas? How much pressure would it exert if the temperature were increased to 750°C?

11. Find the number of mercury molecules, each with a mass of 3.3×10^{-25} kg and an effective speed of 283 m/sec, that would maintain normal atmospheric pressure against the walls of a containing vessel with a volume of 100 cm³. What is the temperature of the gas?   *Ans.* 1.15×10^{21}; 640°K

12. A carefully evacuated vessel has a volume of 5 liters. It develops a small leak through which 100 million molecules of air pass each second. How long will it take for the pressure of the air in the vessel to reach 0.001 atm if the temperature remains constant at 17°C?

13. How long would it take a toy balloon with an original volume of 1 liter and a pressure of 90 cm Hg at 27°C to lose half its molecules if 10^{12} molecules escaped each second?   *Ans.* 1.45×10^{10} sec or 460 years

14. A helium tank has a volume of 10 liters, is at 27°C, and is filled to a pressure of 1.5×10^7 newtons/m² (148 atm). A leak develops in the valve, and after a week the pressure is 9×10^6 newtons/m² when the temperature is 7°C. Find the mass of helium that was in the tank when it was full and the fraction of the original mass which has leaked out.

15. Find the external work done and the increase in internal energy if 4 moles (0.112 kg) of nitrogen at 27°C and 1×10^5 newtons/m² pressure are expanded at constant pressure until the volume increases 50 per cent.   *Ans.* 4,990 joules; 12,500 joules

16. One mole (4 g) of He at 0°C occupies a volume of 22.6×10^{-3} m³ at a pressure of 10^5 newtons/m². If 200 cal of heat are added to this mole of helium at constant pressure, find the final temperature of the gas, the external work done by the gas, and the increase in the internal energy of the gas.

17. A gram-molecular weight (28 g) of nitrogen at 27°C is supplied with 2,000 joules of heat. It expands, doing 400 joules of work. What is the increase in internal energy? What is the increase in temperature?   *Ans.* 1,600 joules; 77 C°

18. Argon is a monatomic gas with an atomic weight of 40. Find the specific heat of argon at constant pressure and at constant volume. How much external work is done when 4 kg of argon is heated from 0 to 5°C at constant pressure? How much is the internal energy increased?

19. A cylinder contains 400 cm³ of neon at 0°C and 76 cm Hg pressure. Neon is a monatomic gas with an atomic weight of 20.2. What is the mass of this quantity of gas? If the temperature of this gas is raised to 100°C and the pressure is reduced to 38 cm Hg, find the new volume of the gas and the increase in the internal energy of the gas.
                                                         Ans. 0.36 g; 1,090 cm³; 22.3 joules

CHAPTER 21 *The success of the kinetic theory of gases prompts us to apply the basic ideas to liquids and solids and to changes from one phase to another. Here we can scarcely hope to achieve quantitative understanding because the assumption that interactions between the particles are negligible is no longer valid, and we do not have simple formulas by which to calculate them. Nevertheless, we proceed to apply the ideas qualitatively, and we shall find that they give us considerable insight toward an understanding of the melting of solids and the evaporation of liquids.*

Change of Phase

21.1 Change of Phase

The kinetic theory of matter leads to an understanding of many properties of liquids and solids, as well as of gases. When we reduce the temperature of a gas, we reduce the average kinetic energy of translation of the molecules. As the molecules move more and more slowly, attractive forces between molecules, which played a negligible role at high temperatures, become important. Eventually, groups of molecules stick together. The gas is beginning to liquefy.

In the liquid phase molecules wander about freely, but they have difficulty in leaving the surface (Sec. 13.11). If the temperature of the liquid is reduced, the energy of the molecules decreases. Eventually, the translational kinetic energy becomes so small that the molecule is trapped by the attractive forces exerted by its neighbors. Once the molecule is able only to vibrate about some equilibrium position, the material loses its fluid properties and retains its shape. We then speak of it as a *solid*. If each atom of the material is located in a particular place in a regular array, we have a *crystalline solid,* of which diamond, quartz, and calcite are examples. In some cases each atom is confined to a small region about an equilibrium point by the attractive forces of neighboring particles, but no perfectly repetitive structure is formed. This is the case when glass cools and when butter solidifies. The structure is not crystalline, but amorphous.

As a solid is cooled, the energy associated with random motions of the particles is reduced. At a temperature of $0°K$, the motions of all atoms would be reduced to their lowest possible value. At one time it was believed that this would correspond to a state of absolutely no motion, but modern quantum mechanics has shown there is necessarily some zero-point energy.

21.2 The Melting Point

If ice is heated, the temperature rises until it reaches 0°C and then remains stationary until all the ice is melted. Once all the ice is melted, the temperature of the water begins to rise. *The temperature at which the solid changes into liquid is called the melting point.* At the melting point more heat serves to hasten the melting process without any change of temperature.

The temperature at which the liquid changes into the solid state is its *freezing point.* For crystalline substances such as ice or copper, the freezing point and the melting point coincide and are sharply defined. Substances that are not crystalline, such as wax or glass, gradually soften and do not have definite melting points. In the cases of certain fats, the melting point is not the same as the freezing point. For example, butter melts between 28 and 32°C and solidifies between 20 and 23°C.

21.3 Supercooling

If a pure liquid is carefully protected from mechanical disturbances, it may be cooled below the temperature at which it normally solidifies. Thus water has been cooled to about −40°C without becoming ice. The liquid at such a temperature is in a state of unstable equilibrium and immediately solidifies if it is disturbed or if a crystal of the solid is dropped into it.

21.4 Heat of Fusion

To melt a solid such as ice, it is necessary to supply a given quantity of thermal energy to each unit mass. This is true even though the temperature of the ice at the beginning is the same as the temperature of the water at the end of the process. The ice has a crystalline structure, and the energy is necessary to tear down this structure. Water, in changing back to ice (in general, a liquid in changing back to a solid), gives up the heat that it absorbed in melting. *The heat of fusion of a substance is the heat necessary to convert a unit mass of solid into liquid at the same temperature and pressure.* To change 1 kg of ice to water at 0°C requires 80 kcal; to convert 1 lb of ice to water at 32°F requires 144 Btu. Heats of fusion of several solids are listed in Table of Data 1 in the Appendix.

Example In an experiment designed to measure the heat of fusion of ice, 25 g of ice at 0°C were dropped into 195 g of water at 30°C contained in a copper calorimeter of mass 100 g. The final temperature was 18°C. Find the heat of fusion of ice.

$$\text{Heat gained} = \text{heat lost}$$
$$0.025L + 0.025 \times 1 \times (18 - 0) = 0.195 \times 1 \times (30 - 18)$$
$$+ 0.100 \times 0.093 \times (30 - 18)$$

where L is the latent heat of fusion, and $0.025L$ is the heat needed to melt the ice.

$$0.025L + 0.450 = 2.45$$
$$L = 80 \text{ kcal/kg}$$

21.5 Change of Volume during Freezing

It is a familiar fact that ice floats and that pipes or bottles filled with water burst when frozen. One cubic foot of water makes about 1.09 ft^3 of ice. Cast iron and type metal behave like water in this respect, expanding when they solidify. For this reason they are suitable for making castings in which it is desired to reproduce the detail of a mold. Most metals and other substances contract on solidification. This is one reason why gold and silver coins are stamped rather than cast.

That the forces exerted by freezing water are large may be seen from the fact that they are sufficient to burst strong water pipes on a cold night. These forces are of importance in the formation of soils from rocks. The water penetrates into the crevices in the rocks and freezes. The expansion breaks off fragments, which after a time become soil. Alternate freezing and thawing of soils tends to pulverize them. Ice forming in the interstices of the soil serves to loosen compact land and give it better tilth.

The fact that water expands when it freezes is responsible for the fact that ice forms on top of a lake or stream rather than the bottom. A layer of ice is an excellent insulation which protects all but shallow water from freezing to the bottom. Fish and other water life can carry on in the water below the ice layer.

21.6 Effect of Pressure on the Melting Point

Since an increase of pressure causes a body to contract, such an increase favors the liquid phase for any substance which contracts on melting and results in a lower melting point. Ice contracts when it melts; therefore the melting point is lowered by application of pressure. Careful experiments show that this lowering is $0.0075°C$ for an increase of 1 atm of pressure (Fig. 21.1). If a substance expands upon melting, its melting point is raised by the application of pressure.

The effect of pressure on the melting point of ice may be shown by supporting, on a piece of ice, a loop of wire from which a heavy weight is hung. The pressure of the wire lowers the melting point so the ice is in a condition to melt as soon as the necessary heat is supplied. This heat is taken from the water above the wire, causing it to freeze again. This process continues until the wire cuts its way through the ice, leaving the block as solid as it was at the beginning. The process is called *regelation*.

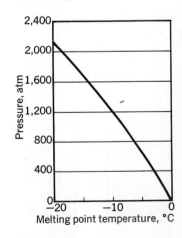

FIGURE 21.1

How the melting point of ice is reduced as pressure rises.

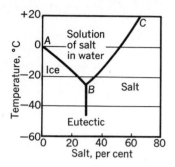

FIGURE 21.2

The freezing point of a salt solution as a function of salt concentration by weight.

21.7 Freezing Point of a Solution

When any material is dissolved in water, the freezing point of the solution is lower than the freezing point of water. This is also true for other liquids. The freezing point of a solution is lower than that of the pure solvent. This fact is used to prevent the water in the cooling system of an automobile from freezing.

For solutions that are not too concentrated, the lowering of the freezing point is proportional to the number of dissolved particles per unit volume. A given number of salt (NaCl) molecules lowers the freezing point more than an equal number of sugar molecules because the salt ionizes, thus producing two particles per dissolved molecule.

When a dilute solution begins to freeze, only solvent freezes out. This makes the remainder of the solution more concentrated and lowers its freezing point still further, until the solution becomes saturated. Then dissolved substance and solvent freeze out in such a way that the concentration of the solution remains unchanged. Figure 21.2 represents the relation between the freezing point and the percentage of salt in a solution. Curve AB shows the relation between temperature and concentration of the salt. The temperature at which the solvent and the dissolved substance crystallize out as a mixture is called the *eutectic temperature*. If the temperature of the solution is higher than the eutectic temperature and the solution is saturated, the dissolved substance crystallizes out as the temperature is lowered (curve BC).

21.8 Saturated Vapor

The molecules of a liquid move with a wide range of instantaneous velocities. When the liquid is heated, this range and the average speed increase. Some of the molecules near the surface attain sufficient kinetic energy to escape the forces of attraction which confine the less energetic molecules to the liquid (Fig. 21.3). When the space above the surface of the liquid is enclosed, some molecules of vapor return to the surface of the liquid and are captured. As more molecules escape, the number returning to the surface also increases. When the number of molecules returning to the surface is equal to the number escaping, the space above the liquid is said to be saturated, and above the liquid we have a *saturated vapor*. The pressure exerted by a saturated vapor

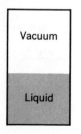
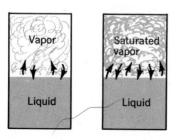

FIGURE 21.3

When a liquid evaporates and the vapor is saturated, the number of molecules escaping the liquid per unit time is equal to the number returning to the liquid per unit time.

depends on the nature of the liquid (Fig. 21.4) and on the temperature. If the temperature is held constant and an attempt is made to increase the pressure on a saturated vapor, part of the vapor condenses. *The saturated vapor pressure of any given liquid depends only on the temperature.*

The saturated vapor pressures of several liquids as functions of temperature are plotted in Figure 21.5. As the temperature increases, the pressure of the saturated vapor rises. A vapor-pressure curve may be obtained by measuring the difference in level between the surfaces of mercury in the apparatus of Figure 21.6 as the temperature is increased.

21.9 Evaporation and Boiling

Even at relatively low temperature the most energetic molecules evaporate from the surface of a liquid. *Evaporation is the escape of molecules from the surface of a liquid.* As the temperature of a liquid is raised, evaporation proceeds more rapidly. Eventually bubbles of vapor form in the liquid and rise to the surface. That temperature at which vapor bubbles form in the volume of the liquid and rise to the surface is the *boiling point* or *boiling temperature.*

We shall now examine the boiling point from a somewhat different point of view. Consider a bubble of vapor within the liquid. This bubble will collapse unless the pressure of the saturated vapor within it is as great as the pressure in the adjacent liquid. The pressure at the bubble is the applied pressure at the surface of the liquid plus the hydrostatic pressure due to the liquid above the bubble plus the pressure due to surface tension. Even for a relatively small bubble near the surface, the latter two contributions to the total pressure are normally negligible in comparison with the applied pressure. Thus, *the*

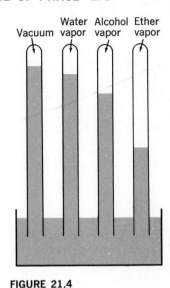

FIGURE 21.4
When a small volume of a liquid is introduced into the Torricelli vacuum above a mercury column, the mercury level is reduced below the vacuum level by the saturated vapor pressure of the liquid.

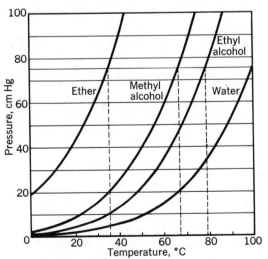

FIGURE 21.5
Saturated vapor-pressure curves of four liquids. The dashed lines indicate the boiling points at 1 atm (76 cm Hg) pressure.

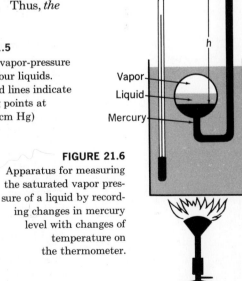

FIGURE 21.6
Apparatus for measuring the saturated vapor pressure of a liquid by recording changes in mercury level with changes of temperature on the thermometer.

boiling point is the temperature at which the pressure of the saturated vapor of the liquid is equal to the applied pressure.

The distinction between *evaporation* and *boiling* should now be clear. Both involve the change of phase from liquid to gas, which is called *vaporization*. Evaporation is vaporization from the surface alone, whereas boiling is vaporization within the volume of the liquid. Since the boiling point of a liquid is the temperature at which the vapor pressure is the same as the applied pressure, it follows at once that when the applied pressure is changed, the boiling point also changes. At 1 atm (76 cm Hg) pressure, water boils at 100°C. The curves of Figure 21.5 show how the boiling points of four familiar liquids vary with pressure. (For water the boiling point is tabulated as a function of pressure in Tables of Data 3 and 4 in the Appendix.)

< The influence of pressure on the boiling point can be shown by filling a flask half full of water and boiling it vigorously for some time to remove the air from above the water. Remove the flask from the flame and immediately insert a stopper, rendering the flask airtight. Invert the flask, and pour cold water on the bottom. This cold water causes some of the vapor in the flask to condense, and the pressure on the hot water in the flask is reduced sufficiently to allow the water to begin boiling again.

The effect of pressure on the boiling point of water is well illustrated in the action of geysers. If it is 100 ft down from the surface of a narrow column of water to a cavity surrounded by hot rocks, the pressure at these rocks is about 4 atm, three of the four being due to the column of water. At this pressure water boils between 140 and 150°C. Once water in the cavity begins to boil, bubbles rush up the column carrying quantities of water with them, thus reducing the pressure at the cavity and encouraging more rapid boiling until the temperature of the water in the cavity is lowered to the point at which boiling ceases.

In the pressure cooker the increased pressure results in a higher boiling point for water and a higher cooking temperature. On the other hand, when sirups or milk are to be evaporated, they may be placed in "vacuum pans" so that boiling can be carried out at a reduced temperature, thereby eliminating undesirable changes which would occur at the normal boiling temperature.

When a ship is driven by a rapidly rotating propeller, the pressure on one side of the propeller decreases as the angular velocity is increased. When the pressure falls below its saturated vapor pressure, the water flashes into vapor, producing cavities in the liquid. This phenomenon is known as *cavitation*.

21.10   Heat of Vaporization

Just as a certain amount of heat is required to convert a unit mass of ice into water without changing its temperature, so a certain amount of heat is required to change a unit mass of water into steam without changing its temperature. When the steam condenses, this heat is liberated.

The heat of vaporization of a substance is the heat necessary to change a unit mass of the liquid to the vapor state without any change in the temperature and pressure. For water at 100°C and 1 atm pressure, it is found to be 540 kcal/kg or 970 Btu/lb. It takes more than five times as much heat to change 1 g of water at 100°C into steam at 100°C as it takes to heat that same gram of water from 0 to 100°C. The heats of vaporization of several other liquids are listed in Table of Data 2 in the Appendix.

< The heat of vaporization depends on the temperature (and pressure) at which the change takes place. The higher the temperature, the easier it is to evaporate the liquid; i.e., the higher the temperature, the lower the heat of vaporization (Fig. 21.7).

The following experiment may be used to determine the heat of vaporization of water. Fill a calorimeter with a known mass of water. Pass dry steam from a boiler into the calorimeter. Measure the temperature of the water in the calorimeter at the beginning and after steam has been condensed in it. The mass of condensed steam is found by weighing the calorimeter after the steam has been condensing for a time sufficient to produce the desired rise in temperature. The latent heat of vaporization of water can now be calculated as illustrated below.

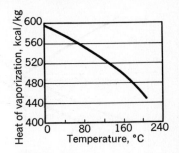

FIGURE 21.7

The heat of vaporization of water decreases as temperature is raised.

Example Dry steam at 212°F is condensed in a large calorimeter of water equivalent 0.60 lb, which contains 6.2 lb of water at 42°F. The final temperature of 82°F is reached after 0.25 lb of steam has been condensed. Find the latent heat of vaporization V as given by these data.

$$\text{Heat gained} = \text{heat lost}$$
$$6.2 \times 1 \times (82 - 42) + 0.60 \times (82 - 42) = 0.25V + 0.25 \times 1 \times (212 - 82)$$
$$248 + 24 = 0.25V + 32.5$$
$$V = 960 \text{ Btu/lb}$$

The correct value is 970 Btu/lb.

When a liquid is evaporating, heat is taken from the remaining liquid and the surrounding bodies. The withdrawal of this heat may cause their temperatures to decrease. For this reason the evaporation of water sprinkled on the sidewalk causes the air to become cooler. Evaporation of perspiration from the skin lowers the temperature of the body.

21.11 Boiling Point of a Solution

When water has some substance such as sugar dissolved in it, the temperature at which it boils is raised. The amount the boiling point is raised is proportional to the amount of the substance dissolved in the water. In making candies or sirups, the temperature is used as a

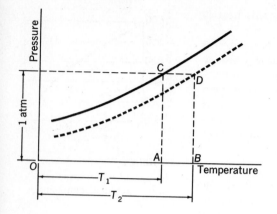

FIGURE 21.8

The saturated vapor pressure of a solution (dashed line) is lower than that of the solvent (solid line) at any temperature.

means of determining the concentration of the solution. By observing the temperature at which the solution is boiling, it is possible to determine when the candy or sirup has been boiled sufficiently long. When vegetables, fruits, meats, etc., are boiled in water, some of their contents dissolve in the water. This raises the boiling point slightly, so that the water boils above 212°F. The effect of a dissolved substance on the vapor pressure and the boiling point is shown in Figure 21.8. The continuous curve gives the relation between the temperature and the vapor pressure of the pure solvent, and the dotted curve the same relation for the solution.

When a solid is dissolved in a liquid, the vapor that rises above the liquid does not contain the dissolved substance. To obtain pure water from water containing solids in solution, it is only necessary to evaporate the water and condense the vapor. The solids are left behind.

21.12 Sublimation

If a substance such as solid camphor or solid iodine is left for some time in a closed vessel, vapor which is given off by the solid condenses on the sides of the vessel to form small crystals. The escape of molecules directly from a solid without passing through the liquid phase is

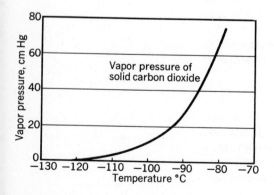

FIGURE 21.9

The saturated vapor pressure of solid carbon dioxide (dry ice) increases rapidly with temperature.

called *sublimation.* In like manner, vapor may go directly to the solid state. For most solids, the vapor pressure is very small, but for some our sense of smell tells us that vapor is being given off. The vapor pressure of ice at 0°C is 4.6 mm Hg; as the temperature decreases, the vapor pressure decreases.

The heat of sublimation is the heat necessary to change a unit mass of a substance from the solid to the vapor state without change of temperature. A vapor-pressure curve (Fig. 21.9) showing the vapor pressure when a solid is in equilibrium with its vapor may be plotted for a solid just as for a liquid; it is called a *sublimation curve.*

21.13 Triple Point

Under certain conditions of temperature and pressure a liquid may be in equilibrium with its vapor. On a temperature-pressure diagram these conditions are represented by the vapor-tension curve. Similarly, a solid may be in equilibrium with its vapor; the conditions are represented by the sublimation curve. In like manner, a curve may be drawn showing the relation between the temperature and pressure when a solid is in equilibrium with its liquid. If all these curves are drawn for a substance such as water (Fig. 21.10), they intersect at a point called the *triple point.* It indicates the temperature and pressure at which the solid, vapor, and liquid can exist together without one of them gaining in mass at the expense of the others. At this temperature and pressure, the solid, liquid, and vapor are in equilibrium.

The triple point for water can be reached by the following experiment: Some water is placed on a watch glass under a bell jar. Evacuation of the bell jar produces boiling, the heat for which is removed from the water, which is cooled. Eventually the temperature falls to the point at which water is simultaneously boiling and freezing. With care one can reach the triple point for water, which is at a temperature of 0.0100°C and a pressure of 4.6 mm Hg. If evacuation is continued and the pressure is reduced below 4.6 mm Hg, only the solid and vapor phases can exist in equilibrium. A wafer of ice remains on the watch glass.

21.14 The Critical Point

If an *unsaturated* vapor is enclosed in a cylinder *HFEG* (lower part of Figure 21.11), and piston *M* is moved in while the *temperature of the vapor remains constant,* the pressure at first increases as the volume is decreased, as represented by the curve *AB.* Near *A,* Boyle's law is almost followed, but deviations increase as *B* is approached. At *B* the vapor is *saturated,* and liquefaction begins. Along *BC* the volume decreases while the pressure remains constant (Boyle's law does not apply to saturated vapors). Meanwhile, the quantity of vapor decreases, and that of liquid increases. At *C* liquefaction is complete. A further application of pressure to the piston causes a small decrease in the

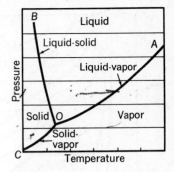

FIGURE 21.10
Equilibrium among the solid, liquid, and vapor phases of a material occurs at the triple point *O.*

FIGURE 21.11
Compression of vapor in cylinder (bottom) is graphed as an isothermal or constant-temperature curve *AB,* showing changes in pressure with volume; pressure holds constant as liquefaction occurs from *B* to *C.*

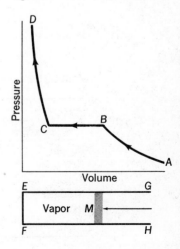

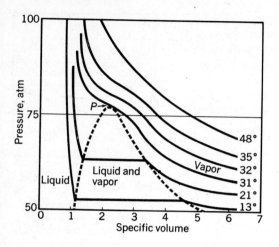

FIGURE 21.12

Isothermal curves for carbon dioxide at six different temperatures.

volume of the liquid, and the curve CD representing the relation between the pressure and the volume of the liquid becomes very steep. The curve $ABCD$ shows the relation between the volume and the pressure when the *temperature is kept constant;* it is called an *isothermal curve.*

If this process is carried out at higher and higher temperatures (Fig. 21.12), the horizontal part of the curve becomes shorter, until a temperature is reached at which the horizontal portion disappears and is replaced by a slight bend in the curve. At a temperature just below this, it is possible to liquefy the vapor by the application of pressure alone; at temperatures above this, it is impossible to liquefy the vapor, however great the pressure. The highest temperature at which it is possible to liquefy a vapor is called the *critical temperature.* The point P (Fig. 21.12) at which the horizontal part of the isothermal just disappears is known as the *critical point.* The pressure and specific volume (volume per unit mass) of the vapor at the point P are known as the *critical pressure* and *critical volume,* respectively.

The isothermals of Figure 21.12 refer to carbon dioxide. Its critical temperature is $31.1°C$, and its critical pressure 77 atm. If a heavy-walled glass tube closed at both ends is partly filled with liquid car-

TABLE 21.1   *Critical Temperatures, Boiling Points, and Freezing Points of Common Gases*

Name of gas	Freezing point, °C	Boiling point, °C	Critical temperature, °C	Critical pressure, atm
Helium	−272	−268.9	−267.9	2.26
Hydrogen	−259	−252.8	−239.9	12.8
Argon	−189	−186.0	−122.0	41.3
Nitrogen	−210	−195.8	−147.1	33.5
Oxygen	−219	−183.0	−118.8	49.7
Water (steam)	0	100.0	374	218

bon dioxide, the remainder of the tube being filled with the saturated vapor of carbon dioxide, at room temperature there is equilibrium between the liquid and its vapor. As the temperature of the tube is increased, the density of the liquid decreases while the density of the vapor increases. As a result, the meniscus marking the boundary between liquid and vapor becomes less distinct. At the critical temperature the densities of liquid and vapor become equal and the meniscus disappears.

To liquefy a gas, it is necessary to cool it below its critical temperature and to apply sufficient pressure to produce liquefaction (Table 21.1). Most of the so-called "permanent" gases have low critical temperatures and require the application of large pressures. The boiling and freezing points quoted are for a pressure of one standard atmosphere.

Questions

1. How does the pressure of air above a water surface affect the saturated vapor pressure of the liquid and the rate of evaporation?

2. Why does the heat of vaporization increase as the temperature is lowered?

3. Why does 100°C steam produce a far worse burn than 100°C water?

4. How is regelation involved in packing a snowball? Why is very cold snow powdery?

5. What is the distinction between a vapor and a gas? How does the pressure of each vary as a function of volume when the temperature is kept constant?

6. If 100 cm^3 of saturated pure ether vapor at 25°C exert a pressure of 53 cm Hg, what pressure is exerted if the volume is reduced to 50 cm^3 without changing the temperature? Explain why the pressure is not increased.

7. What role does surface tension play in the violent boiling, called *bumping,* which often occurs when water is heated to boiling in a smooth-walled container? Why is bumping reduced by placing rough, inert crystals in the container?

Problems

1. If the specific heat of snow is 0.5 kcal/(kg)(C°), how much heat energy is required to turn 10 kg of snow at −10°C into steam at 100°C?   *Ans.* 7,250 kcal

2. Ice has a specific gravity of 0.917. What is the weight of 1 ft^3 of ice? How much heat is required to melt 1 ft^3 of ice at 32°F?

3. What power is required to melt 10 kg of ice at 0°C and to raise the temperature of the water to 100°C in 300 sec?   *Ans.* 25.1 kW

4. How much heat is required to change 20 lb of ice at 2°F to steam at 340°F? The specific heat of ice is 0.50 Btu/(lb)(F°), and that of steam is 0.48 Btu/(lb)(F°).

5. How many kilocalories are required to heat 500 g of mercury from 20 to 357°C and to vaporize it at that temperature?   *Ans.* 39.6 kcal

6. A steel sphere with a mass of 161.74 g is placed in an atmosphere of steam at 100°C and, after reaching equilibrium, is weighed with the water condensed on it. The observed mass is 162.98 g. What was the original temperature of the sphere?

7. A specimen of copper is heated to 200°C and placed on a mass of ice. If 57.5 g of ice is melted, what is the mass of the copper specimen?   *Ans.* 0.25 kg

8. A 200-g sphere of iron is heated in an oil bath and then placed on a block of ice, causing 50 g of ice to be melted. What was the temperature of the iron?

9. Five ice cubes at 0°C, each of 25 g mass, are dropped in a 50-g glass containing 290 g of water at 20°C. If losses are negligible, how many grams of ice are left when the water and glass have cooled to 0°C?   *Ans.* 50 g

10. One hundred grams of ice at 0°C are dropped into 381.4 g of water at 30°C contained in a 200-g copper calorimeter. The final temperature is 8°C. Find the heat of fusion of ice.

11. Four ice cubes, each of mass 15 g and at 0°C, are placed in a 50-g glass which contains 200 g of water. If the glass and the water are initially at 25°C, find the final temperature of the system and the mass of ice remaining, if any.   *Ans.* 1.67°C; none

12. Fifty grams of ice at −20°C are placed in a calorimeter of 20 g water equivalent which initially contains 280 grams of water at 40°C. If the specific heat of ice is 0.5 kcal/(kg)(C°), find the heat required to warm the ice to 0°C, the heat required to melt the ice at 0°C without changing its temperature, and the final temperature of the calorimeter and its contents.

13. The condenser at an electric generating plant receives steam at 100°C and changes it to water at 50°C. The cooling is done by water which enters at 10°C and leaves at 40°C. How much cooling water is required for each kilogram of steam condensed?

Ans. 19.7 kg

14. Ten grams of steam at 100°C are condensed in a 200-g calorimeter containing 150 g of water. The calorimeter and water were initially at 10°C and the final temperature is 40°C. Find the heat lost by the steam, the heat gained by the calorimeter, and the specific heat of the calorimeter.

15. Steam at 100°C is received by a radiator, and water at 80°C leaves. (*a*) How many grams of steam are required per hour if the radiator delivers 2×10^3 kcal/hr? (*b*) What fraction of the heat is associated with the cooling of the water?

Ans. (*a*) 3.58 kg; (*b*) 3.6 per cent

16. A 200-g copper calorimeter contains 400 g of water at 15°C. How many grams of steam at 100°C must be added to raise the temperature to 65°C?

17. Twenty-five grams of steam at 100°C were passed into a 200-g copper calorimeter. The calorimeter contained 300 g of water and a certain amount of ice, all at 0°C. The final temperature was 20°C. How much ice was in the calorimeter?   *Ans.* 91.3 g

18. Ten grams of steam at a temperature of 100°C were passed into an aluminum calorimeter containing an unknown mass of water. The initial temperature of the water was 8°C, its final temperature was 36°C, and the mass of the calorimeter was 150 g. Find the initial mass of water in the calorimeter.

19. How many pounds of coal must be burned to produce 500 lb of steam at 282°F if one starts with water at 50°F and if 80 per cent of the heat of combustion of the coal goes into the water? Take the heat of combustion of coal to be 11,000 Btu/lb and the specific heat of steam to be 0.5 Btu/(lb)(F°).   *Ans.* 66 lb

20. How much steam at 150°C must enter a calorimeter to turn 120 g of ice at −20°C to water at 30°C? The specific heats of ice and steam are both approximately 0.5 kcal/

(kg)(C°). Assume that negligible heat is needed to raise the temperature of the calorimeter.

21. If 500 g of ice at 0°C and 50 g of steam at 100°C are mixed with 480 g of water at 30°C in a calorimeter with a water equivalent of 20 g, find the final temperature.

Ans. 6.7°C

22. It takes 540 kcal or 2.26×10^6 joules to change 1 kg of water at 100°C to steam at the same temperature at one standard atmosphere pressure. At 100°C, 1 kg of water occupies 0.001 m³, and 1 kg of steam 1.671 m³. Find the external work done in evaporating 1 kg of water at 100°C and 1 atm pressure. Find the change in the internal energy of the system during the evaporation.

23. A calorimeter contains 250 g of water and 50 g of ice at 0°C. The mass of the calorimeter is 150 g, and its specific heat is 0.12 kcal/(kg)(C°). How many grams of steam at 100°C must be introduced into the water to make the final temperature 40°C?

Ans. 27.9 g

24. If the specific heat of water vapor at constant pressure is roughly 0.5 kcal/(kg)(C°), and the heat of vaporization at 100°C is 540 kcal/kg, calculate the *approximate* heat of vaporization of water at 90°C. *Hint:* By conservation of energy, it should take the same amount of energy to change 1 g of water at 90°C to 1 g of water vapor at 100°C whether the evaporation is done first or last. Compare your value with that given in the steam tables in the Appendix. Why is your value only approximate?

25. A calorimeter of 30 g water equivalent contains 270 g of water at 10°C. Into this calorimeter 200 g of ice at −50°C are dropped; then 10 g of steam at 120°C are introduced. The specific heats of steam and ice are, respectively, 0.48 and 0.50 kcal/(kg)(C°). Find the final temperature of the system. What remains in the calorimeter?

Ans. 0°C; 336.2 g water and 143.8 g ice

CHAPTER 22 *To warm water, to melt a solid, or to vaporize a liquid we increase the internal energy of the system by adding heat. In a calorimetry experiment we may find the specific heat of a material by dropping a known mass of the material at high temperature into a known mass of water and determining the equilibrium temperature. In all these cases heat is transferred from one body to another or from one part of a system to another. In this chapter we study the processes by which these heat transfers are accomplished.*

Heat Transfer

22.1 Heat-transfer Processes

As we saw in Sec. 18.3, heat is energy in transit from one body to another or from one part of a substance to another by virtue of temperature differences. There are three natural processes by which heat is transferred from one point to another.

1. *Conduction is the process by which heat energy is transferred from particle to particle by collisions or direct interactions.*

Heat is transferred by conduction from the bowl to the handle of a spoon when the bowl is placed in a hot liquid. Conduction occurs in solids, liquids, and gases. It is the only method by which heat is transferred through opaque solids. The atoms in the hotter part of the material vibrate with greater amplitude than those in the colder part. These atoms with greater thermal energy pass part of this energy to their neighbors, which in turn pass energy to their own neighbors. In most materials this transfer occurs because of interatomic interactions, but in metals free electrons are responsible for most of the transfer of thermal energy between atoms. These same electrons are responsible for electric conductivity, and it is for this reason that the best thermal conductors are also the best electric conductors.

2. *Convection is heat transfer by the actual movement of the heated material itself.*

Steam produced in a boiler may be transported to radiators throughout a building. The transfer of heat by movement of the hot steam is a convective process. Convection is ordinarily the most important heat-transfer process for liquids and gases. The distribution of heat in practically all houses and buildings is achieved by means of convection currents of heated air, hot water, or steam.

3. *Radiation consists of electromagnetic waves which transmit energy from a source to an absorber.*

The earth's primary source of energy is the radiation from the sun. Part of this energy is in the form of visible light, but much more of it comes in the form of infrared rays which have wavelengths too long for the eye to see. Radiation traverses a vacuum as well as transparent media.

The atoms and molecules of a body at a higher temperature emit energy as radiation, which passes to a cooler body, where it is absorbed and reconverted to thermal energy. Radiation is of primary importance for bodies at high temperatures and for transmission across regions in which there is no material medium. For temperatures only 100°C or so above or below room temperature, radiation is relatively unimportant compared to conduction and convection for most material mediums.

If a steam radiator provides heat in a room, all three processes play a role in transferring the heat. Conduction brings the heat from the steam to the outside of the radiator. From here the primary heat transfer is by convection, although radiation does play a role in distributing the heat. The first evidence that convection is of principal importance is the fact that a person several feet from the radiator feels equally warm on both sides. It is characteristic of radiation transfer that the energy moves in straight lines from the heat source to the point where it is absorbed. The familiar "roast one side, freeze the other" situation which arises at an outdoor bonfire on a cold night is typical of radiative transfer.

22.2 Conduction

If heat is to be conducted through a material, there must be a difference in temperature between two regions. If a constant temperature difference is maintained between the two faces of a slab of material (Fig. 22.1), the heat Q conducted through this slab is proportional to the area A of the slab, the temperature difference $t_h - t_c$ between the two faces, and the time the temperature difference is maintained. It is inversely proportional to the thickness d of the slab.

$$Q = \frac{kA(t_h - t_c) \text{ time}}{d} \qquad \text{22.1}$$

The proportionality constant k for a given material is called the *coefficient of thermal conductivity*. Coefficients for a number of materials are listed in Table 22.1. In the metric system k is usually given as *the quantity of heat in calories which flows through one square centimeter of area in one second when a temperature difference of one Celsius degree is maintained across a thickness of one centimeter.* In the British system of units, k is numerically equal to *the number of Btu conducted per hour through an area of one square foot when a temperature difference of one Fahrenheit degree is maintained across a thickness of one inch.*

In problems of thermal conductivity it is imperative that one use the actual temperatures of the slab faces in Eq. (22.1). For example,

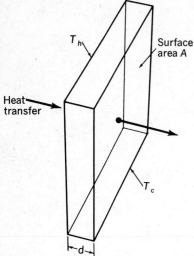

T_h

Surface area A

Heat transfer

T_c

d

FIGURE 22.1
The heat transferred per unit time through a slab of material depends on its thickness, area, and constituency and on the temperature difference between its surfaces.

if one calculates the heat conducted through a glass window when the indoor temperature is 70°F and the outdoor temperature is 0°F, one obtains a heat loss which is far too great if one puts 70°F as t_h and 0°F as t_c. Actually, the temperature of the inner surface of the glass under conditions of this sort might well be 20° lower than the 70°F of the air in the room, while the outer face of the glass may similarly be some 20 F° or more warmer than the outside air. There are major temperature drops in the thin air layers adjacent to each side of the glass. Equation (22.1) gives acceptable values of Q only when the actual surface temperatures are used.

An apparatus for measuring the coefficient of thermal conductivity of a good conductor such as copper is represented in Figure 22.2. It consists mainly of a rod, the coefficient of thermal conductivity of which is to be determined. This rod is typically about 30 cm long and has a diameter of about 3 cm. On one end is soldered a copper box through which steam may be passed to make the temperature of that

TABLE 22.1 *Thermal Conductivities*

Substance	Thermal conductivity, cal/(sec)(cm)(C°)*	Substance	Thermal conductivity, cal/(sec)(cm)(C°)*
Aluminum	0.50	Rock or glass wool	0.00009
Air	0.000055	Sand (white dry)	0.00093
Brass	0.24	Silver	0.99
Concrete	0.0041	Soil (dry)	0.00033
Copper	0.918	Steel	0.11
Cork	0.00011	Water	0.00143
Glass	0.0015	Wood (across grain)	0.0003
Ice	0.00396	Zinc	0.265

* To obtain value in Btu-in./(hr) (ft²) (F°), multiply by 2,900.

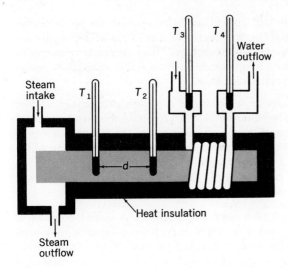

FIGURE 22.2
Measuring the thermal conductivity of a solid rod.

end of the rod about 100°C. Around the other end is soldered a coil of copper tubing through which cold water is circulated. The temperature of this water as it enters is found by means of the thermometer T_3, and its temperature as it leaves is read on the thermometer T_4. The difference in temperature between incoming and outgoing water multiplied by the mass of water gives numerically the quantity of heat that has flowed down the rod. The coil and the rod are carefully lagged with felt to prevent heat losses. Two small holes drilled at right angles to the axis of the rod contain thermometers T_1 and T_2 by which the fall of temperature across the thickness d is measured.

Example In measuring the thermal conductivity of a rod (Fig. 22.2), the following data were obtained. Temperature of incoming water = 20.0°C; temperature of outgoing water = 30.0°C; temperature t_h read by thermometer $T_1 = 80.0$°C; $t_c = 60.0$°C; distance between thermometers = 10 cm; area of rod = 20 cm²; mass of water flowing through box = 650 g in a time of 180 sec. Find the coefficient of thermal conductivity.

Heat gained by water = mass of water × temperature change × sp ht

$$= 650 \times 10 \times 1 = 6500 \text{ cal}$$

$$Q = \frac{kA(t_h - t_c)}{d} (\text{time})$$

$$6{,}500 = k \times 20 \times \tfrac{20}{10} \times 180 = k \times 20 \times 2 \times 180$$

$$k = \frac{6{,}500}{20 \times 2 \times 180} = \frac{6{,}500}{7{,}200}$$

$$= 0.90 \text{ cal/(sec)(cm)(C°)}$$

The ratio of the temperature change Δt to the thickness over which it occurs is called the *temperature gradient*. In the example above it is given by $\Delta t/d = (t_h - t_c)/d = (80 - 60)$C°/10 cm = 2 C°/cm.

The thermal conductivity of carbon increases with the temperature. On the other hand, the thermal conductivities of metals ordinarily decrease with an increase of temperature. The thermal conductivity changes abruptly when a substance such as sulfur (Fig. 22.3) passes from one crystalline state to another.

< Very often the walls of a house or a refrigerator consist of two or three layers of different materials. To compute the heat conducted through such a system of layers, we make use of the fact that the only heat which can be conducted through the second layer is that which passes through the first layer, and so forth. When equilibrium is established, the heat conducted per unit area per second through each of the layers is the same.

Example The wall of a shed in which ice is stored consists of an outer layer of wood 2 cm thick and an inner layer of rock wool 3 cm thick. Find the heat conducted through 50 m² of the wall in 1 hr when the outer wood surface is at 20°C and the inner rock-wool surface is at 5°C. Also find the temperature of the wood–rock-wool interface.

Let t be the temperature of the interface. The heat conducted through both layers is the same, so that

$$
\begin{aligned}
Q &= \left[\frac{ka\,\Delta t(\text{time})}{d} \right]_{\text{wood}} = \left[\frac{ka\,\Delta t(\text{time})}{d} \right]_{\text{rock wool}} \\
&= \frac{3 \times 10^{-4} \times 50 \times 10^{4}(20 - t) \times 3{,}600}{2} \\
&= \frac{9 \times 10^{-5} \times 50 \times 10^{4}(t - 5) \times 3{,}600}{3}
\end{aligned}
$$

Solving for t yields $t = 17.5°C$, the temperature of the interface. If we put this value into the equation for Q, we obtain

$$
Q = \left[\frac{3 \times 10^{-4} \times 50 \times 10^{4}(20 - 17.5) \times 3{,}600}{2} \right]_{\text{wood}} = 6.75 \times 10^{5}\ \text{cal}
$$

It may be of interest to check this answer by showing that the same heat is conducted through the rock wool.

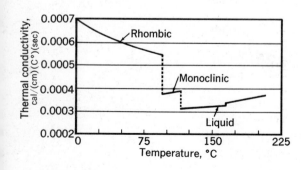

FIGURE 22.3
The thermal conductivity of sulfur changes when the crystalline form changes.

22.3 Convection

The transfer of heat from one place to another by the motion of the heated substance is known as convection. The convection is said to be *forced* if the heated material is moved by means of fans or pumps, as is the case in a forced-air heating system in a home where fans blow the hot air from the furnace throughout the rooms. *Natural* convection arises from the change in density that takes place when a fluid is heated.

For example, when a gas or a liquid is heated, it expands and becomes lighter than the cold fluid. When water is heated on a stove, the liquid at the bottom is warmed, expands, and rises to the top. Meanwhile the cooler and denser water sinks. The flows thus set up in the liquid are known as *convection currents*. There is no simple formula which permits the calculation of heat transfer by convection in the general case. The heat transferred to or from a surface at one temperature in contact with a fluid at a different temperature depends on the geometry and orientation of the surface, the nature and properties of the fluid, and many other factors.

22.4 Radiation

Sunlight falling on an object warms it above the temperature of the surrounding air. In like manner, radiation from a roaring fire in a fireplace warms objects on which it falls. Radiation passes through the air without producing appreciable heating. Radiation from the sun passes through millions of miles of empty space until eventually it falls upon absorbing matter, where it is transformed into the mechanical energy of random motion.

All bodies, whether cold or hot, radiate. If two bodies are exactly alike in every way, except that one is at a higher temperature, the hotter body radiates more heat than the colder one. When a body is at a higher temperature than its surroundings, it radiates more heat than it receives; when it is at a temperature lower than that of its surroundings, it receives more energy than it radiates. The energy radiated by a body increases rapidly as its temperature is raised; it is proportional to the fourth power of the absolute temperature.

The rate at which heat is radiated depends not only on the temperature of the body, but also on the character and area of the radiating surfaces. Some surfaces are good radiators, others poor. Generally, polished surfaces are poor radiators; rough, blackened ones are good radiators.

There is an intimate relationship between the rate at which a surface radiates energy and the rate at which the same surface under the same conditions absorbs heat. Good radiators are also good absorbers of heat. That this must be true can be seen easily. Consider a polished reflecting sphere and a rough black sphere which are put in an enclosure and eventually reach the same temperature as the enclosure

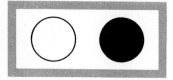

FIGURE 22.4

Two spheres, one black, the other reflecting, remain at the enclosure temperature once thermal equilibrium is reached.

(Fig. 22.4). Radiation from the enclosure falls upon each at the same rate, but the polished surface reflects most of the incident energy, while the blackened surface absorbs the energy striking its surface. Therefore, the blackened surface is receiving energy at a more rapid rate than the polished one. However, if the bodies and the enclosure are all at the same temperature, they remain at the same temperature. Therefore, the blackened body, which is receiving energy at a greater rate, is also radiating at a greater rate. Under equilibrium conditions each body is absorbing energy at the rate at which it is radiating.

The arguments of the preceding paragraph apply to the situation in which equilibrium has been reached and all bodies are at the same temperature. If the blackened sphere and the polished one are placed in the sunlight on a bright day, the blackened sphere attains a substantially higher temperature than the polished one. In this case the bodies and their surroundings (which must include the sun) never attain identical temperatures. However, it is still true that *a good absorber is a good radiator, and a poor absorber a poor radiator.*

22.5 Black-body Radiation

The best emitter of radiation is necessarily the best absorber. A perfect absorber of radiation is known as *an ideal black body. A black body is one which absorbs all the radiation incident upon it.* Although no body with a perfect absorbing surface exists, a surface covered with a thick coating of lampblack absorbs about 99 per cent of the heat radiation incident upon it. An almost perfect black body can be produced by making a small opening in the wall of a rough cavity (Fig. 22.5). Radiation incident on this small hole enters the cavity, in which it is reflected from wall to wall until completely absorbed. Meanwhile, each point of the surface of the cavity emits radiation which falls on other points of the cavity, where part is reflected and part absorbed. Radiation of all wavelengths is reflected back and forth in this cavity until there is a uniform density of radiation throughout it. If the temperature of the wall is increased, the radiation level is also increased.

FIGURE 22.5

An ideal black body is formed by a cavity of rough internal surface with a very small opening.

If radiation emerging from the opening of the cavity is examined with suitable instruments, it is found that a wide range of wavelengths is present. The energy associated with each wavelength can be measured. The distribution of the energy in this spectrum changes with temperature. The total radiation emitted from such a cavity, called *black-body radiation,* increases rapidly with temperature. Stefan found that if R is the energy radiated per unit area per second,

$$R = \sigma T^4$$

22.2

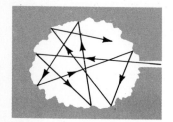

where σ is a constant equal to 5.67×10^{-8} watt/$(m^2)(K°)^4$, and T is the absolute temperature. This is known as *Stefan's law* (or the Stefan-Boltzmann law). If the temperature of a black body is doubled, the rate at which energy is radiated is increased by a factor of 16.

If the radiator is not a black body, it radiates less than a black body of identical size and temperature. If the *absorption factor* α represents the fraction of incident radiation absorbed by the surface of the radiator, the energy radiated per unit area per second is

$$R = \alpha \sigma T^4 \qquad\qquad \textbf{22.2}a$$

Thus a body which absorbs only half the radiation incident upon it has $\alpha = 0.5$, and it emits only half as rapidly as a black body of the same size and shape. For copper α is roughly 0.3; thus a copper radiator radiates only 0.3 as much power per unit area as does a black body at the same temperature.

As the temperature of a black body is increased, the power emitted at every wavelength increases, but not in the same proportion. The curves of Figure 22.6 show the relation between intensity emitted and wavelength. As the temperature is increased, the wavelength at which the maximum intensity is radiated moves toward smaller values. If λ_m is the *wavelength at which the radiation is maximum* for the absolute temperature T,

$$T\lambda_m = 2898°\mathrm{K}\mu \qquad\qquad \textbf{22.3}$$

where $\mu = 10^{-6}$ m. This relation is known as *Wien's displacement law.*

For temperatures up to 600°C or about 900°K, essentially all the radiation is in wavelengths too long for the human eye to see. However, by the time the temperature reaches 1000°K, the black body emits some waves which the eye can detect (Fig. 22.6), and the body appears dull red. As the temperature is increased further, energy is emitted in the blue and violet regions of the visible spectrum, and the color of the body appears to change from red to orange to yellow and eventually to white.

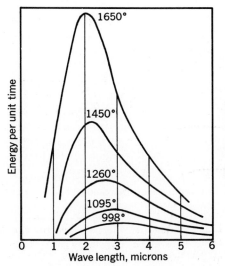

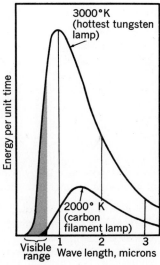

FIGURE 22.6

Black-body radiation at several temperatures, showing the energy emitted per unit time in a small wavelength range as it varies with the wavelength.

$<$ 22.6 The Surface Temperature of the Sun

If we assume that the sun is roughly a black body, we can estimate its surface temperature by applying either Stefan's radiation law or the Wien displacement law. Let us consider first the use of Stefan's law. Measurements at the earth reveal that a surface perpendicular to the sun's rays when the sun is directly overhead receives roughly 1,400 watts/m². The energy received per unit area per unit time on a surface perpendicular to the sun's rays is called the *solar constant*. The solar constant of 1,400 watts/m² is equivalent to about 2 cal/cm²-min. If we assume that the sun's energy is emitted equally in all directions, the total power in watts emitted is given by 1,400 times the area in square meters of a sphere of radius equal to the distance from the sun to the earth. The power radiated by the sun is therefore

$$P = 1{,}400 \text{ watts/m}^2 \times 4\pi \times (1.5 \times 10^{11} \text{ m})^2$$
$$= 4 \times 10^{26} \text{ watts}$$

If we divide this by the area of the sun's surface, we obtain, as the energy emitted per square meter per second, the value

$$R = \frac{4 \times 10^{26} \text{ watts}}{4\pi \times (7 \times 10^8 \text{ m})^2} = 6.5 \times 10^7 \text{ watts/m}^2$$

If we insert this in Stefan's law, assuming the sun is a black body, we obtain

$$R = \sigma T^4 \qquad \text{or} \qquad 6.5 \times 10^7 = 5.67 \times 10^{-8} T^4$$
$$T^4 = 1.14 \times 10^{15}$$
$$T = 5800°\text{K}$$

If the spectral distribution of the radiation from the sun is studied, and a curve of intensity is plotted as a function of wavelength, it is found that maximum energy is radiated at approximately 0.49 micron (μ). If we put this value in Wien's displacement law, we obtain

$$0.49T = 2898°\text{K}$$
$$T = 5900°\text{K}$$

Both these values have been obtained on the assumption that the sun is a black body. Actually, this is not the case. The curves of the sun's radiation fall substantially below the black-body curves for 5900°K in the short-wavelength region and are substantially above in the far infrared region.

Our best methods for measuring very high temperatures involve the use of the radiation laws. Instruments called *optical pyrometers* are used to compare the radiation from the body whose temperature is to be measured with the radiation from a calibrated source.

22.7 Newton's Law of Cooling

Whenever a body is at a somewhat higher temperature than its surroundings, the rates at which energy is lost due to conduction, convection, and radiation are all roughly proportional to Δt, the temperature difference between the body and its surroundings. Therefore, *the rate at which the body loses temperature is proportional to the difference between its temperature and that of its surroundings.* This is known as *Newton's law of cooling.* Thus, a cup of coffee loses temperature twice as rapidly when it is 80 C° above its surroundings as when it is 40 C° above.

If the body is somewhat cooler than its surroundings, Newton's law is still applicable. In this case both the "rate of cooling" and Δt are negative, since the body gets warmer and its temperature is lower than that of the surroundings.

Example A pan filled with hot food cools from 92°C to 88°C in 2 min when the room is at 20°C. How long will it take to cool from 71°C to 69°C?

The average of 92°C and 88°C is 90°C, which is 70 C° above room temperature. Under these conditions the pan cools 4 C° in 2 min or 2 C°/min.

$$\frac{\text{Change of temperature}}{\text{Time}} = k \, \Delta t$$

$$\frac{4 \text{ C}°}{2 \text{ min}} = k(70 \text{ C}°) \qquad\qquad \textbf{A}$$

The average of 69°C and 71°C is 70°C, which is 50 C° above room temperature. k is the same for this situation as for the original.

$$\frac{2 \text{ C}°}{\text{Time}} = k(50 \text{ C}°) \qquad\qquad \textbf{B}$$

If we divide (A) by (B), we have

$$\frac{4 \text{ C}°/2 \text{ min}}{2 \text{ C}°/\text{time}} = \frac{k(70 \text{ C}°)}{k(50 \text{ C}°)}$$

$$\text{Time} = 1.4 \text{ min}$$

Questions

1. Why wear woolen mittens to keep your hands warm when the thermal conductivity of wool is far greater than that of air?

2. Why does an automobile with closed windows get so hot inside when it sits out in the sun?

3. A wooden door and a metal doorknob are in thermal equilibrium at 5°C. Why does the metal doorknob feel much colder than the wood?

4. A piece of paper tightly wrapped around a copper rod may be held briefly in a Bunsen flame without catching fire, while the same paper on a wooden rod would ignite quickly. Why does this happen?

5. Steam radiators are seldom painted black, although a black radiator should radiate better than one painted a light color. Do you think blackening radiators would increase their effectiveness substantially? Why?

6. Why are the contents of an automobile radiator less likely to freeze on a cold, clear night if the automobile is under the roof of a carport, even though it is completely exposed to the cold air?

Problems

1. A glass window has an area of 2.5 m² and a thickness of 0.4 cm. The outer surface is at 10.8°C, and the inner surface at 11.6°C. How much heat flows through the window each hour?

Ans. 270 kcal

2. A glass window is 0.5 cm thick, 120 cm wide, and 100 cm high. The temperature of the inner surface is 14.1°C, and that of the outer surface is 12.9°C. How much heat is lost per hour through the window?

3. How many calories will be lost each hour through a glass window 100 cm by 80 cm by 4 mm thick if the inner surface is at 32°F and the outer surface is at 23°F?

Ans. 540 kcal

4. A brass rod 20 cm long and 1.5 cm² in cross-sectional area is thermally insulated. One end is kept at 100°C in a steam bath, and the other end is cooled by circulating water, as shown in Figure 22.2. In 5 min, 100 g of water enter at 15°C. Two thermometers 10 cm apart along the rod read 80°C and 55°C, respectively. Find the heat conducted down the rod each minute and the temperature of the water as it leaves.

5. The heat exchanger for a reactor is designed to transfer 300,000 cal/sec through a steel conductor 2 mm thick. The temperature on one side of the steel is 140°C, and on the other side 138°C. What area is required?

Ans. 27.3 m²

6. How much water would be evaporated per hour per square meter by the heat which flows through a boiler plate which is made of steel 0.5 cm thick when there is a difference in temperature of 2.5°C between the faces of the plate?

7. Find the coefficient of thermal conductivity for asbestos paper if it is found that 10 cal flow each second through a slab 2 mm thick and 50 cm² in area when the temperature of one face is maintained at 98°C, and that of the other at 36°C.

Ans. 6.5 × 10⁻⁴ cal/(C°)(cm)(sec)

8. If the bottom of an aluminum pan is 2 mm thick and the temperature of the inner surface is 110°C while that of the outer surface is 112°C, find the heat conducted through an area of 150 cm² in 1 min.

9. Superheated steam is flowing through a steel pipe that has a length of 4 m. The internal diameter of the pipe is 5 cm, and its external diameter is 5.5 cm. If the outside surface of the pipe has a temperature of 106°C, and the inner surface a temperature of 110°C, how much heat escapes in 5 min? (Assume the wall of the pipe is approximately a thin slab 0.25 cm thick and of width equal to the average circumference of the pipe.)

Ans. 3500 kcal

10. A large meat-storage refrigerator has a window with an area of 0.5 m². If the window is 1.2 cm thick and the temperature of the inner glass surface is 18°C, how many calories per day are lost through the glass when the outer surface has a temperature of 20°C?

11. A brass bar has a length of 60 cm and a cross section of 5 cm². One end is kept in a mixture of water and ice at 0°C, consisting initially of 5 g of ice and 25 g of water. The other end is maintained at a uniform higher temperature until all the ice is

melted, and then the temperature is raised so as always to maintain the same *difference* in temperature between the two ends of the bar. Neglect losses of heat to other bodies. How many calories are needed to melt the ice? What is the difference in temperature between the two ends of the bar if the ice melts in 15 min? How soon after the ice has melted will the temperature of the water be 80°C? *Ans.* 400 cal; 22.2°C; 90 min

12. A brass bar has a length of 30 cm and a cross-sectional area of 2.5 cm². One end is kept in steam at 100°C, and the other in ice at 0°C. Neglecting losses due to radiation, find the number of grams of ice melted in 10 min.

13. A copper-clad, stainless-steel pan has a conducting area of 600 cm² and has a 0.1-mm layer of copper on 1 mm of stainless steel. The coefficient of thermal conductivity of stainless steel is 0.05 cal/(C°)(cm)(sec). (*a*) Find the temperature at the copper–stainless-steel interface when the outer surface is at 110°C and the inner surface is at 108°C. (*b*) How many calories are conducted through the pan each second?
Ans. (*a*) 109.99; (*b*) 596 cal/sec

14. A black body radiates 0.5 watt when its temperature is 500°K. Find the power radiated if the temperature is raised to 1000°K, and find the wavelength at which the radiation rate is greatest at 1000°K.

15. The surface of a radiation pyrometer receives 0.5 cal/sec from a furnace whose temperature is 727°C. How many calories per second will it receive when the temperature of the furnace is raised to 1227°C? *Ans.* 2.53 cal/sec

16. To what temperature must a black body be raised in order to double its total radiation if its original temperature is 727°C?

17. If the surface temperature of a star is 5250°K, what is the wavelength of its radiation maximum? What would the surface temperature of a star have to be if it were to have its radiation maximum in the blue at a wavelength of 0.425 μ?
Ans. 0.550 μ; 6800°K

18. A black body, initially at 27°C, is heated to 327°C. The total radiation emitted at the higher temperature is how many times that emitted at the lower temperature? What is the wavelength of the maximum radiation at the higher temperature?

19. The filament in a tungsten lamp radiates energy at the rate of 120 watts when operating at a temperature of 2400°K. A second lamp operating at a temperature of 3000°K radiates five times as much energy. What is the ratio of the area of the second filament to that of the first? What is the wavelength of the maximum power radiated at each temperature? *Ans.* 2.05; 1.20 μ; 0.96 μ

20. If it takes 10 min for a glass of water to warm from 39 to 41°F in a room at 70°F, approximately how long will it take for its temperature to rise from 49 to 51°F?

21. A glass of 20 g water equivalent contains 270 g of water and 10 g of ice. If it takes 20 min for the ice to melt, approximately how much longer will it take for the temperature to rise to 2°C if the surroundings remain at 20°C? Roughly how long will it take for the temperature to rise from 9.5 to 10.5°C? *Ans.* 15.8 min; 15 min

CHAPTER 23 *In Chap. 7 we learned that energy is the ability or capacity to do work. A body at a high temperature has internal energy. How can part of this internal energy be used to do useful work? What fraction of the energy is available? The answers to the first of these questions—and there are several—tell us how heat engines operate. The maximum possible efficiency of any particular heat engine is limited by the answer to the second question. In this chapter we consider the operation and efficiencies of various types of heat engines.*

Thermodynamics

23.1 Heat and Work

The heat engines that play such a major role in modern life depend on the transformation of heat energy into work. The hot gases of a jet engine push forward on a moving airplane and thereby do work. An automobile engine drives an automobile only when it is supplied constantly with heat from burning gasoline in the cylinders.

Practically all heat engines depend upon the work done by expanding gases to achieve mechanical work output. The simplest situation to discuss, although a difficult one to use for a heat engine, is that in which a gas expands at *constant pressure* (Sec. 20.5). In this case the work done by the gas is the product of the pressure p and the change in volume $V_2 - V_1$, where V_1 and V_2 represent the volume occupied by the gas before and after the expansion, respectively. If the pressure varies during the expansion, the process may be described by a p-V diagram such as Figure 23.1. The work $\mathcal{W}$ done during a small volume increment ΔV is given by Eq. (20.4):

$$\mathcal{W} = p\,\Delta V \qquad\qquad \textbf{23.1}$$

where p is the average pressure appropriate for the small change ΔV. This work is represented by the dotted area in the figure. Clearly, any volume change $V_2 - V_1$ can be regarded as the sum of many small ΔV increments, and the total work done by the gas in producing the volume change $V_2 - V_1$ is represented by the area $ABba$.

The work performed by the expanding gas comes from one or both of two sources: heat supplied to the gas and the internal energy of the gas. In the *thermodynamics* of heat engines we are interested in energy transformations involving the heat supplied to the "working substance" of the engine (usually a gas), the work done by this substance, and changes in its internal energy.

FIGURE 23.1

The work done by an expanding gas at variable pressure, such as in the cylinder at bottom, is measured on a p-V diagram by the area under the curve, which is the product of the average pressure and the change in volume.

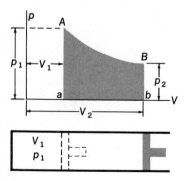

23.2 First Law of Thermodynamics

When the principle of conservation of energy is used to include heat energy specifically, we may state it in the form: *When heat energy is added to a system, the energy appears either as increased internal energy of the system or as external work done by the system.* This statement of conservation of energy is known as the *first law of thermodynamics.*

When we add heat energy to a gas, this energy must appear in one or both of two possible forms—either as an increase in the internal energy of the gas, as evidenced by a rise in temperature, or as external mechanical work performed by the gas in increasing its volume. For this case the first law of thermodynamics requires that

Heat added to gas
  = increase in internal energy of gas + mechanical work done by gas

If ΔQ represents a small amount of heat added to the system,

$$\Delta Q = mc_V \,\Delta T + p \,\Delta V \qquad\qquad 23.2$$

where $mc_V \,\Delta T$ is the increase in internal energy, and $p \,\Delta V$ is the external mechanical work done by the gas.

23.3 Thermal Efficiency

In practical heat engines, which achieve mechanical work output through the expansion of hot gases, the variables pressure, volume, and temperature change simultaneously and in a complex manner. To gain quantitative understanding of the transformation of heat to mechanical energy, it is simplest to imagine an engine that uses an ideal gas as working substance and that holds one of these variables constant during each portion of its heat cycle.

As an example of such a cycle, consider a heat engine in which hot gases push a piston back (Fig. 23.2) at a constant high pressure p_1. During this *isobaric process* the gas does the work represented by the area $ABba$. Heat must be supplied to the gas during this expansion. Next let the engine hold the volume of the gas constant and reduce the pressure to p_2 by lowering the temperature of the gas. During this *isovolumic process* no work is done, but heat is removed from the gas. Then let the gas be compressed at constant pressure to its original volume V_1; the work done *on the gas by the piston* is represented by the area $DCba$. During this compression heat must be removed from the gas. Finally, keeping the volume constant at V_1, let the engine heat the gas to its original pressure p_1. This completes a cycle which may be repeated over and over. To find the net useful work done by the gas during one cycle, the work done *on the gases by the piston* must be subtracted from the work done *on the piston by the gases.* In Figure 23.2 the net work done by the gas is represented by the area $ABCD$. In general, *work done by the gas on the piston is taken to be positive,* while *work done on the gas by the piston is*

FIGURE 23.2

The work done *by a gas* in expanding from A to B, as in the cylinder, is positive, while the work done *on the gas* in compressing it from C to D is negative.

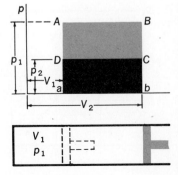

negative. Similarly, heat energy supplied to the gas is taken to be positive, while that removed from the gas is negative.

An important characteristic of any heat engine is its efficiency: *The thermal efficiency of a heat engine is the ratio of the net external work done by the engine to the total heat energy supplied.* In any heat engine only a fraction of the heat developed by the combustion of fuel is converted into work. In a steam engine much of the heat passes out with the exhaust steam. Gasoline engines are more efficient, but, even so, provision must be made for removing the heat not converted to mechanical work.

Example   If 1 lb of coal which has a heating value of 8000 Btu was burned in a machine which raised 500 gal of water 100 ft, what percentage of the heat from the coal was converted into useful work?

Heat supplied = 8000 Btu

Work done = weight × height

= 500 × weight of water per gallon × 100

= 500 × 8.3 × 100 = 415,000 ft-lb = 533 Btu

$$\text{Efficiency} = \frac{\text{mechanical work performed}}{\text{heat supplied}}$$

$$= \frac{533}{8,000} = 6.7 \text{ per cent}$$

23.4 Isothermal and Adiabatic Processes

Consider a gas in a cylinder with walls which are good conductors of heat and with a movable piston at one end. Let the gas expand slowly, maintaining a constant temperature. To do this it is necessary that heat be supplied; otherwise the temperature falls as the gas expands. By the first law of thermodynamics, $\Delta Q = mc_V \Delta T + p \Delta V$. Here we are keeping $\Delta T = 0$, so we must supply heat ΔQ which is equal to the work $p \Delta V$ done by the gas.

A process which is carried out in such a way that the temperature of the working substance remains constant is called an isothermal process. When a gas is compressed isothermally, work is done on the gas, and heat must be removed during the process. The relation between the pressure p and volume V of a gas during isothermal expansion or compression is shown in Figure 23.3 by the line *ST*. The equation of this curve is given by Boyle's law: pV = constant.

If a gas is compressed in such a way that no heat is allowed to enter it or to escape from it, the temperature increases. On the other hand, the temperature falls during expansion. An expansion or compression during which no heat enters or escapes may be realized experimentally by enclosing the gas in a cylinder surrounded by nonconducting materials. *A process in which there is no exchange of heat between the substance and its surroundings is called an adiabatic process.*

In terms of Eq. (23.2), an adiabatic process is one for which $\Delta Q = 0$; no heat is added or removed. In this case the external work done by

FIGURE 23.3
Curve *ST* is isothermal; curve *LM* is adiabatic. The slope of the adiabatic curve at any point is greater than the slope of the isothermal curve through the same point.

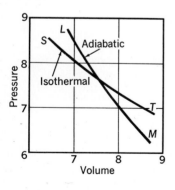

the gas is equal to the decrease in its internal energy: $p \Delta V = -mc_V \Delta T$. The relation between the volume and the pressure of a gas during an adiabatic expansion is shown by the curve LM in Figure 23.3. The curve for the adiabatic process is steeper than the corresponding curve for the isothermal process. Consider two identical gas samples, one of which undergoes an adiabatic expansion, and the other an isothermal expansion. If the pressure, temperature, and volume of the two samples are the same at the beginning, and if they expand to the same final volume, the temperature and pressure of the sample expanded adiabatically are less than the temperature and pressure of the gas expanded isothermally. *When a gas expands adiabatically, the product pV^γ is constant,* where γ is the ratio of the specific heat of the gas at constant pressure to the specific heat at constant volume (Sec. 20.6).

23.5 Carnot Cycle

An ideal engine was devised by Carnot to analyze the fundamental principles involved in heat engines. This engine was imagined to consist of a cylinder filled with gas and closed by a movable piston. By allowing the gas in the cylinder to expand isothermally and then adiabatically, and later compressing the gas isothermally and then adiabatically, the gas in the cylinder is carried through a cycle and made to yield work.

Suppose that the gas in the cylinder has a volume and pressure represented by point A in Figure 23.4. If the gas is expanded isothermally in contact with a source which supplies heat to keep the temperature at T_h (h for hot), the volume increases and the pressure decreases. After the isothermal expansion the volume and pressure are represented by point B on the curve. The area under curve AB represents the work done by the gas during this expansion. From point B the gas expands adiabatically until the pressure and volume have the

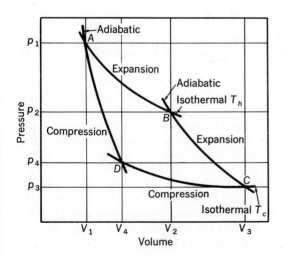

FIGURE 23.4

The p-V diagram for a Carnot cycle is bounded by two isothermals and two adiabatics.

values indicated by point C. During this adiabatic change, in which the cylinder must be insulated so that no heat is added or removed, the temperature of the gas falls to T_c (c for cooler). The area under curve BC represents the work done by the gas during this adiabatic expansion.

Conditions are again changed, and the gas is compressed isothermally at temperature T_c until it has the pressure and volume indicated by point D. To do this, we must remove heat from the cylinder during the compression. The point D is so chosen that the cycle can be closed by an adiabatic compression along the curve DA. The area under CD represents the *work done on the gas* during the isothermal compression, and that under DA represents work done *on the gas* during the adiabatic compression.

The net work output of the cycle is represented by the area enclosed in $ABCD$. It is the difference between the work done *by the gas* during the isothermal expansion AB and the adiabatic expansion BC and the work done *on the gas* during the isothermal compression CD and the adiabatic compression DA.

During the isothermal expansion along AB at temperature T_h, Q_h units of heat flow into the gas. During the adiabatic expansion along BC, no heat flows into the gas or out of it. During the isothermal compression along CD, Q_c units of heat are rejected by the gas at temperature T_c. During the adiabatic compression along DA, no heat flows into the gas or out of it. During the cycle, $Q_h - Q_c$ units of heat are transformed into mechanical energy. If $\mathcal{W}$ denotes the work done by the engine during this cycle,

$$\mathcal{W} = Q_h - Q_c \qquad \textbf{23.3}$$

23.6 The Efficiency of a Carnot Engine

The efficiency of a Carnot engine depends only on the temperatures between which it works. By definition, for a Carnot engine,

$$\text{Eff} = \frac{Q_h - Q_c}{Q_h} \qquad \textbf{23.4}$$

In establishing his absolute thermodynamic temperature scale, Lord Kelvin showed that

$$\frac{Q_h}{T_h} = \frac{Q_c}{T_c} \qquad \textbf{23.5}$$

where Q_h and Q_c are the heats transferred in a Carnot cycle at absolute temperatures T_h and T_c, respectively. Hence, the efficiency of a Carnot engine becomes

$$\text{Eff} = \frac{T_h - T_c}{T_h} \qquad \textbf{23.6}$$

where T_h is the temperature of the hot source from which heat is taken, and T_c the temperature of the cold body to which the heat not transformed into useful work is delivered.

No real engine can have an efficiency greater than that of a Carnot engine working between the same two temperatures. If a real engine could have a greater efficiency than a Carnot engine working between the same temperatures, we could use it to drive a Carnot engine in reverse and transfer net energy from the cold to the hot body with no other change. This would violate the second law of thermodynamics (Sec. 23.8).

Example Find the efficiency of an ideal engine working between temperatures of 127°C and 77°C.

$$\text{Eff} = \frac{T_h - T_c}{T_h} = \frac{400 - 350}{400} = 12.5 \text{ per cent}$$

To obtain high efficiencies, we want heat engines to have T_h as high, and T_c as low, as is practical. Modern electric generating plants using steam turbines often employ lakes or rivers to condense the steam, thereby obtaining the lowest practical T_c.

23.7 Heat Engines

In the sections above we have discussed the operation of engines of a highly idealized form. It may be instructive to see how some practical heat engines use heat energy to perform mechanical work.

Internal-combustion Engines. The four-stroke-cycle *gasoline engine* (Fig. 23.5) is perhaps the most common heat engine. During the *intake stroke* a mixture of gasoline vapor and air enters the partially evacuated cylinder through the intake valve *A*. When the cylinder is full, the valve closes and the piston moves back, compressing the mixture. When the *compression stroke* is near its end, a spark ignites the mixture. The oxidation of the fuel releases heat energy, resulting in a great increase in the temperature and pressure of the gas in the chamber. As a consequence, there is a large force driving the piston forward during the *power stroke*. In the *exhaust stroke* valve *B* is open, and the combustion products are forced out. The cycle is then repeated. During each cycle only one of the four strokes is a working stroke during which heat is transformed into work. The working strokes of other cylinders, or a flywheel, provide the energy to carry the piston through its other three strokes. On the compression stroke of a gasoline engine, the temperature of the air and gasoline vapor increases rapidly because external work is done in compressing the gas. If the gas is compressed such that its final volume is less than about one-tenth its original volume, the gasoline may ignite spontaneously because of the high temperature. When such ignition occurs before the cylinder is near the top of its stroke, *knocking* results, with serious loss of efficiency. The ratio of the initial volume of gas to the final volume in the cylinder is called the *compression ratio*. The greater the compression ratio, the greater the efficiency of the engine, but the greater the difficulty in bringing the explosive mixture safely to the point at which the spark is desired.

FIGURE 23.5

Steps in the operation of a four-stroke-cycle gasoline engine.

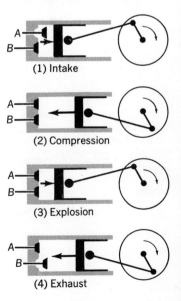

(1) Intake

(2) Compression

(3) Explosion

(4) Exhaust

Modern developments in high-octane fuel have permitted substantial increases in the compression ratios of automobiles, but a serious practical limitation remains.

In the *diesel engine* preignition is avoided by compressing air without fuel vapor. In this way compression ratios of 16 to 1 or more may be obtained; this results in compressed-air temperatures of 500 to 600°C. When the desired compression ratio is reached, fuel is injected into the cylinder, where it ignites spontaneously because of the high temperature. Thus, no spark is required. The diesel engine can use ordinary fuel oil, or even powdered coal. Because the diesel engine is more efficient than an ordinary gasoline engine, and because it can burn lower-grade fuel, large internal-combustion engines are usually diesels.

Steam Turbines. Modern electric generators are often driven by steam turbines in which steam impinges upon a set of rotating blades (Fig. 23.6). The steam is deflected from the rotating blades to a set of fixed blades, where its direction is reversed once more so that it impinges upon a second set of rotating blades fastened to the same shaft as the first set. In a modern steam turbine a number of sets of rotating and fixed blades may be used (Fig. 23.7). As the steam transfers energy to the blades, its temperature drops, the pressure falls, and the volume of the steam increases. To allow for this, the wheels upon which the blades are assembled increase in diameter from the high-pressure end to the exhaust end. The steam may be superheated to above 560°C and supplied at a pressure of 3,500 lb/in.². Under such circumstances the thermal efficiency (Sec. 23.3) may be about 40 per cent.

Jet Engines. If a firecracker is set off in a tube closed at one end, the tube is driven forward by the increased pressure on the closed end. At the open end the hot gases escape. The momentum transferred to the tube is equal to the momentum of the escaping gases in the opposite direction. In jet propulsion it is the reaction from the escaping gases themselves, and not the interaction of the escaping gases with

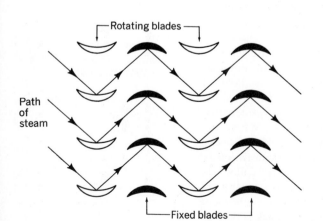

Path of steam

Rotating blades

Fixed blades

FIGURE 23.6
Steam recoiling from the moving blades is directed by fixed blades against the next set of rotating blades.

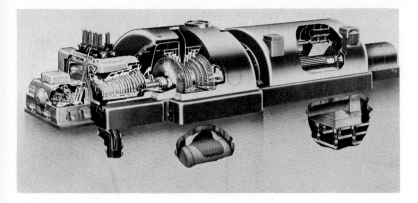

FIGURE 23.7
A modern steam turbine.

the air, which provides the thrust. This is why jet motors are sometimes called *reaction motors*. For many years jet motors have been used in fireworks for rockets, pinwheels, and other displays. Only in recent years have they been adapted for propelling aircraft and large missiles.

The principles underlying rocket propulsion have been discussed in Sec. 8.4. Rocket engines can operate in a vacuum, since they carry with them all the materials needed for combustion. Other jet engines require oxygen from the air for the burning of fuel. In the *turbojet engine* (Fig. 23.8) fuel is oxidized in a combustion chamber. The resulting hot gases escape through a turbine which drives a compressor to provide the air necessary to burn fuel. Many modern aircraft use turbojet engines. They are particularly suited to aircraft flying at high speeds and high altitudes, where air resistance is low. It is precisely in this region that propellers are not able to exert substantial thrust against the rare air. At low speeds and low altitudes, propeller aircraft are more efficient and have a number of superior features. A combination of the desirable (and undesirable) features of the propeller and jet engine can be achieved by operating a propeller from the shaft of the turbojet engine. Such a combination is called a *turbo-prop engine*.

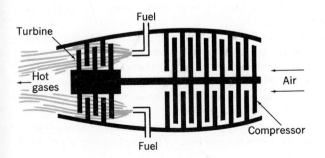

FIGURE 23.8
Schematic diagram of a turbojet engine.

23.8 Second Law of Thermodynamics

In the Carnot engine, the most efficient conceivable engine, a quantity of heat Q_h is taken from the hot reservoir at a temperature T_h. Some of this heat is rejected to a cold reservoir at temperature T_c, and the rest of the energy is converted into work. Only if we have a heat source which is at a temperature T_h greater than that of its surroundings can we get useful work from thermal energy. This idea was formalized by Kelvin in a statement of what he called the second law of thermodynamics: *There is no natural process the only result of which is to cool a heat reservoir and do external work.* This law follows directly from the fact that *heat by itself flows only from bodies at higher temperature to bodies at lower temperature.* Indeed, we may state the second law in the form: *Heat can be made to go from a body at lower temperature to one at higher temperature only if external work is done.* Every electric refrigerator is evidence that we can make heat go from a colder to a warmer body, but the second law of thermodynamics tells us that work must be done to produce this unnatural heat flow.

There is a vast store of thermal energy in the ocean. However, we cannot simply take this thermal energy and convert it into work to operate a submarine. Only if we have some body at a lower temperature than the ocean to which we can transfer part of the energy can we make an engine operate from the ocean's heat energy. Even then we can convert into work only the *difference* between the heat energy provided at the source and the heat energy rejected to the cold reservoir.

On the other hand, we can always convert mechanical energy into heat energy completely. Thus, the second law of thermodynamics indicates a certain *irreversibility* of natural processes. For example, we can always convert the kinetic energy of an automobile into heat in the brake drums and tires, but we cannot reconvert all this heat energy to kinetic energy.

If we have 50 g of water at 0°C and 50 g at 100°C, we can always mix them to obtain 100 g at 50°C. But, if we have 100 g of water at 50°C, we cannot pour half of it into one vessel and have it at 0°C and the other half into a second vessel and have it at 100°C. This would be in violation of the second law of thermodynamics, which tells us that many natural processes occur only in one direction. The world is filled with irreversible processes. For example, people age, eggs rot, and zinc dissolves in acid.

If the second law of thermodynamics is applicable throughout the universe, and if heat always flows from bodies at higher temperatures to those at lower temperatures, eventually the entire universe will come to the same temperature. Then, although the total energy in the universe will be the same as before, none of the energy will be available for doing mechanical work. Thus, the second law of thermodynamics tells us that although the total energy is constant, the available energy becomes always less. This implication of the second law of thermodynamics has aroused wide philosophical interest and leads to what philosophers of the nineteenth century called the *wärmetod* or *heat death*.

23.9 The Refrigerator and the Heat Pump

The process of reducing the temperature of a body below that of its surroundings is essentially the reverse of the process employed in a heat engine. One may imagine a Carnot cycle operated in reverse so that the gas is expanded isothermally at a lower temperature T_c and then compressed isothermally at a higher temperature T_h.

In a typical electric refrigerator (Fig. 23.9) liquid freon is pumped into the cooling coils, where the pressure is reduced. As a consequence, the liquid vaporizes and the gas expands. Both processes remove heat from the surroundings, which are cooled. The gas is pumped out of the cooling chamber, and in an external set of coils it is compressed and liquefied. In both of these processes large amounts of heat are given up. This heat is removed by water cooling in large systems or by air cooling in small systems. The liquid is then ready to pass through the same cycle. In the refrigerator heat is transferred from a lower to a higher temperature, but the work necessary to do this must be supplied by the "pump." This pump is usually operated by an electric motor, although a gas flame can also be used.

Some modern homes are heated by means of *heat pumps* which take heat from ground water or some other heat reservoir and transfer it into the house by means of processes similar to those in the refrigerator. Let us consider a system using water in a well. The heat pump takes heat from the water, which may be at a lower temperature than the house, and transfers or "pumps" it into the house. Just as in the refrigerator, the cycle may involve the vaporization and expansion of a

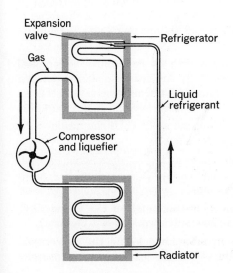

FIGURE 23.9

Schematic diagram of the operation of a refrigerator whose refrigerant is circulated and compressed by an electric pump.

liquid in coils in the water. In the house a compression and liquefaction of the vapor is accomplished with the release of heat there. One of the major advantages of the heat pump is that in the summer it may be used to reduce the temperature inside the house by transferring heat to the water in the well. In this case the vaporization and expansion occur in the house, thereby removing heat, and the compression and liquefaction occur in the well, where the heat is transferred to the water.

Questions

1. What are some examples of common irreversible processes in nature?

2. An electric refrigerator transfers heat from the cold cooling coils to the warm surroundings. Does this violate the second law of thermodynamics? Why not?

3. Why are the efficiencies of heat engines so low?

4. What is gained by using a high compression ratio in an internal-combustion engine? What are the disadvantages?

5. What are the advantages of jet engines? Why haven't they been used more in the past?

6. Can a kitchen be cooled indefinitely by leaving the door of an electric refrigerator open? Explain.

Problems

1. A perfect Carnot engine utilizes an ideal gas. The source temperature is 227°C, and the sink temperature is 127°C. Find the efficiency of this engine, and find the heat received from the source and the heat released to the sink when 10,000 joules of external work is done. *Ans.* 0.20; 50,000 and 40,000 joules

2. A brake is applied to the driving shaft of an engine that develops 3 hp. The brake and the shaft are immersed in a calorimeter so that all the work done against friction is transformed into heat and goes to increase the temperature of the water in the calorimeter. If the weight of the water in the calorimeter is 120 lb, how much will its temperature rise per minute?

3. A steam engine develops 2,500 hp. How many Btu of heat must be supplied per minute if the over-all efficiency is 10 per cent? If the engine operates between 240°F and 140°F, what fraction of the efficiency of an ideal Carnot engine does this engine have? *Ans.* 1.06 × 10⁶ Btu/min; 0.70

4. Steam is injected into a turbine at 277°C and exhausted at 77°C. If the turbine is 60 per cent as efficient as an ideal heat engine, find its efficiency.

5. A Carnot engine takes 660 kcal from a heat source at 277°C, does some external work, and delivers the balance of the energy to a heat sink at 127°C. Find how much work is done and how much heat is delivered to the sink. *Ans.* 753,000 joules; 480 kcal

6. Compute the efficiency of an ideal heat engine operating between 177°C and 27°C. If this engine takes 500,000 joules from the source, how much work does it perform?

7. At the beginning of the compression stroke of an automobile engine, the gas occupies a volume of 12 in.³ at atmosphere pressure. At the end of the compression the pressure is 12.9 atm, and the volume 2.0 in.³. What is the compression ratio? What is the temperature according to the general gas law, if the original temperature was 27°C?

Ans. 6; 372°C

8. A six-cylinder gasoline engine makes 1,800 rev/min. Each piston has an area of 60 cm² and a length of stroke of 15 cm. If the average gauge pressure during a power stroke is 5×10^5 newtons/m², find the power developed.

9. A gasoline engine makes 1,200 rev/min. It has eight cylinders and develops 60 hp. The cylinder is 4 in. in diameter, and the length of the stroke is 5.5 in. Find the average net pressure that is developed during each working stroke. *Ans.* 71.7 lb/in.²

10. A Carnot refrigerator takes 60 kcal from a freezing chamber at $-23°C$ and rejects heat at 27°C. How much work must be done? How many calories are rejected?

11. If it were possible to make an ideal refrigerator utilizing a Carnot cycle, how many joules of mechanical energy would be required to remove 10,000 joules from the cold compartment at $-13°C$ and deliver it to the outside air at 27°C? How much work would be required to remove this same 10,000 joules from a cold compartment at $-73°C$ and reject it at 27°C? *Ans.* 1,540 joules; 5,000 joules

12. A heat pump takes heat from a water reservoir at 7°C and delivers it to a series of pipes in a house at 27°C. Assuming that the energy needed to operate the pump is twice that of an ideal Carnot pump, how much mechanical energy is needed to supply the house with 10^6 kcal?

13. A gas subject to a constant pressure of 2×10^5 newtons/m² is supplied with 30 kcal by an electric heater. If it expands from 0.35 m³ to 0.55 m³, what is the increase in the internal energy of the gas? What is γ for this gas? *Ans.* 85,600 joules; 1.47

14. How much heat must be added to 5 g of nitrogen gas in a cylinder originally at 0°C to double the volume if the pressure is kept at 1 atm? How much external work is done? What happens to the difference between the energy supplied and the work done?

15. Find the work necessary to compress adiabatically 5 liters of neon ($\gamma = \frac{5}{3}$) at 0°C and 76 cm Hg pressure to a volume of 1.25 liters. *Ans.* 1,160 joules

16. Show, for the adiabatic expansion of a given mass of ideal gas from a state characterized by pressure p_1, volume V_1, and temperature T_1 to a state characterized by p_2, V_2, and T_2, that $T_1 V_1^{\gamma-1} = T_2 V_2^{\gamma-1}$ and $T_1^{\gamma/(\gamma-1)}/p_1 = T_2^{\gamma/(\gamma-1)}/p_2$.

17. A quantity of nitrogen ($\gamma = 1.4$) is compressed to occupy a volume of 1 liter at 10 atm pressure and 27°C. If it is allowed to expand adiabatically to 1 atm pressure, find the new volume and temperature. How much work was done by the gas during the expansion? *Ans.* 5.18 liters; 155°K; 1,210 joules

18. Air is admitted to the cylinder of a diesel engine at atmospheric pressure and 27°C. If the gas is compressed adiabatically to $\frac{1}{16}$ of its original volume, find the pressure and temperature after the compression.

CHAPTER 24 *The weather is determined by the interplay of many factors, most of which we have met in preceding chapters. Radiation from the sun provides the energy to evaporate vast quantities of water from the seas; part of the water vapor condenses to form clouds, rain, and snow. Solar radiation also establishes temperature differences which lead to convection currents and further heat transfer. In this chapter we relate much of what we have been studying to the weather.*

Atmospheric Physics

24.1 Weather and the Atmosphere

Nowhere in our daily lives do we meet heat phenomena on a more grandiose scale than in our contacts with the weather. The weather and its patterns can be explained in terms of the mechanical and heat principles which we have been studying. Meteorology is a major facet of physical science devoted to the study of weather patterns, to predicting the weather to come, and to explaining weather phenomena.

In our everyday life we meet the sun's radiation, which is our prime source of energy. We observe giant convection currents which we call *winds.* We see the changes of phase of water to vapor, and sometimes to snow and ice. The weather at any one point is determined by a myriad of conditions, some general and readily understood, others local and of very special nature. In the sections which follow we shall try to outline some of the principal considerations. However, before we can discuss weather patterns in any great detail, we must become somewhat familiar with the atmosphere of the earth, with how the sun's radiation produces daily and seasonal variations in temperature, and with how the amount of water vapor in the air influences the situation.

It is only in the lower few miles of the earth's atmosphere that weather phenomena occur. This portion in which winds, clouds, and weather occur is called the *troposphere.* It extends to a height of about 7 miles over the United States, about 5 miles above the North Pole, and roughly 11 miles at the equator. The greater height at the equator is due to the higher average temperature there and to the rotation of the earth. Above the troposphere is a region called the *stratosphere,* which extends to a height of approximately 50 miles. The stratosphere is particularly well suited for long-distance flying, since the meteorological conditions are roughly constant there, with no

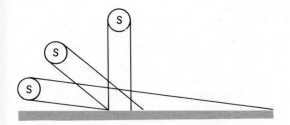

FIGURE 24.1
The position of the sun affects the energy received each second by any particular area of the earth's surface.

clouds or storms. The stratosphere gets its name from the idea that the region is stratified in layers with roughly constant properties. Above the stratosphere is the *ionosphere,* a region where many molecules are ionized and at which radio waves are strongly reflected.

24.2 The Sun's Radiation

On a clear day a surface placed normal to the sun's rays receives approximately 330 cal/m²-sec from the sun. If the rays from the sun strike the surface of the earth at an angle other than 90°, the energy in a given bundle of rays is spread out over a larger area (Fig. 24.1). Specifically, the amount of power received is proportional to the intensity of the beam and to the cosine of the angle between the rays and the perpendicular to the surface. Figure 24.2 shows the importance of the angle at which the sun's rays reach the earth. A glance shows how much more energy reaches a unit area in a day during a summer month than during the winter. This is the primary factor which establishes our seasons. In addition to the change in the area over which a given bundle of rays is spread, another factor which helps to diminish the amount of heat from the sun's rays as the sun approaches the horizon is the greater distance the rays must travel in the earth's atmosphere. Consequently, there is somewhat greater absorption.

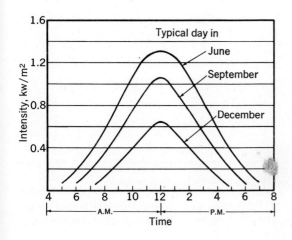

FIGURE 24.2
How solar radiation at the earth's surface varies in intensity with time of day and year at a latitude of roughly 40°N.

24.3 General Circulation of the Air

The inequalities of solar radiation received in different regions of the earth's surface are in part responsible for the general circulation of the atmosphere. If the earth were not in rotation, one might expect a relatively simple circulation pattern in which air in equatorial regions would be heated and rise. The more dense air at greater latitudes would then push underneath, and we would have a pattern with air at the surface of the earth flowing toward the equator. The warmed air would rise and flow at high altitudes toward the polar regions, where it would cool and descend. This oversimplified picture is complicated by the rotation of the earth.

The earth revolves on its axis once each day. A point at the equator is carried eastward with a speed of roughly 1,050 mi/hr, one at latitude 40° at a speed of about 800 mi/hr. At the poles there is no eastward velocity. If a mass of air in the Northern Hemisphere starts moving toward the south, its eastward velocity component is less than that of points on the earth's surface farther south. As it approaches these points, it appears to come from the north *and east.* Similarly, a mass of air moving northward has a greater eastward velocity component than points on the earth's surface farther north. When this air reaches these northern points, it is traveling eastward faster than the ground; therefore, the wind comes from the south *and west.*

The combination of unequal heating in equatorial and polar regions and the rotation of the earth lead to the general atmospheric circulation indicated in Figure 24.3. At any given point on the earth's surface there may be local factors which profoundly influence the wind distribution.

24.4 Humidity

The next important factor governing the weather is the humidity, which is a measure of the amount of water vapor in the air. *The absolute humidity is the mass of water vapor per unit volume in the atmosphere.*

From the point of view of weather the actual mass of water vapor per unit volume is considerably less important than how nearly saturated the air is. At a high temperature the air can hold vastly larger quantities of water vapor per unit volume than at a low temperature. We can expect water to condense out of the atmosphere only when the air is saturated or supersaturated in some region. The ratio of the actual mass of water vapor per unit volume to the mass per unit volume which the air could hold at the same temperature if saturated is the relative humidity:

Relative humidity $= \dfrac{\textit{mass of water vapor per unit volume}}{\substack{\textit{mass of water vapor per unit volume if air were}\\ \textit{saturated at the same temperature}}}$

Since the pressure exerted by the water vapor is proportional to the mass per unit volume, the relative humidity is also given as the ratio

FIGURE 24.3

General atmospheric circulation in the Northern Hemisphere.

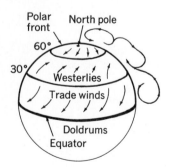

of the vapor pressure of the water to the saturated vapor pressure at the same temperature (Table of Data 4 in Appendix).

One method of determining the absolute humidity is the chemical hygrometer. In this instrument a measured volume of air is passed through a series of U tubes which are filled with a substance that absorbs water vapor. These tubes are weighed before and after passing the known volume of air through them. The absolute humidity is obtained by dividing the mass of water absorbed in the tubes by the volume of air passed through.

The relative humidity of the air may be measured with a number of different types of instruments. Some of these depend on the hygroscopic properties of hair or of a thin strip of an appropriate material. When the moisture content of hair changes, its length also changes. Instruments based on this property are convenient, but are ordinarily not very accurate. The wet- and dry-bulb hygrometer consists of two thermometers, one of which reads the true temperature of the air. The other thermometer is covered with a wet cloth and reads a temperature that depends on the rate of evaporation of the water into the air. If the air is saturated, the rate of evaporation is no greater than the rate of condensation, and the wet bulb has the same temperature as the dry one. The drier the air, the greater the evaporation from the wet bulb, and the lower the temperature indicated by that thermometer. Charts showing the relative humidity in terms of the readings of the two thermometers have been prepared and may be found in many handbooks.

The moisture of the air is important to our health and comfort. When the relative humidity is high in hot weather, perspiration evaporates slowly from the skin, and we have hot "sticky" weather. If the relative humidity is low at the same high temperature, water evaporates rapidly from the skin, and the body is cooled because it supplies the heat of vaporization. Extremes of heat and cold are felt less when the humidity is relatively low. The relative humidity has a marked effect on the physical conditions and behaviors of many materials, such as wood and wool. Lack of moisture often causes furniture to shrink and become unglued. An excess of moisture results in swelling. In many forms of manufacturing it is necessary to control the humidity. One of the important functions of any good air-conditioning system is to maintain a desirable humidity.

24.5 Clouds, Fog, and Dew

On a humid summer day water condenses on the outside of a glass filled with ice water. The temperature of the outside glass surface is low, and the air in close proximity is cooled. As the temperature of air is lowered, the amount of water vapor it can hold is reduced. Eventually air in contact with the glass becomes saturated. If the temperature is lowered still more, water vapor condenses on the cold surface. *The temperature at which the air is saturated is called the dew point.*

Water will condense on any surface which has a temperature lower than the dew point. One way of determining the dew point is to lower the temperature of a polished metal container by evaporating ether from it. When the dew point is reached, a thin film of water is formed on the polished surface.

When the sun goes down at night and the surface of the earth begins to cool, some objects lose heat more rapidly than others. When warm, moist air comes in contact with these objects, some of the moisture from the air is deposited in the form of *dew*. If the temperature happens to be below the freezing point, water vapor is deposited as *frost*. On a typical clear night exposed objects cool faster than the air. As soon as their temperatures fall below the dew point, moisture condenses on them.

If the air cools until it reaches the dew point, moisture condenses out on minute particles in the air. Such a collection of water particles is called a *fog* if the particles are sufficiently small (less than about 30 μ in diameter) so that they do not fall to the earth as rain. Fog often forms in low areas during the night. In the morning, the water particles reevaporate as the air warms. If fog is formed in a region above us, we speak of it as a *cloud*. Whether we use the term fog or cloud to describe the formation depends on whether we are in it or observing it from some distance. Not all clouds, of course, are formed of water droplets. The high fleecy-white cirrus clouds are composed of ice crystals; they exist where the temperature is below freezing.

A cloud is often found above an island. During the day the sunlight produces greater warming of the island than of the surrounding ocean. The warm air above the island rises. As it moves upward, its temperature falls because the pressure becomes less and the gas expands. The expansion is essentially adiabatic. In a standard atmosphere this expansion results in a drop of temperature of 1 C° for every 340 ft increase in altitude. Eventually the air above the island is cooled to the point at which it becomes saturated; here a cloud begins to form. A cloud of this type is characterized by a flat bottom, which suggests that the temperature at that particular height is uniform over a wide area.

FIGURE 24.4

Temperatures on land affect wind directions. (*a*) Sea breezes blow from ocean to shore by day when temperatures are higher on land, and (*b*) land breezes blow from shore to ocean by night when temperatures are lower on land.

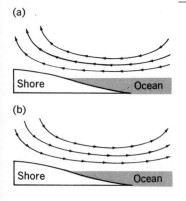

(a)

(b)

24.6 Local Temperature Differences

Along shores and coastal areas there are movements of air, known as land and sea breezes, which are caused by diurnal variations in the temperature. As the sun shines on land adjacent to the sea, differences in temperature are developed. In the daytime the land becomes warmer than the water. Convection currents are set up in the air over the land. As the air rises, the pressure over the land is decreased, and there is a movement of air from water to land (Fig. 24.4a). At night the land cools more rapidly than the water. Convection currents are again set up, but they are now from shore to water (Fig. 24.4b).

24.7 The Weather Map

As a consequence of unequal heating of various parts of the earth's surface and of the rotation of the earth, huge convection currents which we call winds are established. In regions where excessive heating has occurred there are updrafts and reduced pressure, while in cold regions one expects increased density and pressure. Regions of high pressure are known as *highs,* and regions of low pressure as *lows.* These regions are shown on typical weather maps by drawing lines known as *isobars.* An isobaric line connects all neighboring places at which the pressure is the same. Such lines are shown in Figure 24.5. The characteristic pattern of highs and lows in the United States moves from west to east with a speed of roughly 500 mi/day.

Barometers make it easy to detect and measure changes in atmospheric pressure, which may vary from hour to hour or from day to day. These variations are important for weather prediction. When the air contains an unusually large fraction of water vapor, the pressure is ordinarily below normal, since water vapor is lighter than air. Thus a falling barometer is often associated with a storm, while a high atmospheric pressure is characteristic of dry air.

FIGURE 24.5

Weather map showing a well-defined low around Tennessee with associated warm front extending toward the east, cold front to the southwest, and extensive rain area.

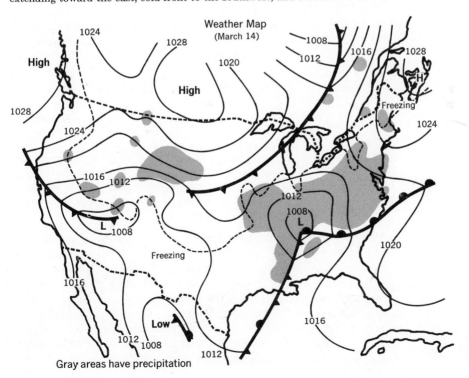

Gray areas have precipitation

Over fairly extended regions we have large bodies of air which are nearly homogeneous in the horizontal plane with respect to both temperature and pressure. Such a body is called an *air mass*. It is, of course, never homogeneous in the vertical plane; even in the horizontal plane there are gradual variations. An air mass may cover thousands of square miles and extend to heights of many thousand feet. It acquires its characteristics by moving for some time over an area where conditions are reasonably uniform. One which has developed over northern Canada is called a *polar continental* or *polar Canadian* air mass, while one which has originated in the northern regions of the Pacific Ocean is called a *polar Pacific* or *polar maritime* air mass. One which has originated over a tropical land mass is described as *tropical continental,* and one over tropical water as *tropical maritime.*

As an air mass moves, it is modified by heating or cooling, by the addition or removal of moisture, and by mixing with other air. Weather conditions are determined to a great extent by the characteristics of air masses and by the direction of their movements.

When air masses at different temperatures and pressures meet, the surface of separation is called a *front.* Across a front there is a sharp transition in weather conditions, which may include temperature, pressure, humidity, and wind velocity. Several different types of fronts are recognized (Fig. 24.6).

A *warm front* is a surface on which the direction of motion of the air is such that warm air replaces cold air. On the weather map, warm fronts are represented by black semicircles pointing in the direction toward which the warm air is moving. Figure 24.7 shows a warm front advancing. Because the warm air is less dense, it rides over the colder air, and, in the early stages of the warm front, high clouds are formed by the condensation of moisture in this invading mass of warmer air. As the warm front moves in, lower clouds are formed, and, if the warm front involves air of high relative humidity, rain is produced. It ordinarily takes about a day from the first signs of approaching warm air before the warm front passes on the earth's surface.

A *cold front,* in contrast to a warm front, is defined as the surface along which cold air is replacing warm. It is represented by small black wedges along the front, pointing in the direction in which the cold air is moving. If the cold air which moves in under the warmer

FIGURE 24.6

Symbols for fronts.

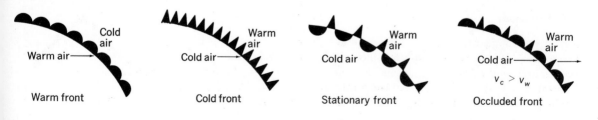

Warm air→ Cold air Warm front

Cold air→ Warm air Cold front

Cold air Warm air Stationary front

Cold air→ Warm air $v_c > v_w$ Occluded front

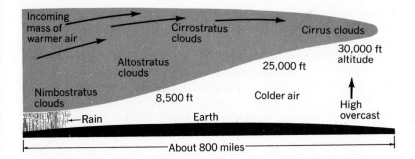

Incoming mass of warmer air

Cirrostratus clouds

Cirrus clouds

30,000 ft altitude

Altostratus clouds

25,000 ft

Nimbostratus clouds

8,500 ft

Colder air

High overcast

Rain

Earth

About 800 miles

FIGURE 24.7
Advancing warm front.

air is at a much lower temperature, and if the warm air is reasonably humid, the cold air pushes the warm air upward into violent thunderheads. Ordinarily, a cold front moves more rapidly than a warm front, and there is not a great deal of warning before it arrives. As the cold front passes, there is often a hard shower which removes much water vapor from the air and leaves crisp bright weather in its wake. Cold fronts move about 25 mi/hr and are steeper and faster than warm fronts. When a cold front overtakes a warm front, the result is an *occluded front,* represented by a combination of cold-front and warm-front symbols pointing in the direction of motion of the front.

A *stationary front* is a surface separating cold and warm air when the surface is not moving.

24.8 Cyclones and Anticyclones

An atmospheric condition characterized by a low-pressure region surrounded by closed isobars is called a *cyclone.* As air from the south moves northward (Fig. 24.8), it is deflected to the east in the Northern Hemisphere, while colder air from the north is deflected toward the west. Thus the circulation about a cyclone is counterclockwise in the Northern Hemisphere. Often warmer air moving from the south forms a warm front, and colder air from the north a cold front, as indicated in the figure.

A high-pressure region on the weather map is known as an *anticyclone.* About this high-pressure region winds circulate clockwise in the Northern Hemisphere. A high-pressure area is ordinarily characterized by bright, clear weather. The pattern of cyclones and anticyclones which migrates across the country is largely responsible for exchange of heat between high and low altitudes.

24.9 Tornadoes

Tornadoes are gigantic whirling funnels of air. The motion of the air is characterized by a cyclonic upward spiral that causes rapid expansion, cooling, and condensation. This condensation forms the dark cloud of the tornado funnel. The width of the storm may vary from 30 yd to 1 mile, and the forward velocity may vary from 20 to 40 mi/hr. The

FIGURE 24.8
Cyclonic circulation about a low, showing typical warm and cold fronts.

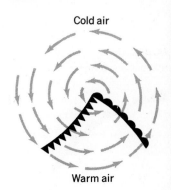

Cold air

Warm air

tapering end of the funnel may skip over one area and descend on another. It often has a whirling and serpentine appearance. The whirling velocity of the air causes a decrease in pressure at the center of the funnel. The wind velocity is excessive, both in horizontal and vertical directions. Vertical wind speeds may be as much as 200 mi/hr, and horizontal speeds may exceed this figure.

Questions

1. Why do ground fogs appear less often on cloudy overcast nights than on clearer nights?

2. Why should the temperature fall less than the ordinary 1 C° for every 340-ft increase in altitude if the air is unusually moist?

3. Why do the trade winds and the westerlies blow in opposite directions?

4. Why is cyclonic circulation counterclockwise in the Northern Hemisphere and clockwise in the Southern Hemisphere?

5. Why are the bases of neighboring cumulus clouds often at about the same level?

Problems

1. A chemical hygrometer gains 0.55 g in mass when 45 liters of air at 23°C are passed through it. Calculate the absolute humidity of the air and the relative humidity if saturated air at 23°C contains 20.6 g/m³. *Ans.* 12.2 g/m³; 59 per cent

2. Assume the density of the atmosphere is 1.29 kg/m³ regardless of the height (of course, the density of the atmosphere does depend on what is above it). If a barometer reads 76 cm Hg at sea level, what is the height of the atmosphere? Convert your answer to miles.

3. Find the relative humidity and the absolute humidity on a day when the temperature is 30°C and the dew point is 10°C. *Ans.* 29 per cent; 8.8 g/m³

4. How great is the vapor pressure of water in a room at 20°C if the humidity is 60 per cent? What mass of water vapor is present in each cubic meter of air?

5. A room has a temperature of 30°C. When a surface in the room is cooled to 20°C, moisture just begins to condense on it. Find the dew point, the approximate absolute humidity, and the relative humidity. *Ans.* 20°C; 16.6 g/m³; 55 per cent

6. A room is 10 m long, 7 m wide, and 4 m high. The temperature is 20°C. How much water must be evaporated in the room to raise the relative humidity from 10 to 40 per cent?

7. The solar constant is 1,400 joules/m²-sec. How much energy falls each minute on 1 m² of a lake at latitude 37° on a clear day at high noon in June, when the sun is 23° north of the equatorial plane? In December, when the sun is 23° south of the equatorial plane? *Ans.* 81,500 joules; 42,000 joules

8. The relative humidity of an auditorium that has a volume of 1,000 m³ is 25 per cent at the beginning of a concert and 60 per cent at the end of the concert. If the temperature of the room is assumed to remain at 20°C throughout the concert, how many grams of water have been added to the room?

9. Air that is saturated at $30°C$ rises vertically until its volume is doubled. At the same time, its temperature decreases until it is $10°C$. Find the number of grams of water that will condense out of each cubic meter of the air, measured at the original temperature and pressure. *Ans.* 11.4 g

10. Find the amount of water vapor contained in a room which is saturated at $10°C$ if the room has a volume of 5,000 m^3. If the air is heated to $20°C$, no water vapor is added, and the pressure remains the same, find the relative humidity.

11. An air-conditioning system delivers 2,900 m^3 of air each hour at $17°C$ and 60 per cent relative humidity. To do so, it takes in 3,000 m^3 of air at $27°C$ and 80 per cent relative humidity. Find the absolute humidity of the air taken in and the mass of water vapor removed per hour. (For saturated air the absolute humidity in grams per cubic meter is: $11°C$, 10; $13°C$, 11; $15°C$, 12.5; $17°C$, 14.3; $19°C$, 16.2; $21°C$, 18.2; $23°C$, 20.3; $25°C$, 22.9; $27°C$, 25.8.) *Ans.* 20.6 g/m^3; 37 kg

12. An air-conditioning system delivers 1,500 m^3 of air each hour at $20°C$ and 40 per cent relative humidity. How much water must be removed each hour if the incoming air has a relative humidity of 90 per cent at $30°C$?

13. One mole of dry air at $27°C$ and 1 atm pressure expands adiabatically as it rises to 5,400 m altitude, where the pressure is ½ atm. Calculate the temperature at 5,400 m, the decrease in the internal energy of the gas, and the work done by the gas. On the average, how many meters did the air have to rise to be cooled 1 C°? (Compare your result with the value of 1 C° for each 340 ft quoted in Sec 24.5 for a standard atmosphere.) *Ans.* 246°C; 1,120 joules; 1,120 joules; 100 m

PART IV   LIGHT

CHAPTER 25 *We turn now to a study of light, one of the first branches of physics to undergo substantial development. In part because of its ancient origins, it will seem at first that there is little connection between light and the parts of physics which we have been studying. However, very soon we find velocity and energy entering the discussion, and a little later we use the physics of wave motion to treat interference, diffraction, and polarization of light. In advanced physics, light becomes a facet of electromagnetism, a topic we introduce in Part V.*

One of our principal contacts with the world around us is through light. Not only are we personally dependent on light to convey visual information, but most of what we know about the stars and the solar system is derived from light waves impinging on our eyes and on optical instruments. Similarly, our concept of the structure of atoms comes largely from observing the radiations they emit. We have many instruments which make use of light in their operation. Important among them are the microscope, the telescope, and many kinds of spectrometers.

Light and Illumination

25.1 The Nature of Light

Much of the early knowledge of light dealt with its general behavior when it strikes materials: how it is reflected and how it is bent when it goes from one medium to another. Fortunately, the fundamental nature of light is not important in studying these phenomena, and the great science which we know as *geometrical optics* was well established before an understanding of the nature of light evolved in the nineteenth century.

Most objects emit no visible light; rather they are visible by light which is reflected from them. The sun is our chief source of light and heat, but many other bodies are *luminous* and serve as light sources. Any body which is heated to a sufficiently high temperature becomes self-luminous through *incandescence*. A gas through which an electrical discharge is passed also emits light, the color depending on the gas evolved. Entire panels of certain solid materials may be electrically excited to produce light through *electroluminescence*. Other solids emit light when bombarded by electrons or ultraviolet radiation; the television screen is an example of such a *fluorescent* source. A few chemical reactions result in the emission of visible light, even though the chemicals themselves are at a low temperature; the firefly is a *chemiluminescent* source.

Early in the nineteenth century it was established that light has wave properties. In Chap. 30 we present evidence of the wave nature of light; for the moment we assert without proof that visible light involves transverse electromagnetic waves with wavelengths between roughly 380 and 780 millimicrons (1 m$\mu = 10^{-9}$ m). Light exhibits not only wave properties, but also some which we may describe as "particle" properties. In some experiments the particle characteristics dominate, in others the wave characteristics. This "wave-particle duality" was a source of great confusion until the development of modern quantum mechanics.

In addition to visible light, there are radiations characterized by longer and shorter wavelengths than the eye can see, but with physical properties identical with those of visible light. Sometimes the term *light* is used to denote only those radiations which we see, while at other times we use *light* in a broader sense to mean electromagnetic radiation, regardless of visibility. From the psychophysical point of view, "light" is radiant energy capable of producing a standard response in the human eye. In the broader physical sense, "light" is visible light plus invisible radiations having the same fundamental properties.

25.2 Rectilinear Propagation of Light

Under ordinary circumstances light travels in straight lines, not bending appreciably around objects. Indeed, we depend on light to tell us when a meter stick is straight. The rectilinear (straight line) propagation of light is shown by the fact that a small source of light casts sharp shadows. A point source S (Fig. 25.1) illuminates all points on a screen above A and below B. No light arrives at the screen between A and B because it is stopped by the opaque body M. The fact that the boundary of the shadow is sharp shows that light from S does not bend appreciably into the shadow of the opaque body.

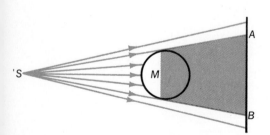

FIGURE 25.1

An opaque body casts a sharp shadow when illuminated by a point source.

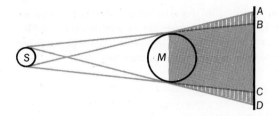

FIGURE 25.2
Umbra and penumbra comprise the shadow of an opaque body illuminated by a source of significant angular dimension.

When the source of light is not small, the boundary of the shadow is no longer sharp (Fig. 25.2). Points on the screen above A and below D are fully illuminated by S. The screen between B and C receives almost no light. The screen between A and B and between C and D is partially illuminated and in a less dense shadow than the part between B and C. This outer shadow gradually shades off from complete shadow at B to complete illumination at A, giving the blurred appearance that characterizes most shadows. The region of total shadow is called the *umbra,* while the partially shadowed region is the *penumbra.*

When the source of illumination is larger than the object casting the shadow (Fig. 25.3), the only region of complete shadow is the cone ENF having the object M as a base. If the screen is placed at A, there is a small umbra surrounded by a large penumbra; if at D, the umbra is absent.

The best illustration of shadows on a large scale is found in eclipses. When the moon is interposed between the sun and the earth and its shadow falls on the earth, the sun is wholly or partly obscured by the moon, and there is a total or partial eclipse of the sun. If the earth is sufficiently near the moon and passes through the complete shadow represented by the cone FNE (Fig. 25.3), the eclipse is *total*. If, however, the earth is farther from the moon and passes through only the partial shadow, the eclipse is said to be *annular*. Sometimes the moon passes through the shadow of the earth; there is then an eclipse of the moon.

The pinhole camera illustrates the rectilinear propagation of light. If the pinhole is circular, the light from each point on the object strikes the photographic plate in the form of a small circle (or ellipse).

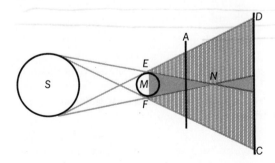

FIGURE 25.3
Shadow cast by an object smaller than the illumination source.

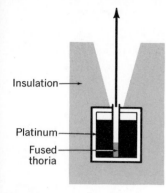

FIGURE 25.4
International standard light source.

If the pinhole is large, the circles overlap badly, and the image is blurred. The smaller the hole, the sharper the image (unless the hole is so small that diffraction becomes important), but the longer it takes to expose the picture. Note that the image is *inverted*.

25.3 Standard Sources and Luminous Flux

To compare light sources and illumination, we make measurements in terms of arbitrary standards. In the early days the standard source was the *British standard candle*, made of spermaceti and burned at the rate of 120 grains/hr. At that time the *lumen*, which is the unit of *light flux*, was the light emerging through an opening made by cutting an area of one square foot out of a spherical surface of radius one foot when a standard candle emitted light at the center of the sphere. These standards are not of current scientific value, but modern standards have been chosen in such a way that we still measure source intensities in *candles* and light flux in *lumens*.

The present standard candle is based on the following arbitrary, but highly reproducible, operation. The standard source, developed by the National Bureau of Standards and adopted by the International Commission of Weights and Measures in 1948, consists of a glowing cavity of the temperature of melting platinum. A schematic diagram of the standard source is shown in Figure 25.4. A cylindrical tube of thorium oxide, surrounded by pure platinum at its melting point and with powdered thorium oxide in the bottom, acts as an ideal blackbody radiator. The tube is closed at the top except for a small hole, the area of which is $\frac{1}{60}$ cm². When this source, operating at the freezing temperature of platinum, is observed from above, its luminous intensity is one international *candle*. We measure the luminous intensities of other light sources in *candles* (sometimes called *candlepower*).

Imagine an ideal point source S of radiation at the center of a sphere (Fig. 25.5) emitting light equally in all directions and having a luminous intensity of I candles. Actually such an isotropic source is not something we can make, but we can discuss its properties. The total luminous flux F emitted is arbitrarily chosen to be $4\pi I$ lumens. Thus an isotropic 1-candle source emits 4π lumens of flux, and *one lumen is the luminous flux which falls upon one square meter of the area of a sphere of one meter radius when an isotropic source of one candle is at the center of the sphere.*

FIGURE 25.5
Ideal point source S at the center of a sphere of radius R. The solid angle ω subtended by an area A of the spherical surface is given by A/R^2 steradians.

The solid angle subtended by 1 m² of the surface of a sphere of 1 m radius is called a *steradian*. The solid angle subtended by an area A of the surface of a sphere of radius R (Fig. 25.5) is given by $\omega = A/R^2$. Thus the entire sphere subtends an angle of 4π steradians. A one-candle source emits one lumen per steradian.

Typical light sources, such as fluorescent and incandescent lamps, emit different luminous fluxes in different directions. Consequently, the apparent source intensity depends on the direction from which it is viewed, just as is the case with the standard source. In Sec. 25.5 we describe a means of measuring the intensity of a practical source.

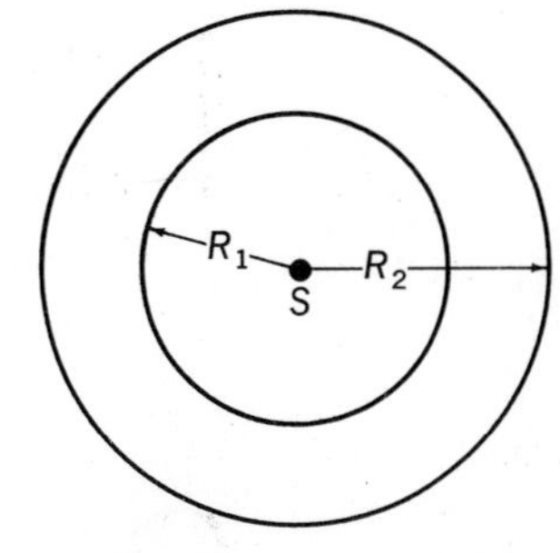

25.4 Illuminance

When luminous flux strikes a surface, the surface is illuminated. We define the *illuminance* (or *illumination*) E of the surface as the *luminous flux incident per unit area.* In the metric system we measure the illuminance in lumens per square meter, or *luxes;* in the British system in lumens per square foot, which are sometimes called *foot-candles.* Consider light proceeding from a point source S of I candles. As the light advances, it is distributed over a larger and larger area. If the medium through which the light travels does not absorb any energy, the total light energy passing any spherical surface concentric with S is constant. The light falling on a unit area of a sphere of radius R is given by the ratio of the luminous flux F emitted to the area $4\pi R^2$ of the sphere:

$$E = \frac{F}{4\pi R^2} = \frac{4\pi I}{4\pi R^2} = \frac{I}{R^2} \qquad \text{25.1}$$

For concentric spheres (Fig. 25.6), the luminous flux F is constant; thus

$$E_1 = \frac{F}{4\pi R_1{}^2} \qquad \text{and} \qquad E_2 = \frac{F}{4\pi R_2{}^2}$$

The amount of light per unit area arriving from a point source varies inversely as the square of the distance from the source.

When the light rays are not incident along a normal to the surface, but make an angle i with the normal (Fig. 25.7), the illuminance is given by

$$E = \frac{I \cos i}{R^2} \qquad \text{25.2}$$

If the eye were equally sensitive to radiant energy of all wavelengths, we could measure the illuminance E of a surface in terms of the amount of energy falling on a unit area of the surface in unit time. However, the eye is more sensitive to some wavelengths than to others (Sec. 29.5). Therefore, if we are interested in light from the point of view of vision, we must compare illuminances on surfaces by use of the eye or an instrument deliberately constructed to respond like the eye. One such instrument is similar to an exposure meter used by photog-

FIGURE 25.6
The total light flux passing each sphere from the point source S is the same, though it falls on differing areas. The flux per unit area is inversely proportional to the square of the distance from the source.

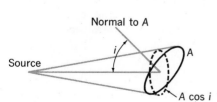

FIGURE 25.7
The illuminance falling on a surface at an angle of incidence i is proportional to $\cos i$.

raphers. The output of a photoelectric cell is adjusted so that it reads the illuminance directly. The instrument differs from an exposure meter in that suitable filters over the cell give it a response which is proportional to the luminous flux. If the eye and the camera film had identical responses to all wavelengths, the same instrument could be used for both purposes.

Table 25.1 lists a few typical illuminances. The figures are approximate; one reason is that different surfaces reflect vastly different fractions of the incident light. A gray surface receiving an illuminance of 50 lumens/m² does not appear as bright as a white one under the same illuminance, since more light is reflected back from the white surface. Hence, one may find a lower illuminance acceptable for reading a book printed on good white paper than for reading a newspaper.

The *luminous efficiency* of a light source is the ratio of light flux emitted by the source to the power supplied to the source. Table 25.2 lists some typical luminous efficiencies of modern light sources. For an incandescent lamp, the higher the temperature at which the source operates, the greater the luminous efficiency.

25.5 The Photometer

A photometer is a device for comparing the intensities of two sources. To make this comparison, the distances of the sources from a screen are adjusted until they produce the same illuminance. Under these circumstances, if I_1 is the intensity of one source, I_2 that of the other source, and R_1 and R_2 their respective distances from the screen when they produce equal illuminance,

$$\frac{I_1}{R_1{}^2} = \frac{I_2}{R_2{}^2}$$

25.3

Example A standard 32-candle lamp at a distance of 60 cm from a screen gives the same illumination as a lamp of unknown intensity

TABLE 25.1 *Typical Illuminances*

Situation	Illuminance, lumens/m²
Brilliant day, sun overhead	100,000
Overcast day	8,000
Minimum recommended for fine work	100
Night football or baseball	40
Office, classrooms, reading room	25
Street lights	0.5
Full moonlight	0.2
Starlight	0.0003

TABLE 25.2 *Typical Luminous Efficiencies*

Source, watts	Luminous flux, lumens	Efficiency, lumens/watt
TUNGSTEN LAMP		
10	80	8
40	470	12
100	1,600	16
1,000	22,000	22
FLUORESCENT LAMP		
6	240	40
10	450	45
30	1,800	60
40	3,000	75

at a distance of 120 cm from the screen. Find the intensity of the unknown lamp.

$$\frac{I_1}{R_1{}^2} = \frac{I_2}{R_2{}^2}$$

$$\frac{32 \text{ candles}}{(0.6 \text{ m})^2} = \frac{I_2}{(1.2 \text{ m})^2}$$

$$I_2 = 128 \text{ candles}$$

If two sources have different colors, it is impossible to obtain proper balance with a simple photometer. However, if an arrangement is made whereby a screen is illuminated first by one source and then by a second, it is possible to find a frequency of alternation such that the color difference disappears. Then the observer can adjust the source distances until the sources produce equal illuminances. A photometer constructed for this process is called a *flicker photometer*.

25.6 The Velocity of Light

Light travels through empty space and through air with a speed of approximately 186,000 mi/sec. In 1 sec light travels a distance more than seven times around the earth at the equator. It takes light a little over 8 min to reach us from the sun, and 4 years from the next nearest star. Several methods have been devised for determining the speed of light.

The first successful measurement of the speed of light was made by the Danish astronomer Römer about 1675. Römer studied the periods of Jupiter's moons, four of which are visible in a small telescope. The innermost of these moons revolves around Jupiter in about 42.5 hr. Römer found that as the earth moved from *B* to *C* (Fig. 25.8) the measured periods of this moon were all somewhat longer than average;

FIGURE 25.8
Römer's method for determining the speed of light, using the diameter of the earth's orbit and the passage behind Jupiter of one of its moons.

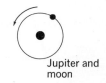

Jupiter and moon

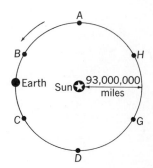

the periods were shorter than average while the earth moved from G to H. He concluded correctly that the longer periods were due to the fact that, while the moon revolved around Jupiter, the earth was moving farther away. The shorter periods occurred when the earth moved closer to Jupiter during the revolutions of the moon. From his measurements Römer estimated that 22 min are required for light to travel the diameter AD of the earth's orbit. Subsequent measurements show that the time required for light to traverse AD (186,000,000 miles) is 1,000 sec and that the speed of light is 186,000 mi/sec.

In Figure 25.8 no account was taken of the motion of Jupiter, which is also revolving in its orbit about the sun. This motion is an additional complication, although Jupiter's speed is considerably less than that of the earth. It takes almost 12 years for Jupiter to make one revolution about the sun.

One of the most famous determinations of the velocity of light was that of Michelson. Figure 25.9 is a simplified diagrammatic representation of his experiment. Light from an intense source is focused by a lens and reflected from an octagonal mirror which, for the moment, is at rest. This mirror is adjusted so that the beam of light travels to a stationary mirror and is reflected back to the octagonal mirror and finally to the eye of an observer. In Michelson's determination a stationary mirror was placed on Mount San Antonio, and the octagonal mirror on Mount Wilson, in California. The distance between mirrors was carefully surveyed and found to be 35.4 km. Then the octagonal mirror was put into rapid rotation. Each time one of the eight sides passed the position indicated in the figure, a flash of light was sent to the stationary mirror on Mount San Antonio and returned. If, when it returned, the mirror was in some different position, the light was reflected in some direction other than that of the eye. However, when

FIGURE 25.9
Simplified representation of Michelson's apparatus for measuring the speed of light.

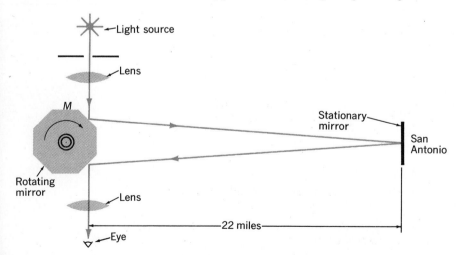

the speed of rotation of the mirror was made great enough so that the mirror rotated through exactly one-eighth of a revolution while the light made the trip to Mount San Antonio and returned, the light was reflected to the eye and observed. When this condition was satisfied, the time in which the mirror made one-eighth of a revolution was exactly equal to the time for the light to travel 70.8 km.

Example In Michelson's experiment the light path from a rotating mirror to a fixed mirror (Fig 25.9) is 22 miles. If an octagonal mirror is rotated at the rate of 31,800 rev/min, the light flashes are observed for the first time. Find the speed of light.

$$\text{Time for 1 rev} = \frac{1}{31,800} \text{ min} = \frac{60}{31,800} \text{ sec}$$

$$\text{Time for } \frac{1}{8} \text{ rev} = \frac{60}{31,800 \times 8} \text{ sec} = 2.36 \times 10^{-4} \text{ sec}$$

In this time light travels 44 miles, so that

$$c = \frac{44 \text{ miles}}{2.36 \times 10^{-4} \text{ sec}} = 186,000 \text{ mi/sec}$$

Many other methods of determining the speed of light have been devised, several of which are capable of far higher precision than the Michelson measurement. The results of many determinations by many different physicists using a wide variety of methods lead us to believe that the speed of light in free space is 2.99793×10^8 m/sec.

25.7 Frequency and Wavelength

The relation between frequency, velocity, and wavelength is the same for light waves as it is for sound waves. Hence,

$$c = \nu\lambda$$

where c is the velocity, ν the frequency, and λ the wavelength. Waves of yellow light have been found to have a wavelength equal to about 590 mμ. Taking the velocity of light to be 3×10^8 m/sec, the frequency of yellow light is

$$\nu = \frac{c}{\lambda} = \frac{3 \times 10^8 \text{ m/sec}}{590 \times 10^{-9} \text{ m}} = 5.08 \times 10^{14}/\text{sec}$$

The wavelength of light is usually expressed either in angstroms or in millimicrons. One angstrom $= 10^{-8}$ cm $= 10^{-10}$ m, while the millimicron is 10^{-9} m, as its name implies.

Questions

1. Is the source intensity of an incandescent lamp the same in all directions? What do we mean by source intensity in this case?

2. How, in principle, would you calculate the illuminance at a point illuminated by a large, spread-out source such as a fluorescent lamp?

$1 \overset{0}{A} = 10^{-10}$ m

$c = 3 \times 10^{8}$ m

3. Do a photometer and a photographic light meter read the same physical quantity? If not, how do they differ?

4. If the sun is closer to us in winter than in summer, why is the illuminance on a horizontal surface greater on a clear summer day than on a clear winter day?

5. In Michelson's method of measuring the speed of light, what was the advantage of using eight- and twelve-sided mirrors rather than four- or six-sided ones?

Problems

1. Find the frequencies associated with electromagnetic waves of wavelength (a) 5,000 Å (visible light), (b) 0.5 Å (X rays), (c) 50 μ (infrared), and (d) 500 m (radio).

Ans. 6×10^{14}, 6×10^{18}, 6×10^{12}, and 6×10^{5} sec^{-1}

545 M

188 M

5.5 M

5.17 m

2. Standard radio broadcasting stations use frequencies between 550 and 1,600 kc, while the longer-wavelength television channels use frequencies in the 54- to 72-Mc bands. Find the wavelengths which correspond to these frequencies (10^{3} cycles/sec = 1 kc; 10^{6} cycles/sec = 1 Mc).

3. It is desired to use a pinhole camera with film 3 in. high to take a picture of a house 27 ft high. The film is 6 in. from the pinhole. How far should the camera be from the house to include the full height of the house? Ans. 54 ft

4. Light of a certain wavelength has 16,000 waves to the centimeter in air. What is its frequency? Find the number of waves per centimeter when the light is traveling in water if the speed of light in water is three-fourths as great as it is in air and the frequency remains constant. What is the wavelength in each medium?

5. A lens of 5 cm diameter is 50 cm from a lamp which is essentially a point source with a luminous intensity of 80 candles. Find the illuminance at the lens. How many lumens are incident on the lens if the lamp lies on the axis of the lens?

Ans. 320 lumens/m^2; 0.628 lumen

6. A small screen is 20 ft from a 60-candle source. The normal to its surface makes an angle of 30° with a line drawn from the source. What is the illuminance?

7. A lamp of unknown luminous intensity is placed at a distance of 2.5 m from a 40-candle standard. The proper setting of a photometer screen placed between the sources is found by experiment to be 1.4 m from the standard lamp. What is the luminous intensity of the lamp? Ans. 24.7 candles

8. An arc lamp at a distance of 50 ft from a screen produces the same illumination as a 100-candle lamp at a distance of 6 ft from the screen. What is the luminous intensity of the arc lamp?

9. A 32-candle lamp is placed 0.4 m in front of a screen. How far from the screen must a 120-candle lamp be placed in order that the illuminance on the screen may be three times as great as it was with the first lamp? Ans. 0.447 m

10. Two lamps of 80 and 30 candles are placed 150 cm apart. At what position between them will the illumination on both sides of an interposed screen be equal?

11. The luminous efficiency of a 200-watt light bulb is 20 lumens/watt. If such a bulb is used as a street light, what is the illumination in foot-candles (lumens per square foot) on a horizontal street (a) 15 ft directly below the lamp and (b) 20 ft from the point directly below the lamp. Assume that there is no reflector and that light is emitted equally in all directions. Ans. (a) 1.41 ft-candles; (b) 0.31 ft-candles

12. If a 100-candle incandescent lamp sends out light uniformly in all directions, how many lumens per square foot are received on a screen 5 ft from the lamp when the angle of incidence is 20°?

13. A screen is placed 1.2 m from a lamp. When a sheet of smoked glass is placed between the screen and the lamp, the lamp must be moved so that it is at a distance of 0.75 m from the screen in order to produce the same illuminance on the screen. Calculate the percentage of light transmitted by the sheet of glass. *Ans.* 39 per cent

14. An astronomical unit of distance is the light-year, by which is meant the distance light travels in a year. Compute this distance in miles. The nearest star is at a distance of 4 light-years. To how many miles does this correspond?

15. A football field is illuminated at night from six towers, each with twenty-four 1,000-watt lamps with luminous efficiencies of 25 lumens/watt. If one-third of the luminous flux reaches the used area which is 120 by 75 m, find the average illuminance at the field. *Ans.* 133 lumens/m²

16. If the separation of the mirrors in a Michelson-method determination of the speed of light is 18 miles and the rotating mirror has eight sides, how rapidly must the mirror be turning when light is first reflected to the eye?

17. What minimum speed of rotation is necessary for a 12-sided mirror used in measuring the speed of light with Michelson's arrangement (Fig. 25.9) if the distance from the fixed mirror to the rotating one is 35.4 km? *Ans.* 353 rev/sec

18. In determining the speed of light by the Michelson method a 12-sided mirror is used. The rotating mirror is 30 km from the stationary mirror, and the minimum rotational speed for light to reach the eye is 415 rev/sec. What speed do these values predict for light?

19. A photocell actuates a relay which controls the opening and closing of the door of a supermarket. At least 0.3 lumen must reach the photocell through an opening of 6 cm² area if the relay is to operate. What source intensity would be required if a point source is to be used 1.2 m from the relay? (In an actual installation one would use a lamp of much lower candlepower. How would the installation deviate from the setup of the problem?) *Ans.* 720 candles

20. Fizeau devised a method of measuring the speed of light in which a beam of light passed between two teeth of a toothed wheel, was reflected back by a mirror, and arrived back at the wheel just in time to pass through the next slot between the teeth. Fizeau's wheel has 720 teeth, and the mirror was 8.6 km from the toothed wheel. He observed no light returning through the wheel when it was rotating at 12.6 rev/sec, and maximum brightness of returning light at 25.2 rev/sec. Find Fizeau's value for the speed of light.

3.12×10^5 km/sec

CHAPTER 26   *Now that we know a little about the nature of light, we shall devote the next four chapters to* geometrical optics, *so named because we consider only the geometrical paths followed by light rays as they are reflected and refracted at various surfaces.   In subsequent chapters we shall treat* physical optics, *in which the wave properties of light play a dominant role.   But our immediate objective, an understanding of the gross operation of optical instruments, can be achieved without any mastery of physical optics.   All we require is a reasonable understanding of reflection and refraction, the first of which we discuss in this chapter.*

Reflection of Light

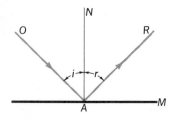

FIGURE 26.1

Reflection of a ray of light from a plane mirror.

FIGURE 26.2

Irregular or diffuse reflection.

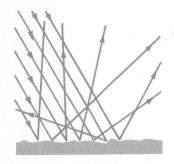

26.1 Laws of Reflection

When a beam of light traveling in a homogeneous medium comes to a second medium, part of the light is reflected.   At a silvered surface the fraction of the light reflected is almost 100 per cent, while at the surface of clear glass it is only a few per cent.   In Figure 26.1, *OA* is a ray incident on a plane mirror, and *AR* a reflected ray.   The angle between *OA* and *AN*, the perpendicular or normal to the surface, is called the *angle of incidence;* the angle *NAR* between normal and reflected ray is the *angle of reflection.*   The laws governing reflection, developed in Sec. 15.8, are:

First law of reflection: The incident ray, the reflected ray, and the normal to the surface lie in the same plane.

Second law of reflection: The angle of incidence is equal to the angle of reflection.

When light falls on a rough, opaque surface (Fig. 26.2), the incident light is scattered in all directions.   If the surface is so smooth that the distances between successive elevations on the surface are less than about one-quarter the wavelength of the light, there is little random scattering, and the surface is said to be *polished.*   Thus, a surface may be polished for radiation of long wavelength, but not polished for light of short wavelength.   A polished reflector or *mirror* is said to exhibit *regular* (or specular) *reflection.*   Rough surfaces produce *diffuse reflection.*

26.2 The Plane Mirror

When a luminous object such as a small candle flame is placed in front of a plane mirror MM' (Fig. 26.3), a point O on the object sends light in all directions. Several rays which leave this point and strike the mirror are shown in the figure. To an observer in front of the mirror all the reflected rays appear to come from the point I behind the mirror. An observer, therefore, sees a bright spot which appears to be behind the mirror and which we call the *image* of the object. For every point on the luminous source there is a corresponding point on the image. The image behind the mirror is a *virtual image,* because the light rays do not actually come from that point. However, every ray of light which leaves a point on the object and is reflected from the mirror *appears to come* from the corresponding point on the image.

The ray ON (Fig. 26.3) falls normally on the mirror and is reflected directly back on itself. It is clear from the figure that the triangles ONA and INA are similar and equal triangles. Therefore, the image point is as far behind the mirror as the object point is in front.

Reflection may also be considered in terms of wave fronts and Huygens' principle (Secs. 15.7 and 15.8). Such a treatment leads to the same conclusions so far as the location of the image of an object point is concerned. In terms of this description, spherical waves diverge from each point on the object, have their curvatures reversed (Fig. 15.10) at the reflecting surface, and thereby appear to have originated at the corresponding image point.

Figure 26.4 shows an object in front of a mirror. It is evident from the figure that the image is as far behind the mirror as the object is in front of the mirror and that image and object have the same size. However, *the image is reversed with respect to the reflecting plane.* This is shown more clearly in Figure 26.5, in which the image $O'X'Y'Z'$ of a set of axes $OXYZ$ is indicated. Note that the axis $O'X'$ points in a direction opposite to that of the axis OX. Such an

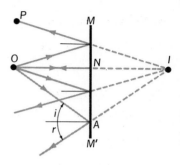

FIGURE 26.3

Image I of a point source O formed by reflection from a plane mirror.

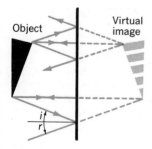

FIGURE 26.4

The image formed by a plane mirror is the same size as the object and as far behind the mirror as the object is in front.

FIGURE 26.5

The image formed by a plane mirror is reversed with respect to the reflecting plane.

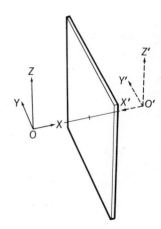

image is *perverted*. Object and image are related in the same way that a right hand is related to a left. If a person salutes with his right hand before a plane mirror, his image appears to salute with the left hand.

26.3 The Concave Spherical Mirror

A concave spherical mirror is part of a spherical shell with its inner surface polished. The center C of the sphere from which the mirror was taken is called the *center of curvature* of the mirror; the radius of the sphere is called the *radius of curvature* of the mirror. The middle point V of the mirror M (Fig. 26.6) is known as the *vertex,* and the straight line CV through the vertex of the mirror and its center of curvature C is the *principal axis.*

Consider a ray of light AB coming up to the mirror parallel to the principal axis. At the mirror the ray is reflected with angle of reflection equal to angle of incidence. Since AB is parallel to the axis, angles i and θ are equal. Triangle FBC is isosceles; therefore BF is equal to FC. If B is not too far from V, BF and VF are nearly equal. Hence, VF is nearly equal to FC; therefore, F is halfway between the mirror and the center of curvature C. This point F is known as the *principal focus* of the mirror. *The distance from the vertex V to the principal focus F is the focal length f of the mirror.* The focal length of a mirror is one-half the radius of curvature R:

$$f = \frac{R}{2}$$

26.1

Any ray of light which comes to the mirror parallel to the principal axis is reflected so that it passes through the principal focus F, provided the angle θ in Figure 26.6 is small. If a ray of light passes along the line FB, it is reflected back in the direction BA. It is true in general that, if a ray takes a certain path through an optical system in one direction, a ray sent backward along the path on which the original ray leaves traverses the same path and comes out along the line on which the original ray entered.

If an object OP is placed before a concave mirror (Fig. 26.7), we may locate an image of point O by drawing a suitable ray diagram.

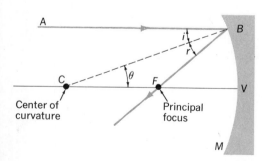

FIGURE 26.6

A ray parallel to the principal axis is reflected from a concave mirror so that it passes through the principal focus.

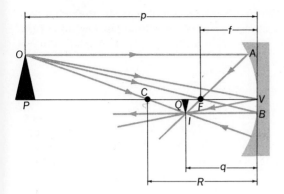

FIGURE 26.7
Concave mirror forming a real image.

The ray OA parallel to the principal axis is reflected back through F, the principal focus.   The ray OF strikes the mirror at point B and is reflected back parallel to the principal axis CV.   A ray from O through C comes to the spherical surface along the radius and is reflected directly back on itself.   All three reflected rays pass through a common point I.   Indeed, if we draw any number of rays which leave point O and are reflected by the mirror, we find that *every ray which leaves point O and strikes the mirror passes through point I.*   The point I is the image of point O.   In this case it is a *real image,* since the rays of light actually cross at this point.   If we put a piece of white paper at I, we see a real image of O.   A similar construction can be made for other points on the object; for each object point we can thus locate the corresponding image point.   In this case the image is *inverted.*

If an object were placed at IQ, the image would be formed at OP. The points P and Q are called *conjugate points;* an object at one has an image at the other.

Let p, q, and f denote, respectively, the distances of object, image, and principal focus from the mirror.   These three distances are related by a simple formula which can be derived with the aid of Figure 26.7 as follows: The triangles OPV and IQV are similar; hence

$$\frac{OP}{IQ} = \frac{PV}{QV} = \frac{p}{q} \qquad\qquad \textbf{26.2}$$

Also, triangles OPF and BVF are essentially similar, so

$$\frac{OP}{BV} = \frac{PF}{FV} = \frac{p-f}{f} = \frac{p}{f} - 1 \qquad\qquad \textbf{26.2a}$$

Since $BV = IQ$, the left-hand members of Eqs. (26.2) and (26.2a) are equal, and

$$\frac{p}{q} = \frac{p}{f} - 1$$

If we divide through by p and rearrange, we obtain

$$\frac{1}{p} + \frac{1}{q} = \frac{1}{f} \qquad\qquad \textbf{26.3}$$

Example An object is situated at a distance of 80 cm from a concave mirror of radius of curvature 60 cm. Find the position of the image.

$$p = 80 \text{ cm} \qquad f = \frac{60 \text{ cm}}{2} = 30 \text{ cm}$$

$$\frac{1}{p} + \frac{1}{q} = \frac{1}{f}$$

$$\frac{1}{80} + \frac{1}{q} = \frac{1}{30}$$

$$q = \frac{2,400}{50} = 48 \text{ cm}$$

When an object is at a great distance, $q = f$, and the image is at the principal focus. As the object is moved toward the mirror, the image moves away. When the object distance is equal to the radius of curvature, the image distance is also the radius of curvature; object and image are identical in size. As the object is moved still closer to the mirror, the image moves away, until it reaches infinity when the object is at the principal focus. From Figure 26.7 we observe that, since the triangles OPV and IQV are similar,

$$\frac{\text{Length of image}}{\text{Length of object}} = \frac{\text{image distance}}{\text{object distance}} = \frac{q}{p} \qquad \textbf{26.4}$$

The ratio of the length of the image to the length of the object is known as the *linear magnification*.

Example Find the size of the image of a body 2.5 cm high when placed 50 cm in front of a concave mirror whose focal length is 20 cm.

$$p = 50 \text{ cm} \qquad f = 20 \text{ cm}$$

$$\frac{1}{p} + \frac{1}{q} = \frac{1}{f}$$

$$\frac{1}{q} = \frac{1}{20} - \frac{1}{50}$$

$$q = 33.3 \text{ cm}$$

$$\frac{\text{Height of image}}{\text{Height of object}} = \frac{33.3}{50} = 0.667$$

$$\text{Height of image} = 0.667 \times 2.5 = 1.67 \text{ cm}$$

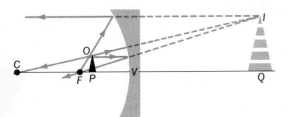

FIGURE 26.8

A concave mirror forms a virtual, erect, magnified image of an object inside the principal focus.

If an object lies inside the principal focus of a concave mirror, a diagram such as that of Figure 26.8 indicates that the image lies behind the mirror. It is *upright, virtual,* and *enlarged.* If we solve for q for the case in which p is less than f, we find that it is *negative.*

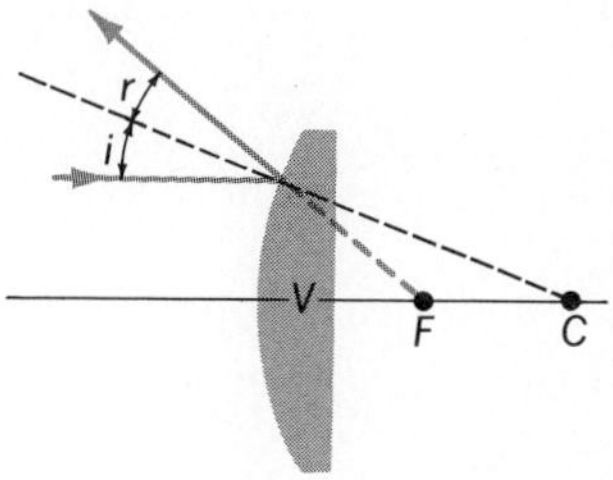

26.4 The Convex Mirror

In the case of the convex mirror (Fig. 26.9), a ray of light parallel to the principal axis is reflected away from the principal axis. However, if we extend the reflected ray backward, the line crosses the principal axis at point F, the principal focus for this convex mirror. The principal focus is *virtual.* Rays parallel to the principal axis are reflected away from the axis in such a way that they appear to come from the principal focus. The mirror is a *diverging* mirror, because rays initially parallel diverge after reflection.

If we place an object in front of a convex mirror (Fig. 26.10), the rays of light which leave a point O on the object and are reflected at the mirror never actually cross, but if we extend these rays behind the mirror, the extensions cross at point I. In a convex mirror a real object forms an *erect, virtual* image, *reduced* in size.

Equation (26.3) is applicable to the convex mirror, provided that we assign a negative sign to the focal length. Further, for a virtual image formed behind the mirror, the image distance q is negative.

FIGURE 26.9
A convex mirror has a virtual principal focus.

Example A bright spot situated 60 cm in front of a convex mirror forms an image 20 cm behind the mirror. Find the focal length of the mirror.

$$\frac{1}{p} + \frac{1}{q} = \frac{1}{f}$$

$$p = 60 \text{ cm} \qquad q = -20 \text{ cm}$$

$$\frac{1}{60} - \frac{1}{20} = \frac{1}{f}$$

$$f = -30 \text{ cm}$$

26.5 The Standard Rays and the Sign Convention

The same formula can be used for both concave and convex mirrors if we are careful to use the proper signs for various quantities. We establish conventions for choosing these signs as follows:

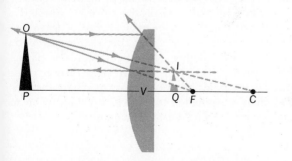

FIGURE 26.10
Convex mirror forming a virtual, erect, reduced image of the object at the left.

1. The object distance p is positive when a ray of light parallel to the principal axis goes from the object to the mirror.

2. The focal length f is positive if this ray parallel to the principal axis strikes the mirror and is reflected so that it passes through the principal focus. If, instead of passing through the principal focus after reflection, it diverges from the principal axis, the focal length is negative.

3. The image distance q is positive if the ray from the object parallel to the principal axis passes through the image after reflection. If, after reflection, the ray goes away from the image, the image distance is negative.

It is of great help in solving optics problems to draw scaled ray diagrams. In such a diagram, the intersection of any two rays which leave a point on the object and are reflected from the mirror is sufficient to establish the corresponding point on the image. It is desirable to use three rays and thus guard against errors. We shall place emphasis on three rays, which we call the *standard rays* and which can be drawn with a ruler. These three standard rays and their paths are as follows:

1. The ray which goes from a point on the object along the line parallel to the principal axis leaves the mirror along a line which passes through the principal focus.

2. A ray which leaves a point on the object along a line connecting that point with the principal focus is reflected along a line parallel to the principal axis.

3. A ray from a point on the object through the center of the curvature of the mirror is reflected directly back on itself.

FIGURE 26.11

Spherical aberration occurs when rays parallel to the principal axis of a spherical mirror of large aperture are reflected so that the outer rays do not cross at the principal focus, but over a surface called the *caustic surface*.

< **Spherical Aberration and Parabolic Mirrors**

If the width of a mirror (Fig. 26.11) is comparable to its radius of curvature, parallel rays after reflection do not all meet at the single point F, the principal focus. Rays that are reflected from a limited region of the mirror in the neighborhood of its vertex V are brought to a focus at F, but the rays that strike the mirror at points distant from the vertex of the mirror cross the axis at points nearer to the mirror than F. The effect of this *spherical aberration* is to destroy the sharpness of the image that would otherwise be formed by the mirror.

If the section of the mirror is a parabola rather than a circle, incident rays parallel to the principal axis are all brought to focus at a single point F, regardless of the size of the mirror. Similarly, all reflected rays which originated at a point source at F leave the parabola parallel to the principal axis. For this reason parabolic mirrors are often used for searchlights. If a light source is placed inside the focus of a parabolic mirror, the rays of light diverge after reflection. If it is outside the focus, the rays converge after reflection. This fact is used in automobile headlamps to give a broad "bright" beam from one filament and a narrow "dim" beam from another.

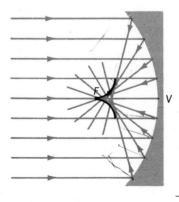

Questions

1. How could you locate the center of curvature of a concave mirror with only a sharpened pencil and your eye?

2. What is the shortest plane mirror in which a 6-ft man can see himself completely?

3. If you wish to take a photograph of yourself in a plane mirror and you stand 4 ft from the mirror, for what distance should the camera be set? Why?

4. A trick mirror makes a man's head look small and his hips large. How is this mirror made?

5. If a ground-glass surface is wetted with water, it becomes more transparent. Why?

6. A burning candle stands between two plane mirrors which touch along a vertical line. How many images of the candle does an observer see if the angle between the mirrors is (*a*) 90°, (*b*) 60°, or (*c*) 30°?

Problems

Draw a suitable ray diagram for each problem.

1. A plane mirror lies face up, making an angle of 15° with the horizontal. A ray of light shines down vertically on the mirror. What is the angle of incidence? What will be the angle between the reflected ray and the horizontal? *Ans.* 15°; 60°

2. Prove that a ray of light reflected from a plane mirror rotates through an angle 2θ when the mirror is rotated through an angle θ about an axis perpendicular to both the incident ray and the normal to the surface.

3. An object 2 cm high is placed 25 cm from a concave mirror with a focal length of 10 cm. Where is the image located? How high is it? *Ans.* 16.7 cm; 1.33 cm

4. As the position of an object reflected in a concave mirror of 25 cm focal length is varied, the position of the image varies. Plot the image distance as a function of the object distance, letting the latter change from $-\infty$ to $+\infty$. Where is the image real? Where virtual?

5. An object 1.6 cm high is 24 cm from a concave mirror whose radius of curvature is 16 cm. Locate the image. Is it real or virtual? Is it erect or inverted? What is its size? *Ans.* 12 cm; real; inverted; 0.80 cm high

6. An object 2 cm high is located 10 cm in front of a concave mirror which has a radius of curvature of 30 cm. Find the position, size, and character of the image.

7. An object 1.6 cm high is 24 cm from a convex mirror with a radius of curvature of 16 cm. Locate the image. Is it real or virtual? Is it erect or inverted? What is its size? *Ans.* −6 cm; virtual; erect; 0.4 cm high

8. An object is placed 3 ft from a convex mirror which has a focal length of 2 ft magnitude. Find the image distance and the ratio of the height of the image to the height of the object. $-1.2 ft$ 0.4

9. A man's eye is 14 cm from the center of a spherical reflecting Christmas-tree ornament which is 8 cm in diameter. Find the image position and the linear magnification. *Ans.* −1.75 cm; ⅛

10. What will be the magnification obtained by using a concave mirror with a focal length of 16 in. if the mirror is held 10 in. from the face?

11. A magnifying mirror produces an erect virtual image 2.5 times as high as an object 24 cm from it. Find the radius of curvature of the mirror.   *Ans.* 80 cm

12. A fortuneteller uses a polished sphere of 5 in. radius. If her eye is 8 in. from the sphere, where is the image of the eye?

13. An object is placed in front of a concave mirror having a radius of curvature of 18 cm. It is desired to produce first a real image and then a virtual image three times as high as the object. Find the object distance required in each case.

Ans. 12 cm; 6 cm

14. A magnifying mirror has a radius of curvature of 0.50 m. How far must a face be from a mirror if the image is to be erect, virtual, and with linear dimensions three times those of the face?

15. An object 3 cm high is 30 cm from a concave mirror of 20 cm focal length. Find the image distance and image height. If the object is moved 5 cm closer to the mirror, how far does the image move?   *Ans.* 60 cm; 6 cm; 40 cm

16. Where must an illuminated object be placed with reference to a concave mirror with a radius of curvature of 2 m in order to have its image focused on a screen 6 m from the mirror?

17. An incandescent lamp is located 2.4 m from a wall. It is desired to throw on the wall an image magnified three diameters, using a concave mirror. What must be the radius of curvature of the mirror? Where must it be placed?

Ans. 1.8 m; 3.6 m from wall

18. Show that the path of the reflected ray from O of Figure 26.3 which passes through point P after reflection is the shortest possible path which reaches the mirror. (This is an example illustrating Fermat's principle of least time, which states that the actual path of a light ray between two points is such that it takes less time for the light to traverse this path than it would take to traverse any other path which varies slightly from the actual path.)

CHAPTER 27 *In the preceding chapter we discussed what happens when light is reflected at a surface, and we learned how images are formed by spherical reflectors. Next we examine the bending of light rays as they pass through an interface which separates one medium from another. It is this phenomenon of refraction which we must understand if we are to appreciate how lenses form images and how optical instruments such as microscopes and cameras operate.*

Refraction and Dispersion

27.1 Refraction

When light passes obliquely from one medium to another, there is a change in the direction of propagation. *The bending of light rays as they pass from one medium to another is called refraction.* As a consequence of refraction, a ruler which is dipped obliquely into water appears to bend sharply at the surface of the water.

Figure 27.1 shows a ray *OA* incident obliquely on a plane water surface *RS*. Upon reaching the surface, the ray *OA* undergoes a sharp change in direction, proceeding along the line *AI*. The angle *OAN* between the incident ray and the normal *NN′* to the surface is the angle of incidence *i*, while the angle *IAN* is the angle of refraction *r*. When a ray of light is refracted at a surface, two laws are obeyed:

1. *The incident ray, the refracted ray, and the normal to the surface lie in the same plane.*

2. *The ratio of the sine of the angle of incidence to the sine of the angle of refraction is a constant independent of the angle of incidence.*

The second law of refraction is called *Snell's law* in honor of its discoverer.

The ratio sin *i*/sin *r* depends on the media on the two sides of the interface at which refraction occurs. In order to compare the refraction associated with various media, we refer refraction measurements to a common medium. A vacuum has been chosen as the standard medium, and we now define:

The index of refraction of a medium is the ratio of the sine of the angle of incidence measured in vacuum to the sine of the angle of refraction measured in the medium.

When we say the index of refraction of glass is 1.50 or the index of refraction of water 1.33, we are automatically implying that the light is incident from a vacuum and falls upon the material whose index is quoted. Table 27.1 lists the indices of refraction of a number of common transparent materials. It is apparent that the index of refraction

FIGURE 27.1
Light ray being bent or refracted.

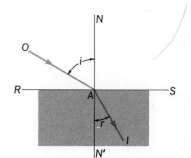

TABLE 27.1 *Indices of Refraction (For light of $\lambda = 589\ m\mu$—Na D radiation)*

Substance	n	Substance	n
Air	1.00029	Glycerin	1.47
Carbon dioxide	1.00045	Water	1.333
Canada balsam	1.53	Crown and plate glass	1.52
Ethyl alcohol	1.36	Flint glass	1.63
Carbon disulfide	1.63	Heavy flint glass	1.66
Diamond	2.42	Quartz	1.54

of air differs little from unity. In most situations it makes no significant difference whether light is incident on a medium from vacuum or from air.

The correct explanation for refraction was given by Huygens, as we have seen in Sec. 15.9. Whenever a wave motion passes from one medium in which its speed is V_1 to another in which its speed is V_2, the wave pattern changes its direction in such a way that $V_1/V_2 = \sin i/\sin r$, where i is the angle of incidence, and r the angle of refraction.

In general, for any medium the index of refraction n is given by

$$n = \frac{\sin i\ (\text{in vacuum})}{\sin r\ (\text{in medium})} = \frac{c}{V} \qquad \textbf{27.1}$$

where c is the speed of light in vacuum, and V the speed in the material.

27.2 Relative Indices of Refraction

In defining the index of refraction of a material we chose to have light incident from a vacuum. Often an interface separates two transparent media of substantial density, such as glass and water. The laws of refraction are valid in such cases; the ratio $\sin i/\sin r$ is called the *index of refraction of the second medium relative to the first*. In general, the ratio of the sine of the angle of incidence to the sine of the angle of refraction is equal to the ratio of the speed of light in the first medium V_1 to the speed of light in the second medium V_2:

Index of refraction of medium 2 relative to medium 1

$$= n_{2,1} = \frac{\sin i}{\sin r} = \frac{V_1}{V_2} \qquad \textbf{27.2}$$

When light goes from one medium to another in which its velocity is smaller, it is bent toward the normal; when it goes from one medium to another in which its velocity is greater, it is bent away from the normal.

If light is going from medium A into medium B, it is convenient to write the law of refraction in the form

$$n_A \sin \theta_A = n_B \sin \theta_B \qquad \textbf{27.3}$$

where n_A and n_B are the indices of refraction, and θ_A and θ_B are the

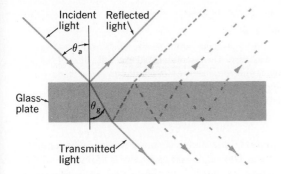

FIGURE 27.2

Refraction and reflection at parallel plane surfaces.

angles between the normal and the rays in medium A and medium B, respectively. This relationship applies whether the ray is going from A into B or from B to A.

If the light is going from A to B, the index of refraction of B relative to A is

$$n_{B \text{ relative to } A} = \frac{\sin \theta_A}{\sin \theta_B} = \frac{V_A}{V_B} = \frac{n_B}{n_A} \qquad \textbf{27.3}a$$

On the other hand, if the light goes from B to A, the index of refraction of A relative to B is

$$n_{A \text{ relative to } B} = \frac{\sin \theta_B}{\sin \theta_A} = \frac{V_B}{V_A} = \frac{n_A}{n_B} \qquad \textbf{27.3}b$$

27.3 Refraction through Slabs with Parallel Faces

If a ray of light (Fig. 27.2) falls on a plate of glass with parallel faces, it is bent toward the normal as it enters the glass. As it leaves the glass, it is bent away from the normal. Since the faces of the plate are parallel to each other, the normals to the first and second faces are parallel to each other, and therefore the angle θ_G between the normal and the ray in the glass is the same at both surfaces. Consequently, the direction of the ray emerging from the glass is the same as its direction on entering; however, the ray is displaced laterally.

Whenever light goes from one transparent medium to another with different optical properties, there is always a reflected beam as well as a refracted one. Figure 27.2 shows this schematically. There is reflection at the lower surface of the plate as well as at the upper. Light which undergoes several reflections is said to be *multiply reflected*.

When a ray of light from air traverses several parallel layers of transparent substances (Fig. 27.3), it is refracted at each surface. If it returns to air, its direction is unchanged, but it is laterally displaced from its original path.

27.4 Total Reflection

When a ray of light passes from an optically dense medium such as water to a rarer medium such as air, it is bent away from the normal so that the angle of refraction is greater than the angle of incidence

FIGURE 27.3

Paths of a light ray through parallel layers of different materials.

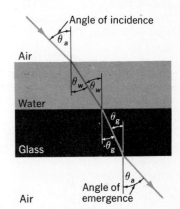

(a) (b) (c)

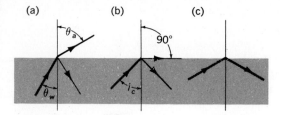

FIGURE 27.4

When light goes from water to air, (a) the refracted ray is bent away from the normal, (b) at the critical angle of incidence the refracted ray is parallel to the surface, (c) the light is totally reflected when the angle of incidence exceeds the critical angle.

(Fig. 27.4a). If the angle of incidence is made larger, the angle of refraction becomes 90°, and the refracted ray travels along the surface of separation between the two mediums. *The angle of incidence for which the angle of refraction is 90° is called the critical angle.*

Example The index of refraction of water is 1.33. What is the critical angle for light going from water to air?

In general for light going from medium A to medium B,

$$n_A \sin \theta_A = n_B \sin \theta_B$$

Therefore,

$$n_{\text{water}} \sin i_c = n_{\text{air}} \sin 90°$$
$$1.33 \sin i_c = 1.00 \times 1.00$$
$$\sin i_c = 0.75$$
$$i_c = 49°$$

If the angle of incidence is made larger than the critical angle, light no longer enters the rarer medium. Since none of the light enters the second medium, this type of reflection is known as *total reflection*. It takes place at a surface separating an optically rarer from a denser medium when the light comes from the denser to the rarer medium and the angle of incidence exceeds the critical angle. The prism ABC (Fig. 27.5) produces total reflection of the ray OL, since the angle of incidence of 45° exceeds the critical angle for glass.

FIGURE 27.5

Total reflection by an isosceles right-angle prism.

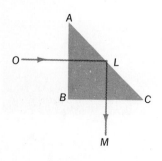

It would be erroneous to believe that when the critical angle of incidence is reached, there is a sudden transition from all light refracted to all light reflected. At any angle of incidence there is always some reflected light.[1] At normal incidence the fraction of the incident intensity reflected is given by $[(n_2 - n_1)/(n_2 + n_1)]^2$, where n_1 and n_2 are the indices of refraction of the first and second mediums. As the angle of incidence is increased, a greater fraction of the incident light is reflected, and a smaller fraction refracted. It is easy to observe with a pane of glass that as the angle of incidence increases the fraction of the light reflected becomes larger.

There are many applications of total reflection. Light can be "piped" down a bent tube of glass or lucite. As the light goes down the tube, it strikes the surfaces at angles of incidence greater than the

[1] These remarks apply to ordinary light; the reflection of polarized light is discussed in Sec. 31.4.

critical angle and is totally reflected. Thus the light is transmitted down the tube until it reaches the end, where the angle of incidence is less than the critical angle, and the light emerges. Such "light pipes" may be used to get illumination in surgical operations at places where it is difficult to operate a lamp because of the heat involved. Light can also be piped in streams of water; colored fountains depend on total reflection to keep the light in the water stream until it finally strikes at an angle of incidence greater than the critical angle and escapes.

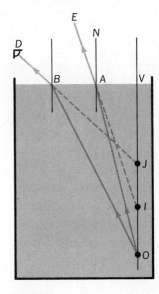

FIGURE 27.6

The apparent depth of an object in water is less than its actual depth by an amount which depends on the angle of incidence.

27.5 Apparent Thickness of a Transparent Body

One of the consequences of refraction is the fact that a body immersed in a transparent medium appears nearer to the observer than it actually is. Let OA and OB represent rays from an object under water (Fig. 27.6); both are bent away from the normal when they reach the surface. An eye at E sees light which appears to come from the image at I; an eye at D would "see" the object at J.

The index of refraction of the water is given by

$$n = \frac{\sin EAN}{\sin AOV} = \frac{\sin AIV}{\sin AOV} = \frac{AV/IA}{AV/OA} = \frac{OA}{IA}$$

If the eye receives only rays very near the normal to the surface, we may write OV for OA, and IV for IA. Then

$$n = \frac{OV}{IV} = \frac{\text{actual depth}}{\text{apparent depth}} = \frac{p}{q} \qquad \text{27.4}$$

The greater the inclination at which the object is viewed, the less is its apparent depth.

27.6 Atmospheric Refraction and the Mirage

Although the index of refraction of air under standard conditions deviates from unity by less than 0.03 per cent, there are situations in which atmospheric refraction is far from negligible. One of the most interesting occurs in the *mirage*. On hot sunny days there may be a layer of very hot air in contact with the ground. This air has a lower density and a slightly smaller index of refraction than the air above it. Light from a distant mountain or treetop approaches this layer of hot air at a large angle of incidence and is totally reflected (Fig. 27.7).

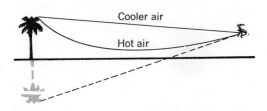

Cooler air

Hot air

FIGURE 27.7

A mirage may be observed when air near the ground is hotter than the air higher up.

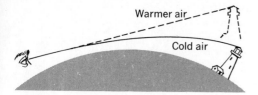

Warmer air

Cold air

FIGURE 27.8

Looming occurs when air near the surface is substantially cooler than the air above.

The light appears to have come from the image just as though it had been reflected from the surface of a lake.

When the air next to the ground is substantially colder than higher air, rays of light are deviated downward (Fig. 27.8). An image of a ship may appear above the ship itself. This phenomenon is called *looming*. It is rather common when an observer is looking over a snow field or over a body of water which is substantially colder than the air several feet above the surface. Cases have been reported in which a lighthouse has been seen at a distance of 40 miles when the curvature of the earth would have completely cut off the light had there been no looming.

When one looks at an object over the hot burner of a stove or over a hot pavement, one may observe a wavy, shimmering effect. This arises from the bending of the light as it passes from colder to warmer to colder air. The twinkling of stars is in part due to similar phenomena in that the light travels through unstable layers in the atmosphere in which the index of refraction is constantly changing by significant amounts.

A ray of light entering the earth's atmosphere from the sun or some other heavenly body is refracted unless it enters at zero angle of incidence. For this reason, the altitude of the sun ordinarily appears too great and must be corrected. Because of variations in the density of the atmosphere, the correction is not easy to calculate. Ordinarily, when the sun is at the horizon, the correction is about one-half degree, which is slightly more than the angle subtended at the earth by the sun's diameter. At the horizon the sun is apparently raised by a little more than its diameter. As a consequence, the sun is really below the horizon when we watch it rise or set. When the sun (or moon) is near the horizon, the rays from the lower edge are bent more than those from the upper edge. This produces a shortening of the vertical diameter, so that the sun appears elliptical.

27.7 Refraction at a Spherical Surface

Consider a ray OP in medium A which is incident upon a spherical surface of medium B (Fig. 27.9) with center of curvature at C. This ray is refracted at the surface, and

$$n_A \sin \theta_A = n_B \sin \theta_B \qquad \text{27.3}$$

By definition,

$$\sin \phi = \frac{z}{R} \qquad \tan \alpha = \frac{z}{p + x} \qquad \tan \beta = \frac{z}{q - x}$$

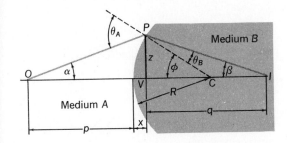

FIGURE 27.9
Refraction at a spherical surface.

Since $\theta_A + \angle OPC = 180° = \angle OPC + \alpha + \phi$, we have $\theta_A = \alpha + \phi$. Similarly, $\phi = \theta_B + \beta$.

We now confine our development to the case in which θ_A, θ_B, α, and ϕ are all small angles. If an angle is small, its sine, its tangent, and the angle itself (in radians) are essentially equal. For this case x is negligible compared with p and q, and we may write

$$\sin \theta_A = \theta_A = \alpha + \phi = \frac{z}{p} + \frac{z}{R}$$

and

$$\sin \theta_B = \theta_B = \phi - \beta = \frac{z}{R} - \frac{z}{q}$$

Then, by Eq. (27.3),

$$\frac{n_A z}{p} + \frac{n_A z}{R} = \frac{n_B z}{R} - \frac{n_B z}{q}$$

or

$$\frac{n_A}{p} + \frac{n_B}{q} = \frac{n_B - n_A}{R} \qquad\qquad 27.5$$

The line OC is the principal axis for this optical system. Equation (27.5) is valid only for rays which make small angles with this axis. The radius R is positive when it is measured from the surface to the center of curvature in the direction in which the light is traveling. Thus R is positive for a surface convex to the incident light and negative for a surface concave to the incident light. Similarly, q is positive if the image is on the side of the surface toward which the light is propagating and negative if on the side from which the light approaches.

27.8 Refraction by a Prism

A wedge-shaped portion of a refracting medium bounded by two plane surfaces is called a *prism*. If the prism is optically denser than the surrounding medium, a ray of light incident on one of the faces is bent toward the normal to that face on entering the prism. On emerging from the opposite face, the ray is going from a denser to a rarer medium and is bent away from the normal to that face. The angle D (Fig. 27.10) through which the ray is deflected in passing through the

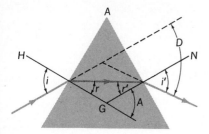

FIGURE 27.10
Refraction by a prism.

prism is called the *angle of deviation*. When the angle at which the ray enters one face is equal to the angle at which it leaves the opposite face, the angle of deviation has its least value and is known as the *angle of minimum deviation*.

< By observing the angle of minimum deviation and the angle between the faces of the prism, it is possible to find the index of refraction of the material of which the prism is made. Let A be the angle of the prism, D the angle of minimum deviation, and n the index of refraction. Since the angle between the faces of the prism is the supplement of the angle between the normals HG and NG (Fig. 27.10),

$$A = r + r'$$

The deviation at the first face is $i - r$, and at the second face $i' - r'$. Hence, the total deviation is

$$D = i - r + i' - r' = i + i' - A$$

The angle of deviation is minimal when the angle of incidence is equal to the angle of emergence. In this case, $i = i'$, $r = r'$, $A = 2r$, $D = 2i - A$, and

$$i = \frac{A + D}{2}$$

From the law of refraction,

$$\text{Index of refraction} = n = \frac{\sin i}{\sin r}$$

$$n = \frac{\sin [(A + D)/2]}{\sin (A/2)} \qquad \qquad \textbf{27.6}$$

Example In a 60° glass prism, the angle of minimum deviation is found to be 48°. What is the index of refraction of the prism?

$$\text{Index of refraction} = \frac{\sin [(A + D)/2]}{\sin (A/2)}$$

$$n = \frac{\sin 54°}{\sin 30°} = \frac{0.809}{0.500} = 1.62$$

27.9 The Dispersion of Light by a Prism

If a very narrow beam of white light is passed through a prism (Fig. 27.11) in a darkened room, it is spread out into a band of colors known as a *spectrum*. Violet light, which has the shortest wavelength

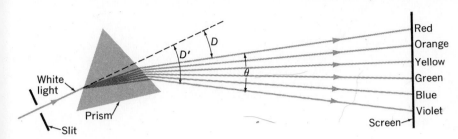

FIGURE 27.11

A prism refracts red light less than violet, resulting in the dispersion of white light into a spectrum.

of the visible, is bent most, while red, with the longest wavelength, is bent least. *The separation of white light into its component colors is called dispersion.*

Since different colors are deviated different amounts by the prism, it is clear that the index of refraction and the speed of light in the prism must be different for the various colors. In ordinary crown glass, red light is approximately one per cent faster than violet.

The question may well be raised as to why we did not notice dispersion in connection with experiments performed earlier with the deviation of light by a prism. In these experiments a much wider beam of light was used, and the level of illumination in the room was great. Because of the width of the beam, the blue from one part of the beam fell on the red from another, on the orange from still another, and so forth. This led to a white core, but at the edges of the deviated beam there were doubtless evidences of dispersion. However, the colors were so dim compared with the bright central image that they probably were not noticed.

27.10 Achromatic Prism

When light of more than one color falls on a prism, the emerging beam is not only deviated, but spread out into a spectrum. If a second prism is placed just beyond, with its vertex at the base of the first, the second prism tends to gather the different colors together again and combine them into white light. The net dispersion produced by the two prisms is the difference between the dispersions produced by the individual prisms. The deviation produced by the second prism is opposite that produced by the first prism, and the net deviation is the difference between the two. If the two prisms were identical, the net effect would simply be that of passing the light through a parallel-faced plate—no dispersion and no deviation. However, if the prisms are made of different kinds of glass, they may have the same net dispersion, but quite different deviations. A flint-glass prism which produces the same dispersion as a crown-glass prism of larger central angle gives a smaller deviation. By placing together crown- and flint-glass prisms which have the same dispersion, it is possible to construct

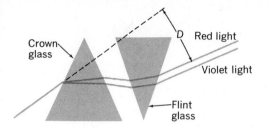

FIGURE 27.12
Achromatic prism combination producing deviation without dispersion. The red from the incident ray shown recombines with the yellow, green, blue, and violet components of neighboring rays to give white light once more.

a prism that deviates the light without spreading it into a spectrum (Fig. 27.12). Such a prism is called an *achromatic* prism.

If the angle of the flint-glass prism is increased until the deviation it produces is equal to that produced by the crown-glass prism, the dispersion of the flint-glass prism is substantially greater. When two such prisms are put together, the combination produces *dispersion without deviation*. When white light passes through such a combination of prisms, called a *direct-vision spectroscope,* it is dispersed into a spectrum, but its general direction is unchanged.

27.11 The Rainbow

No doubt the first evidence of dispersion seen by man was the rainbow. The formation of the rainbow was explained by Descartes about 1637. Let us consider a situation in which the sun is in the west and it is raining in the east. Rays of sunlight enter water droplets (Fig. 27.13), where they are refracted and dispersed. If a ray enters a drop at the proper place, it will be partly reflected at the internal surface of the drop and leave the drop as shown in insert A of the figure. Descartes showed that when the angle θ is 42° red light is strongly reflected, while violet light appears prominently at 40°. The other colors of the spectrum are intensely reflected at angles between 40° and 42°. Each color is strongly reflected at that angle for which it can pass through the droplet with minimum deviation. If an observer stands at O, and if the line SO represents the direction of the incident sunlight, all those raindrops which lie on

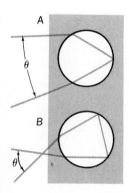

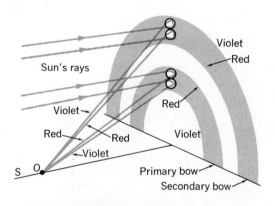

FIGURE 27.13
Formation of a rainbow.

the surface of a cone of angle 40° about SO send an excess of violet light to the observer, while those which lie on a conical surface of angle 42° about SO return red light.

In addition to the primary bow which we have just discussed, there is sometimes a secondary bow in which the colors are reversed, with violet on the outside and red on the inside. This secondary bow is produced by refraction, dispersion, and two internal reflections inside the raindrop, as shown in insert B. For the secondary bow, the angle between the incident and emergent rays is about 51° for red and 54° for violet.

When exceedingly tiny drops are involved, as may be the case in a garden spray, diffraction effects may become large, and the structure of the bow much more complicated.

Questions

1. A swimming pool of clear water is flat where the depth is 3 ft. If a person stands at the center of this region, why does it appear to him that he is standing at the deepest point?

2. What is looming? How can it be explained?

3. How and why does the earth's atmosphere alter the apparent shape of the sun and moon when they are near the horizon?

4. Why are optical systems using totally reflecting prisms usually designed so the light enters and leaves the surfaces normally?

5. Why are colors observed in the light from a cut diamond?

6. Why does the air shimmer over a hot stove? Why do stars twinkle?

Problems

1. Find the angle of refraction of light incident on a water surface at an angle of 52°. What is the speed of light in water?   *Ans.* 36.2°; 2.25×10^8 m/sec

2. Calculate the index of refraction of an aniline by which light incident from air at an angle of 50° is refracted at an angle of 29°. What is the speed of light in this medium?

3. A glass dish with a plane parallel bottom and refractive index 1.50 is half filled with water. Then carbon disulfide is poured on top of the water. Finally, a glass cover is placed on top of the dish, the cover being flat. A beam of light making an angle of 55° with the vertical is incident on the horizontal cover. Find the angles which the beam makes with the vertical as it passes through glass, carbon disulfide, water, glass, and air.
Ans. 33°; 30.2°; 37.8°; 33°; 55°

4. Find the sine of the critical angle of incidence for an air-water interface and the angle of refraction in water if light is incident from air at an angle of 32°.

5. The index of refraction of glass is 1.5. Find the speed of light in glass, the angle of refraction in glass if light is incident from water at an angle of 40°, and the critical angle of incidence for a glass-water interface.   *Ans.* 2×10^8 m/sec; 35°; 62.6°

6. A ray of light passes from flint glass to water. What is the critical angle of incidence?

7. Light, in passing from air into a liquid, is deviated $20°$ when the angle of incidence is $62°$. Under what conditions will total reflection occur at this interface?

Ans. i in liquid $> 49.3°$

8. The bottom of a glass vessel is a thick plane plate that has an index of refraction of 1.55. The vessel is filled with water. What is the largest angle of incidence in the water for which a ray can pass through the glass bottom and into the air below? How does this compare with the critical angle of incidence for a water-air interface?

9. A beam of white light is incident on a block of flint glass at an angle of $55°$. What is the angular separation in the glass of two rays of light, one of wavelength 4,860 Å and the other of wavelength 6,560 Å, if the index of refraction for the former is 1.67 and that for the latter is 1.65?

Ans. 23.5 min of arc

10. Show that Eq. (27.4) follows directly from Eq. (27.5) if the refracting surface is plane, i.e., has a radius of curvature of infinity.

11. A fish is 3 ft below the surface of a pool. What is its apparent depth when viewed from above?

Ans. 2.25 ft

12. A ray of light makes an angle of incidence of $38°$ with a glass prism of index of refraction 1.5 and refracting angle $60°$. Through what angle is the ray deviated by the prism? Does this represent minimum deviation?

13. What is the index of refraction of a $58°$ glass prism which produces an angle of minimum deviation of $38°$?

Ans. 1.53

14. A ray of light is passed through a prism having a refracting angle of $60°$. Rotation of the prism causes the ray to be deviated various amounts, the least of which is $47°$. Determine the index of refraction of the glass of which the prism is made.

15. A hollow prism is made of plane-parallel plates of glass. The angle between the faces is $56°$. What is the angle of minimum deviation when the prism is filled with carbon disulfide and a sodium D line having a wavelength of 589 mμ is passed through it?

Ans. 43.4°

16. Given a $50°$ prism of crown glass, find the angle of minimum deviation. At what angle of incidence must the light strike the prism? Find the deviation if the angle of incidence is $5°$ less.

17. Experiment shows that the index of refraction of a heavy flint glass is 1.717 for D light (yellow) and 1.742 for F light (blue). Find the angle of dispersion of these two colors produced by a $60°$ prism if the light strikes the prism with an angle of incidence of $52°$.

Ans. 4°5′

18. A hemispherical glass paperweight has an advertising trademark sealed against the plane surface at its center. If the radius of the sphere is 5 cm and the index of refraction of the glass is 1.50, find the image position of the trademark when it is viewed along the axis.

19. A fish is swimming in a spherical bowl 40 cm in diameter. If the fish is actually 12 cm from the point on the bowl closest to the observer, what is its apparent distance from that point? (Assume the glass of the bowl is of uniform and negligible thickness.)

Ans. −10.6 cm

20. Show that if a ray of light is incident on a plane parallel glass plate of thickness d at a small angle of incidence θ, it emerges from the plate parallel to its original direction but displaced a distance $\theta d(n-1)/n$, where n is the index of refraction of the glass. (Recall that, for small angles, $\sin\theta = \theta$ in radians.)

21. A clear plastic ball with a diameter of 8 cm has a flaw which is actually 2 cm under the surface. The index of refraction of the plastic is 1.40. Find the position of the image of the flaw when it is viewed along a diameter passing through the flaw from (a) the near side and (b) the far side.   *Ans.* (a) -1.67 cm; (b) -7.5 cm

22. Show that the deviation produced by a thin wedge of transparent material of angle A is given approximately by $D = (n-1)A$ if the angle of incidence is small. *Hint:* For small angles, $\sin\theta = \theta$ in radians.

CHAPTER 28   *Now that we know how light rays are bent when they pass from one material to another, we are ready to apply this knowledge to lenses, which are the basic elements of most optical instruments.   When light rays pass through a lens, they undergo refraction at both surfaces, and, except in very special cases, they emerge traveling in a direction different from that in which they were incident.   In this chapter we see how a lens deviates rays to form an image of an object.   We shall find that much of what we learned in Chap. 26 about image formation by spherical mirrors is applicable to lenses as well.*

Lenses

28.1 Simple Lenses

Lenses are bodies of transparent material shaped to converge or diverge a beam of light.   Simple lenses are bounded by faces which are small sections of spheres.

Consider a beam of parallel rays falling on the prism in Figure 28.1*a*. The rays are deviated by the prism but remain parallel to one another. If we wish to bring these rays together at a point, we must deviate the uppermost ray more than the lowest one.   This can be accomplished by grinding the surfaces so that they have the cross section indicated in Figure 28.1*b*.   If the surfaces of a glass blank are small sections of spheres, they will deviate the upper ray more than any of the others; the higher the ray, the greater the deviation.   Of course, this does not guarantee that all incident parallel rays will pass through the same point.   However, if we do not use too large a section of the spherical surfaces, the emerging rays will all pass very close to the same point.

If a lens brings a bundle of parallel rays together at a point focus, the lens is said to be *converging*.   If it separates such a bundle of parallel rays, the lens is *diverging*.   If glass or plastic lenses are used in air, they are converging if they are thicker in the middle than at the edges, diverging if they are thinner at the middle.   Figure 28.2 shows six possible types of spherical lenses with their names.

Consider the lens of Figure 28.3.   The left surface is a section of a spherical surface having point C_1 as its center, while the right surface is a portion of a sphere having point C_2 as its center.   *The principal axis of this lens is the line connecting the centers of curvature of the two lens surfaces.*   If one of the surfaces is plane, we define the principal axis as the line which passes through the one center of curvature and is perpendicular to the plane surface.

FIGURE 28.1

(*a*) Parallel rays deviated by a prism remain parallel. (*b*) A lens with spherical surfaces brings parallel rays to a focus.

(a)

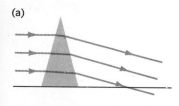

(b)

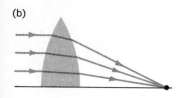

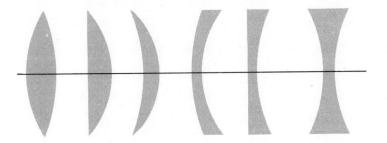

FIGURE 28.2
Lens shapes, from left to right, are double-convex, plano-convex, concavo-convex (converging meniscus), convexo-concave (diverging meniscus), plano-concave, and double-concave.

Rays of light which approach a converging lens parallel to the principal axis are deviated so that they pass (Fig. 28.4) through a common point, the *principal focus,* on the principal axis. If rays of light parallel to the principal axis are incident from either side of the lens, they are deviated by the same amount and pass through the principal focus on the opposite side of the lens. Thus, a lens has *two principal foci,* one on each side. For thin lenses, the principal foci are equidistant from the lens. By a thin lens we mean one whose thickness is negligible compared with the distance to the principal foci and to the objects and images concerned. In this text we confine our attention to thin lenses.

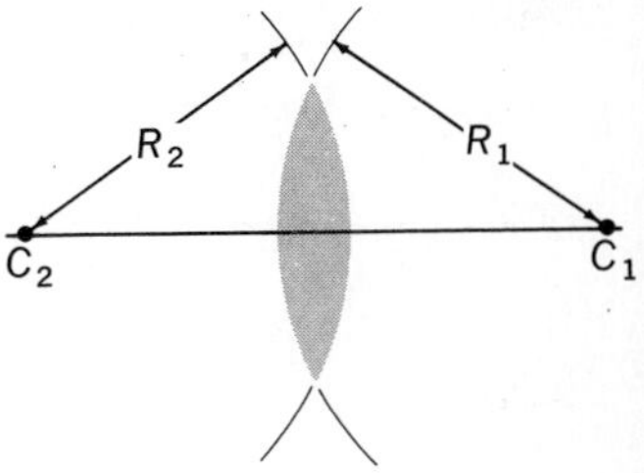

If the rays incident on a lens are parallel, the incident wave front is a plane perpendicular to the rays. The part of the wave front which goes through the edges emerges ahead of the central part because it has less distance to go in glass, where the speed is reduced. By Huygens' principle it can be shown that the emerging wave front is spherical and converges on the principal focus.

In the case of a diverging lens, rays parallel to the principal axis are bent as shown in Figure 28.5. These rays never intersect, but they all appear to come from the virtual principal focus F.

FIGURE 28.3
The principal axis of a lens is the line connecting the centers of curvature of the two lens surfaces.

28.2 Standard Rays for Lenses

In Figure 28.6 we have an object OP a distance p from a converging lens. Every ray of light which leaves point O on the object and passes through the lens passes through point I. In the figure we have shown

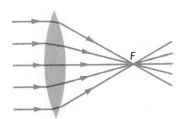

FIGURE 28.4
A converging lens deviates rays parallel to its principal axis so that they pass through the principal focus.

FIGURE 28.5
Rays parallel to the principal axis of a diverging lens are deviated so they appear to come from a virtual focus.

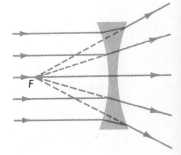

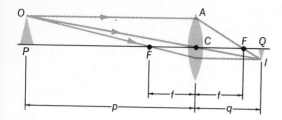

FIGURE 28.6

Formation of a real image by a converging lens.

only three rays, but any other ray from point O which traverses the lens proceeds through point I. Therefore, at point I we have an image of point O. For the entire object OP we find an image IQ, which in this case is real and inverted.

Whenever we are concerned with locating an image by ray tracing, we shall use three standard rays. These rays are analogous to those discussed for mirrors and are as follows:

1. A ray parallel to the principal axis is deviated so that it passes through the principal focus of a converging lens, or diverges as though it came from the principal focus of a diverging lens.

2. A ray of light which approaches the lens along a line which passes through the principal focus for parallel rays coming from the opposite side of the lens is deviated so that it leaves the lens parallel to the principal axis.

3. A ray through the optical center of the lens passes through the lens undeviated. In a thin lens we may take the optical center to be the center point of the lens.

In Figure 28.6 these three standard rays are, respectively, $OAFI$, OFI, and OCI.

28.3 Single Lenses

Let us denote the distance from the object to the lens by p, and that from the image to the lens by q. The distance from the lens to either principal focus is the *focal length*. It is easy to show that the equation

$$\frac{1}{p} + \frac{1}{q} = \frac{1}{f} \qquad \textbf{28.1}$$

applies as well to lenses as to mirrors.

Equation (28.1) can be derived as follows: The triangles OPC and IQC (Fig. 28.6) are similar, and hence $OP/IQ = CP/CQ = p/q$. Also, triangles ACF and IQF are similar, so that $AC/IQ = FC/FQ = f/(q-f)$. Since $AC = OP$, we have $AC/IQ = OP/IQ = p/q = f(q-f)$. Therefore, $pq - pf = qf$. If we divide by pqf and rearrange, we obtain $1/p + 1/q = 1/f$.

We note further that $IQ/OP = q/p$. Since IQ is the length of the image, and OP the length of the object, we have

$$\text{Linear magnification} = \frac{\text{length of image}}{\text{length of object}} = \frac{q}{p} \qquad \textbf{28.2}$$

For the lens of Figure 28.6, if we place an object at *IQ*, we find its image at *OP*. Points *P* and *Q* are *conjugate points* of the lens—an object at either point has an image at the other.

If an object is inside the principal focus of a converging lens, the image formed is *erect, virtual,* and *enlarged* (Fig. 28.7). In this case, the image distance is negative.

If a real object is placed before a diverging lens, an erect, virtual, and reduced image is formed (Fig. 28.8). In applying the general lens formula to the diverging lens, the focal length is taken as *negative*. In Figure 28.8 the image distance *q* is also negative.

In calculations involving the lens relation [Eq. (28.1)], one must be careful that the proper signs are taken for object distance, image distance, and focal length. The sign convention used in this text for both lenses and mirrors is as follows:

1. If the direction of an incident ray is from the object toward the lens (or mirror), the object distance is positive; if its direction is from the lens toward the object, *p* is negative.

2. The focal length is positive for a converging lens (or mirror) and negative for a diverging lens (or mirror).

3. The image distance is positive if a ray goes from the lens (or mirror) toward the image. It is negative if the ray goes away from the image when it leaves the lens (or mirror).

28.4 Combination of Lenses

When light passes first through one lens and then through a second, the position of the final image can be calculated by repeated use of the general lens equation. *The object for the second lens is the image formed by the first.* If the second lens is interposed before the rays actually cross, as in Figure 28.9, its object is still taken to be the image which the first lens would have formed had the second not been pres-

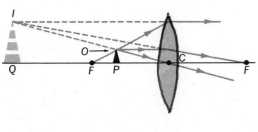

FIGURE 28.7

A converging lens forms an erect, virtual, enlarged image of an object inside the principal focus.

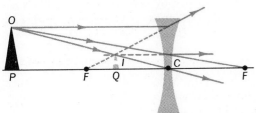

FIGURE 28.8

A diverging lens forms an erect, virtual, reduced image of a real object.

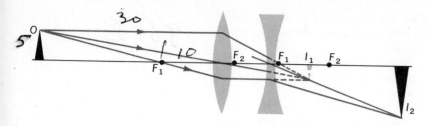

FIGURE 28.9

Image formed by a pair of lenses which are separated.

ent. In this case the second lens has a *negative* object distance, since the light is deviated by this lens before its "object" is formed. If there is a third lens, the image formed by the second lens acts as its object. The final image formed by a very complicated optical system, such as that of a submarine periscope, can be located by successive applications of the relations governing simple lenses and mirrors. In every case the object for any single component is the image formed by the preceding one. Great care must be taken to assign the proper sign to each distance.

Example An object 5 cm high is 30 cm from a lens of 10 cm focal length. A diverging lens of focal length -8 cm is placed 9 cm beyond the converging lens (Fig. 28.9). Find the position and height of the final image.

For the first lens,

$$\frac{1}{p} + \frac{1}{q} = \frac{1}{f}$$

$$\frac{1}{30} + \frac{1}{q} = \frac{1}{10} \qquad \frac{\text{size of image}}{\text{size of object}} = \frac{15}{30}$$

$$q = 15 \text{ cm} \qquad \text{size of image} = 2.5 \text{ cm}$$

For the second lens $p = -6$ cm, and

$$\frac{1}{-6} + \frac{1}{q} = \frac{1}{-8} \qquad \frac{\text{size of image}}{\text{size of object}} = \frac{24}{6}$$

$$q = 24 \text{ cm from second lens} \qquad \text{size of final image} = 10 \text{ cm}$$

Example If the diverging lens of the preceding example had been only 4 cm from the first lens, where would the final image have been located?

The image which would be formed by the first lens is still 15 cm from the first lens. The image distance for the second lens is now -11 cm.

$$\frac{1}{p} + \frac{1}{q} = \frac{1}{f}$$

$$\frac{1}{-11} + \frac{1}{q} = -\frac{1}{8}$$

$$q = -29.3 \text{ cm}$$

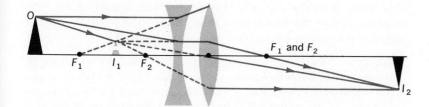

FIGURE 28.10

Diverging and converging lens together.

Example An object is 25 cm from a diverging lens of 15 cm focal length. A converging lens of focal length 10 cm is 5 cm beyond the diverging lens (Fig. 28.10). Find the position of the final image.

For the first lens,

$$\frac{1}{p} + \frac{1}{q} = \frac{1}{f}$$

$$\frac{1}{25} + \frac{1}{q} = \frac{1}{-15}$$

$$q = \frac{-75}{8} \text{ cm}$$

For the second lens,

$$p = {}^{75}\!/_{8} + 5 = {}^{115}\!/_{8} \text{ cm}$$

$$\frac{1}{p} + \frac{1}{q} = \frac{1}{f}$$

$$\frac{8}{115} + \frac{1}{q} = \frac{1}{10}$$

$$q = 33 \text{ cm}$$

28.5 The Telephoto Lens

An interesting application of two lenses in series is found in the telephoto lens (Fig. 28.11). In order to produce a large image of a distant object with a single lens, the focal length must be large. This makes it necessary that a camera of inconvenient length be used, since the length of the camera must be approximately equal to the focal length of the lens. This difficulty can be avoided by a telephoto lens, which consists of a combination of a converging lens A and a diverging lens B placed at a distance d from each other. The converging lens A would form an image of a distant object just outside its focus F_1, but the lens B causes the image to be formed at F'. The image formed at

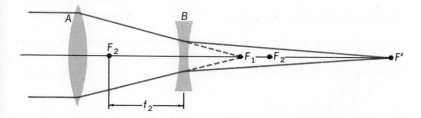

FIGURE 28.11

Telephoto lens.

F' is larger than the one that would have been formed at F_1. The magnification of the lens system is increased without increasing the length of the camera too much.

Example The telephoto lens of Figure 28.11 is used for taking an action shot at a football game. Lens A has a focal length of 12 cm, and lens B a focal length of -6 cm; they are separated by a distance of 8 cm. If the action is 100 m away, find the position of the final image and the magnification of the system. What focal length would be necessary in a single lens to produce an image of the same size? How long would the camera have to be?

For lens A,

$$\frac{1}{100} + \frac{1}{q} = \frac{1}{0.12}$$

$$q = 0.1202 \text{ m} = 12.02 \text{ cm}$$

and the size of the image is $0.12/100$ that of the object.

For lens B, $p = -4.02$ cm and $f = -6$ cm, and

$$\frac{1}{-4.02} + \frac{1}{q} = \frac{1}{-6}$$

$$q = 12.2 \text{ cm}$$

Size of second image $= \dfrac{12.2}{4.02}$ size of first image

$$= \frac{12.2}{4.02} \times \frac{0.12}{100} \text{ size of original object}$$

Magnification $= 0.00364$

The film is $8 + 12.2 = 20.2$ cm from lens A.

For a single-lens camera to produce the same image size, $p = 100$ m and $q = 0.00364p = 0.364$ m.

$$\frac{1}{p} + \frac{1}{q} = \frac{1}{f}$$

$$\frac{1}{100} + \frac{1}{0.364} = \frac{1}{f}$$

$$f = 0.362 \text{ m}$$

The minimum length of camera is the distance from lens to film, which is 36.4 cm; therefore this camera is almost twice as long as the one using the telephoto lens.

28.6 The Lens-maker's Equation

The focal length of a lens depends on the material of which the lens is made and on the radii of curvature of the two surfaces. It is shown below that the focal length is given by

$$\frac{1}{f} = (n - 1)\left(\frac{1}{R_1} - \frac{1}{R_2}\right)$$

28.3

where R_1 and R_2 are the radii of curvature of the two lens surfaces, and n is the index of refraction of the lens material *relative to its surroundings*. In this relationship R_1 is the radius of curvature of the surface upon which the light is incident, while R_2 is the radius of curvature of the surface by which the light leaves the lens. *R_1 is positive when the surface is convex* and *negative when the surface is concave to the incident light*. The same rule applies to R_2. In general, the radius of curvature of a surface is positive when measured from the surface to the center of curvature in the direction the light is leaving the surface. Thus, for a double-convex lens, the first surface has a positive radius of curvature, and the second a negative one.

Rays from an object point O (Fig. 28.12) are refracted at the first surface of the lens and would form an image at I_1 if everything to the right of the first surface were medium B. By Eq. (27.5),

$$\frac{n_A}{p_1} + \frac{n_B}{q_1} = \frac{n_B - n_A}{R_1} \qquad \textbf{A}$$

I_1 serves as object for the second surface; since the light goes from the second surface to I_1, the object distance is negative. Thus $p_2 = -(q_1 - t)$, where t is the lens thickness. For a thin lens t is negligible compared to q_1, so $p_2 = -q_1$, and, for the second surface,

$$\frac{n_B}{-q_1} + \frac{n_A}{q_2} = \frac{n_A - n_B}{R_2} \qquad \textbf{B}$$

Adding Eqs. (*A*) and (*B*) yields

$$\frac{n_A}{p_1} + \frac{n_A}{q_2} = (n_B - n_A)\left(\frac{1}{R_1} - \frac{1}{R_2}\right)$$

or

$$\frac{1}{p} + \frac{1}{q} = \left(\frac{n_B}{n_A} - 1\right)\left(\frac{1}{R_1} - \frac{1}{R_2}\right) \qquad \textbf{28.3a}$$

which is equivalent to Eq. (28.3).

Example A double-convex lens is made of glass having an index of refraction of 1.5. The front surface has a radius of curvature of 10 cm, and the back surface has a radius of curvature of 20 cm (Fig. 28.12). Find its focal length.

$$\frac{1}{f} = (n - 1)\left(\frac{1}{R_1} - \frac{1}{R_2}\right)$$
$$= (1.5 - 1)[\tfrac{1}{10} - (-\tfrac{1}{20})] = \tfrac{1}{2} \times \tfrac{3}{20} = \tfrac{3}{40}$$
$$f = \tfrac{40}{3} = 13.3 \text{ cm}$$

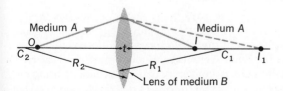

Medium A   Medium A

Lens of medium B

FIGURE 28.12
Light rays from object point O are refracted at both surfaces of the lens to form an image at I.

Object

Pincushion

Barrel

FIGURE 28.13

The image of an object may suffer from pincushion or barrel distortion.

The reciprocal of the focal length of a lens in meters is the dioptric power of the lens in diopters. Thus, a lens of focal length 50 cm has a power $P = 1/0.5 = 2$ diopters. (The power is given in diopters only when the focal length is measured in meters.) The powers of lenses used in typical eyeglasses range from about 0.2 to 4 diopters.

< One of the great advantages of using the powers of lenses is associated with the fact that when two thin lenses are in contact the power of the combination is equal to the sum of the individual powers. If f represents the focal length of the combination of two thin lenses in contact,

$$\frac{1}{f} = \frac{1}{f_1} + \frac{1}{f_2}$$

28.4

where f_1 and f_2 are the focal lengths of the two lenses.

28.7 Defects of Lenses

If we had an ideal lens, every ray of light from any given point on the object would cross at exactly the same point on the image. Further, the image would be similar to the object in every respect. Any circle on the object would be a perfect circle on the image, and any square on the object would lead to a perfect square on the image. If the object were all in one plane, the image would be all in one plane. Actually no such ideal lens exists. For a single lens, the rays from a point on the object ordinarily fall over a small region of the image. If most of the rays from a point on the object cross at the desired image point but some of them cross off on one side, a defect called *coma* occurs. With some lenses the image of a rectangular object (Fig. 28.13) is distorted so that it is *barrel-shaped;* in other cases it may look like a *pincushion.* The detailed explanation of these defects is beyond the scope of this book, but there are three types of image defect which can be readily explained.

Spherical Aberration. When rays of light parallel to the principal axis of a spherical lens pass through zones near its edges, they cross the axis nearer the lens than those rays which pass through nearer to the center. Instead of converging to a sharp focal point, they cross the axis at slightly different points and form a blurred image. This defect is known as *spherical aberration.* It can be minimized by using only a small portion of the lens; for a lens of small aperture and long focal length, spherical aberration becomes small. Spherical aberration can be reduced by proper choice of the curvatures of the lens surfaces. When the bending is roughly the same at each lens surface, deviation is minimum, and so is spherical aberration.

Chromatic Aberration. When rays of white light parallel to the principal axis pass through an ordinary lens, they are refracted in such a way that different colors are brought to focus at different distances from the lens (Fig. 28.14). Since violet rays are bent more than the red, the focal length for violet light is smaller. Such a lens cannot bring all the rays of white light from a point on the object to a single point on the

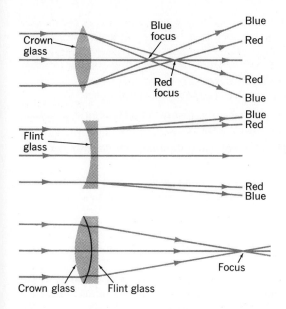

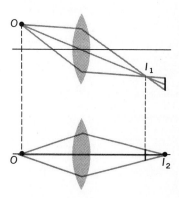

FIGURE 28.14

Chromatic aberration (middle and top) is corrected by two lenses with compensating dispersion to form an achromatic doublet.

image. As a result the image is not sharp and is likely to have colored rings or markings. This image defect is called *chromatic aberration.* It may be corrected to a large extent by combining a converging lens of crown glass with a diverging lens of flint glass. These lenses are chosen so that the dispersion of one is equal and opposite to that of the other. In this way no major separation of light into colors occurs. On the other hand, the bending or refractive power of one lens exceeds that of the other; thus there is a resultant bending of the rays in spite of the fact that the lenses deviate the rays in opposite directions. Lenses which are free from dispersion are called *achromatic lenses.* Two lenses, combined to form an *achromatic doublet,* can bring only two colors to exactly the same focus; the other colors are not perfectly corrected. For better correction of chromatic aberration, one must use more lenses.

Astigmatism. Rays of light from an object point far from the principal axis pass through the lens obliquely and do not converge to a common image point. Figure 28.15 shows side and top views of several rays from the object point O. Rays in the vertical plane converge on I_1, while those in the horizontal plane converge on I_2. Thus, the rays from this single point at O focus in two lines I_1 and I_2, called *focal lines.* At a point midway between I_1 and I_2, a roughly circular patch of light corresponds to the closest available approximation to a point image. In quality optical systems astigmatism is corrected by the use of two or more lenses with the proper separation between them.

In a high-quality camera or microscope a combination of several lenses is utilized to perform the function of a single *ideal* lens. The different kinds of glass used in these lenses, their radii of curvature, and their separations are carefully chosen by the optical designer to minimize image defects.

FIGURE 28.15

Astigmatism and astigmatic focal lines.

Questions

1. What happens to the focal length of a lens when it is immersed in water? Does it matter whether the lens is converging or diverging?

2. How large must a lens be to produce a complete image of a distant object?

3. If a plano-convex lens is used to form an image of a distant object, should the plane or the convex surface be on the side of the object? Why?

4. As a self-luminous object moves closer to a lens, does its image get brighter or dimmer? Why? Explain with equations.

5. If a cylindrical lens is used to form an image of a point source, what will the image look like? Is it really an image in the sense of the discussion in Sec. 28.2?

Problems

Draw a ray diagram whenever appropriate.

1. A converging lens has a focal length of 16 cm. An object 3 cm high is placed 40 cm in front of the lens. Find the position and height of the image.   *Ans.* 26.7 cm; 2 cm

2. An object 60 cm from a lens results in a real image 40 cm from the lens. Find the focal length of the lens. If the image is 1 cm high, how high is the object?

3. An object 2 cm tall is placed 50 cm from a lens of 75 cm focal length. Find the image distance and the height of the image.   *Ans.* −150 cm; 6 cm

4. A converging lens has a focal length of 20 cm. Find the image distance for an object at each of the following distances from the lens: 5 cm, 15 cm, 20 cm, 30 cm, 50 cm, and 100 cm.

5. An illuminated arrow 2 cm high is placed 108 cm from a diverging lens of focal length −36 cm. Find the position and the height of the image.   *Ans.* −27 cm; 0.5 cm

6. A candle is placed at a distance of 1.2 m from a diverging lens with a focal length of −0.4 m. Where is the image located? How high is it relative to the object?

7. The image formed by a converging lens is erect, virtual, and four times as high as the object. If the focal length of the lens is 12 cm, find the object and image distances.
     Ans. 9 cm; −36 cm

8. An object 2 cm high is located 20 cm in front of a plano-convex lens of 30 cm focal length. The lens is made of glass of index of refraction 1.50. Find the image distance, the height of the image, and the magnitude of the radius of curvature of the convex side of the lens.

9. A lens, made of glass with index of refraction 1.5, has surfaces with radii of curvature of magnitudes 30 and 60 cm. If this is a double-convex lens, what is its focal length? If double-concave, what is the focal length? What is the power in each case?
     Ans. 40 cm; −40 cm; 2.5 and −2.5 diopters

10. A plano-convex lens is made of flint glass, which has an index of refraction of 1.69 for violet light and 1.64 for red light. If the radius of curvature of the curved surface of the lens is 30 cm, what is the difference between the focal lengths of the lens for these two colors?

11. A double-convex lens is made of glass of index of refraction 1.5 and has radii of curvature of 24 and 48 cm. Find the focal length of this lens in air and in water.

Ans. 32 cm; 128 cm

12. A plano-convex lens is made of glass of index of refraction 1.5. The curved surface has a radius of 12 in. An object is placed 60 in. in front of the lens. Where is the image? If the object and lens were both immersed in clear water, where would the image be formed?

13. A glass lens having an index of refraction of 1.52 and radii of curvature of $+40$ and -20 cm is cemented to another glass lens having an index of refraction of 1.66 and radii of curvature of -20 and -60 cm. Find the focal length of the combination and its power.

Ans. 58.8 cm; 1.7 diopters

14. A plano-convex lens has a radius of curvature of 20 cm and an index of refraction of 1.75. A plano-concave lens has the same radius of curvature and an index of refraction of 1.50. What is the focal length of the combination if the two lenses are placed in contact to form a plane slab?

15. An object 4 cm high is 120 cm from a converging lens of 40 cm focal length. A diverging lens of focal length -100 cm is placed 20 cm beyond the converging lens. Find the position and height of the final image.

Ans. 66.7 cm; 3.33 cm

16. A converging lens that has a focal length of 40 cm is in contact with a diverging lens that has a focal length of -50 cm. What are the focal length and power of the combination?

17. A converging lens and a diverging lens are placed 12 cm from each other. Where will this combination of lenses produce an image of a distant object if the converging lens has a focal length of 20 cm and the diverging lens a focal length of -6 cm?

Ans. -24 cm

18. An object is 90 cm from a converging lens of 30 cm focal length. A diverging lens of -60 cm focal length is placed 25 cm beyond the converging lens. Find the position of the final image and the ratio of its height to that of the object.

19. A converging lens with a focal length of 24 cm is placed 40 cm in front of a diverging lens having a focal length of -30 cm. An object is placed 30 cm in front of the converging lens. Find the position and linear magnification of the image produced by the two lenses.

Ans. -48 cm; 2.4

20. A beam of sunlight falls on a diverging lens of focal length -15 cm; 20 cm beyond this is placed a converging lens of 25 cm focal length. Where should a screen be placed to receive the final image of the sun?

21. Two double-convex lenses have focal lengths of 40 cm. They are separated by 20 cm. An object 5 cm high is placed 100 cm in front of the first lens. Find the position of the image formed by the system of two lenses. How high is the image?

Ans. 21.6 cm; 1.53 cm

22. Prove that when two thin lenses are in contact the power of the combination is the sum of the powers of the two lenses. *Hint:* Assume a distant object and use the fact that the image formed by the first lens acts as object for the second.

23. A telephoto lens system (Fig. 28.11) consists of a converging lens of 15 cm focal length and a diverging lens of -8 cm focal length separated by a distance of 10 cm. If the system is used to photograph an object 100 m away, how far must the film be from the converging lens? How far would the film be from the lens in a camera using a single lens if the final image were the same size in both cases? *Ans.* 23.6 cm; 40.5 cm

24. Show that if $s = p - f$ (Fig. 28.6) is the distance of an object from the principal focus for parallel rays coming from the opposite side of a lens, and $s' = q - f$ is the distance of the image from the other principal focus, then $ss' = f^2$. (This is known as the *Newtonian form* of the lens equation.)

CHAPTER 29 *Now we know how lenses and mirrors form images, and, in principle at least, we can trace the path of a ray which falls successively upon any number of reflecting and refracting surfaces. This is the knowledge we require to understand the operation of optical instruments—eyes, cameras, projectors, microscopes, and telescopes—which are the subject of this chapter.*

Optical Instruments

29.1 The Photographic Camera

One major application of lenses is in the photographic camera (Fig. 29.1). In a quality camera a combination of lenses acts as a single ideal lens and produces a real image of an external object on a film. The distance between lens and film can be altered to focus the image. In some cameras this adjustment is made by a bellows, and in some by sliding one tube inside another.

The image of a distant object is formed in the focal plane, which contains the principal focus. Therefore, if two cameras of different focal lengths are set up to take the same picture, the lengths of the images are directly proportional to the focal lengths. If both cameras are using the same kind of film, the total amount of light which must reach unit area on each film for proper exposure is the same. The luminous flux entering the camera is directly proportional to the area of the lens opening, which in turn is proportional to the square of the diameter of the circular opening. Consequently, the exposure times for the two cameras are the same if the ratios of focal length to diameter of the opening are the same. *The ratio of focal length to diameter of the opening is called the f number.* If a camera is set at $f/3$, the diameter of the lens opening is one-third the focal length. If the opening is reduced to $f/6$, for the same exposure a time four times as great is required. If a picture must be taken in a very short

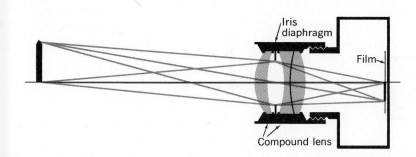

FIGURE 29.1
Photographic camera.

time, a lens with a small f number must be used, and this in turn means a large opening. To produce a lens with a large aperture for which lens defects have been satisfactorily corrected is an expensive process. For this reason a camera with an $f/1.5$ lens may cost several times as much as one with an $f/3$ lens.

The smaller the opening through which light is admitted, the greater the depth of focus for a camera. A smaller cone of rays is used to form the image of a point when the opening is small; therefore the circle on which they fall is smaller when a point is not quite in focus. On the other hand, a smaller opening calls for a longer exposure. If one is taking pictures of fast action such as that in a football game, a compromise between short exposure time and great depth of focus must be made.

29.2 The Projection Lantern

In the projection lantern the fundamental optical parts are essentially those of a camera. The lantern produces a large image at some distance of a small object close by. All the light which forms the image must come from the object. Since the image has a much greater area than the object, it is necessary that the object be strongly illuminated if a bright image is desired. Basically, the projection lantern consists of a powerful source of light (Fig. 29.2), large condensing lenses, and a projecting lens. The condensing lenses collect light from the source and send it through the slide, so that this slide is brilliantly illuminated. The objective then projects a real image of the slide on the screen. Since the slide is just outside the principal focus of the projecting lens, the image on the screen is enlarged, real, and inverted.

Example Find the focal length of the lens which must be used in a lantern to produce the image of a slide 8 cm square upon a screen 3 m square at a distance of 10 m from the lantern. Assume that the image covers the entire screen.

$$\text{Magnification} = \frac{q}{p} = \frac{300}{8}$$

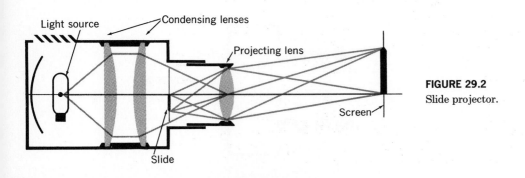

Light source

Condensing lenses

Projecting lens

Screen

Slide

FIGURE 29.2
Slide projector.

Since $q = 1,000$ cm,

$$\frac{q}{p} = \frac{1,000}{p} = \frac{300}{8} \quad \text{and} \quad p = 26.7 \text{ cm}$$

$$\frac{1}{p} + \frac{1}{q} = \frac{1}{f}$$

$$\frac{1}{26.7} + \frac{1}{1,000} = \frac{1}{f}$$

$$f = 25.9 \text{ cm}$$

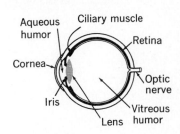

FIGURE 29.3
Human eye.

29.3 The Eye

Like the camera, the eye can be looked upon as a light-tight enclosure having a lens at one end and a sensitive film of nerve fibers at the other end. The eyeball is roughly a hollow sphere of dense fibrous tissue (Fig. 29.3) about 1.5 cm in diameter. Light enters through a transparent tissue called the *cornea* into a clear fluid known as the *aqueous humor.* It then passes through the *lens,* a flexible structure with index of refraction somewhat greater than that of the aqueous humor and of the jellylike *vitreous humor* on the other side. The light is brought to focus on the *retina,* which plays the role of a sensitive screen. The amount of light which enters the eye is regulated by a circular diaphragm called the *iris.* It is this diaphragm which is responsible for the color of the eye. It is provided with muscles which diminish or dilate the *pupil,* which is the opening through which the light enters the lens.

The principal bending of light occurs at the cornea, which has a radius of curvature much less than the remainder of the eyeball. The cornea provides roughly two-thirds of the bending required to focus the image of a distant object on the retina, while the lens provides a power of about 20 diopters. When a normal eye is adjusted for very distant objects, it is relaxed, and the lens has its thinnest shape with surfaces of maximum radii of curvature. To bring the image of a near object in focus on the retina, the muscles of the ciliary body which encircles the lens contract, thereby making the radii of curvature smaller, particularly that of the front surface. Thus the focal length of the lens is reduced, and the image focused on the retina.

The remarkable ability of the eye to adjust its focal length is called *accommodation.* The greatest and shortest range at which a given eye can see distinctly are called the *far point* and *near point,* respectively. For a normal eye the far point is at infinity; the near point may be 6 cm for a child and usually increases with age.

29.4 Defects of Vision

If the image formed by a distant object falls in front of the retina, an eye is *nearsighted* or *myopic* (Fig. 29.4a). This may occur because the lens has too short a focal length, because the eyeball is too long, or for some other reason. Such an eye may see a near object distinctly, since the image moves back as the object approaches. To correct for

(a)

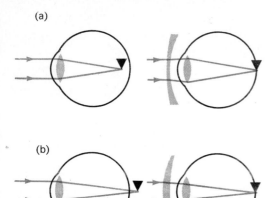

(b)

FIGURE 29.4

How eyeglass lenses correct vision. (*a*) In nearsightedness the image of a distant object falls in front of the retina; a diverging lens corrects the condition. (*b*) In farsightedness the image of a nearby object falls behind the retina; a converging lens provides correction.

myopia, a diverging lens is placed in front of the eye. The image formed by this lens serves as the object for the eye.

Example A nearsighted eye cannot see objects clearly when they are more than 3 m distant. Find the power of the weakest correcting lens which will just allow this eye to form a sharp image of the moon on the retina.

The image formed by the lens serves as object for the eye. The lens desired must form an image of a distant object 3 m from the eye. Therefore, $p = \infty$ and $q = -3$ m.

$$\frac{1}{p} + \frac{1}{q} = \frac{1}{f}$$

$$\frac{1}{\infty} + \frac{1}{-3} = \frac{1}{f}$$

$$f = -3 \text{ m}$$

$$\text{Power} = \frac{-1}{3 \text{ m}} = -0.33 \text{ diopter}$$

In the *farsighted* or *hyperopic* eye the image of a nearby object is formed behind the retina (Fig. 29.4*b*). This defect may arise because the lens is too flat or the eyeball too short. As the object is moved farther away, the image moves nearer to the retina, so this eye may see distant objects clearly. To correct for farsightedness, a converging lens is placed in front of the eye. This makes the equivalent focal length of the eye shorter.

Example The near point of an eye is 90 cm. What is the lowest power lens which will permit this eye to see print clearly at a distance of 25 cm?

The image formed by the lens acts as object for the eye. The lens must produce an image of the print at 25 cm at a distance of 90 cm in front of the eye.

$p = 25$ cm $q = -90$ cm

$$\frac{1}{p} + \frac{1}{q} = \frac{1}{f}$$

$$\frac{1}{25} + \frac{1}{-90} = \frac{1}{f}$$

$$f = 34.8 \text{ cm}$$

$$\text{Power} = \frac{1}{0.348} = 2.89 \text{ diopters}$$

Another common defect of the eye is *astigmatism*. This occurs when the lens or the cornea does not have a truly spherical surface. The curvature is not the same in different planes containing the axis of the eye. Then the focal length is not the same in different planes. When light from an object is received by the normal eye, there is an attempt by the eye to adjust so that light from all parts of the object forms sharp images. With an astigmatic eye this is not possible, because the optical system has different focal lengths for light in different planes. Consequently, the image formed is indistinct (Fig. 29.5). This defect may be overcome with lenses that have cylindrical surfaces.

29.5 Luminous Flux and the Eye

The eye has two mechanisms by which it adjusts for changes in the level of illumination. The first is varying of the diameter of the *pupil* through the motion of the iris. In bright light the pupil closes down; in dim light it opens. However, this adjustment covers only a relatively minor range, and the total amount of light entering the eye can be changed by the iris by only a factor of about 16. The eye, however, can see in brilliant sunlight and in dim moonlight, a range of illumination which covers a factor of millions. The principal mechanism which the eye uses to adapt for changes in illumination is that of changing the sensitivity of the retinal surface. To understand this, we must consider the retina in more detail.

(a)   (b)

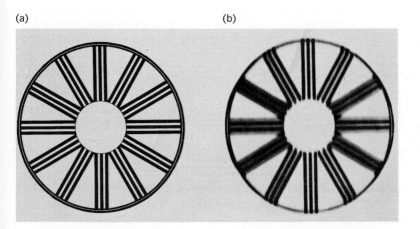

FIGURE 29.5
(*a*) The spokes of the wheel appear equally sharp to the normal eye. (*b*) To the astigmatic eye, the radial lines differ in sharpness. [Image (*b*) was formed with a cylindrical lens in the optical system.]

Just under the surface of the retina is a mosaic of photosensitive cells, of which there are two kinds, named *rods* and *cones* after their shapes. Both rods and cones have higher indices of refraction than the surrounding material. Light is transmitted down their length by total internal reflection. There are no rods or cones where the optic nerve leaves the eye. The image formed on this region, called the blind spot, is not seen. The cones are responsible for color vision; the rods give only achromatic perceptions of white, gray, and black. The rods are grouped in bunches, with each bunch having a connection to the brain, while each cone usually has a private line to the brain. Cones are largely concentrated in the central region of the retina, the *fovea*. As we go away from this central region, the number of cones per unit area decreases. The number of rods per unit area increases to a maximum at 20° from the optic axis and then decreases slowly.

The cones of the foveal area give us acute and color vision under conditions of high to adequate illumination. The solid line of Figure 29.6 shows how cones respond to equal intensities of various wavelengths. For equal amounts of light energy a yellow-green light of $\lambda \approx 560$ mμ appears brightest to the normal light-adapted eye. One watt of radiant energy at this wavelength corresponds to 680 lumens of luminous flux. Under illuminances lower than about 0.5 lumens/m^2 the cones do not respond well. The rods are sensitive to very small amounts of radiant energy. The dashed curve of Figure 29.6 shows that the rods have maximum sensitivity at $\lambda \approx 510$ mμ; they are relatively more sensitive to blues and less sensitive to reds than the cones. This is one reason for using blue lights for aisles of theaters and darkened railroad trains.

On the rods the eye builds a photosensitive pigment called *rhodopsin* or *visual purple*. When light strikes a rod, rhodopsin is bleached, and a signal goes to the brain. In bright daylight little rhodopsin is present. In darkness the rhodopsin is built up in the rods, and the eye becomes *dark-adapted*. It takes about 30 min to build up a maximum concentration. When this has been accomplished, the eye is very sensitive to light. This accounts for the blinding effect of bright headlamps from an approaching car at night; these same lights would produce no problem at all in daytime, when little rhodopsin is present.

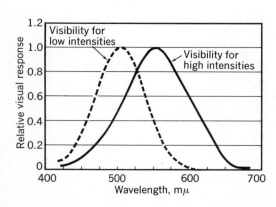

FIGURE 29.6

Relative illuminances produced by equal intensities of monochromatic radiation. The solid curve is for cones, the dashed curve for rods.

When the eyes are focused on a distant object, the visual axes are parallel. For viewing a near object there is a movement of the eyeballs which causes the visual axes to converge. Such a movement is necessary in order that the image in both eyes may fall on the proper area of the retina. Because of the distance between them, the eyes view an object from slightly different angles. Each retina receives a slightly different picture; this helps us judge distance, solidity, and depth.

29.6 Simple Microscope

For most distinct vision, an object must be about 25 cm from a normal eye. If the object is placed at a greater distance, the image on the retina is smaller, and its details are not seen so distinctly. When the object is placed too near, the image on the retina is blurred unless an additional converging lens is used to aid the eye. A lens used in this way constitutes a *simple microscope* or *magnifying glass*. When the object OP (Fig. 29.7) is inside the principal focus, the lens forms an erect, virtual, magnified image IQ which in turn serves as object for the eye, placed just to the right of the lens. To obtain the greatest advantage, the eye should be as near as possible to the lens. In this way, the field of view is made as large as possible.

When an object is examined with the aid of a simple microscope, the object is brought nearer to the eye than would be possible for distinct vision without the magnifying glass. In Figure 29.7 the angles subtended at the center of the lens by the object OP and the image IQ are the same. If QE is the distance of most distinct vision, and if the lens were absent, the eye could not see OP distinctly until it were removed to $O'Q$. Hence, by using the lens, the usable visual angle subtended by OP has been increased from α to β. The *angular magnification M* of a microscope is the ratio of the angle subtended at the eye by the image formed by the microscope to the angle subtended by the object when it is at the point of most distinct vision. For the simple microscope of Figure 29.8 the angular magnification, also known as the *magnifying power,* is given by

$$M = \frac{\beta}{\alpha} = \frac{IQ/QE}{O'Q/QE} = \frac{IQ}{OP} = \frac{QE}{PE}$$

If we take $QE = 25$ cm, the distance of most distinct vision for

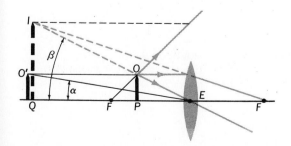

FIGURE 29.7

A simple microscope produces a virtual, erect, magnified image.

a normal eye, and observe that PE is the object distance p, we have, by Eq. (28.1), $1/p + 1(-25 \text{ cm}) = 1/f$, and

$$M = \frac{25 \text{ cm}}{p} = \frac{25 \text{ cm}}{f} + 1$$

for an eye placed as close as possible to the lens.

It is usually less tiring to use a simple microscope if the final image is at infinity, since then the eye muscles are relaxed.   In this case

$$\beta = \frac{OP}{f} \quad \text{and} \quad \alpha = \frac{OP}{25}$$

so that

$$M = \frac{25 \text{ cm}}{f}$$

With a single converging lens used at the eye, angular magnifications up to about 4 are possible before aberrations become a serious problem. By using eyepieces composed of two lenses it is possible to correct for aberrations and increase the angular magnification to 15 or 20.

29.7 Compound Microscope

To obtain great magnification, a compound microscope is used.   It utilizes a group of lenses acting as an ideal single converging lens L of short focal length (Fig. 29.8).   This lens, called the *objective,* produces a real, magnified image IQ of a small object placed just outside its focus.   The image IQ is viewed through the eyepiece L', which acts as a simple microscope.   This *ocular* produces an enlarged, virtual image $I'Q'$ of the real image IQ.

The magnification of a compound microscope depends on the focal lengths of objective and eyepiece.   The objective might have a focal length of 5 mm and form a real image 20 cm from the objective.   By Eq. (28.1), $1/p + 1/200 = 1/5$, or $p = {}^{200}\!/_{39}$ mm.   The linear magnification produced by the lens is then

$$\frac{q}{p} = \frac{200}{{}^{200}\!/_{39}} = 39$$

If now the eyepiece has a focal length of 2.5 cm and is adjusted for a final image at infinity, the angular magnification is $25/f = 10$.   The over-all angular magnification is $39 \times 10 = 390$.

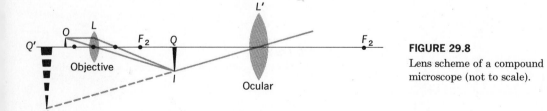

FIGURE 29.8

Lens scheme of a compound microscope (not to scale).

29.8 Astronomical Telescope

The principle of the astronomical telescope is the same as that of the compound microscope (Fig. 29.9). The objective lens is modified so that the instrument may be used to view distant objects. The objective, a large converging lens of long focal length, forms a real, inverted image IQ of a distant object OP. This real image is formed in the focal plane of the ocular, by which an enlarged virtual image $I'Q'$ of the real image IQ is produced at infinity.

Because of the great distance of the object from the telescope, the rays from any point are essentially parallel when they reach the objective. Hence, the image formed lies essentially in the focal plane of the objective. The angular magnification of the telescope is determined by the angles that the object subtends and appears to subtend at the eye (Fig. 29.9). The angle α that the object OP subtends at the eye when no lenses are present is $OEP = IEQ$. The angle β that the image $I'Q'$ subtends at the eye is $I'GQ' = IGQ$. For a distant object, with the ocular adjusted to place $I'Q'$ at infinity, F_1, Q, and F_2 coincide. Then the length of the telescope is $f_0 + f_e$, and

$$\text{Angular magnification} = \frac{\beta}{\alpha} = \frac{QI/f_e}{QI/f_0}$$

$$= \frac{f_0}{f_e} = \frac{\text{focal length of objective}}{\text{focal length of eyepiece}}$$

The image formed by an astronomical telescope is inverted. For terrestrial uses of the telescope it is desirable that the image be erect. This condition is realized by inserting a third convex lens between the objective and the eyepiece in such a way that the image formed by the objective is again inverted before it is viewed by the eyepiece.

Example The focal length of the objective of a telescope is 150 cm, and the focal length of the eyepiece is 2 cm. Find the angular magnification of the telescope for distant objects.

$$\text{Angular magnification} = \frac{\text{focal length of objective}}{\text{focal length of eyepiece}}$$

$$= {}^{150}\!/_2 = 75$$

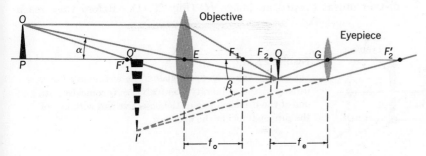

FIGURE 29.9

Lens scheme of an astronomical telescope. Actually IQ is formed at the principal focus of the objective lens, and the final image $I'Q'$ is placed at infinity by adjusting the eyepiece so that IQ is at its principal focus F_2.

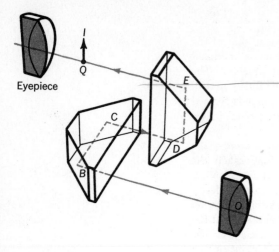

FIGURE 29.10

Optical scheme of one telescope of prism binoculars.

In very large telescopes the objective lens is replaced by a concave mirror. The great mirror in use at the Mount Palomar Observatory has a diameter of 200 in.

29.9 Prism Binoculars

A terrestrial telescope of reasonable field and magnification becomes unreasonably long. The prism binocular has largely replaced the old "spy glasses." Each side of the binocular achieves a long optical path by making the light traverse almost three times the length of the binoculars (Fig. 29.10). The beam of light OB from the objective is reflected internally at B and C by a right-angled prism. In this way its direction is reversed, and it travels back to a second right-angled prism which is placed at right angles to the first. Here it is again reflected internally at D and E and then passes through the eyepiece. The image, after the reflections by the two right-angled prisms, is restored completely to the upright position. The eyepiece, serving as a simple microscope, magnifies this image.

29.10 Opera Glass or Galilean Telescope

The opera glass uses an objective which converges the rays from a distant object toward an image IQ (Fig. 29.11). Before they reach

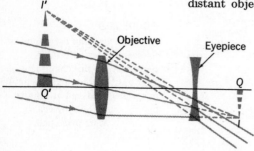

FIGURE 29.11

Optical scheme of an opera glass. The final image $I'Q'$ is usually placed at infinity, in which case Q coincides with one of the principal foci of the objective and with one of the principal foci of the eyepiece.

this image they pass through a diverging lens which acts as eyepiece. In passing through this lens, rays that were converging are made to diverge. To an eye on the right-hand side of the eyepiece, the rays appear to have come from the virtual, erect image $I'Q'$.

To focus the opera glass, the eyepiece is adjusted so the rays emerging from it are parallel and the final image is at infinity. Then,

$$\text{Angular magnification} = \frac{\text{focal length of objective}}{\text{focal length of eyepiece}} = \frac{f_0}{f_e}$$

The length of the opera glass is $f_0 - |f_e|$; thus the glasses need not be as long as a telescope of comparable magnifying power. A major disadvantage of the opera glass is its small field of view.

Questions

1. How does the eye accommodate to see objects which are at different distances?

2. How does the eye adjust to permit it to function under conditions of radically different illuminances?

3. When a swimmer is under clear water, why can't he see nearby objects clearly?

4. How is the camera similar to the eye? How different?

5. Why is a simple microscope useful when its image gets farther away at the same rate at which the linear dimensions of the image increase?

6. Why does the magnification of a telescope increase with the focal length of the objective while the magnification of a compound microscope decreases with increasing focal length?

7. Why is the depth of focus of a camera at $f/11$ far greater than the depth of focus of the same camera at $f/3.5$?

8. Why does a wide-angle lens for a camera have a shorter focal length than the standard lens for the camera?

Problems

1. A myopic (nearsighted) eye has a far point of 80 cm. What is the power of the spectacle lens required for this eye to see distant objects clearly? What would be the far point for this eye with a lens of -0.75 diopter?   *Ans.* -1.25 diopters; 2 m

2. A nearsighted person cannot see objects clearly when they are more than 40 cm from his eyes. Find the power of the weakest lens which will permit him to see distant objects distinctly. If he puts on a pair of -1.5-diopter glasses, where is his new far point?

3. A farsighted eye cannot form a sharp image of an object which is closer than 40 cm. Find the focal length and the power of a lens which will permit the eye to form a sharp image of an object 25 cm distant, but not of an object closer than this.

Ans. 66.7 cm; 1.5 diopters

4. A farsighted eye has a near point of 50 cm. Find the focal length and the power of the lens which will bring the near point to 20 cm. Where would the near point for this eye be with a lens of power 5 diopters?

5. A farsighted eye has a far point of infinity and a near point of 80 cm. A plano-convex lens made of glass whose index of refraction is 1.5 is used to enable the eye to see an object located 25 cm away. What is the largest radius the curved surface may have? Where would the near point and the far point be if this eye were using a 4-diopter lens?

Ans. 18.2 cm; 19 cm; 25 cm

6. The lens of an aerial camera has a focal length of 18 in. What will be the dimensions, on the film plate, of a square of the earth's surface 2 miles on a side, photographed from a height of 6 miles?

7. A camera has a lens of 50 mm focal length. When it is set at *f*/6, what is the diameter of the lens opening? If the setting is changed to *f*/9, how much more exposure time is required? If the camera is originally set to photograph distant objects, how far must the lens be moved to focus on a flower 40 cm away?

Ans. 8.3 mm; 2.25 times; 7.14 mm

8. An enlarging camera has a lens with a focal length of 6 in. It is used to enlarge a negative of dimensions 2 by 2.5 in. How far from the lens must the negative be placed in order that the enlargement be 8 by 10 in.?

9. A camera lens is set at *f*/3 for a picture which includes a distant point source of light. If the film is actually 5 mm too far from the lens for the point source to be in focus, what is the diameter of the circle of light on the film? If the lens had been at *f*/9, what would the diameter have been? *Ans.* 1.67 mm; 0.56 mm

10. The lens of a camera has a focal length of 20 cm. It is used to photograph an object that is 3 m from it, and then an object that is 30 m from it. How much must the lens of the camera be moved?

11. The lens of a projection lantern is to be 5 m from a screen on which an image with a height of 1.25 m is desired. The height of the slide is 7.5 cm. What should be the focal length of the projecting lens? *Ans.* 28.3 cm

12. A projection lantern is desired which will throw an image 6 ft wide of a slide 4 in. wide on a screen 20 ft from the lens. What must be the focal length of the projecting lens?

13. A source emits monochromatic light of 560 mμ wavelength. If the radiant flux (energy per unit time) through an aperture is 0.5 watt, what is the luminous flux through this aperture? If the source had emitted light of 600 mμ wavelength, what would the flux have been (Fig. 29.6)? *Ans.* 340 lumens; 204 lumens

14. A converging lens used as a reading glass has a focal length of 8.33 cm. What is the angular magnification if the lens is used to produce an image at a distance of 25 cm from the eye?

15. A double-convex lens of 6.25 cm focal length is used as a simple microscope. If it is held close to the eye to form an image 25 cm from the eye, where should the object be located? What is the angular magnification? What would the angular magnification be if the final image were at infinity? *Ans.* 5 cm; 5; 4

16. The objective of a compound microscope has a focal length of 0.5 cm, and its eyepiece has a focal length of 2 cm. If the distance between the objective and the eyepiece is 22 cm, what is the angular magnification of the microscope when the image is at infinity? Where must the object be placed?

17. A metric scale is placed at a distance of 25 cm from the eyes and observed with one eye unaided. The other eye observes a closer similar scale through a converging lens placed close to the eye.   A magnified millimeter division appears to be the same size as a 5-mm division seen with the naked eye when the image formed by the lens is also 25 cm from the eyes.   Find the focal length of the lens.   *Ans.* 6.25 cm

18. A compound microscope has an objective lens of focal length 4 mm which forms an image 16 cm from the lens.   The eyepiece produces a magnification of 10.   What is the total magnification?

19. A crude microscope consists of an objective of 0.6 in. focal length and an eyepiece of 2 in. focal length.   The lenses are placed 7 in. apart.   A person uses the microscope to form an image at infinity.   Where must the object be placed?   What is the linear magnification of the objective?   The angular magnification of the eyepiece?   The overall magnification?   *Ans.* 0.682 in.; 7.33; 5; 37

20. What is the diameter of the image of the moon formed at the prime focus by the 200-in. reflector on Mount Palomar if the mirror has a prime focal length of 55 ft and the moon subtends an angle of 0.009 radian at the earth?

21. An 8-mm microscope objective forms an image at a distance of 168 mm.   The eyepiece has a focal length of 40 mm.   Find the lateral magnification of the objective and the angular magnification of the microscope.   If an eye can see two dots as separate when they are 100 μ apart, how close together could two dots be and still be resolved by this microscope?   *Ans.* 20; 125; 0.8 μ

22. A telescope which consists of an objective that has a focal length of 80 cm and an eyepiece with a focal length of 2 cm is used to view an object that is 8 m from the objective.   What must be the distance between the eyepiece and the objective for a final image at infinity?

23. The world's largest refracting telescope at the Yerkes Observatory has an objective lens 40 in. in diameter and a focal length of 62 ft.   If the image formed by this objective is viewed through an ocular (eyepiece) of 2 in. focal length, find the angular magnification for viewing at great distances.   *Ans.* 372

24. The objectives of a pair of binoculars have apertures of 35 mm diameter and focal lengths of 240 mm.   The oculars (eyepieces) have focal lengths of 34 mm.   Find the angular magnification.   Why are these binoculars designated as 7 × 35?

25. The eyepiece of a telescope has a focal length of 5 cm.   When the final image is viewed at infinity, the objective and the eyepiece are 105 cm apart.   Find the angular magnification of the telescope.   *Ans.* 20

CHAPTER 30   *From the geometrical laws of reflection and refraction we have seen how lenses and optical instruments function.   However, there are limitations on optical instruments due to the fundamental nature of light.   Further, there are many optical phenomena which cannot be explained in terms of geometrical laws alone.   To become acquainted with them we turn now to* physical optics.   *We begin by discussing interference of light beams.   This interference shows that light has wave properties and offers us a means of measuring the wavelengths associated with the colors of the visible spectrum which we met in Chap. 27.*

Interference and Diffraction

30.1 Double-slit Interference

In 1801 Thomas Young performed a celebrated experiment which led to the general acceptance of the wave theory of light.   Huygens and others had advanced the wave theory much earlier, but their arguments were inconclusive until Young showed that light beams produce interference phenomena (Sec. 15.10).

In order to understand Young's experiment, consider a source of light placed behind the screen containing a narrow slit S (Fig. 30.1). A second screen having two narrow slits A and B is placed in front of the first screen in such a way that the openings are equally illuminated by the light from S.   If the illumination on a third screen DF is examined, it is found that a series of light and dark bands (Fig. 30.2b) result.   At point D, where we might expect the center of a shadow, there is a bright line.   This, of course, means that light from the source S arrives at the screen at a point which it could not reach if light travels in perfectly straight lines.   Thus, any explanation requires acceptance of the fact that light bends, to some extent at least, around obstacles.   *The bending of light when it passes an obstacle is called diffraction.*

To explain the pattern of Figure 30.2b, we accept the tentative hypothesis that light is a wave motion and that Huygens' principle is applicable.   Then we can understand the origin of the bright and dark lines by the following reasoning: A wave front from S reaches slits A and B.   Each point on this wave front acts as a new source of Huygens' wavelets.   Since A and B are equidistant from S, the Huygens' sources at A and B both send out crests at the same time, and half a cycle later both send out troughs.   The waves from A and B arrive at the screen DF in such a way that at some points crests meet crests (Fig. 30.2) and troughs meet troughs, thereby giving constructive interference and a bright line. At other points the troughs meet crests and crests meet troughs, resulting in destructive interference or darkness. The bright and dark bands on the screen are called *interference fringes*.

The experiment which we have just described with slits differs from that of Thomas Young in that he used pinholes in the screens rather than slits. In his experiment, interference fringes were also formed, but these fringes were not straight lines.

Let us now see how we can determine the wavelength of light from the interference pattern observed. Note that a bright fringe is produced at D (Fig. 30.1) which is in the heart of the shadow of the slit. This bright line arises from the constructive interference of the light coming through slits A and B. The waves from these two slits arrive in phase, since the light travels exactly the same distance in both cases. For the first bright fringe above D, the light must travel one wavelength farther from slit B than from slit A. For the nth bright fringe above D, the light from B goes n wavelengths farther than that from A. Suppose for the moment that the nth bright fringe is formed at point E. For this particular case the distance BC is n wavelengths if $CE = AE$. On the other hand, for a dark fringe at E the path difference BC must be some odd number of half wavelengths so that the waves interfere destructively.

We can calculate the path difference BC as follows: Let d represent the distance between slits A and B, X represent the distance from the double slit to the screen DF, and y represent the distance ED. Then

$$(AE)^2 = X^2 + \left(y - \frac{d}{2}\right)^2 \qquad \text{and} \qquad (BE)^2 = X^2 + \left(y + \frac{d}{2}\right)^2$$

$$(BE)^2 - (AE)^2 = X^2 + y^2 + yd + \frac{d^2}{4} - X^2 - y^2 + yd - \frac{d^2}{4} = 2yd$$

$$(BE - AE)(BE + AE) = 2yd$$

Then

$$BE - AE = \frac{2yd}{BE + AE} = \frac{2yd}{2X}$$

since BE and AE are almost exactly equal to X. Therefore, we have

$$\text{Path difference} = BC = \frac{yd}{X} \qquad\qquad\qquad \textbf{30.1}$$

The central bright fringe at D occurs for zero path difference. If we count this fringe as zero, the nth bright fringe in either direction

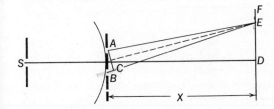

FIGURE 30.1
Interference of light passing through two parallel slits A and B.

(a)

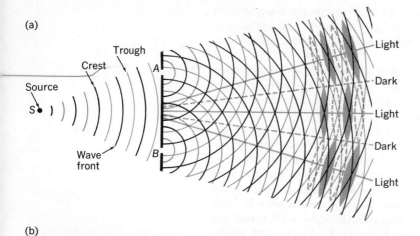

(b)

FIGURE 30.2
(*a*) Interference of light from parallel slits *A* and *B*, (*b*) interference fringes produced in the double-slit experiment.

comes when the path difference BC is $n\lambda$, which we know from Eq. (30.1) to be yd/X. For the dark fringes, on the other hand, the difference in distance traversed from the two slits must be some odd integral number of half wavelengths. The first dark fringe occurs for $yd/X = \lambda/2$, the second for $yd/X = 3\lambda/2$, and so forth.

We have required that our slit S be illuminated with monochromatic light. If we use white light, the red wavelengths interfere constructively at different places than do the blue. As a result, we observe white light at the central point D; then there is a spectrum on each side of D in which the path difference is one wavelength, then another spectrum in which the path difference is two wavelengths, etc. However, in a short distance the spectra overlap seriously, and the illumination appears uniform.

TABLE 30.1

Name of unit	Abbreviation	Value, m
Micron	μ	10^{-6}
Millimicron	$m\mu$	10^{-9}
Angstrom	Å	10^{-10}
X unit	xu	10^{-13}

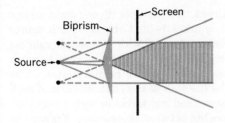

FIGURE 30.3
Fresnel's biprism experiment; interference occurs in the cross-hatched region.

Example   The distance between slits A and B in Young's interference experiment is 0.25 cm.   The distance X from the slits to the screen on which the fringes are formed is 100 cm, and the distance from the central bright fringe to the third dark one is 0.059 cm.   Find the wavelength of the incident light.

For the third dark fringe the path difference BC must be 2.5λ.

$$2.5\lambda = \frac{yd}{X} = \frac{0.059 \text{ cm} \times 0.25 \text{ cm}}{100 \text{ cm}}$$

$$\lambda = 5.9 \times 10^{-5} \text{ cm}$$

The eye responds to waves ranging in wavelength roughly from 3.8×10^{-7} m (violet) to 7.8×10^{-7} m (red).   Other detectors respond to other wavelength regions (Sec. 32.2).   For many kinds of waves the meter is an inconveniently large unit.   Some of the units in which wavelengths are reported are listed in Table 30.1.

30.2 Coherent Sources

Shortly after Young's work, Fresnel was able to produce interference fringes similar to those of Figure 30.2*b* in other ways.   One of his methods involves placing a source of light behind a biprism (Fig. 30.3) and finding interference fringes in the crosshatched region where the light which went through the upper prism and the light through the lower prism overlapped.   Still another method devised by Fresnel involved the use of two mirrors set so that the angle between their surfaces is very near to zero.   The Fresnel double-mirror arrangement is shown in Figure 30.4.

In Young's experiment and in the two interference experiments of Fresnel, light must come from a single source.   No interference would

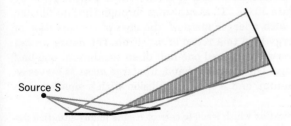

FIGURE 30.4
Fresnel double-mirror method for producing interference.

be observed in Young's experiment, for example, if one light source were placed behind slit *A* and another behind slit *B*. Each source would send out a very large number of waves with completely random phases. At one instant the crest of one wave might meet the trough of another, but an instant later crest might be meeting crest. The light reaching any area would be the sum of the contributions of each of the sources. When two sources send out waves in such a way that there is no regular phase relationship between these waves, the sources are *incoherent*. If there is a regular phase relationship between the waves, the sources are *coherent*.

In the interference experiments which we have discussed, light comes from a single source. A single wave front is separated into two parts which travel different paths. When the parts are recombined, interference results. In order to produce interference, there must be two "apparent" sources initiating light waves with a well-defined phase relationship. This cannot be achieved with independent light sources. For electromagnetic waves in general it can be done in one of two ways: (1) we may start with a single source, send portions of the wave fronts by different paths, and recombine them in some region or (2) we may drive a source in such a way that it radiates coherently either with a master source or with another source controlled by the same master.

30.3 Lloyd's Mirror and Phase Change at Reflection

Lloyd was able to obtain interference fringes with a light source and a single mirror in the manner indicated in Figure 30.5. Light coming directly from the source and light reflected from the plane mirror overlap in the crosshatched region. If a screen is placed at the end of the mirror, one might expect a bright fringe at point *P* where the screen and mirror come in contact. However, a dark fringe is observed at this point. This fact is explained by a change in phase of one-half wavelength (or 180°) which occurs when light is reflected at the interface between two media if the light approaches the interface through the medium in which it has the higher speed. *When light in a medium is reflected at the surface of a second medium which has a greater index of refraction, there is a half-wavelength phase shift; there is no phase shift when the second medium as a lower index of refraction.*[1]

< It may be helpful to consider an analogue to this phase shift at reflection. If a small mass *m* is set into vibration as a pendulum bob, the *x* component of the displacement as a function of time is given by the sine wave of Figure 30.6*a*. If, as *m* swings through the equilibrium position, it collides with a larger mass *M*, the laws of conservation of momentum and energy lead to a recoil of *m*. From the figure we can see that the small mass has missed one-half of an oscillation; one-half wavelength is missing. On the other hand, if a large mass *M* serves as the bob of the pendulum, and if it has a collision with a smaller mass

FIGURE 30.5

Lloyd's mirror experiment.

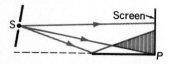

[1] This is an oversimplification which leads to correct results in any situation discussed in this text.

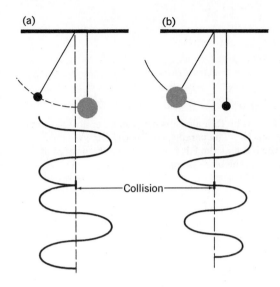

FIGURE 30.6

Mechanical analogue of the 180° phase shift in reflection shows how the smaller mass changes direction in a collision, but the larger mass does not.

m as it swings through the equilibrium position (Fig. 30.6*b*), the larger mass continues in its original direction with somewhat reduced amplitude. There is no phase shift when the larger mass collides with the smaller one, but a half-wavelength change in phase when the smaller mass collides with the larger.

30.4 Interference in Thin Films

Consider the thin air film between two optically plane pieces of glass when the plane surfaces touch at one edge and are slightly separated at the other end (Fig. 30.7). When monochromatic light falls normally from above on this air wedge, part of the light is reflected at the upper surface of the wedge, and part of the light passes to the bottom, where some of the light is reflected, this time with a change in phase of one-half wavelength. If the air wedge is viewed from above, a series of light and dark bands (Fig. 30.8) is observed.

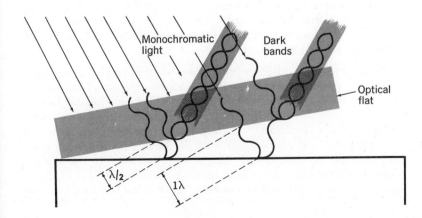

FIGURE 30.7

Thin air wedge illuminated from above produces fringes by the interference of light reflected at the two surfaces of the wedge.

FIGURE 30.8

Interference by thin air films between an optical flat and gauge blocks. The parallel, equispaced fringes indicate that the block at the left is plane, while the pattern at the right shows the block is worn.

In the region in which the two plates touch there is a dark band because, although the two reflected waves go the same total distance, there is a change in phase for the reflection in which the light goes from air to glass. The first light fringe occurs when the air wedge is one-fourth wavelength thick. The wave reflected from the lower plate goes one-half wavelength farther than the wave reflected at the upper surface, and there is a half-wavelength phase shift at the lower reflection. Therefore, the waves reflected at the two sides of the air wedge meet in phase, and a light band results. When the thickness of the air wedge is one-half wavelength, the wave reflected at the lower plate goes one wavelength farther, but the half-wavelength change in phase on reflection again puts the two waves out of phase by one-half wavelength, and a dark band results. When the air wedge is three-quarters of a wavelength thick, constructive interference occurs once more, and so forth. There is a bright band whenever the thickness of the air wedge is an odd number of quarter wavelengths, and a dark band whenever the thickness of the air wedge is an even number of quarter wavelengths. If n represents the number of a bright fringe, counting the first bright fringe after the point of intersection of the planes as one, the thickness of the wedge at the nth bright fringe is given by $(2n - 1)\lambda/4$.

The interference of light waves is used when a working gauge block for checking vernier and micrometer calipers with great accuracy is compared with a master block. The two blocks are placed next to each other on a flat surface, and an optically flat glass plate is placed on top of them (Fig. 30.8). If the two are exactly the same height, the optical flat is in contact with both blocks across their entire upper surfaces, and no interference fringes are observed. If the working block is shorter than the master block, parallel fringes are observed, and the amount by which the working block is low can be calculated.

Example When the optical flat of Figure 30.8 is viewed from above with helium yellow light of $\lambda = 587.6$ mμ, there is a dark fringe where the flat touches the working block, a second dark fringe one-third the way across the block, a third one two-thirds the way across, and a fourth one just before the master block is reached. How much shorter is the working block than the master?

At the line of contact the separation is a negligible fraction of a wavelength. At the second dark fringe the air wedge is $\lambda/2$ thick, at the third λ, and at the last $3\lambda/2$. Therefore, the working block is $3\lambda/2$ shorter than the master block.

$$\frac{3\lambda}{2} = \frac{3}{2} \times 587.6 = 881 \text{ m}\mu$$

If a plano-convex lens is placed on an optical flat and illuminated with monochromatic light from above, a series of light and dark rings is observed. This pattern is known as *Newton's rings*. These light and dark rings are analogous to the light and dark straight fringes observed with plane surfaces. In the region where the lens touches the optical flat, there is destructive interference. Where the thickness of the air film is one-quarter wavelength, a bright circular fringe exists, while there is a dark circle where the thickness is $\lambda/2$, etc.

Consider a very thin film of transparent material with surfaces parallel to each other (Fig. 30.9). If one of these surfaces is illuminated by a beam of light of a single wavelength, light is reflected from the upper and lower surfaces. An incident ray such as AB is partly reflected from the upper surface, but most of the light enters the film, and a small part of it is reflected at C. In a similar manner, part of the ray DE is reflected at E, and the remainder of the light enters the film. Some of it is reflected at F, etc. If rays parallel to AB and DE illuminate the upper surface XY of the film, parallel rays EF, GH, etc., are reflected from the upper surface. There are also rays which are parallel to EF, GH, etc., which are reflected from the lower surface MN of the film. The rays reflected from the lower surface MN are super-

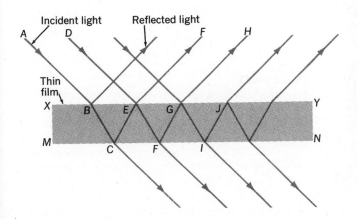

FIGURE 30.9

Interference of light produced by differences in the path lengths of light reflected from the two surfaces of a thin film.

posed on those reflected from the upper surface XY. These two sets of reflected beams have nearly the same brightness but differ in phase, because those which are reflected from the lower surface of the film have traveled a distance equal to BCE farther than those reflected at the upper surface, while the latter have undergone a phase shift of one-half wavelength. The two sets of beams may interfere constructively or destructively, depending on the angle of incidence, the wavelength of the light, and the thickness and refractive index of the film. The condition for destructive interference does not occur at the same place for different wavelengths. Hence, when the film is illuminated by white light, certain wavelengths reinforce each other where light of other wavelengths destroy each other. The result is a series of colored fringes giving the appearance of a rainbow. The colors of thin films of oil illustrate this type of interference.

30.5 The Michelson Interferometer

An interesting example of a device in which part of a wave front is sent along one path and part along a different one is the Michelson interferometer (Figs. 30.10 and 30.11). Light emerging from a source S falls on a glass plate A, which reflects half and transmits the remainder. The reflected part goes to mirror C, by which it is reflected, and returns along its original path. The part which went through plate A passes through a second glass plate B, is reflected at mirror D, and returns to mirror A. There it is reflected in such a way that its direction coincides with the direction of the ray which was reflected at mirror C and which subsequently passed through the glass plate A. The wave front from source S has been split into two wave fronts. Both are received by the eye, one of them after reflection at C, and the other after reflection at D. The plane parallel glass plate B

FIGURE 30.10
Michelson interferometer.

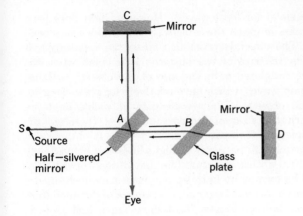

FIGURE 30.11
Optical paths in a Michelson interferometer.

is introduced to compensate for the extra thickness of glass through which the ray reflected at C has passed in reaching the eye.

If the distance from plate A to mirror C is the same as the distance from plate A to mirror D, the two rays of light travel the same distance, and they are therefore in phase. Under these conditions, the central rays reinforce each other. If, however, the distance AD is greater than the distance AC by one-quarter of a wavelength of the light, the central rays are out of phase and destroy each other. Rays which make small angles with the central ray travel slightly different distances and interfere alternately constructively and destructively (Fig. 30.12). If mirror D is moved along the line AD, the light and dark circles interchange position for each quarter wavelength the mirror is moved.

30.6 Diffraction

When light passes an obstacle, it does not proceed in exactly straight lines, but spreads out somewhat into the geometrical shadow. Ordi-

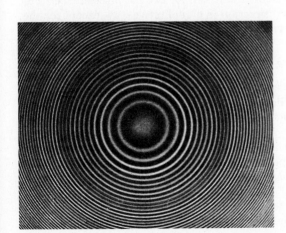

FIGURE 30.12
Interference fringes produced with a Michelson interferometer.

FIGURE 30.13

If light from a distant, monochromatic point source passes
through a "key-hole" aperture
in an opaque screen and the
shadow is observed some
distance beyond the screen, the
diffraction pattern below is
found. Above is the shadow
predicted on the assumption of
rectilinear propagation.

narily this effect is small for light waves. However, light does bend
slightly around corners in much the same way that water waves bend
around obstacles. The effect is prominent when the wavelength is
large compared with the size of the obstacle; it is small when the
wavelength is short compared with the size of the obstacle. Thus,
radio waves and sound waves, which have relatively long wavelengths,
bend readily around objects. The wavelengths of visible light are
small compared with the sizes of ordinary obstacles; therefore the
bending is not conspicuous for light waves.

If light always traveled in perfectly straight lines and obeyed only
the laws of geometrical optics, a picture like that of the upper half of
Figure 30.13 would be formed by light from a distant monochromatic
source passing through a small keyhole aperture some distance from
the film. The lower half of Figure 30.13 shows an actual picture.
Not only has there been some spreading of light into the region of the
geometrical shadow, but interference between wavelets from various
portions of the wavefront passing the aperture has led to a series
of light and dark fringes. *The spreading of a wave motion into
the geometrical shadow of an object and the other deviations from
the predictions of geometrical propagation are called diffraction.*

To account for the fact that light bends around obstacles, we need
only invoke Huygens' principle, which tells us that for any kind
of wave motion we may regard each point on a wave front as a
new source. Whenever we are dealing with diffraction phenomena, we
are treating a case in which various parts of the same wave front act
as coherent sources and the secondary wavelets from these coherent
sources interfere. For interference in a Young's double-slit experiment
we take two limited sections of a wave front, send them by different
paths, and combine them to get constructive and destructive interference. In diffraction much larger sections of the wave front may be
involved. The general theory calls for finding the net interference
effect at a given point for a large number of waves with a continuous
variation in phase. The mathematical treatment of such diffraction
phenomena is more difficult than than for two-slit interference. For
this reason we discuss diffraction in a qualitative way, except for the
case of the diffraction grating.

30.7 Diffraction Grating

If a series of very fine equidistant parallel slits is ruled on a plate
of glass with a fine diamond point, we have a *diffraction grating.*
Where the diamond point has made a furrow on the glass, the light
cannot pass regularly. Between the furrows, where the surface of the
glass is undisturbed, the glass is transparent. The plate of glass is
then somewhat like a picket fence. In effect, there are strips through
which the light can pass separated by strips through which it cannot
pass.

Let *AB* (Fig. 30.14) represent such a grating on which parallel light
is falling so that the direction of the rays is perpendicular to the plane
of the grating. Figure 30.14 shows the Huygens wavelets that start

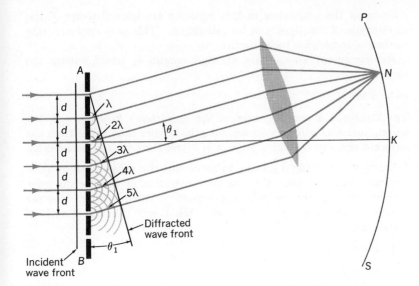

FIGURE 30.14
Diffraction grating. Reinforcement occurs when $n\lambda = d \sin \theta$, where d is the distance between adjacent slits, or the grating space.

out from the slits. These wavelets destroy or reinforce each other, according to whether they are in phase or out of phase at a given point.

Through the slits in the grating come beams of parallel light. If these rays, coming in the direction perpendicular to the plane of the grating, are brought to a focus on the screen PS by the lens, a bright line is formed at K. If the light is viewed in a direction making an angle θ with the normal to the grating, parallel rays of light emerging from the slits in this direction travel unequal distances to reach the screen, and when they are brought to a focus by the lens they may either reinforce or destroy each other. If the angle θ is made such that a ray of light from one slit is one-half wavelength behind the corresponding ray from the adjacent slit, then the rays from one slit are out of phase with the rays from the adjacent slit, and they destroy each other. Hence, there will be darkness. If the angle between the normal to the grating and the ray is increased, the rays from the lower slits will be further and further behind the rays from the upper slits. When the difference in path between corresponding rays from adjacent slits amounts to one wavelength, wavelets from all the slits are again in phase and interfere constructively. If these rays are focused by the lens, a bright image of the slit is formed on the screen at N. Whenever

$$\sin \theta = \frac{n\lambda}{d} \qquad n \text{ an integer}$$

the wavelets from different slits reinforce each other, and the screen is illuminated.

The angle θ_1 at which reinforcement is first obtained after leaving the central line K can easily be measured on the divided circle of a spectrometer. For this first reinforcement,

$$\lambda = d \sin \theta_1 \qquad\qquad \textbf{30.2}$$

Since all the quantities in this equation are known except λ, the wavelength of the light can be calculated. This is a very accurate method of measuring wavelengths.

Reinforcement also occurs at other angles θ_n which satisfy the equation

$$n\lambda = d \sin \theta_n \qquad\qquad \textbf{30.3}$$

The integer n gives the *order* of the spectrum. When $n = 2$, the waves from each slit go two wavelengths farther than those from the adjacent slit. In the third order n is 3, and the path difference is 3λ.

Example In using a grating to determine the wavelength of light, it was observed that the angular separation of the second-order spectrum from the central image was 45°. The number of lines per inch on the grating was 14,500. What was the wavelength of the light?

$$2\lambda = d \sin \theta_2$$

$$\lambda = \frac{d}{2} \sin \theta_2$$

$$= \frac{1}{2} \times \frac{0.0254 \text{ m/in.}}{14,500/\text{in.}} \times 0.707$$

$$= 621 \times 10^{-9} \text{ m} = 621 \text{ m}\mu$$

Example For a certain color of yellow light, the angular separation between the central image and the first-order spectrum produced by a plane grating was 17°. The grating has 5,000 rules to the centimeter. What is the wavelength of the light?

$$\text{Wavelength} = d \sin \theta_1$$

$$\lambda = \frac{1 \text{ cm}}{5,000} \times \sin 17°$$

$$= \frac{1}{5,000} \times 0.292$$

$$= 0.0000584 \text{ cm, or } 5,840 \text{ Å}$$

30.8 Diffraction by a Straight Edge

Suppose that light is diverging from a narrow slit L (Fig. 30.15a) and that it passes by the straight edge of an opaque screen. If the light were propagated exactly in straight lines, there would be uniform illumination on the screen above the line LO and complete darkness below it. However, the illumination does not become zero immediately below O, but fades away continuously. There is almost complete darkness a small distance below O. Immediately above O the illumination is not uniform, but shows a series of bright and dark bands parallel to the edge. The appearance of the fringes thus produced is seen in Figure 30.15b.

Consider now the case of a fine wire AB (Fig. 30.16a) placed in front of a narrow slit L. The shadow of this wire on the screen MN is found to be bounded on each side by a system of parallel fringes (Fig. 30.16b). Each edge of the wire behaves like a straight edge.

(a)

(b)

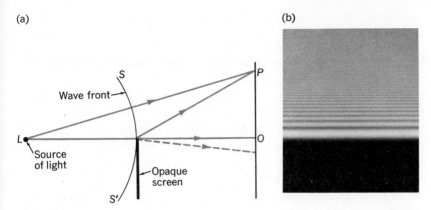

FIGURE 30.15

Light passing a straight edge (*a*) produces a diffraction pattern (*b*) with monotonically decreasing intensity below *O* and a series of fringes in the region *OP*.

Further at the very center of the shadow there is constructive interference of waves diffracted around each side of the wire, so the center is bright relative to the main part of the shadow, though still dark compared with regions *CN* and *DM*.

30.9 Diffraction by a Circular Aperture

Another striking illustration of diffraction is observed when light from a luminous point passes through a small circular aperture such as a pinhole. When this aperture is viewed by means of a magnifying glass, there appears a brilliant spot which is surrounded by a series of bright and dark rings, essentially like the circular portions of the diffraction fringes of Figure 30.13. When images are formed in an optical instrument, even the most perfect optical parts cannot produce a point image of a point source. Instead there is a diffraction pattern consisting of a bright circle surrounded by a series of light and dark rings. Ultimately these diffraction patterns limit the angular separation of two sources which can be distinguished as separate.

(a)

(b)

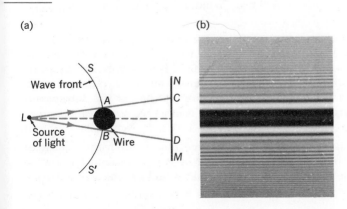

FIGURE 30.16

Light passing a fine wire is diffracted (*a*), producing the diffraction pattern (*b*).

Questions

1. How do the colors observed in Newton's rings, oil films, and soap bubbles arise? Explain.

2. An observer sees a green fringe passing through a given point in an oil film. Would other observers looking at the same point necessarily see green there? Explain.

3. How do the spectra of sunlight formed by diffraction gratings differ from those formed by prisms. Which color is deflected most by prisms? By gratings?

4. Would a diffraction grating with 5,000 lines/cm be useful for studying infrared spectra with wavelengths around 3 μ? Explain.

5. Two spectral lines of different colors are observed by means of a grating, and it is seen that the third-order image of one line coincides with the fourth-order image of a second line. What is the ratio of the wavelengths of the two colors?

6. What happens to the distance between the interference fringes from two slits as the slits are moved closer together?

7. Newton's rings can be observed by transmitted light as well as by reflected light. Would the point of contact be light or dark by transmitted light? Show that the transmitted rings are dark where the reflected ones are bright, and vice versa.

Problems

1. Monochromatic light from a narrow slit illuminates two parallel slits 0.22 mm apart. On a screen 110 cm away interference bands are observed 2.5 mm apart. Find the wavelength of the light. *Ans.* 5×10^{-5} cm

2. Yellow light of wavelength 5,800 Å from a single source is passed through two narrow slits separated by 0.8 mm. On a screen 120 cm away an interference pattern is formed. Calculate the separation of intensity maxima in this pattern.

3. The two parallel slits used for a Young's interference experiment are 0.5 mm apart. The screen on which the fringes are projected is 1.5 m from the slits. What is the distance between the fringes for monochromatic red light of wavelength 600 mμ? How far is the third dark fringe from the central bright one? *Ans.* 1.8 mm; 4.5 mm

4. A thin air wedge is formed between two optical flats by slipping a piece of paper under one edge of the upper flat. Twelve bright fringes are observed per centimeter across the upper flat with light of $\lambda = 500$ mμ. What is the thickness of the paper if the flats are 5 cm long?

5. Two plane pieces of optical glass are pressed together at one edge and separated by a fine wire at the other edge. The distance between the wire and the edges of glass that are in contact is 10 cm. When light of wavelength 5,000 Å is incident normally on the surface of one of the pieces of glass, interference fringes are observed. If these fringes are 0.15 cm apart, what is the diameter of the wire? What is the thickness of the air wedge at the third bright fringe from the line of contact of the plates? *Ans.* 1.67×10^{-3} cm; 6.25×10^{-5} cm

6. Two flat glass plates which are almost parallel produce interference fringes by successive reflections from the surfaces of normally incident light. If the light has a wavelength of 4,000 Å, what is the difference in thickness that would be indicated in passing from one bright fringe to the next? If there are six bright fringes per centimeter of length along the plates, what is the angular separation between the surfaces?

7. Newton's rings are observed by reflected light of wavelength 589 mμ. The central area is dark and is surrounded by light and dark circles. Find the thickness of the air film at the first, third, and fifth bright circles.   *Ans.* 147, 736, and 1,325 mμ

8. Newton's rings are observed by reflected light of wavelength 500 mμ. The central area is dark and is surrounded by light and dark circles. Find the thickness of the air film at the fourth bright circle. Explain your method.

9. What is the thinnest film of oil (index of refraction 1.40) floating on water in which green light (λ = 500 mμ in air) is essentially eliminated by destructive interference from a beam of white light incident normally on this film? If the oil film were on glass (index of refraction = 1.50), what thickness would be required?   *Ans.* 179 mμ; 89.3 mμ

10. When the movable mirror of a Michelson interferometer is moved 0.08 mm, how many fringes pass the reference mark if light of wavelength 5,890 Å is used?

11. A film of oil with an (unrealistically low) index of refraction 1.25 rests on a puddle of water (n = 1.333). When yellow light of λ = 500 mμ is incident normally on the film and the reflected light is viewed from above the film, destructive interference is observed. What are the three smallest thicknesses the oil film could have? What are the three smallest thicknesses the film could have for constructive interference?

Ans. 100, 300, and 500 mμ; 0, 200, and 400 mμ

12. When a Michelson interferometer was used to measure the wavelength of monochromatic light, it was found that 400 fringes passed the observing microscope when the movable mirror was displaced 0.088 mm. What was the wavelength of the light?

13. One arm of a Michelson interferometer utilizing light with λ = 500 mμ contains a cell 7.50 cm long between plane parallel windows. How many fringe shifts would be observed if all the air were evacuated from this cell? The index of refraction of the air was initially 1.00029.   *Ans.* 87

14. A glass grating is ruled with 5,500 lines/cm. Light striking the grating normally forms a second-order image diffracted at an angle of 40° from the normal. What is the wavelength of the light?

15. If 4,500-Å radiation falls normally on a grating ruled with 5,000 lines/cm, how many orders may be observed on each side of the direct beam? Determine the angles at which the orders are observed.   *Ans.* 4; 13°; 26.8°; 42.5°; 64.1°

16. Light is incident normally on a grating which has 250 lines/mm. Find the wavelength of a spectral line for which the deviation in second order is 12°.

17. Compute the longest wavelength which can be observed in third order by a transmission diffraction grating with 6,000 lines/cm.   *Ans.* 555.6 mμ

18. The fourth-order spectrum contains a certain color diffracted at an angle of 55°. If the grating is ruled with 300 lines/mm, what is the wavelength of the light?

19. A grating is ruled with 6,000 lines/cm. Calculate the angles of diffraction for first-order red and blue light, the wavelengths being, respectively, 7,000 and 4,000 Å. Determine the angular separation in radians. A lens of 50 cm focal length is placed in the path of light just beyond the grating. Determine the linear separation of the red and blue lines. (This is essentially the basis for a grating spectrometer.)

Ans. 24.8°; 13.9°; 0.19 radian; 9.5 cm

CHAPTER 31 *The phenomena of interference and diffraction show that light has wave properties and offer us a means for measuring wavelengths. Next we ask whether these waves are longitudinal, like sound waves, or transverse, like waves in a stretched string. There is a phenomenon called* polarization *which establishes that light waves are transverse, i.e., that the vibrations take place at right angles to the direction in which the light is traveling. In this chapter we describe and interpret a number of experiments which support the assertion that light waves are transverse.*

Polarization

31.1 Polarization

When a crystal of tourmaline (Fig. 31.1) is cut parallel to the crystallographic axis and a ray of light passes through it, the transmitted beam in no way differs from the incident beam so far as the unaided eye can detect. If the light that has passed through one tourmaline crystal is allowed to pass through another with its axis parallel to the first, the light is almost completely transmitted by the second crystal. If now the second crystal is rotated around the ray of light so that the axes of the two crystals are inclined to each other, the intensity of the transmitted light decreases. When the axes of the crystals are at right angles to each other, none of the light from the first crystal passes through the second. If the rotation of the second crystal is continued until the axes of the crystals are again parallel, the light from the first crystal is transmitted through the second. It is evident that the light, in passing through the first crystal, acquires properties that ordinary light does not possess.

To understand this experiment, consider a stretched string (Fig. 31.2) in which the particles are vibrating perpendicular to the length of the string. If a block of wood with a slot in it is placed over the string, the vibrations are not affected when the slot is parallel to the direction of vibration. However, when the slot is at right angles to this direction, the vibrations do not pass. If the slot makes various angles with the direction of vibration of the string, the component of the vibratory motion parallel to the slot passes through. If a second slot is placed over the string, the vibrations that pass the first slot also pass the second when the two slots are parallel. When the slots are perpendicular to each other, the vibrations that pass the first slot do not pass the second.

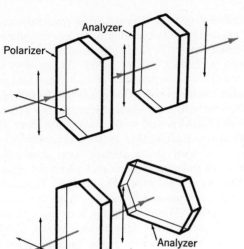

FIGURE 31.1
Polarization of light by tourmaline crystals.

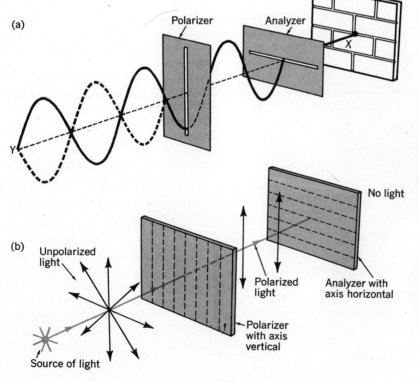

FIGURE 31.2
Polarization of transverse waves in a stretched string (*a*) is analogous to polarization of light rays (*b*).

The action of the tourmaline may be understood if we consider ordinary light to consist of a transverse wave motion in which the vibrations take place in all directions in a plane perpendicular to the direction in which the light is traveling (Fig. 31.2b). When such a beam passes through a crystal, one component of the vibrations is absorbed, the other component transmitted. Consequently the emerging beam differs from ordinary light in that all the vibrations are in one direction. Such a beam of light is said to be *plane-polarized*. If it falls on a second crystal of tourmaline, that crystal transmits only those vibrations which are parallel to its transmission direction. When ordinary light falls on a polarizing agent and plane-polarized light is produced, we call the agent a *polarizer* (Fig. 31.2b). To determine whether a beam of light is polarized or not, we pass the light through a second polarizing agent. When the latter is rotated, there is no change in transmitted intensity if the light is unpolarized, while the intensity goes from the maximum to zero if the beam is plane-polarized. A polarizing agent used in this way is called an *analyzer*. If the incident light is partially plane-polarized, the intensity is maximum for one orientation of the analyzer and minimum for another, but there is no zero. When two polarizing agents are arranged with their axes perpendicular so that they cut out all light, they are said to be *crossed*.

FIGURE 31.3
Polaroid sheet crossed on itself to show how transmitted light is absorbed in varying degrees.

31.2 Polaroid Sheets

Tourmaline crystals are somewhat colored and are not very often used in the study of polarization phenomena. When a polarizing agent of large aperture is desired, polaroid sheets are ordinarily used (Fig. 31.3). A polaroid consists of two thin sheets of plastic with a thin layer of ultramicroscopic polarizing crystals of iodosulfate of quinine (also known as *herapathite* after Herapath, who studied the polarizing properties in 1852) between them. The tiny needlelike crystals are aligned with their axes parallel by subjecting them to a strong electric field as the plastic in which they are embedded solidifies.

Actually a pair of crossed polaroids is not perfectly effective for eliminating the far red and far violet radiations, so that one can see a little deep purple through crossed polaroids.

31.3 Light Vibrations

Light is a complex system of wave motions consisting of alternating electric and magnetic fields at right angles to each other. In a plane-polarized wave the electric vibrations all lie in the same plane, while the magnetic vibrations are in a plane at right angles to that containing the electric vibrations. In discussing polarized light, it is necessary to consider only one of these types of vibration; it is customary to focus attention on the *electric vibrations,* since most common optical phenomena are due to the interaction of the electric vector with the charged particles in matter. The plane of vibration is defined as the plane determined by the electric vibrations and the direction of propagation.

A beam of ordinary light consists of a very large number of waves, each with its own plane of vibration, with every direction of vibration perpendicular to the rays having equal probability. We represent such a beam, looking head on, by the end-on view of Figure 31.4a. When we pass such a beam through a tourmaline crystal, it comes out plane-polarized. Only an infinitesimal part of an unpolarized light beam

(a)
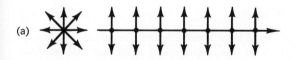

(b)

FIGURE 31.4

Pictorial representation of (*a*) ordinary light, (*b*) plane-polarized light with electric vibrations horizontal, and (*c*) plane-polarized light with electric vector vertical.

(c)
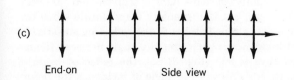

End-on   Side view

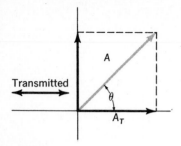

FIGURE 31.5

Resolution of electric vector into rectangular components.

contains vibrations in any single direction. However, if we have a polarizer set to transmit only vertical vibrations, approximately half the incident intensity is transmitted. Those vibrations which are not exactly vertical also contribute to this beam. Actually, a polarizer transmits all *components* which are parallel to its select direction. We can look on a beam of unpolarized light as being composed of two equal beams plane-polarized at right angles to one another. Any vibration which is not in one or the other of these two directions can be resolved into two components, one in each direction. Hence, we sometimes represent unpolarized light by showing only two of the many directions of vibration. We use a dot to represent vibration perpendicular to the plane of the paper, and arrows to indicate vibrations in this plane (Fig. 31.4).

If a beam of plane-polarized light falls on an analyzer set to transmit a plane of vibrations making an angle θ with that of the incident beam, a portion of the incident beam is transmitted. To calculate the fraction transmitted, we proceed as follows: We resolve (Fig. 31.5) the vibration amplitude A of the incident beam into two components, one parallel to the preferred plane of the analyzer and the other perpendicular. The polarizer passes the parallel component and rejects the perpendicular one. The amplitude transmitted A_T is given by

$$A_T = A \cos \theta \qquad\qquad \textbf{31.1}$$

Since the intensity is proportional to the square of the amplitude, the fraction of the incident intensity I transmitted is given by

$$\frac{I_T}{I} = \frac{A_T{}^2}{A^2} = \cos^2 \theta \qquad\qquad \textbf{31.2}$$

Example An analyzer is set to transmit vibrations at 37° to those of an incident plane-polarized beam. Find what fraction of the incident intensity is transmitted.

$$A_T = A \cos \theta = A \cos 37° = 0.8A$$

$$\frac{I_T}{I} = \frac{A_T{}^2}{A^2} = 0.64$$

31.4 Polarization by Reflection

When a beam of unpolarized light is reflected at the surface of glass or water, the reflected beam is unpolarized for normal incidence and for grazing incidence. For any other angle of incidence, the reflected ray contains more vibrations parallel to the reflecting surface, while the transmitted beam contains more vibrations in the plane of incidence (Fig. 31.6a). If the angle of incidence is about 45°, and if the reflected light is examined by an analyzer, some light is transmitted for every orientation of the polarizer, but the intensity is maximum when the analyzer passes electric vibrations parallel to the reflecting surface.

When the angle of incidence is such that the angle between the reflected and refracted rays is 90° (Fig. 31.6b), the reflected beam is completely plane-polarized. We call the angle of incidence the *polar-*

(a)   (b)

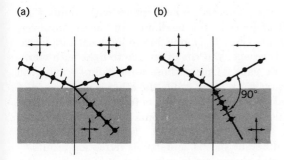

FIGURE 31.6
Partial polarization by reflection and refraction occurs at most angles (a), but complete plane polarization of the reflected beam occurs at the polarizing angle (b).

izing angle and indicate it by i_p. For this case the angle of refraction r is the complement of the angle of incidence i_p, so that $\sin r = \cos i_p$. If n is the index of refraction of the reflecting material relative to the air, we have

$$n = \frac{\sin i_p}{\sin r} = \frac{\sin i_p}{\cos i_p} = \tan i_p \qquad\qquad 31.3$$

The relation $n = \tan i_p$ is known as *Brewster's law.*

Although the reflected beam is completely plane-polarized for incidence at the polarizing angle, the refracted beam is only partially plane-polarized. Most of the intensity is associated with the transmitted beam, which includes all vibration components in the plane of incidence and part of those perpendicular to this plane.

Light reflected from metallic and other conducting surfaces is not polarized. A well-silvered mirror may reflect 98 per cent of the incident light; both types of polarization are reflected. In order to have plane polarization by reflection, we must have a dielectric medium which is not a good conductor of electricity.

Sunlight reflected from the surface of a lake or from an asphalt pavement is partially plane-polarized. Glasses equipped with polarized lenses oriented so that they transmit only vertical vibrations cut out most of the reflected light and only half the unpolarized light. It is for this reason that polaroid glasses reduce glare which is due primarily to reflected light.

31.5 Double Refraction

If a crystal of calcite (often called *Iceland spar*) is placed over a page of print, two images are seen in the calcite. If these images are examined through a polaroid analyzer, it is found that each of the images is produced by plane-polarized light, with the planes of vibration at 90° to one another. Thus, ordinary light entering the crystal is split into two plane-polarized beams which travel through the crystal in different directions. This phenomenon, known as *double refraction,* is shown by many transparent crystals.

Suppose that a flash of light is created at point P inside the calcite and that we look at the wave front a very short time Δt later. In glass or water the wave front is expected to be a sphere with radius $V \Delta t$, where V is the speed of light in the medium. In calcite, however, there are two wave fronts (Fig. 31.7), one due to light with its vibration perpendicular to the page, and the other due to light with vibrations in the plane of the page. One of these wave fronts is spherical and is called the *ordinary* wave front, while the other is an ellipsoid of revolution and is called the *extraordinary* wave front. In calcite there is one direction in which these two wave fronts travel with the same speed. This direction is called the *optic axis*. In other directions the two wave fronts have different speeds, and double refraction results.

In order that a crystal show double refraction, it must be *anisotropic;* i.e., it must have different properties in different directions. Calcite and quartz are examples of anisotropic crystals. Water and glass have the same properties in all directions and are therefore *isotropic.* However, a piece of glass can be made anisotropic if it is subjected to stress.

For calcite the optic axis of a typical cleavage crystal is oriented as shown in Figure 31.7. If we use Huygens' principle to trace light through a calcite crystal, we find that the Huygens' wavelets for the extraordinary wave are ellipsoidal rather than spherical (Fig. 31.8). To find the new wave front for the extraordinary wave, we find the surface which is tangent to these wavelets. This is a plane in the crystal parallel to the ordinary wave front, but the light which enters the crystal at point A in the figure moves along the line AX which represents the path of the *extraordinary ray.* The construction for the ordinary ray is just as it would be for an isotropic medium. Thus, an ordinary ray goes straight through the crystal, while the extraordinary ray moves off to one side. If we place a calcite crystal over a dot on a piece of paper and rotate the crystal, the image formed by the ordinary ray stands still, while the image due to the extraordinary ray rotates about it.

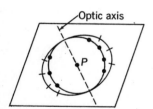

FIGURE 31.7

Calcite exhibits two wave surfaces, the circular one formed with electric vibrations perpendicular to the plane of the paper, and the ellipsoidal one by electric vibrations in the plane of the paper.

FIGURE 31.8

Double refraction in calcite, showing the Huygens wavelets and the paths of ordinary and extraordinary rays.

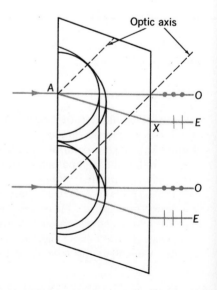

31.6 Nicol Prism

One method of separating the ordinary from the extraordinary ray is by use of a *Nicol prism* (Fig. 31.9). A rhomb of Iceland spar *AMBN* is cut into two parts by a plane *MN*, which makes an angle of about 22° with *MB*. When the cut surfaces have been polished, they are cemented together with Canada balsam, the index of refraction of which is less than that of calcite for the ordinary ray and greater than that of calcite for the extraordinary ray. The refractive indices are Canada balsam 1.55, ordinary ray in calcite 1.658, and extraordinary ray 1.468.

The ray of light *LC* entering the face of the rhomb at *C* is broken into the ordinary and extraordinary rays which are polarized at right angles to each other as indicated by the dots and crosslines in the figure. When the ordinary ray reaches the surface of separation of the Iceland spar and the Canada balsam at *D* at an angle greater than the critical angle, it is totally reflected and emerges from the rhomb in the direction *OO'*. This surface of the rhomb is ordinarily painted black, and the ray is absorbed in this black coating. The extraordinary ray is transmitted in the direction *CE* and emerges from the rhomb at the face *BN*. In this way, there is obtained a beam of plane-polarized light.

31.7 Polarization by Selective Absorption

We have introduced polarization phenomena with the aid of tourmaline crystals and polaroid sheets. These materials produce plane-polarized light by the phenomenon of *selective absorption,* which is exhibited by a number of minerals and organic compounds. Materials which yield polarized light by selective absorption are not only *anisotropic* and double-refracting, but in addition they strongly absorb one of the polarized beams while transmitting the other.

31.8 Polarization by Scattering

When light rays pass through the air, they interact with air molecules and dust particles. Part of the energy is scattered. Particles with dimensions much smaller than the wavelength of the radiation scatter short wavelengths more strongly than long ones. Indeed, the scattering is proportional to the fourth power of the frequency. Since the violet part of the light from the sun has a frequency approximately

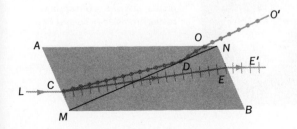

FIGURE 31.9
Total reflection eliminates the ordinary ray in a Nicol prism.

double that of red waves, the violet rays are scattered about $2^4 = 16$ times as strongly as the far red.

Light from the sun is scattered in passing through the atmosphere, and some of this scattered light is rescattered to our eyes. Since this scattered light is much richer in blues and violets than in the longer wavelengths, the sky is blue. By the same token the sun, even at midday, looks far more orange than it would if it were viewed from a rocket ship above the earth's atmosphere. Much of the blue and violet has been scattered out before the light reaches the earth's surface. At sunrise and at sunset the sun's rays go through far greater thicknesses of atmosphere; for this reason the sun appears redder at these times.

If the light of the sky is examined through a polaroid, it is found that this light is partially plane-polarized if the sky is viewed from almost any angle. Light scattered at an angle of 90° with the incident rays is plane-polarized.

31.9 Interference with Polarized Light

If plane-polarized light is incident on a thin sheet of some double-refracting material, the beam is spread into ordinary and extraordinary rays, which travel with different speeds. When they emerge from the double-refracting material, the vibrations are likely to be out of phase. If the light is now passed through an analyzer which transmits only horizontal vibrations, this analyzer selects only the horizontal components of the vibrations from both ordinary and extraordinary rays. These horizontal components may interfere with one another, either constructively or destructively. In particular, if highly convergent light is passed through the double-refracting crystal, the paths of various rays in the crystal differ in length, and there is then constructive interference for a given wavelength for some directions and destructive interference for others. Consequently, interference pat-

(a)

(b)

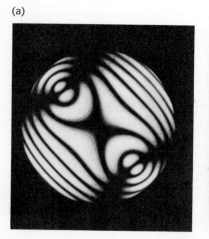
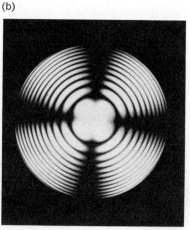

FIGURE 31.10
Interference patterns from crystals of (a) mica and (b) quartz placed in converging monochromatic polarized light.

terns are formed (Fig. 31.10). If the original light contains all the wavelengths in the visible spectrum, the interference pattern is vividly colored. If either the polarizer or analyzer is rotated through 90°, the colors change to the complementary colors, because those for which the interference was initially constructive then have destructive interference, and vice versa.

When a sheet of cellophane is placed under stress, it becomes double-refracting. Interference colors may be observed when such a sheet is placed between two polaroids. It is possible to determine where the stresses are and how great they are by careful analysis of such an interference pattern. One of the most useful methods of studying the stresses in various structural shapes involves making a plastic model, subjecting it to external stresses, and studying the interference patterns produced (Fig. 31.11). Such studies permit a fairly complete analysis of the stress distributions. Once one knows what stress distribution is most likely to cause difficulty, one can change the shape in such a way as to produce a more desirable distribution.

31.10 Rotation of the Plane of Polarization

When a beam of monochromatic plane-polarized light passes through certain substances, the plane of polarization is rotated. Thus, if a plate of quartz cut so that the faces are perpendicular to the axis of the crystal is placed between crossed Nicol prisms, the light is no longer extinguished by the second Nicol prism. If, however, the second Nicol prism is rotated, a new position can be found at which the light is again extinguished. Rotation of the plane of polarization is called *optical activity.*

The angle through which the plane of polarization is rotated depends on the kind of substance interposed between the Nicol prisms, the thickness of the substance, the wavelength of the light, and the temperature. The rotation may be either clockwise or counterclockwise. In this respect there are two kinds of quartz. One kind rotates the plane of polarization clockwise; the other rotates it counterclockwise. Some liquids and gases also cause a rotation of the plane of polarization. Molecules in which a carbon atom is attached by

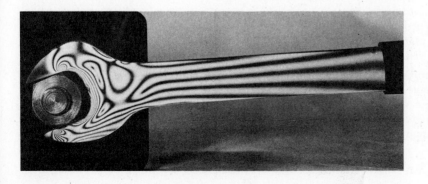

FIGURE 31.11
Stress distribution in an open-end wrench made of Photo Stress® plastic, photographed by polarized light.

valence bonds to four different atoms or groups of atoms often show optical activity. Optical activity is a matter of importance in organic chemistry and is fundamental to stereochemistry.

Questions

1. How should the plane of vibration be oriented in polaroid sunglasses if they are to be effective in cutting the glare of reflected light from a lake?

2. Why do only anisotropic media exhibit double refraction?

3. Why is the sun red at sunset? Is this red light polarized or partially polarized? Explain.

4. Why is the sky blue? Is the light from the blue sky polarized or partially polarized? Explain.

5. How could you make an estimate of the index of refraction of polished black marble by use of a piece of polaroid and a reflected beam?

6. Proposals have been made to use polaroid for reducing the dangers of night driving by eliminating the glare of blinding headlights. Explain how this could be done. (Remember that the driver must still see reflected light from his own head lamps.) What are the disadvantages of such a system?

Problems

1. Find the angle of incidence for which light reflected from water of refractive index 1.333 is plane-polarized. *Ans.* 53°

2. Determine the angle of incidence (polarizing angle) for which light reflected from glass of index of refraction 1.54 is plane-polarized.

3. Light reflected from a flint-glass surface is plane-polarized when the angle of incidence is 59°. What is the index of refraction of the glass? *Ans.* 1.66

4. Determine the critical angle of incidence for the ordinary ray passing from calcite to Canada balsam in a Nicol prism.

5. Two Nicol prisms have their planes of vibration parallel. One of the prisms is then turned so that its plane of vibration makes an angle of 35° with that of the other. What fraction of the amplitude incident on the second Nicol prism is transmitted? What percentage of the light incident on the second Nicol prism is transmitted? *Ans.* 0.819; 67 per cent

6. Light of a certain wavelength passes through a Nicol prism and is thus polarized. It then passes through a second Nicol prism whose plane of vibration makes an angle of 70° with the plane of vibration of the first prism. What percentage of the light incident on the second Nicol prism is transmitted?

7. Two polaroids are crossed. If the analyzer is now rotated through an angle of 50°, what percentage of the plane-polarized light from the polarizer is transmitted, assuming the polaroid is a perfect transmitter of one polarization and a perfect absorber of the other? What percentage of the ordinary light incident on the polarizer is transmitted through the analyzer? *Ans.* 58.7 per cent; 29.3 per cent

OPTICAL SPECTRA

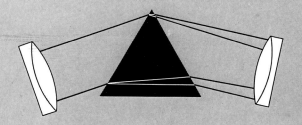

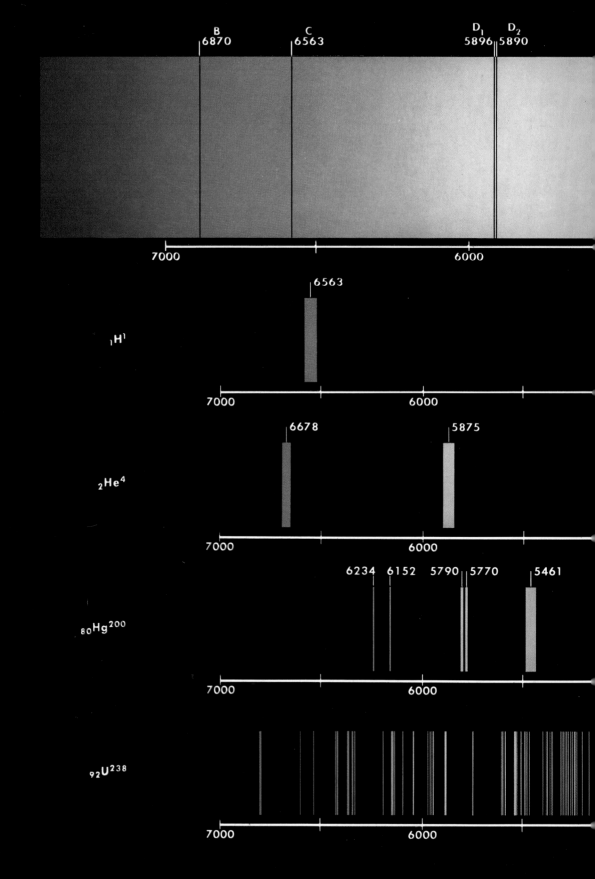

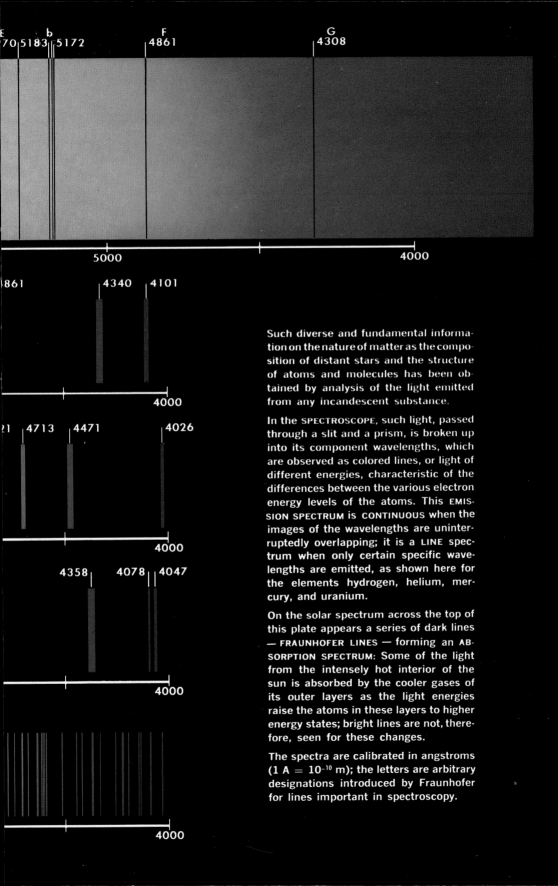

E   b
70|5183||5172   F   G
                      4861   4308

5000   4000

861   4340 4101

4000

21 4713 4471   4026

4000

4358| 4078||4047

4000

4000

Such diverse and fundamental information on the nature of matter as the composition of distant stars and the structure of atoms and molecules has been obtained by analysis of the light emitted from any incandescent substance.

In the SPECTROSCOPE, such light, passed through a slit and a prism, is broken up into its component wavelengths, which are observed as colored lines, or light of different energies, characteristic of the differences between the various electron energy levels of the atoms. This EMISSION SPECTRUM is CONTINUOUS when the images of the wavelengths are uninterruptedly overlapping; it is a LINE spectrum when only certain specific wavelengths are emitted, as shown here for the elements hydrogen, helium, mercury, and uranium.

On the solar spectrum across the top of this plate appears a series of dark lines — FRAUNHOFER LINES — forming an ABSORPTION SPECTRUM: Some of the light from the intensely hot interior of the sun is absorbed by the cooler gases of its outer layers as the light energies raise the atoms in these layers to higher energy states; bright lines are not, therefore, seen for these changes.

The spectra are calibrated in angstroms (1 A = 10^{-10} m); the letters are arbitrary designations introduced by Fraunhofer for lines important in spectroscopy.

CHAPTER 32 *We have learned that a beam of white light can be dispersed into a spectrum by either a prism or a diffraction grating. An exciting feature of these spectra is the appearance of color, an aspect of light which greatly enriches our vision, but one about which we have said little. Now we shall discuss color vision and point out some of its mysteries. But color is only one facet of spectra, and in this chapter we consider also the classification of spectra and the importance of the fact that any given type of atom has its own unique spectrum.*

Spectra and Color

32.1 Emission Spectra

When a beam of white light is passed through a prism, the light is dispersed into a spectrum (Sec. 27.9). Light from an incandescent lamp or a candle contains all the colors of the rainbow (Fig. 32.1). However, if we put salt (NaCl) in the flame of a bunsen burner, the light emitted is a yellow characteristic of sodium. If a lithium salt is put in the flame, a bright red is produced.

The systematic examination of the spectra of various light sources was initiated by Kirchhoff about a century ago. The spectra of elements gave us one of the most important clues in the development of modern atomic theory. There are several ways in which emission spectra may be classified. We shall group them as follows:

Continuous Spectra. When the spectrum of the light from an incandescent solid or liquid is examined, it shows no regions of darkness (Fig. 32.1). The spectra of an incandescent lamp and a carbon arc are of this type and are known as *continuous spectra,* since they contain light of every wavelength over a broad region.

Bright-line Spectra. When atoms in the gaseous state are excited to emit radiation, the spectrum consists of a number of *narrow bright lines* with wavelengths characteristic of the element that emits them. The optical spectra of hydrogen, helium, mercury, and uranium are shown in the preceding color insert. Such spectra may be excited by passing an electrical discharge through the gas or by raising the temperature of the atoms sufficiently. Each element has its own characteristic *bright-line* spectrum.

Band Spectra. When radiation is emitted by excited molecules, the spectrum often appears in the form of bands of light with regions of darkness between. Such molecular spectra are often referred to as *band spectra.* However, when band spectra are studied in spectrometers of great resolving power, it is found that a band results from a large group of lines very close together. Overlapping of the lines gives rise to the band structure.

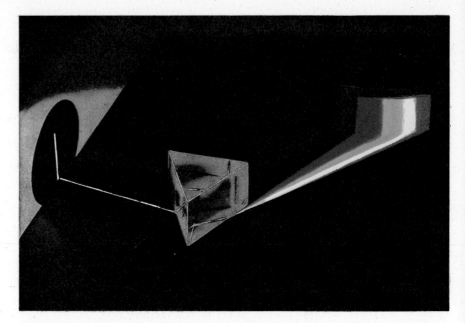

FIGURE 32.1 White light dispersed into its component colors by a prism.

32.2 Spectroscopy

In spectral measurements we are concerned directly with the wavelengths of the radiation, which range from many kilometers to far less than a billion billionth of a meter. The observation and interpretation of spectra is known as *spectroscopy*. It deals not only with visible light, but also with electromagnetic waves of longer and shorter wavelengths including radio, radar, infrared, ultraviolet, X rays, and gamma rays. The wavelength regions of these radiations are suggested in Table 32.1 and in Figure 32.2. Actually there is substantial overlapping of regions; the boundaries are not sharp. Except for their inability to excite vision, radiations with wavelengths only a little longer (near infrared) or a little shorter (near ultraviolet) than visible

TABLE 32.1

Kinds of waves	Limits of wavelengths
Radio, television, and radar	10^4 km to 10^{-4} m
Infrared radiation	10^{-3} to 7×10^{-7} m
Visible spectrum	7.8×10^{-7} to 3.8×10^{-7} m
Ultraviolet radiation	4×10^{-7} to 10^{-8} m
X rays	10^{-8} to 10^{-14} m
Gamma rays	10^{-10} to 10^{-12} m
Secondary cosmic rays	10^{-10} m to —

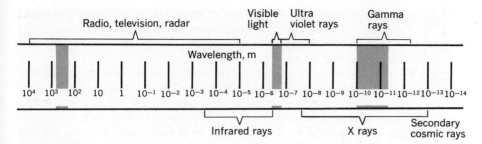

FIGURE 32.2
Electromagnetic spectrum.

light have optical properties very close to those of radiations in the optical range.   Infrared and ultraviolet rays are reflected and refracted like visible ones and can expose suitably prepared photographic film.   For wavelengths far from those of the optical region, some phenomena occur which are not apparent with visible light.

As an example of how potent a tool spectroscopy is, consider the element *helium;* its spectrum was observed in light from the sun some 25 years before helium was discovered on the earth.   Thanks to study of the spectra of the stars, we know a great deal about their chemical composition, even though no sample has ever been placed in the hands of a chemist.   To this day spectroscopy is one of the most active branches of physics and chemistry; both research and industrial applications are legion.

Since each element has a unique spectrum, an examination of the light emitted by a substance gives direct evidence of its composition. This method is very useful in detecting small quantities of substances. It is a rapid and sensitive method of analysis.   The spectrum of an ele-

FIGURE 32.3
Spectrometer, showing how rays made parallel by a collimator are brought to a focus by the telescope.

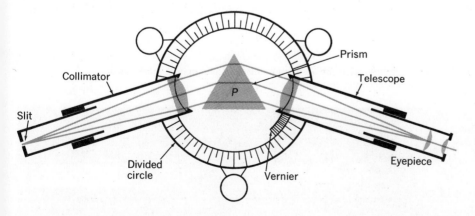

ment can be excited in a variety of ways, among which are passing an electrical discharge through a gas containing the element, heating the element in a furnace, and introducing it into an electric arc. The origin of spectral lines is discussed in Chap. 48.

For the study of optical spectra, a spectroscope or a spectrometer is used. One essential part of a typical spectrometer (Fig. 32.3) is the collimator, which consists of a tube with a slit at one end and a converging lens at the other. The slit is located at the principal focus of the lens so that the light rays which emerge from the lens when the slit is illuminated are parallel. These rays pass through a prism which disperses the light to a telescope mounted so that it can rotate about the vertical axis of the instrument. The angle through which the telescope is rotated is read on a divided circle.

32.3 Dark-line Spectra; Fraunhofer Lines

The spectrum of the sun is crossed by a number of fine dark lines known as *Fraunhofer lines* (see color insert following page 404). They are produced by absorption in the atmospheres of the sun and the earth. The core of the sun emits white light. Surrounding this central part is an atmosphere of cooler vapors and gases. When light passes through this solar atmosphere, the wavelengths corresponding to the light that would be emitted by these luminous vapors is absorbed by them. For example, sodium vapor in the sun's atmosphere absorbs those wavelengths which sodium vapor emits when luminous. These wavelengths are therefore almost completely absent when the solar spectrum is examined. From the Fraunhofer lines it has been possible to determine what elements are abundant in the sun's atmosphere. Figure 32.4 compares the emission spectrum of iron with the solar spectrum, showing that iron vapor is present in the solar atmosphere.

A dark-line spectrum can be produced in the laboratory by passing an intense beam of continuous radiation through the vapor of some element which absorbs from the continuous spectrum wavelengths which the element emits in its bright-line spectrum; e.g., when white light from a carbon arc is sent through sodium vapor, there is strong absorption of the wavelengths of the yellow sodium-D lines.

FIGURE 32.4

The correspondence of many Fraunhofer lines with the absorption lines of iron vapor is apparent in these emission spectra from 3,900 to 4,000 Å for iron and for the sun (center).

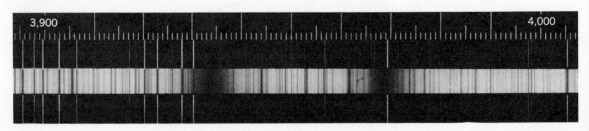

32.4 The Doppler Effect

When a sound source is moving toward or away from an observer, the frequency observed is different from the source frequency (Sec. 17.9). A similar effect is observed in light. The Doppler effect provides a means of determining the motions of distant stars. If a star is moving away from the earth, the frequency of a spectral line observed at the earth is lower than the emitted frequency so that the observed wavelength is greater than normal; if the star is approaching the earth, the wavelengths are shifted toward smaller values. By measuring the displacements of the lines, the speed of the moving star can be determined.

The Doppler effect in light waves differs in one very important respect from that in sound waves. In sound waves it is the velocity of the source (or of the observer) *relative to the air* which is of importance. In the case of light waves there is no comparable medium. So long as the velocity of the light source relative to the observer is small compared with the speed of light,

$$\frac{\nu_{observed}}{\nu_{source}} = \frac{c}{c - v} \qquad\qquad 32.1$$

where c is the speed of light, and v the velocity of source toward observer.

The Doppler effect is used for measuring speeds of missiles and of automobiles. For example, when a radar transmitter on a police car sends out very-high-frequency waves, these waves are reflected by oncoming automobiles. The reflected waves have a different frequency and are "beat" (Sec. 16.10) against the initial frequency, yielding a *beat frequency* equal to the difference between the two. In this case the source is the image of the transmitter reflected from the vehicle, which acts as a plane mirror. Therefore, the speed of the source is twice the speed v of the oncoming vehicle. Let the frequency emitted by the radar be ν, and that received be ν_r. Then Eq. (32.1) yields

$$\frac{\nu_r}{\nu} = \frac{c}{c - 2v}$$

The beat frequency F is given by

$$F = \nu_r - \nu = \frac{2v\nu}{c - 2v} = \frac{2v\nu}{c}$$

since $2v$ is negligible compared with c.

Example A radar transmitter sends out a signal at 100 Mc. An automobile is approaching, and the beat frequency observed is 19 beats/sec. Find the speed of the approaching car.

$$F = \frac{2v\nu}{c}$$

$$F = 19 \text{ beats/sec} \qquad \nu = 10^8 \text{ cycles/sec} \qquad c = 186,000 \text{ mi/sec}$$

$$19 = \frac{2v \times 10^8}{186,000}$$

$$v = 1.77 \times 10^{-2} \text{ mi/sec} = 64 \text{ mi/hr}$$

32.5 Color Classification

When we look at a group of colored objects, there are three psycho-physical characteristics in terms of which we can make a qualitative color description. They are *hue, saturation,* and *lightness* (or, for a self-luminous object such as a light bulb, the *brightness*). The *hue* we can give in terms of the color which the object most closely resembles, such as blue, orange, purple, or yellow-green in the hue circle of Figure 32.5. In the system of color notation developed by Munsell, the complete hue circle consists of 100 hues.

The term *saturation* has to do with the extent to which the hue is influenced by the addition of other colors. If blue is the only color present, the saturation approaches unity. On the other hand, if other colors are present, but there is enough blue so that the object has a blue hue, the saturation is low (Fig. 32.6). In mixing paints, for example, a paint of lower saturation can always be made by mixing white with the color. Thus, it is easy to produce a wide range of variations in saturation for the same hue. As we go from zero to 100 per cent in saturation, we go from whites and grays to pure colors. Whites and grays are *achromatic* and correspond to zero saturation.

Lightness is connected with the relative amount of light which reaches the eye from the object. If the object is illuminated by white light and reflects all the incident light, it has maximum lightness and appears white; if it reflects none of the light, it is black. It is possible to arrange achromatic grays in a scale of brightness and to match against these grays samples of a given hue which reflect the same fraction of the incident light (Fig. 32.6).

One simple way of representing colors is in a three-dimensional color cylinder or color tree (Fig. 32.7) in which the lightness (or brightness) is plotted, going from black to grays to brilliant white along an axis. Around this axis can be drawn concentric circles, with the various hues given by the angles, and the saturations by the distance from the central white-black axis.

It is not necessary that all visible wavelengths be present to excite the sensation of white light; indeed only two properly chosen wavelengths need be present, and a wide variety of pairs is possible. Two wavelengths (or two colors) which, when mixed together, give white light are said to be *complementary.* Red and blue-green are complementary, and so are blue and yellow. The complementary of green is reddish purple (magenta) which is not a spectral color, but arises from a combination of spectral colors.

32.6 The Measurement of Color

Suppose a projector (Fig. 32.8) throws on the screen S_1 an arbitrary color X. Let us illuminate the adjacent area S_2 by means of three lanterns, each of which sends out a light of a single narrow wavelength region, A at 425 mμ (blue), B at 551 mμ (green), and C at 650 mμ (red). For almost any color we can find one and only one combination of relative intensities of these three lights which exactly matches the color X. We can then describe color X in terms of the amounts of light from A,

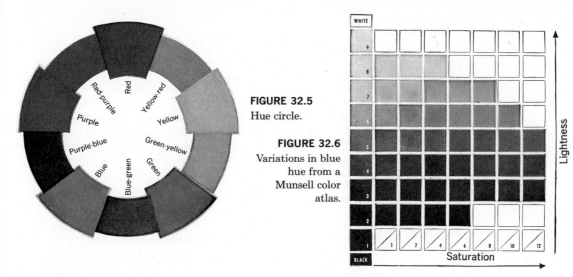

FIGURE 32.5
Hue circle.

FIGURE 32.6
Variations in blue hue from a Munsell color atlas.

FIGURE 32.7
Color tree vividly shows the three-dimensional relationship between lightness, hue, and saturation.

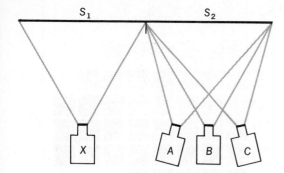

FIGURE 32.8

Color of almost any hue or saturation thrown on screen S_1 can be matched on screen S_2 by blending (adding) three monochromatic primaries in specific amounts.

B, and C. Thus, we can describe this color with three specific numbers.

Although we may match almost all colors in this way, there are some which we cannot match by adding everything on the screen at the right. Colors which we cannot match are outside the *gamut* of these *primaries*. However, if we move the proper one of the lamps to the other side and add its light to the unknown color, it is possible to achieve a match. For example, if we try to match a pure green of $\lambda = 500$ mμ with the lamps, we find that we always have too much red, but if we move lamp C to the other side, we find that we can match $\lambda = 500$ mμ plus some red from C with light from lamps A and B. One way of saying this is to say we can match $\lambda = 500$ mμ with light from A and B and a *negative* amount of light from C. This, however, introduces the complication of negative numbers for specifying some colors.

We have chosen for our illuminants blue, green, and red, because with them we can match the widest gamut of colors. In this sense red, green, and blue are *primary* colors. However, if we use any three different wavelengths, we can still match any color if we allow the use of negative contributions and assume that the sources A, B, and C can be varied in intensity over an infinite range.

To avoid the difficulties associated with negative numbers, and for other reasons, the International Commission on Illumination agreed in 1931 on a standard *operational procedure* for determining the color of a surface. (This method can be shown to be equivalent to the type of experiment in which we match the color with three primary sources, except that the sources chosen do not exist in the realm of *real colors*.) The surface is placed in a spectrophotometer. This instrument contains an optical system in which the light from a standard lamp is dispersed into a spectrum by a prism. One narrow range of wavelengths at a time is allowed to fall upon the surface under test, and the amount of light reflected is compared with the amount of the same wavelength range reflected from a standard white surface. A plot is made of the relative reflectance of the surface under test as a function of wavelength. Several such *spectral-reflectance* curves are shown in Figure 32.9. From the spectral-reflectance curve it is possible to calculate the coordinates x and y for the color of the surface on the ICI *chromaticity diagram* (Figs. 32.10 and 32.11).

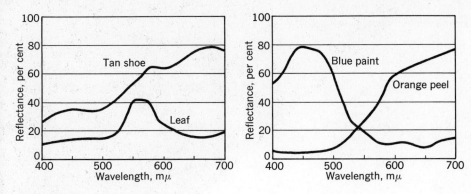

FIGURE 32.9
Spectral-reflectance curves for various objects.

The horseshoe-shaped boundary (Fig. 32.10) is called the *spectrum locus,* since here we find the pure colors of the continuous spectrum. Point B on the diagram represents a white surface illuminated by sunlight at noon, while point C represents average daylight from an overcast sky. The other points on the inner curve represent the colors of black bodies at the temperatures indicated on the diagram. Point C is ordinarily chosen as the illumination standard.

Any color above the dotted lines in Figure 32.12 may be regarded as a mixture of illuminant C and a single spectral frequency. Thus the point N in this figure could be reached by mixing daylight and sodium D radiation. The line CN extended to the spectrum locus gives us 589.3 mμ, which is called the *dominant wavelength* for the color specified by N. Since the yellow of point N lies between C and the spectrum color, it is not *saturated yellow,* as is the spectrum color.

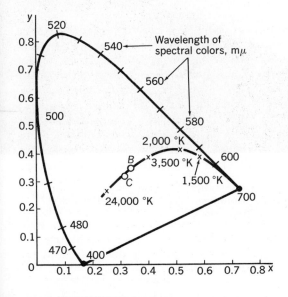

FIGURE 32.10
Chromaticity diagram shows the spectrum locus and the colors of black bodies at the temperatures indicated. Point C represents average daylight from an overcast sky and is chosen as the illumination standard.

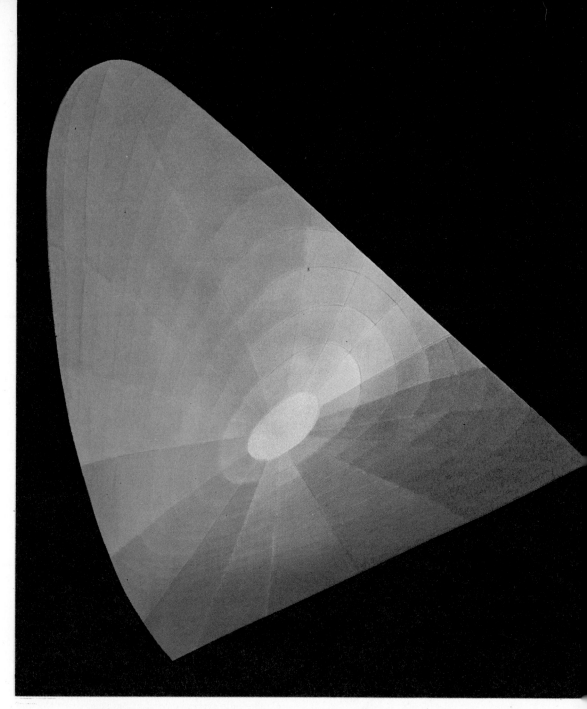

FIGURE 32.11

Chromaticity diagram has radial boundaries between segments to separate the various hues, with oval boundaries representing lines of constant saturation. The horseshoe-shaped outer boundary corresponds to the positions of pure spectrum colors.

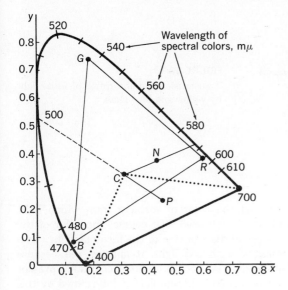

FIGURE 32.12

Chromaticity diagram showing method of specifying a color in terms of dominant wavelength and purity. The phosphors of color television screens glow in the primaries R, B, and G, permitting mixtures to reproduce any color in the triangle RBG, a close approximation to the full spectrum of visible color.

The distance from C to N divided by the distance from C to the spectrum locus gives the *purity* of the color. For point N the purity is 40 per cent.

Any two colors on opposite sides of a line through C on the chromaticity diagram are complementary. The point P below the dotted line is a purple, and not a spectral color. If we extend the line CP, it reaches the spectral curve at 500 mμ. Point P is said to have the coordinate 500c, where the c ($=$ complementary) is added to indicate that the point P is on the opposite side of C from the 500-mμ spectral color to which it is complementary. We may assign a purity to the color represented by P if we use a straight line connecting the end points of the visible region as the analogue of the spectrum locus.

By use of the ICI chromaticity diagram it is possible to specify measurable physical quantities, dominant wavelength and purity, which correspond to the psychological *hue* and *saturation*. From the spectral-reflectance curve for a surface it is possible to compute the *luminous reflectance,* where the word *luminous* means that the value takes into account the visual response of a standard observer and the color characteristics of the light source. The luminous reflectance is the physical analogue of *lightness.*

For color television, phosphors are available which give the primaries R, G, and B of Figure 32.12 when they are bombarded by an electron beam. The screen is made up of these phosphors. By appropriate variations in intensities, all the colors in the triangle RBG can be obtained. Although this triangle does not include all visible colors, it covers a sufficiently wide range so that rich color communication is possible.

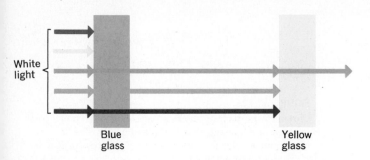

Blue
glass

Yellow
glass

FIGURE 32.13
Transmission and absorption of white light
by yellow and blue glass.

32.7 Color of Bodies

Thus far we have discussed the color of surfaces from which light
from a standard illuminant is reflected. Of course, the color of the
object depends on the spectral distribution of the incident light. If a
white surface is illuminated with red light, it appears red because
it reflects only red light to the eye. Since no other colors are present
to be reflected, the color of the body is completely determined by this
reflected red light. An object that appears red in white light is also
red in red light, but it is black in any light which it does not reflect or
transmit. Bodies that have the same color when viewed in daylight
may not have the same color in lamplight. Light from an ordinary
incandescent lamp is richer in red rays than in blue.

A piece of glass which appears blue may actually reflect and transmit
other colors such as the neighboring green and violet (Fig. 32.13).
Similarly, a yellow glass plate may transmit red and green. If both
glasses are placed in a beam of white light, the only color which can
pass through both is green. This is an example of color by the
subtractive process, in which we start with white light and remove
various wavelength regions by absorption. The mixing of pigments is

FIGURE 32.14
Background color affects
identical hues.

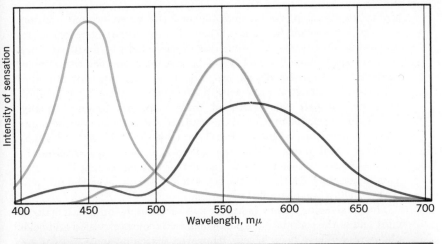

FIGURE 32.15

Response curves (above) of retinal cones to primary colors in the daylight spectrum (below), according to the three-component theory of color vision.

another example of a subtractive process. Mixing suitable yellow and blue pigments may give rise to a green paint just as green light passes through the combined filters of Figure 32.13.

32.8 Color Vision

Color vision is known to arise from the stimulation of the cones in the retina. The processes which occur are not completely understood, but current research[1] in this subject is yielding new insight into the remarkable versatility of the eye in perceiving color. The apparent hue of an object is affected by its surroundings (Fig. 32.14) and, indeed, by the immediate past exposure of the retina. When any area of the retina is subjected to continued stimulation by intense red light and then subjected to white light, the area "sees" blue-green. In general, a retinal area strongly stimulated by any color responds to subsequent white light with a *fatigue image* dominated by the color complementary to the original stimulus.

A reasonable explanation for the ability to match any color with three spots of light (Sec. 32.6), developed by Maxwell and Helmholtz, is built upon the assumption that there are three types of cone response, each of which is excited to some extent by the whole visual spectrum (Fig. 32.15). However, the blue response is particularly

[1] A fascinating and highly readable report of definitive studies in this area may be found in E. H. Land, "Experiments in Color Vision," *Scientific American,* May, 1959, p. 84.

strong for wavelengths around 450 mμ, the green around 550 mμ, and the red around 600 mμ. When all three types of response are aroused about equally, the sensation of white light is produced. It is not necessary that all wavelengths be present to get the sensation of white light. As we have seen, properly chosen amounts of radiation of only two wavelengths can excite a sensation of perfect white light, since such a pair can excite all three responses roughly equally. Purples arise from excitation of the blue and red sensations without any substantial amount of green. Purple is not a spectral color, but a mixture of spectral colors. Yellow is a true spectral color; nevertheless, the simultaneous excitation of the red and green sensations in roughly equal amounts gives the eye the sensation of yellow, even though none of the "yellow wavelengths" are present.

The three-color theory is highly successful in dealing with spots of light and is the foundation upon which both color television and color photography have been based. However, matching spots of light is a far cry from seeing colors in complete images under normal conditions. Then the colors of images arise from the interplay of longer and shorter wavelengths over the total visual field. For example, if a photographic transparency of a colored scene taken with red light is projected on a screen with yellow light of $\lambda = 599$ mμ, the resulting image is yellow with various areas lighter and darker than others. Now if the image of a second transparency of the same scene taken with green light and projected with yellow light of $\lambda = 579$ mμ is superposed, the resulting image includes reds, greens, blues—a broad range of colors, paler and less saturated than the original scene, but still a reasonably faithful reproduction. Thus it appears that color is not determined uniquely by the wavelengths reaching the eye, but rather the various wavelengths bear information by which the eye assigns colors to various objects. Apparently, to see colors the eye needs information concerning long and short wavelengths in a scene, but this information can be brought to the eye by as little as two narrow bands of wavelengths.

32.9 Fluorescence

Although many bodies return only those visible wavelengths which fall upon them, some bodies absorb light of one wavelength and emit light of longer wavelength. This process is called *fluorescence*. Many dyes emit vivid visible radiation under ultraviolet light. Fluorescence is used in a wide variety of applications ranging from the theater to the identification of ores in mining. In fluorescent lamps ultraviolet light from an electric discharge in mercury vapor is absorbed by fluorescent materials, called *phosphors*, which coat the insides of the tubes. By suitable choice of phosphors a wide range of colors of fluorescent light is available.

Some materials continue to emit visible light for some time after exposure to ultraviolet light. Such materials are said to be *phosphorescent*.

Questions

1. Pieces of cloth appear red, yellow, green, and blue-violet in daylight. How is their appearance modified when seen under candlelight?

2. How does the Doppler effect enable us to determine the angular velocity of the sun? The component along the line of sight of the velocity of a distant star?

3. How can only three colors (and black) be used to print color pictures? Can any color be reproduced in this way?

4. Green color can be seen in (*a*) a green leaf, (*b*) a mercury arc, (*c*) a dress, and (*d*) a stained-glass window. What is the origin of the green in each case?

5. A "daylight" incandescent bulb has a blue glass envelope. Why?

PART V   ELECTRICITY AND ELECTRON PHYSICS

CHAPTER 33 *The twentieth century may well be called the* age of electricity. *Developments in the nineteenth century made it possible to generate, deliver, and control vast amounts of electrical energy at reasonable cost. The results are everywhere apparent. Electrical energy is used for lighting, heating, cooking, refrigeration, washing, drying, ironing, and air circulation in many modern homes. Electrical energy dominates the world of communication; the telephone, telegraph, radio, and television are direct outgrowths of advances in our understanding of electricity.*

Less obvious, but no less important, is the role of electricity in our economic development. The automobile and aluminum industries, to mention only two, could not have evolved in their present form until man learned how to generate and control electrical energy. So important is electricity in our everyday life that our standard of living would be tremendously lowered without it. Electrical servants have replaced human servants in the average home. In the short course of less than a century the science of electricity has developed from a curiosity to a dominant position in our technology.

Although most of the common uses of electrical phenomena involve electric charges in motion, the fundamental concepts are best developed by considering first electrostatics, *the science of stationary electric charges. Electrostatics is both the historical and the logical starting point in the study of electricity.*

Electric Charges at Rest

33.1 Charges by Contact and Separation

As early as 600 B.C. it was known that amber rubbed with fur had the interesting property of attracting light pieces of straw or paper. A rubber comb run through the hair may exhibit this same property. Such bodies are said to be *electrified,* a term derived from the Greek word for *amber.* Experiments reveal that it is possible to electrify any kind of material by rubbing it with a suitable second material and then separating the two. An electrified body is said to bear an *electric charge.* When a charged body and an uncharged one are brought together, a portion of the charge is likely to be transferred to the uncharged body.

If a small pith ball is charged by contact with an electrified glass rod, the rod and ball repel each other. Similarly, if a pith ball is charged by contact with an electrified rubber rod, they repel one another. However, a ball charged by contact with the electrified *glass* rod is attracted by the electrified *rubber* rod, while the charged *glass* rod attracts a pith ball charged by contact with the electrified *rubber* rod. This simple experiment suggests (see Figure 33.1) that there are *at least* two different kinds of electric charge. Exhaustive experiments with many substances have led to the conclusion that there are *only* two kinds of charges. The charge on a glass rod rubbed with silk is called *positive,* while that on a rubber rod rubbed with cat's fur is *negative.* From a number of experiments it is possible to establish the qualitative laws of electrostatic reaction: *Like charges repel one another; unlike charges attract one another.*

33.2 The Electrical Structure of Matter

The idea that all matter is composed of tiny particles called *atoms* is well known. Although the word *atom* means "indivisible," atoms have a complex structure. Practically all the mass of an atom is concentrated in a tiny core called the *nucleus.* The nucleus bears a *positive* charge, the magnitude of which depends on the atom in question. All nuclei of a given element bear the same charge. The nucleus with the smallest charge is that of the hydrogen atom, which carries one positive atomic unit equal in magnitude to the negative charge on the electron. The nucleus of the hydrogen atom has a special name, the *proton.* Every other type of atom has a nucleus bearing some integral number of atomic units. All oxygen nuclei have 8 atomic charges, all copper nuclei 29 charges. Indeed, the atomic number of the atom is a measure of how many atomic units of charge its nucleus bears (i.e., of how many protons it contains).

Outside the nucleus of a neutral atom are *electrons,* the number of electrons being equal to the number of positive charges in the nucleus. It is sometimes convenient to think of an atom as sort of a submicroscopic solar system, with the nucleus as the sun and with the electrons revolving about it much as the planets revolve around the sun.

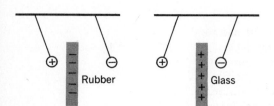

FIGURE 33.1
Different materials assume different charges, but like charges always repel, and unlike always attract.

For an atom which has several electrons there is abundant evidence to indicate that some of the electrons are close to the nucleus and others much farther away (Sec. 48.8). For example, sodium has eleven electrons, of which two are ordinarily close to the nucleus, eight are at a somewhat greater distance, and the eleventh is usually much farther from the nucleus, as indicated schematically in Figure 33.2. This "outside" electron is not very tightly held by the atom; it can be removed readily, which accounts for many of the interesting chemical properties of sodium. In general, any atom which has several electrons will have some which are difficult to remove and one or at most a few electrons which are comparatively easy to take away from the atom. The outer electrons of some atoms, such as lithium and sodium, are particularly easy to remove, while those of other atoms, such as neon and argon, are relatively tightly held. The chemical properties of elements are intimately related to their electronic structures.

If two substances are brought into intimate contact with one another, it is almost certain that one has a greater affinity for electrons than the other. As a result, some of the electrons are transferred to the substance with the greater electron affinity. This leaves one substance with an excess of electrons or a negative charge, while the other is left with a deficiency of electrons and a corresponding positive charge. The transfer of charges does not go on indefinitely because, as the substance with the greater electron affinity accumulates electrons, the excess negative charge repels other electrons, while the other substance, with its excess positive charge, attracts them.

33.3 Conductors and Insulators

In some materials, notably the metals, a small fraction of the electrons are not bound to any one nucleus, but are free to wander among the atoms. Materials in which electrons are free to move about are called *conductors*. In other materials each electron is held by one or two atoms. A material in which charges are not free to move about is called a *nonconductor* or *insulator*. As might be expected, the line between conductors and insulators is not a sharp one. For example, a piece of damp wood is neither a good conductor of electricity nor a good insulator.

In most solid conductors the transfer of charge is by movement of electrons. However, there are many situations in which charges are not conducted by electrons. A solution of sodium chloride in water is a good conductor of electricity, because the molecules break into two parts, a sodium atom with an electron missing and a chlorine atom with one extra electron. These charged particles are called *ions*. The conduction takes place by the movement of both positively charged sodium ions and negatively charged chlorine ions. In liquids and gases, the transfer of charge by ions, both positive and negative, is common.

The early observations of electric charges were made on materials such as amber and glass, which are nonconductors. A piece of glass

FIGURE 33.2

Sodium atom, simplified, showing nucleus with 11 positive charges surrounded by 11 electrons.

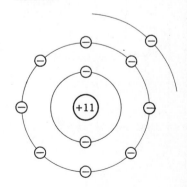

rubbed with silk obtains a positive charge which does not escape readily because the glass is a good insulator. If a copper rod is rubbed with silk, it also becomes charged, but, unless it is carefully insulated, the charge is rapidly conducted away. If one holds the copper rod in one's hand, the charges have no difficulty in traveling along the copper conductor and escaping through the body, since the human body is a fairly good conductor, especially when the skin is moist.

It is possible to charge one end of a hard rubber rod positively and the other end negatively by rubbing one end with a material of great electron affinity and the other end with a material of low electron affinity. Because the rubber is a good insulator, the charges remain on the ends. However, if one tries to do this to a metal rod, the charges do not stay on the ends; rather, there is an immediate flow of electrons. Similarly, if a wire of conducting material is connected between a positively charged metal sphere and a negatively charged sphere, there is a flow of charges. Such a flow is called an *electric current*. In sending electrical energy from one point to another, it is standard practice to produce a flow of charges; since this requires some sort of conducting medium, wires of good conductors, usually copper or aluminum, connect homes with power-generating stations.

33.4 The Law of Conservation of Charge

Since electrification by contact and separation always involves a transfer of charges from one body to another, the amount of positive charge which appears on one is equal to the negative charge which appears on the other. Whenever a certain positive charge appears on one body, an equal negative charge must appear on some other body or bodies.

Charge is one of the fundamental properties of matter. *The total net charge of any isolated system never changes.* This statement expresses the *law of conservation of charge,* one of the basic laws of nature. This law and the laws of conservation of energy and momentum are of great importance in the interactions of atoms and in the reactions of atomic nuclei.

33.5 Coulomb's Law

In 1785 the French physicist Coulomb used a torsion balance (Fig. 33.3) to measure the force between two small charged spheres as a function of the distance between them. He found that *the force between two charges Q_1 and Q_2 is directly proportional to the product of the charges and inversely proportional to the square of the distance r between the charges:*

$$F = k\frac{Q_1Q_2}{r^2}$$

33.1

where the proportionality constant k depends on the units in which the variables of Eq. (33.1) are measured. Coulomb's law is directly applicable only in situations in which the distance r between charges

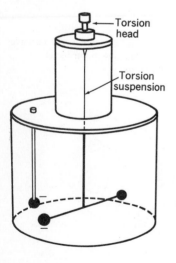

FIGURE 33.3

Torsion balance measures repulsion of charged sphere on end of swinging bar by stationary charged sphere and is similar to that used by Coulomb to study the forces between electric charges.

Torsion head

Torsion suspension

is large compared with the dimensions of the charged bodies. When two charged objects are very small compared with the distance between them, we may consider the charges as concentrated at points, and we refer to them as *point charges*.

Charge may be measured in a number of units, four of which have been widely used. We shall work with only two.

1. The *atomic unit of charge* is the charge on a single proton; the charge on the electron has the same magnitude, but is negative in sign. The atomic unit of charge is exceedingly minute, far too small to be convenient for use in most practical problems in electricity. It is, however, a truly basic unit in that no smaller charge has ever been observed, and all larger charges are believed to be integral numbers of atomic units.

2. The *coulomb* is the practical unit of charge. We shall take it as a new fundamental unit which, with the meter, kilogram, and second, will permit us to formulate the laws of electricity and magnetism in a self-consistent manner. The formal definition of the coulomb in terms of the operations required for a precise measurement of charge involves the use of concepts which are developed in subsequent chapters (Sec. 39.8). We can, however, compare the coulomb with the atomic unit of charge:

1 coulomb = 6.242×10^{18} atomic units (electrons)

or

(electron)
1 atomic unit = 1.6021×10^{-19} coulomb

In electrostatics we seldom meet charges as large as 1 coulomb. Typically we shall be dealing with charges of the order of a microcoulomb (1 μC = 10^{-6} coulomb) or even a micromicrocoulomb (1 $\mu\mu$C = 1 pC = 10^{-12} coulomb).

3. The *electrostatic unit of charge,* sometimes called the *statcoulomb,* is especially convenient for dealing with electrostatic problems. It is defined in terms of Coulomb's law as follows: The electrostatic unit of charge is that charge which repels an identical charge one centimeter away in vacuum with a force of one dyne (10^{-5} newton).

1 coulomb = 3×10^9 electrostatic units of charge

4. The *electromagnetic unit of charge,* sometimes called the *abcoulomb,* is defined in terms of the magnetic field produced at the center of a circular coil by a current.

1 coulomb = 0.1 electromagnetic unit of charge

Complete systems of electrical units have been built around both the electrostatic and the electromagnetic units of charge. These systems are particularly convenient for handling certain special problems. However, it is difficult to learn three distinct systems of electrical units; therefore we shall use only the practical system in the problems of this text.

When the charges Q_1 and Q_2 are in coulombs, the force in newtons, and the distance r in meters, the constant k of Eq. (33.1) for a vacuum has the value 8.9878×10^9 newton-m²/coulomb², which in turn is $10^{-7}c^2$, where c is the speed of light in free space in meters per second. It is customary to write Coulomb's law in the form

$$F = \frac{1}{4\pi\epsilon_0} \frac{Q_1 Q_2}{r^2}$$

33.1a

where $\epsilon_0 = 8.8543 \times 10^{-12}$ coulomb²/newton-m² is called the *permittivity of free space*. From the point of view of Coulomb's law, replacing k with $\frac{1}{4}\pi\epsilon_0$ appears to offer no advantages; however, we shall find in Chap. 35 that Eq. (33.1a) leads to simpler expressions for capacitances; the advantages become still greater in advanced electromagnetic theory.

As we have seen, in vacuum $\frac{1}{4}\pi\epsilon_0 = k$ is almost 9×10^9 newton-m²/coulomb². In air the constant in Coulomb's law is less than in vacuum by the factor $1/1.0006$. For our problems we shall use

$$F = 9 \times 10^9 \frac{Q_1 Q_2}{r^2}$$

33.1b

for charges in either air or vacuum.

When several charges are present in one region, the force on any one of the charges is equal to the vector sum of the forces which each of the other charges would exert on the first one if it acted independently.

Example Charges A, B, and C of $+25$, $+20$, and -8 μcoulombs, respectively, are arranged as shown in Figure 33.4. Find the magnitude of the force on charge A.

$$F_{AB} = 9 \times 10^9 \frac{20 \times 10^{-6} \times 25 \times 10^{-6}}{25} = 0.180 \text{ newton}$$

$$F_{AC} = -9 \times 10^9 \frac{25 \times 10^{-6} \times 8 \times 10^{-6}}{9} = -0.200 \text{ newton}$$

The vertical component of F_{AB} is $\frac{3}{5} \times 0.180 = 0.108$ newton. The horizontal component of F_{AB} is $\frac{4}{5} \times 0.180 = 0.144$ newton.

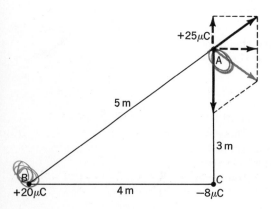

+25μC

A

5 m

3 m

B
+20μC

4 m

C
−8μC

FIGURE 33.4
Charges of $+25$, $+20$, and -8 μcoulombs at the corners of a right triangle.

The vertical component of the resultant force on A is $-0.200 + 0.108 = -0.092$ newton. The horizontal component of the resultant is 0.144 newton.

The magnitude of the resultant is then

$$\sqrt{(0.144)^2 + (0.092)^2} = 0.17 \text{ newton}$$

33.6 Electric Field Intensity

Any region in which electric forces may be detected is called an *electric field*.

The *intensity* (or *strength*) **E** *of an electric field at any point is defined as the ratio of the force* **F** *acting on a small test charge q at that point to the charge q:*

$$\mathbf{E} = \frac{\mathbf{F}}{q} \qquad\qquad 33.2$$

It is desirable that a very small test charge be chosen, since a large test charge would change the charge distribution which creates the field and thus distort the very thing it is being used to measure. Clearly, the electric intensity is a vector quantity. Its direction is the direction of the force on a *positive* charge.

The intensity of the electric field at a distance r from an isolated point charge Q is obtained by performing an imaginary experiment in which a small test charge q is placed at the point where the intensity is desired. By Coulomb's law the force on this test charge is $F = Qq/4\pi\epsilon_0 r^2$. Since $\mathbf{E} = \mathbf{F}/q$, we conclude that the electric intensity at a distance r from a point charge Q is given by

$$E = \frac{Q}{4\pi\epsilon_0 r^2} \qquad\qquad 33.3$$

If an electric field is due to two or more charges, the electric intensity **E** at any point is given by the resultant of the electric intensities due to each charge taken individually.

Example   Find the magnitude of the electric intensity at A of Figure 33.4 due to the charges at B and C.

We have found the magnitude of the force on a charge of 25 μcoulombs at this point to be 0.17 newton. By Eq. (33.2),

$$E = \frac{F}{q} = \frac{0.17 \text{ newton}}{25 \text{ }\mu\text{coulombs}} = 6{,}800 \text{ newtons/coulomb}$$

Example   Find the electric field strength at the point P of Figure 33.5 which is 10 cm from a charge of $+6$ μcoulombs and 40 cm from a charge of -8 μcoulombs.

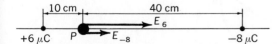

FIGURE 33.5

Electric field stength **E** at point P is the resultant of the fields due to the $+6$ and -8 μcoulomb charges.

The electric field due to the $+6$-μcoulombs charge has a magnitude $9 \times 10^9 \times 6 \times 10^{-6}/(0.1)^2 = 54 \times 10^5$ newtons/coulomb. The field due to the -8-μcoulomb charge has a magnitude $9 \times 10^9 \times 8.0 \times 10^{-6}/(0.4)^2 = 4.5 \times 10^5$ newtons/coulomb. The fields due to both charges are in the same direction—to the right. Therefore, the resultant has a magnitude of 58.5×10^5 newtons/coulomb and is directed toward the right.

33.7 Lines of Force

The electric field in the vicinity of one or more charged bodies is frequently represented by drawing *lines of force* as an aid in visualizing the field. *An electric line of force is a line which is drawn so its tangent at every point has the direction of the electric intensity at that point.* Some of the lines of force associated with a pair of equal and opposite charges are shown in Figure 33.6, while some due to two identical positive charges are indicated in Figure 33.7. Lines of force always begin on positive charges and terminate on negative charges. The lines of Figure 33.7 terminate on negative charges which might, for example, be on the walls of the room.

We may draw as many lines of force as we wish in picturing an electric field. A reasonable number of lines can give us a visualization of the direction of the force on a small positive test charge any place in the field. The line of force through a point tells us the direc-

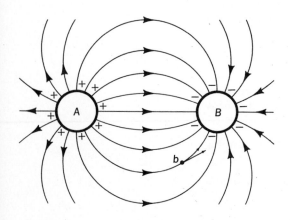

FIGURE 33.6

Lines of force for a pair of equal and opposite charges.

FIGURE 33.7

Lines of force for two identical positive charges; at a *neutral point N* the field is zero.

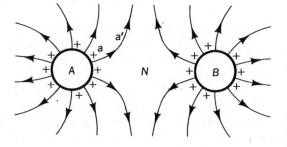

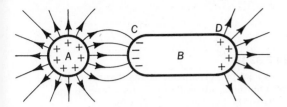

FIGURE 33.8

Equal and opposite charges are induced at ends C and D when an uncharged conductor B is brought into the field of a positive charge A.

tion of the electric intensity at that point, but nothing of its magnitude. However, a qualitative estimate of the magnitude of the field can be obtained from a reasonably detailed plot which shows the lines of force approaching one another as the field becomes stronger. (Why does this happen?) Indeed, in an ideal three-dimensional plot, the number of lines of force per unit area perpendicular to the lines would be *proportional* to the electric intensity.

33.8 Electrostatic Induction

If an uncharged conductor B (Fig. 33.8) is brought into the electric field of a positively charged conductor A, the attractive forces due to the excess positive charge on A cause the electrons in B to be pulled toward end C, leaving the farther end D with a deficit of electrons and, therefore, charged positively. Since B was originally neutral (i.e., contained as much positive as negative electricity), the positive charge on end D is just equal to the negative charge on end C.

If conductor B is connected to earth by a wire, enough electrons come from the earth to B to neutralize the positive charge at D. Meanwhile the electrons on end C are held fast by the attractive force due to the positive charge on A. If the connection to the earth is broken, and B removed from the presence of A, B will have an excess of electrons and therefore will be charged negatively. If B is now again connected to the earth, this excess of electrons will flow to the earth, leaving it uncharged.

A charged sphere in the neighborhood of the surface of the earth (Fig. 33.9) induces a charge on the surface of the earth below it. A charged antenna in the neighborhood of the surface of the earth has a similar effect.

Another illustration involving electrostatic induction is seen in Figure 33.10. If a metal sphere, charged positively, is introduced into an insulated uncharged hollow sphere, some of the electrons of the hollow sphere are drawn to its inner surface, leaving the outer surface charged positively. If the metal sphere A is placed in contact with the inner surface of the hollow sphere, the electrons from the inner surface of the hollow sphere go over to the sphere A and just compensate the deficit of electrons. This leaves both sphere A and the inner surface of the hollow sphere without a charge, while the outer surface of the hollow sphere is charged positively. If the outer surface is now connected to the earth, it gains a sufficient number of electrons to

FIGURE 33.9

A positively charged sphere induces a negative charge on the earth.

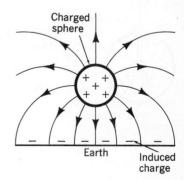

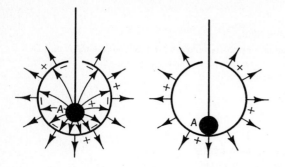

FIGURE 33.10
Faraday's ice-pail experiment shows that the charge induced on the inside wall of the cavity is equal and opposite to the inducing charge on sphere A.

compensate for its deficit, and it is left uncharged. By experiments of this type Faraday was able to show that the charge induced on the outside of an almost closed hollow conductor is equal to the inducing charge on the inside. As his hollow conductor Faraday used a small ice pail, and the operations described in this paragraph are often referred to as the "Faraday ice-pail experiment."

33.9 The Electroscope

A useful instrument for studying electrostatic phenomena is the electroscope, one form of which consists of two thin gold leaves attached to one end of a metal rod which is terminated at the other end by a metal sphere (Fig. 33.11). When the metal sphere is charged, part of the charge goes to the gold foils, which repel each other and therefore diverge. The greater the charge on the leaves, the greater the divergence.

An electroscope can be charged positively or negatively by touching the knob with either a positive glass rod or a negative rubber rod, but there is a substantial danger that so much charge may be transferred that the gold leaf will be torn off. A safer and easier way to charge

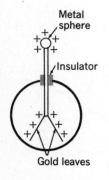

Metal sphere

Insulator

Gold leaves

FIGURE 33.11
Gold-leaf electroscope.

FIGURE 33.12
Charging an electroscope by induction.

(a) (b) (c)

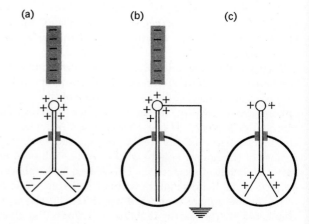

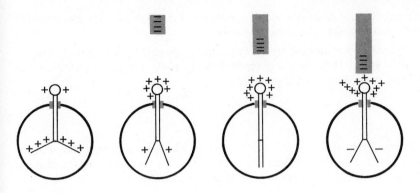

FIGURE 33.13
Charge distribution changes but total charge remains constant as a negatively charged rod comes nearer and nearer to a positively charged electroscope.

an electroscope is by induction. To charge an electroscope positively by induction, a negatively charged rod is brought near the knob, as shown in Figure 33.12a. Electrons in the knob are repelled by the rod and descend to the leaves. The knob is then grounded by touching it (Fig. 33.12b), and the excess electrons on the leaves run off. The connection to ground is then removed, leaving a net positive charge on the electroscope knob. When the negative rod is removed, these charges rearrange themselves so that both the knob and leaves are positively charged (Fig. 33.12c).

If a negatively charged rod is brought near a positively charged electroscope, some of the electrons on the metal sphere are repelled and move to the leaves, where they reduce the net positive charge and hence the divergence of the leaves (Fig. 33.13). As the negative rod is brought still nearer, more electrons go to the leaves, which eventually lose all their charge and converge. If the negative rod is brought still closer, even more electrons go to the leaves, causing them to diverge once more. In this case, although the total charge on the electroscope is positive, the leaves bear a negative charge.

Questions

1. Can two lines of force ever cross? Explain your answer carefully.

2. In one form of Cottrell precipitator for capturing smoke particles, a highly negative wire is suspended vertically in a rising column of polluted air. The wire produces a strong inhomogeneous electric field. Why should such an arrangement remove smoke and soot?

3. A small charged pith ball is brought near to an uncharged metal sphere, and an attractive force is evident. Why? If the sphere is grounded, the attraction is still greater. Why?

4. How can one prove that the force between two charges is proportional to the product of the charges? If someone refused to believe this, what experiment could you devise to convince him?

5. How could you charge an electroscope positively with a negatively charged rod? Explain what happens during each step of the process.

6. Does it make any difference which end of conductor B in Figure 33.8 is grounded by the wire? Justify your answer with an explanation.

7. Three point charges are equally spaced along a line. Q_2 and Q_3 are equal in magnitude but opposite in sign. What is the magnitude of Q_1 if the net force on Q_3 is zero? Is the sign of Q_1 the same as that of Q_2 or of Q_3?

Problems

1. The force on a small test charge is 2.1×10^{-6} newton when the charge is placed in an electric field of intensity 7×10^5 newtons/coulomb. Find the magnitude of the charge. How many electrons would be required to neutralize this charge?

Ans. 3×10^{-12} coulomb; 1.87×10^7

2. Three charges of $+3$, -3, and $+3$ μC are placed in the same straight line 10 cm apart. What force acts on each charge because of the other two?

3. A point charge of 0.03 μC is placed 0.6 m from a point charge of 0.04 μC. What force is exerted on each charge? Find the electric field strength at the point midway between the charges.

Ans. 3×10^{-5} newton; 1,000 newtons/coulomb toward smaller charge

4. How many electrons must be removed from a small pith ball to give it a charge of 10^{-12} coulomb? What is the electric field strength 2 cm from the pith ball?

5. A point charge of 5×10^{-9} coulomb is located 0.3 m from a point charge of 3×10^{-9} coulomb. Find the force exerted on each charge by the other and the electric field strength at a point 0.2 m from the larger charge on the line connecting the two charges.

Ans. 1.5×10^{-6} newton; 1,575 newtons/coulomb toward larger charge

6. Charges of -4 and $+3$ μC are 2 m apart. Find the force they exert on one another and the electric intensity midway between them.

7. The electric intensity in the region between two deflecting plates of an electrostatic deflection television tube is 30,000 newtons/coulomb. Find the force on an electron passing between these plates. What acceleration does the electron experience if it has a mass of 9.11×10^{-31} kg?

Ans. 4.8×10^{-15} newton; 5.28×10^{15} m/sec²

8. A small test charge of 10^{-10} coulomb experiences a force of 8×10^{-6} newton when it is 2 m from a point charge of unknown magnitude. Find the electric intensity at the test charge due to the unknown charge and the magnitude of the unknown charge.

9. Find the force on a charge of 2×10^{-9} coulomb if it is placed in a uniform field of intensity 55,000 newtons/coulomb. How much work is done by the field if the charge moves 0.3 m in the direction of the field? Perpendicular to the field?

Ans. 1.1×10^{-4} newton; 3.3×10^{-5} joule; zero

10. An unknown charge and a charge of -2 μC are 1 m apart. The electric field strength is zero at a point 60 cm from the unknown charge on the line connecting the two charges. Find the unknown charge.

11. Two point charges repel each other with a force of 4×10^{-4} newton when they are 30 cm apart. Find the force if the distance between them is reduced to 15 cm. If one of the charges is -8×10^{-10} coulomb, what is the other?

Ans. 1.6×10^{-3} newton; -5 μC

12. Calculate the ratio of the Coulomb electric force to the newtonian gravitational force between two electrons if the mass of an electron is 9.11×10^{-31} kg. What electric intensity is required to balance the gravitational force on an electron?

13. Two small equally charged spheres, each with a mass of 0.12 g, are suspended from the same point by silk fibers 75 cm long. The repulsion between them keeps them 10 cm apart. What is the charge on each sphere? *Ans.* 9.3×10^{-9} coulomb

14. Two small pith balls, each weighing 0.002 newton, are hung from a common point by nylon threads 15 cm long. When the pith balls are given equal positive charges, they repel one another and stand 15 cm apart, so that each of the supporting threads makes an angle of 30° with the vertical. Find the charge on each pith ball.

15. Three charges A, B, and C are located on the same straight line. The distance from A to B is 20 cm, and that from B to C is 40 cm. The charge at A is 0.04 μC, that at B is 0.08 μC, and that at C is 0.06 μC. What force is exerted on A by the charges at B and C if all the charges are positive? What is the electric intensity midway between A and B? *Ans.* 7.8×10^{-4} newton; 38,160 newtons/coulomb toward A

[handwritten: 9.2×10^{-8} new]

16. In a Bohr model of the hydrogen atom, an electron revolves in a circular orbit of radius approximately 5×10^{-11} m about a nucleus which bears a positive charge equal in magnitude to the electronic charge. Find the force on the electron which provides the centripetal acceleration for the uniform circular motion. How large is the centripetal acceleration?

[handwritten: 1.01×10^{23} m/rev²]

17. A charge of 0.4 μC is placed in a downward-directed electric field of intensity 60,000 newtons/coulomb. Find the work required to move the charge (*a*) 0.5 m to the east, (*b*) 0.5 m upward, and (*c*) 2 m upward at an angle of 37° with the vertical.
Ans. zero; 0.012 joule; 0.0384 joule

18. Charges of -3 and $+5$ μC are placed at two of the vertices of an equilateral triangle with sides 10 cm in length. Find the magnitude of the electric intensity at the third vertex and the force which would act on a charge of 2×10^{-8} coulomb at that vertex.

19. Identical 5-μC charges are placed at opposite ends of a diagonal of a 0.30 by 0.40 m rectangle. Find the values of the charges Q_1 and Q_2 which must be placed at the other two corners to make the resultant force on one of the 5-μC charges zero. Will the force on the other 5-μC charge then also be zero? If not, what will its magnitude be?
Ans. -2.56 μC; -1.08 μC; no; 0.85 newton

20. Charges of 1.5×10^{-9} coulomb are placed at opposite ends of the hypotenuse of a right triangle with sides 3, 4, and 5 m. Find the magnitude of the electric intensity at the other vertex.

21. A charge of 0.2 μC is placed at the origin of a cartesian coordinate system, and a charge of -0.4 μC is placed at $x = 2$ m, $y = 0$. Find the electric intensity at the points (*a*) $x = 4$ m, $y = 0$ and (*b*) $x = 2$ m, $y = 2$ m.
Ans. (*a*) 787.5 newtons/coulomb toward origin; (*b*) 758 newtons/coulomb at $-77.6°$ with x axis

22. Charges of $+3$, -4, and $+5$ μC are placed on the corners of a square with sides 20 cm long. Find the magnitude of the electric field strength at the fourth corner, which is diagonally opposite the -4-μC charge.

23. An electric dipole consists of a charge $+Q$ separated by a distance d from a charge $-Q$. Find the torque on this dipole when it is placed in a uniform field of intensity E (*a*) with its axis perpendicular to E and (*b*) with its axis making an angle θ with E.
Ans. (*a*) QdE; (*b*) $QdE \sin \theta$

CHAPTER 34 *From mechanics we know that the best approach to many problems is through the concept of energy and its conservation. By using the energy approach we avoid the need of knowing and working with force, which may be changing rapidly in space or in time. In electricity a large fraction of our practical problems are most conveniently solved by considering changes in the energy of a charge as it moves from place to place, rather than focusing our attention on the resultant force experienced by the charge at each point in its path. In this chapter we make use of the Coulomb law of force between electric charges and the electric intensity to find the potential energy of a small test charge in the field of a point charge. This leads us to the concept of potential, one of the key ideas of electricity.*

Potential

34.1 Potential Energy in an Electric Field

When a small test charge $+q$ is moved about in the field of a fixed charge $+Q$ (Fig. 34.1), work must be done to move the test charge closer to Q. This work goes into increasing the potential energy of the test charge. On the other hand, as q moves away from Q, the electric field does work, and the potential energy of q decreases. In discussing the movement of electric charges, the concept of electrical potential energy plays an important role, since many problems in electricity involve the law of conservation of energy, and electrical potential energy is one of the forms which must be taken into consideration.

In expressing the electrical potential energy of a charge quantitatively, it is necessary to specify some point at which the potential energy is zero, just as it is necessary to specify a zero configuration in dealing with any other form of potential energy. For example, the potential energy of a given mass relative to the earth (Chap. 7) is proportional to the elevation h. In this case it is necessary to decide from what level h is measured. The potential energy of a 1-kg mass 2 m above a table depends on whether one wishes to use the table or the floor as the point of zero potential energy. In dealing with the particular situation illustrated in Figure 34.1, it is common to consider the potential energy of q to be zero when it is infinitely far from Q. This choice is arbitrary.

Having once chosen a point of zero potential energy, one may define the potential energy of a charge $+q$ at point P as the work necessary

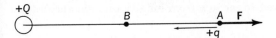

FIGURE 34.1
Work is done in moving a small test charge $+q$ from point A to point B against the electric field of charge $+Q$.

to move the charge from the point at which its potential energy is zero to the point P. If the potential energy of a charge q at a given point is $\mathcal{W}$ joules, the potential energy of a charge $3q$ at this same point is $3\mathcal{W}$ joules, and, in general, for charge nq the potential energy at this point is $n\mathcal{W}$. Since the potential energy of a charge at a given point is directly proportional to the charge itself, it is convenient to introduce the concept of *potential energy per unit charge*. The ratio of the potential energy of a charge at a given point to the charge is called the *potential at the point*. In electrostatics the zero of potential is almost invariably chosen to be at infinity. For this choice the following definition applies: *The potential at a point P is the ratio $\mathcal{W}/q$, where $\mathcal{W}$ is the work required to move a small test charge $+q$ from infinity to the point P.*

The practical unit of potential, the joule per coulomb, is called the *volt,* in honor of Alessandro Volta, whose pioneering work with the battery was a major contribution to the infant science of electricity in 1800. *The potential at a point is one volt when it requires one joule of work to move a positive charge of one coulomb from a point of zero potential to the point in question.*

34.2 The Potential Due to a Point Charge

The potential at a distance r from a point charge of Q coulombs is the *work per unit charge* required to bring a positive test charge from an infinite distance to the point in question. If q is the test charge being transferred, the repelling force exerted on it by Q is $Qq/4\pi\epsilon_0 r^2$. To move q against this force we must apply a force of this same magnitude toward Q. The element of external work $\Delta\mathcal{W}$ required to move q a distance Δr is given by $\Delta\mathcal{W} = (-Qq/4\pi\epsilon_0 r^2)\,\Delta r$ (Fig. 34.2). If Δr is positive (r increasing), this work is negative: Q provides the required force, and no positive external work need be performed. However, when Δr is negative (r decreasing), external work must be done against the electric field of Q, and $\Delta\mathcal{W}$ is a positive quantity.

Since the repelling force on q varies with r in the same way as the gravitational attractive force on a small mass in the earth's gravitational field (Sec. 9.9), we may use the reasoning of that section to conclude

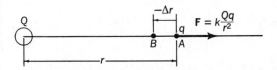

FIGURE 34.2
The external work $\Delta\mathcal{W}$ required to move a small test charge $+q$ a distance Δr in the field of $+Q$ is given by $\Delta\mathcal{W} = (-Qq/4\pi\epsilon_0 r^2)\,\Delta r$. When q is moved from A to B, Δr is negative, and $\Delta\mathcal{W}$ is a positive quantity.

that the work[1] required to move q from infinity to a distance r from charge Q is

$$\mathcal{W} = \frac{Qq}{4\pi\epsilon_0}\left(\frac{1}{r} - \frac{1}{\infty}\right) = \frac{1}{4\pi\epsilon_0}\frac{Qq}{r} \qquad 34.1$$

This is the potential energy of the test charge relative to zero at $r = \infty$. The potential at distance r from Q is then

$$V = \frac{\mathcal{W}}{q} = \frac{1}{4\pi\epsilon_0}\frac{Q}{r} = 9 \times 10^9 \frac{Q}{r} \qquad 34.1a$$

when Q is in coulombs, and r in meters. The potential 1 m from a charge of 1 coulomb in vacuum is 9×10^9 volts.

Example   Find the potential 2 m from a charge of $+6$ μcoulombs.

$$V = \frac{9 \times 10^9 Q}{r} = \frac{9 \times 10^9 \times 6 \times 10^{-6}}{2} = 27{,}000 \text{ volts}$$

When there are a number of charges in a region, the potential at any point is the sum of the potentials due to each charge acting alone. Thus if there are three charges Q_1, Q_2, and Q_3 in a region, the potential at a point which is at distance r_1 from Q_1, r_2 from Q_2, and r_3 from Q_3 is simply given by

$$V = \frac{1}{4\pi\epsilon_0}\left(\frac{Q_1}{r_1} + \frac{Q_2}{r_2} + \frac{Q_3}{r_3}\right) \qquad 34.2$$

The contribution of a negative charge to the potential is negative; the electric field does work in bringing a positive test charge toward a negative charge. A great advantage of working with potential in preference to electric intensities arises from the fact that potential is a scalar quantity, while the electric intensity is a vector.

34.3 The Isolated Sphere

Consider a metal sphere of radius R, far away from all other bodies and bearing a charge of Q coulombs. The electric field associated with this charged sphere is everywhere radial and, for all points outside the sphere, is indistinguishable from the electric field which would be associated with a point charge Q located at the center of the sphere. Thus, a uniformly charged sphere behaves, *so far as all external points are concerned,* exactly as though all its charge were concentrated at the center. The work necessary to bring a unit charge from infinity to the surface of the sphere is the same as the work which would be required to bring the same unit charge from infinity to the distance R from a point charge Q. The potential of the sphere is therefore given by

$$V = \frac{1}{4\pi\epsilon_0}\frac{Q}{R} = 9 \times 10^9 \frac{Q}{R} \qquad 34.3$$

---

[1] It is assumed that all operations in this chapter are carried out in air or *in vacuo*.

Within the sphere the electric field is zero (see Sec. 34.7). Therefore, no work is required to carry a small test charge from any point on the surface of the sphere to any point within the sphere. *The potential at all points inside the sphere is the same as the potential at the surface.* The electric field and the potential are plotted as a function of r in Figure 34.3.

34.4 Surface Charge Density

When a sphere of radius R bears a charge of Q coulombs, the charge per unit area is given by

$$\sigma = \frac{Q}{4\pi R^2} \qquad\qquad 34.4$$

where σ is known as the *surface charge density.*

Consider a large sphere and a small one, both charged to the same potential V and sufficiently far apart so the electric field of either is negligible at the other. If the charges on the two spheres are then Q and q, and the radii of the two spheres are R and r, respectively, V is given by

$$V = \frac{Q}{4\pi\epsilon_0 R} = \frac{q}{4\pi\epsilon_0 r}$$

Let σ_R and σ_r be the charge densities on the respective spheres. Then

$$V = \frac{4\pi R^2 \sigma_R}{4\pi\epsilon_0 R} = \frac{4\pi r^2 \sigma_r}{4\pi\epsilon_0 r}$$

and

$$R\sigma_R = r\sigma_r \qquad\qquad 34.5$$

For isolated spheres at the same potential, the charge densities are inversely proportional to the radii.

The surface of any conductor may be regarded as composed of a large number of spherical segments (Fig. 34.4) of different curvatures. While we may not regard these segments as portions of isolated spheres in order to apply Eq. (34.4) to calculate relative charge densities, it remains qualitatively true for convex surfaces such as those of Figure 34.4 that where the surface has greatest curvature (i.e., smallest radius), the surface charge density is greatest. When a conductor

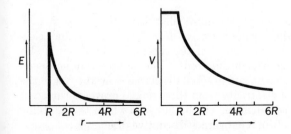

FIGURE 34.3

Electric intensity E and potential V at a distance r from the center of a uniformly charged conducting sphere of radius R.

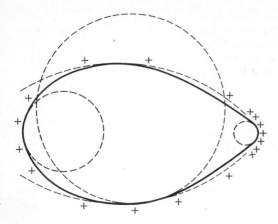

FIGURE 34.4

The surface of a curved conductor is assumed to be made up of sections of spherical surfaces; charge density becomes greater as the radius of curvature becomes smaller.

FIGURE 34.5

Flashover on a sealed bushing.

terminates in a sharp point, the surface density at the point is so great that the molecules of air in the neighborhood of the point may become charged with electricity. Since like charges repel, the charged molecules are repelled from the point, and the body to which the point is attached is discharged. The ionized molecules may emit light which is readily visible in a darkened room. Such a discharge is called a *corona discharge*. If the field is sufficiently great, flashover occurs (Fig. 34.5).

The fact that charged points allow electricity to escape is used in electrostatic machines, where rows of metallic points conduct electricity from moving to fixed parts of the machine. This fact is also important in the design of lightning rods. The pointed conductors on the rod bring about a silent and gradual discharge from the rod to the clouds. The escape of electricity from these points prevents the accumulation of enough electricity on the building on which the lightning rod is mounted to result in a dangerous disruptive discharge.

34.5 Potential Referred to the Earth

In dealing with potential, it is convenient to assign zero potential to some conducting body, just as it is convenient to refer the height of a building to the ground level, while the height of a mountain is ordinarily referred to mean sea level. In many situations the potential of the earth is taken as zero. When one speaks of a 110-volt lighting circuit or of a 180,000-volt transmission line, one ordinarily implies that the earth is taken as zero potential. In a radio or television receiver the chassis is usually regarded as being at zero potential; often it is actually tied to the ground by a direct conductor. In dealing with the electrical circuits of an automobile, it is convenient to regard the frame of the car as being at zero potential, although it is ordinarily insulated from the earth by the tires.

In general, one may assign the potential zero to any convenient point. Then the potential at any other point is the ratio $\mathcal{W}/q$, where $\mathcal{W}$ is the *work* required to move a small charge q from the point at zero potential to the point in question.

34.6 Potential Difference

One of the most important concepts in electrical theory is that of potential difference. Let $\mathcal{W}$ be the external work done against an electric field in moving a small *positive* test charge q from one point to another. The potential difference V between these two points is defined as the ratio of $\mathcal{W}$ to q:

$$V = \frac{\mathcal{W}}{q} \qquad \text{34.6}$$

The potential difference between two points is the work per unit positive charge required to move a small test charge from one point to the other.

Potential difference, as well as potential, is commonly measured in volts (joules per coulomb). *The potential difference between two points is one volt if it requires one joule of external work to move each coulomb of charge from one point to the other.* The potential difference across the terminals of an ordinary automobile battery is 12 volts; this means that 12 joules of external work is required to transfer 1 coulomb of positive charge from the negative terminal to the positive terminal. This energy is supplied by the chemical reaction within the cells, so that chemical energy is converted into electrical energy.

The potential difference between two points A and B is equal to the potential at A minus the potential at B, just as the term *potential difference* implies. Thus, $V_{AB} = V_A - V_B$. Alternatively, *the potential difference between points A and B is the external work per unit charge done against the electrostatic field in moving a small test charge from B to A.* The potential difference is independent of the zero of potential. For example, the potential difference between the positive and negative terminals of an ordinary dry cell is 1.5 joules/coulomb, regardless of whether the earth or some other point is taken as the zero potential reference. The sign of the potential difference depends on which way the charge is moved. The potential of the positive terminal relative to the negative terminal is $+1.5$ volts, while the potential of the negative terminal relative to the positive is -1.5 volts.

In any electrostatic field, external work is required to move a positive charge from a point of lower to a point of higher potential, since the electric field is directed from points of higher to points of lower potential. Suppose a small positive test charge is moved from B to A against an electric field and then returned to B. External work is required to transfer the charge from B to A; when the charge returns to B, work is done on the charge by the electric field. Since the force on a negative charge in an electric field is opposite that on a positive charge, the field moves negative charges from points of lower toward points of higher potential; external work must be done to carry a negative charge from a point of higher to one of lower potential.

34.7 Equipotential Surfaces

It is often convenient to represent the potential distribution in an electric field by means of equipotential surfaces. An equipotential surface is defined as a surface whose points are all at the same potential. Some of the equipotential surfaces for a spherical charge distribution are shown in Figure 34.6. In this particular case the equipotential surfaces are spheres, while the lines of force are radial. The lines of force are perpendicular at every point to the equipotential surfaces. This follows immediately from the fact that it takes no work to move a small test charge from one point to another on the same equipotential surface. The electric field has no component in the direction of the surface and hence must be perpendicular to it.

In Figure 34.6, A and B lie on the same equipotential surface, while C lies on another equipotential surface. No work is done in moving a small test charge from A to B along the equipotential surface, since the displacement is at all points perpendicular to the force on the charge. However, if a charge is moved from C to A, work must be done; regardless of what path is chosen, the force due to the field must have a component in the direction of this displacement for at least some part of the movement. The work required to move a charge from one point to another is independent of the path. The work required to move a small test charge from C to A is the same whether one goes first along the line of force to the equipotential surface AB and then to A, or from C to A along a straight line, or to B and then over to A.

Lines of force and equipotential surfaces are shown in Figure 34.7 for the region around two equal point charges of opposite sign.

In a conductor there is a flow of charge if there is a potential difference between any two points. This flow stops as soon as all points in the conductor are at the same potential. In electrostatics,

FIGURE 34.6

Lines of force (radial) and equipotential surfaces (spheres) for a spherical charge distribution.

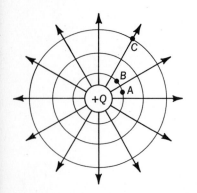

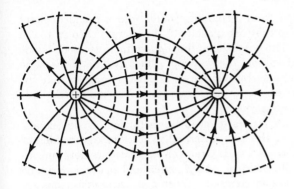

FIGURE 34.7
Lines of force (solid lines) and equipotential surfaces (dashed lines) near two equal but opposite charges.

charges are at rest, and therefore there is no potential difference between points in the conductor. The entire conductor is an equipotential surface. Since there can be no electric field within the conductor, there is no net charge within the conductor. *The entire net charge of the conductor resides on the surface.* Any excess or deficiency of electrons is at the surface. Since the surface of a conductor is an equipotential surface, and since lines of force are always perpendicular to equipotential surfaces, *lines of force always leave perpendicular to the surface of a conductor.*

34.8 The Van de Graaff Electrostatic Generator

An important application of the fact that charges go to the outside of a conductor is the Van de Graaff generator (Fig. 34.8), a major tool of nuclear physics. A belt made of an insulating material carries

FIGURE 34.8
Four-MeV Van de Graaff electrostatic generator.

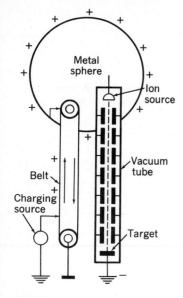

FIGURE 34.9

Van de Graaff electrostatic generator.

charges at high speed from a charging source into a rounded metal shell (Fig. 34.9), where they are picked off; the charges then go to the outside of the shell. The potential of the high-voltage electrode builds up until charges are lost from the shell and gained at exactly the same rate. Often the entire system is placed in a large tank so that the pressure may be raised to several atmospheres to reduce the loss of charge by sparks and corona.

If the Van de Graaff generator is to be useful for physics experiments, one must utilize the high potential to accelerate some kind of charged particle, or *ion*. A Van de Graaff electrostatic accelerator consists of a Van de Graaff generator, an ion source, and an evacuated tube down which the ions are accelerated. When high-energy electrons are desired, the electron source is usually a hot filament inside the high-voltage electrode, which is made negative. For exciting nuclear reactions by bombarding targets with protons, an ion source involving an electric discharge through hydrogen gas is installed in the high-voltage electrode, which is charged positive. In either case charged particles are accelerated down the evacuated tube to the grounded end, where they are focused on a target.

When a particle of charge q falls through a potential difference V in a vacuum, it gains a kinetic energy Vq. This energy is in joules if V is in volts and q is in coulombs. However, if we express q in atomic units of charge, the energy is given in electron volts. *An electron volt is the kinetic energy gained by a particle bearing one atomic unit of charge in falling through a potential difference of one volt.* The negative charge on the electron and the positive charge on the proton both have the magnitude of one atomic unit of charge. Since the atomic unit of charge corresponds to 1.602×10^{-19} coulomb,

$$1 \text{ electron volt} = 1.602 \times 10^{-19} \text{ coulomb} \times 1.000 \text{ volt}$$
$$= 1.602 \times 10^{-19} \text{ joule}$$

Electrostatic generators are highly valuable sources of particles with energies from many thousands of electron volts (keV) to several million electron volts (MeV).

< 34.9 Uniform Electric Field

Consider two large parallel plates, one bearing a charge $+Q$, and the other a charge $-Q$ (Fig. 34.10). The electric field between the two plates (reasonably far from an edge) is constant in both magnitude and

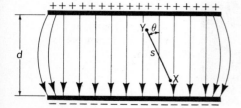

FIGURE 34.10

The electric field between two parallel charged plates is uniform except at the edges, where fringing occurs.

direction. Such a field is said to be *uniform*. If a charge q is carried from the lower plate to the upper one, the work done against the field is $-Eqd$, where d is the distance between plates. The minus sign appears because E and the displacement are in opposite directions. The potential difference V between the plates is $\mathcal{W}/q = -Ed$. Solving for E yields

$$E = -\frac{V}{d} \qquad\qquad 34.7$$

If the test charge q is moved from X to Y (Fig. 34.10) the work done is

$$\mathcal{W} = -qEs \cos \theta$$

and the potential difference is $V = -Es \cos \theta$, or

$$E \cos \theta = -\frac{V}{s} \qquad\qquad 34.8$$

The ratio of the potential difference V between two neighboring points along a line of force to the distance d between the points is a vector called the *potential gradient*. The electric intensity $\mathbf{E}$ is the negative of the potential gradient [Eq. (34.7)]. The component of the potential gradient in any direction is the negative of the component of the electric intensity in that direction [Eq. (34.8)]. $\mathbf{E}$ may be measured in terms of potential difference divided by distance as well as in terms of force divided by charge. Electric field strengths are often expressed in volts per meter, rather than in the equivalent newtons per coulomb. (An electric intensity of one volt per meter is exactly the same as an electric intensity of one newton per coulomb.)

34.10 The Charge on the Electron

The uniform electric field between parallel charged plates was utilized by Millikan and his students to determine the charge on the electron. An extensive series of measurements performed between 1909 and 1917 produced evidence that every electron bears the same charge. Millikan's apparatus is shown schematically in Figure 34.11. Two horizontal plates B and C are placed about 1 cm apart. An atomizer

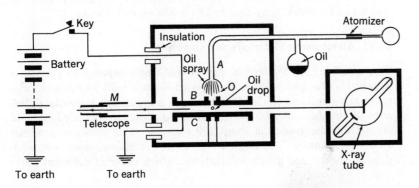

FIGURE 34.11
Millikan's apparatus for measuring the charge on the electron.

A shoots a fine spray of oil into the space above these plates. The drops of oil are so small that they do not settle for a long time. Eventually one or more of the drops finds its way through the opening *O* in the upper plate. A telescope is focused on this drop so that its movements can be observed over a long period of time. The rate at which the drop falls can be measured by means of a micrometer eyepiece in the telescope.

A beam of X rays is next sent into the air between the horizontal plates. By means of these X rays, electrons are detached from the atoms of air. One or more of these electrons may be captured by oil drops. If the upper plate *B* is charged positively, and the lower plate *C* negatively, there is an upward force on a negatively charged oil drop. If the electric field is sufficiently strong, this upward force may equal or exceed the weight of the drop. Under such conditions the drop may be made to hang in the air for a substantial time. If the downward pull of gravity and the upward pull of electrostatic field leave the oil drop essentially at rest, we may write

$$W = Eq = \frac{Vq}{d}$$

where *W* is the weight of the drop, *q* the charge on the drop, *E* the electric field strength, *V* the potential difference between the plates, and *d* their separation. By measuring *W*, *V*, and *d*, it is possible to calculate the charge *q*. Frequently, a number of electrons may be attached to the drop, and, as a result, *q* is several times the charge on a single electron. Careful observations show that whatever charges are present, their magnitudes are always integral multiples of a single elementary charge. This charge *e* is the smallest known unit of electricity. It is the fundamental unit of electric charge and is borne by all electrons.

$e = 1.602 \times 10^{-19}$ coulomb

The procedure just described is an oversimplification of the method used by Millikan, who actually measured the velocity of the oil drop as it moved upward under the influence of the electric field and the velocity of the same drop as it moved downward due to gravity with the electric field turned off. The calculations are straightforward, but somewhat involved; they lead to the result quoted above.

34.11 Atmospheric Electricity and Lightning

On a clear day the surface of a level field freely exposed to the sky is negatively charged, so that there is an electric field downward. Between the earth and the ionosphere there is typically a potential difference of roughly 360,000 volts. In good weather, the electric field strength at the ground is about 100 volts/m. This potential gradient varies continually. In addition to local variations, there are well-defined annual and diurnal variations, which differ at different parts

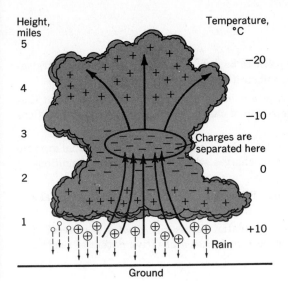

Height,
miles

Temperature,
°C

Charges are
separated here

Rain

Ground

FIGURE 34.12

Charging of clouds can occur when ascending air currents
in thunderheads produce charges by contact and separation.

of the surface of the earth.   Above the earth's surface, the potential
gradient diminishes, and at a height of about 10 km it approaches
zero, a fact which is explained by the rapid increase in the conductivity of the atmosphere at higher altitudes.

The earth's negative charge is believed to come largely from lightning and point discharges under clouds.   During thunderstorms the
violent, ascending air currents in thunderheads (Fig. 34.12) break
large raindrops into small ones.   In this process the water droplets become positively charged, and the air molecules negatively charged.
Electrification occurs particularly strongly in the area of the thunderhead, where the temperature is a few degrees below zero and tiny ice
crystals abound.   Water droplets are driven against ice crystals; the
ice crystals become strongly negative, while the residue of the water
droplets is positive.   These tiny droplets are carried to great elevations, where they freeze.   The result is that the top of the thunderhead
has a large positive charge which eventually spreads out in the upper
atmosphere.   The region near the 0°C isotherm is strongly negative,
while the falling raindrops are positively charged.   Most of the lightning flashes to earth are from the lower negative center to ground, and
these flashes bring the earth its negative charge.   The earth would require 500,000 coulombs of negative charge to produce a potential
gradient of 100 volts/m over its entire surface.   The gradient is not
the same all over the earth, and it is actually reversed over substantial
areas during lightning storms.

Not only do we have lightning strokes between charged clouds and
the earth, but discharges between the lower negative charge center
and the upper positive region also occur.

Questions

1. Is it possible for the potential at a point to be zero while there is a finite electric intensity at that point? Show a charge configuration which satisfies these conditions.

2. Is it possible for the electric intensity at a point to be zero while the potential at that same point is nonzero? Show a configuration of charge which satisfies these conditions at some point.

3. Can charges be arranged so that both the electric intensity and the potential are zero at some point? Show an arrangement of charges which satisfies these conditions at some point.

4. A metal cube bears a positive charge. What is the shape of the equipotential surfaces very close to the cube? Very far away from the cube?

5. If a body bears a positive charge, is its potential necessarily greater than zero? Devise a situation in which a positively charged body has a negative potential relative to the earth.

Problems

1. The potential difference between the terminals of an automobile battery is 12 volts. How much work is done by the battery in transferring 800 coulombs from one terminal to the other?   *Ans.* 9,600 joules

2. How much work is required to move a charge of 3 μC from a point where the potential is -5 volts to one where the potential is $+150$ volts?

3. In a Millikan oil-drop experiment, the charge on the oil drop is that of five electrons. The oil drop is in the electric field arising from a difference of potential of 3,000 volts between two plates that are at a distance of 0.75 cm from each other. Find the force exerted on the oil drop by the electric field. Find the mass of the drop if it is almost in equilibrium in the field.   *Ans.* 3.2×10^{-13} newton; 3.27×10^{-14} kg

4. In a Millikan oil-drop experiment an oil drop of 1.25×10^{-11} g mass is balanced by applying a potential difference of 1,530 volts between plates which are 0.8 cm apart. How many elementary charges are on the oil drop?

5. A conducting sphere of radius 3 cm bears a charge of 2×10^{-9} coulomb. Find the electric intensity and the potential at the surface of the sphere.
                                Ans. 20,000 newtons/coulomb; 600 volts

6. Find the potential at a point 3 m from a charge of 4 μC. How much work is required to bring a 1-μC charge from infinity to this point?

7. A point charge of 4×10^{-8} coulomb is 0.5 m from a charge of -3×10^{-8} coulomb. Find the electric field intensity at the point P midway between the charges, the potential at this same point P, and the work required to bring a charge of 2×10^{-9} coulomb from infinity to point P.   *Ans.* 10,080 newtons/coulomb; 360 volts; 7.2×10^{-7} joule

8. Find the potential and electric intensity midway between point charges of -0.6 and 1.8 μC if they are separated by a distance of 6 m.

9. Two points in the neighborhood of an isolated point charge differ in potential by 80,000 volts. How much work is required to carry 2×10^{-9} coulomb from the point of lower to the point of higher potential? If the points are 0.5 and 3 m from the original charge, find the magnitude of this charge.   *Ans.* 1.6 × 10⁻⁴ joule; 5.33 μC

10. Two large parallel plates are 4 cm apart. If the potential difference between them is 600 volts, calculate the electric intensity between the plates and the force on a 2-μC charge placed anywhere between the plates.

11. The plates of a cathode-ray tube are parallel and 0.6 cm apart. The potential difference between them is 12,000 volts. Find the force on an electron passing between the plates. What acceleration is produced if the electron has a mass of 9.11 × 10⁻³¹ kg?
Ans. 3.2 × 10⁻¹³ newton; 3.5 × 10¹⁷ m/sec²

12. The potential of an isolated conducting sphere of radius 8 cm is 2,000 volts. Find the charge on the sphere and the potential at a distance of 1 m from the center of the sphere.

13. Find the potential difference between two points, one 4 m and the other 1.5 m from a point charge of 6 × 10⁻⁹ coulomb. How much work is required to move a charge of 2 × 10⁻¹⁰ coulomb from the 4-m point to the other?   *Ans.* 22.5 volts; 4.5 × 10⁻⁹ joule

14. How much work is required to carry a charge of 3 × 10⁻⁹ coulomb from an infinite distance to a point midway between two identical 5-μC charges 20 cm apart? How much work is required if one of the charges is −5 μC?

15. Suppose a copper sphere 1.00 cm in diameter had a negative charge arising from one additional electron for each 10⁹ copper atoms. If the sphere contained 4.4 × 10²² atoms, what would be the charge on the sphere, the potential of the sphere, and the electric intensity at the surface?
Ans. −7.1 μC; −1.28 × 10⁷ volts; −2.56 × 10⁹ newtons/coulomb

16. Air at atmospheric pressure breaks down and ionizes when the electric intensity is about 3 × 10⁶ volts/m. Find the approximate maximum potential to which a smooth sphere of 0.200 m radius can be charged in air. What charge is required for this potential?

17. A water droplet with a radius of 5 × 10⁻⁴ m bears a charge of 100 electrons. Find its potential. If this droplet coalesces with an identical droplet, also bearing 100 excess electrons, find the potential of the new larger droplet.
Ans. −2.88 × 10⁻⁴ volt; −4.57 × 10⁻⁴ volt

18. How much work is required to move a charge of 10⁻⁹ coulomb from a point 3 m to a point 0.5 m from a point charge of 7 μC? What is the potential difference between these points?

19. A 50-eV electron passes through a hole in a screen into a region where there is a uniform electric intensity of 400 newtons/coulomb. If the velocity vector is in the direction of the field, how far does the electron move before it reverses its direction of motion? What was the initial speed of the electron?   *Ans.* 0.125 m; 4.2 × 10⁶ m/sec

20. Find the kinetic energy and the speed of an electron which starts from rest and is accelerated through a potential difference of 20 volts.

21. A hollow copper sphere has a radius of 4 cm. If it bears a charge of 1.2 × 10⁻⁹ coulomb, find the potential and the electric intensity (*a*) inside the sphere, (*b*) at the surface of the sphere, and (*c*) at a point 2 m from the center.
Ans. (*a*) 270 volts, zero; (*b*) 270 volts, 6,750 newtons/coulomb; (*c*) 5.4 volts, 2.7 newtons/coulomb

22. Charges of -2, 3, -4, and 5 μC are placed at the corners of a square 0.5 m on a side. Find the potential at the center of the square.

23. A metal sphere having a radius of 5 cm carries a charge of 0.08 μC. It is temporarily connected by a conducting wire to a second uncharged metal sphere having a radius of 15 cm. Find the charge remaining on the smaller sphere. *Ans.* 0.02 μC

24. A charge of 0.016 μC is placed on a conducting sphere of radius 10 cm. This sphere is then connected temporarily by a copper wire to an uncharged conducting sphere of radius 6 cm. Find the charge on each sphere.

25. Find the electric intensity and the potential at the center of a cube with sides of length d (a) if there is a charge $+Q$ at each of the eight corners and (b) if one of the eight charges is changed to $-Q$.

Ans. (a) zero, $4Q/\sqrt{3}\pi\epsilon_0 d$; (b) $2Q/3\pi\epsilon_0 d^2$ toward $-Q$, $\sqrt{3}Q/\pi\epsilon_0 d$

26. A rectangle is 4 by 3 m. If charges of $+0.10$ and -0.08 μC are placed at corners separated by 4 m, find the potentials of the other two corners and the potential difference between them.

27. Find the potential at the center of a uniformly charged thin ring of radius 9 cm which bears a charge of 3×10^{-9} coulomb. What is the potential on the axis of the ring 12 cm from the center? Find the electric intensity at this point.

Ans. 300 volts; 180 volts; 960 newtons/coulomb along axis

28. A spherical conductor of 5 cm radius bears a charge of 4 μC. It is surrounded by a concentric sphere of 9 cm radius bearing a charge of -3 μC. Find (a) the potential difference between the two spheres and (b) the potential and electric intensity at $r = 6$ cm and $r = 10$ cm.

CHAPTER 35   *In the preceding two chapters we have discussed electric charges at rest and the electric fields and potentials associated with the charges.   In this chapter we treat a widely used arrangement in which two neighboring conductors have equal and opposite charges.   Such an arrangement, known as a* capacitor, *may store a substantial amount of energy; hence it is a reservoir for both charge and energy.   Capacitors are widely used in radio, television, and other electric circuits, as we shall see in subsequent chapters.*

Capacitance and Dielectrics

35.1 Capacitors

A device on which electric charges may be stored is called a *capacitor* or a *condenser*.   Capacitors are important components in radio and television circuits, in the ignition systems of automobiles, and in other electrical equipment.   The term condenser originated in the erroneous idea that electricity was a fluid which could be stored in a suitable container.   An early capacitor is the Leyden jar, which consists of a glass jar with a coating of tin foil on the inside and another on the outside.

Capacitors have many different forms.   A typical capacitor consists of two conductors, one of which is charged positively and the other negatively.   Charging is usually accomplished by transferring the charge from one conductor to the other by means of a battery or other source of potential difference.   The charge gained by one conductor is equal to that lost by the other.   When we refer to the charge on a capacitor, we mean the magnitude of the charge on either conductor. Since the two conductors bear equal and opposite charges, the net charge is zero.

Let $+Q$ be the charge on the positive conductor, $-Q$ that on the negative conductor, and V the potential difference between the two conductors.   *The capacitance C is defined as the ratio of the charge to the potential difference:*

$$C = \frac{Q}{V} \qquad\qquad 35.1$$

From the definition it follows that capacitance may be measured in coulombs per volt.   This unit has been named the *farad* in honor of Michael Faraday.   *One farad is that capacitance for which a charge of one coulomb will produce a potential difference of one volt.*   The farad is a very large unit of capacitance; a capacitance of a few microfarads (written μF or mfd) is typical, and capacitances of the order of a few micromicrofarads (μμF), i.e., 10^{-12} farad, are common in radio and television circuits.

The capacitance of a capacitor is independent of the charge. If the charge is doubled, the potential difference between the two conductors is also doubled. The capacitance depends on the size and shape of the conductors, on their relative positions, and on the character of the insulating material between them. Before we develop equations for the capacitances of various arrangements of conductors, it is desirable to consider how the insulating material affects the capacitance.

35.2 The Dielectric Constant

If two parallel metal plates are insulated from one another and connected to an electroscope (Fig. 35.1), there is a potential difference between the plates if they are charged so that one bears $+Q$ and the other $-Q$ coulombs. The potential difference V may be measured in a variety of ways, e.g., by the divergence of the electroscope leaves. If a sheet of glass is inserted between the two plates, the potential difference between the two plates becomes smaller, and the divergence of the electroscope leaves is reduced. Since no charge escaped from the plates while the potential was reduced, the capacitance Q/V of the system with the glass plate in place must be greater than the capacitance without the glass plate.

To understand this phenomenon, consider what happens to the glass plate. The plate is composed of electrically neutral atoms. When it is placed in the electric field, the electrons are attracted by the positively charged conductor, and the nuclei by the negatively charged conductor. The electrons in the glass are not free and cannot leave the atoms to which they are attached, but they can undergo slight displacements toward the positive plate, while the nuclei undergo similar

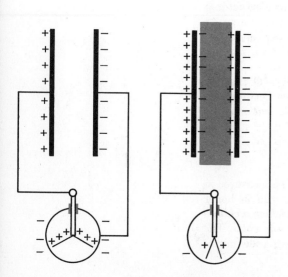

FIGURE 35.1

The potential difference between capacitor plates is reduced by inserting a dielectric sheet because of the bound surface charges induced on the dielectric.

TABLE 35.1 *Dielectric Constants and Dielectric Strengths*

Material	K	Dielectric strength, volts/m	Material	K	Dielectric strength, volts/m
Vacuum	1		Barium titanate (25°)	1,200	
Air (1 atm)	1.0006	3×10^6	Glass	4.8–10	30×10^6
Ammonia (liquid)	22		Mica	4.5–7.5	200×10^6
Ethyl alcohol (0°C)	28.4		Paraffined paper	2	40×10^6
Transformer oil	2.1	5–15×10^6	Polystyrene	2.6	20×10^6
Water (18°C)	81		Porcelain	6	15×10^6
Amber	3		Rubber (hard)	3	21×10^6

displacements toward the negative plate. The net effect of these minute displacements throughout the glass is to produce a layer of negative charge on one side and a layer of positive charge on the other. The presence of the glass results in a layer of negative charge close to the positive metal plate. This negative charge layer reduces the potential of the plate (see Sec. 34.2). Similarly, the positive surface layer near the negative metal plate raises the potential of the latter. The potential difference between the metal plates is decreased. The glass plate increases the capacitance of the capacitor because it places a layer of negative charge close to the positive conductor and a layer of positive charge close to the negative conductor. In a very real sense it reduces the *effective* charge on the conductors, although the actual charge is not changed significantly.

A material is said to be *polarized* when the electrical "center of charge" of the electrons and of the nuclei of a material do not coincide. As a consequence of the polarization, there is a "bound" charge on the surface of the polarized material.

Consider a pair of plates *A*, *B* (Fig. 35.2) connected to a battery which maintains a constant potential difference between them. If the space between the plates is filled with a dielectric such as glass, the charge *Q* on plate *A* is increased several fold through the polarization of the dielectric. Since *Q* increases when the dielectric is introduced, while *V* is held constant by the battery, the capacitance of the plates is increased by the insertion of the dielectric. *The ratio of the capacitance of a capacitor with a given material filling the space between conductors to the capacitance of the same capacitor when the space is evacuated is the dielectric constant*[1] *K of the material.* The dielectric constants of several materials are listed in Table 35.1.

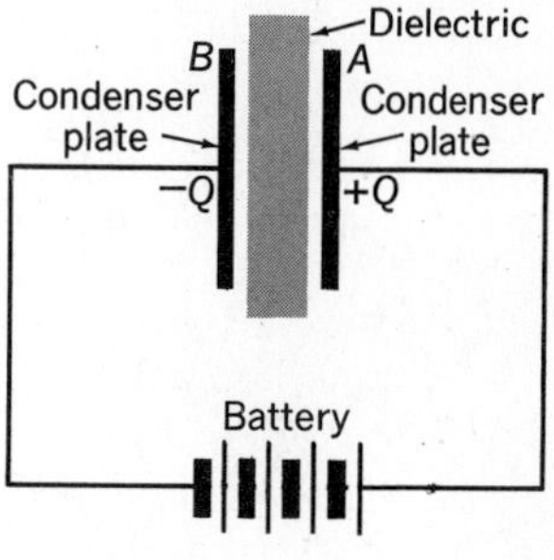

FIGURE 35.2

Dielectric between the plates of a capacitor.

35.3 Piezoelectricity

We have seen that when a slice of dielectric material is placed between two charged plates (or, more generally, in an electric field), there is a

[1] Some authors prefer the name *specific inductive capacity,* and others use the name *relative permittivity.*

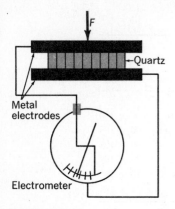

FIGURE 35.3

A piezoelectric cell in which pressure on the crystal faces produces a potential difference between them.

polarization of the medium. In some materials, such as quartz and rochelle salt, this displacement of electric charges is accompanied by small changes in the size and shape of the crystal slice, an effect called *electrostriction*. Electrostrictive effects depend on the orientation of the crystal axes relative to the direction of the electric field.

In view of the fact that the shapes of some crystals change when the internal charges are displaced by an electric field, it is not surprising that changing the shape of a crystal may result in a redistribution of charges. If a thin slice of quartz is compressed (Fig. 35.3), one face becomes positive and the other negative. If the crystal is stretched instead of compressed, the charges on the faces are reversed. Compressing or elongating the crystal results in a potential difference between the faces. This potential difference may be hundreds or even thousands of volts. This phenomenon is known as *piezoelectricity* (*piezo* means "pressure").

If an alternating voltage is applied to a properly sliced quartz crystal, the crystal faces oscillate. By proper choice of the thickness of the slice, the mechanical oscillations can be made to have any desired frequency over a wide range. If a radio-frequency circuit has the same natural frequency as the mechanical oscillations of a quartz crystal, a sharp resonance may be obtained, and the electrical oscillations may be accurately controlled by the mechanical frequency of the quartz crystal. Quartz crystals are often used to control the frequencies of radio and television transmitters.

35.4 The Capacitance of an Isolated Sphere

Consider a single sphere of radius R in vacuum, removed sufficiently far from other bodies so that their influence may be neglected. Let this sphere be charged with Q coulombs, presumably brought to the sphere from an infinite distance. (In this case the second conductor of the capacitor is a sphere of infinite radius, which now bears a charge $-Q$.) According to Eq. (34.3) the potential of the sphere is given by $V = Q/4\pi\epsilon_0 R$. Since $C = Q/V$, it follows immediately that

$$C = 4\pi\epsilon_0 R = \frac{R}{9 \times 10^9} \qquad 35.2$$

where C is in farads when R is in meters.

If we imagine all space to be filled with a medium of dielectric constant K, we have

$$C = 4\pi\epsilon_0 KR = \frac{KR}{9 \times 10^9} \qquad 35.3$$

Obviously, the charge Q has not changed; therefore the increase in C must arise from a decrease in V. The potential of the sphere under these conditions is given by

$$V = \frac{Q}{4\pi\epsilon_0 KR} = \frac{9 \times 10^9 Q}{KR} \qquad 35.4$$

35.5 Capacitance of a Spherical Capacitor

Figure 35.4 shows a capacitor consisting of two concentric spheres. Let a be the radius of the inner sphere, and b the radius of the outer sphere, which is connected to the earth. If the inner sphere bears a charge $+Q$, the outer one must have a charge $-Q$ if its potential is to be zero. (Remember the charge on the inner sphere raises the potential of the outer sphere, so a negative charge is required on the outer sphere to reduce its potential to zero.) If the region between the spheres is filled with a medium of dielectric constant K, the potential V_a of the inner sphere is the sum of the contributions of the charges $+Q$ on the inner sphere and $-Q$ on the outer sphere, so

$$V_a = \frac{Q}{4\pi\epsilon_0 Ka} - \frac{Q}{4\pi\epsilon_0 Kb} = \frac{Q}{4\pi\epsilon_0 K}\left(\frac{1}{a} - \frac{1}{b}\right)$$

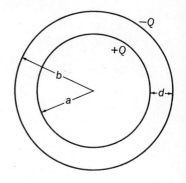

FIGURE 35.4
Capacitor formed by two concentric spheres.

Since the potential of the outer sphere is zero, the potential difference V between the spheres is just the potential of the inner sphere V_a, and the capacitance of the two concentric spheres is

$$C = \frac{Q}{V} = \frac{4\pi\epsilon_0 Kab}{b-a} = \frac{Kab}{9\times 10^9(b-a)} \qquad \text{35.5}$$

35.6 Capacitance of Two Parallel Plates

If the radii of the two concentric spheres considered above are allowed to increase until they are very large while the difference $b - a$ remains constant, the surfaces of the spheres become approximately plane. The product ab becomes almost equal to a^2, since a and b are almost equal when both a and b are very large.

Let S be the area of the sphere of which a is the radius ($S = 4\pi a^2$), and let $d(= b - a)$ be the distance between the spheres (kept constant) as a and b approach infinity. Then

$$C = \frac{4\pi\epsilon_0 Kab}{b-a} = \frac{4\pi\epsilon_0 Ka^2}{d} = \frac{\epsilon_0 KS}{d} = \frac{KS}{9\times 10^9 \times 4\pi d}$$

If this relation is true for the entire spherical capacitor, it is true for a small portion of it, provided the area of that portion is used instead of the entire area of the sphere. If the spheres are very large, and if a small portion of area A is cut out of the spherical surfaces, the capacitor obtained in this artificial way consists of two parallel plates at a distance d apart, each plate with area A. The capacitance in farads of such a capacitor is

$$C = \frac{KA}{9\times 10^9 \times 4\pi d} = \frac{\epsilon_0 KA}{d} \qquad \text{35.6}$$

when A is in square meters and d is in meters.

Example Find the capacitance of a capacitor consisting of two parallel plates that are 0.5 cm apart. Each of the plates has an area of 100 cm². The space between the plates is filled with a medium whose dielectric constant is 3.0.

$$C = \frac{KA}{4\pi d(9 \times 10^9)}$$

$$= \frac{3.0 \times 0.01}{0.005 \times 4\pi \times 9 \times 10^9}$$

$$= 54 \times 10^{-12} \text{ farad or } 54 \ \mu\mu\text{F}$$

< 35.7 Practical Capacitors

Most of the practical capacitors in everyday use represent some modification of the parallel-plate capacitor. A good example is the familiar type used for tuning radio and television circuits (Fig. 35.5). The capacitance is varied by changing the effective area of the plates, which is that area close to a plate bearing the opposite charge. Alternate plates are connected together so that there are only two conductors; several plates are used to get a large area in a reasonable space. A further favorable factor in achieving a large area is that both sides of all but the outermost plates are used.

Another common form of capacitor consists of two thin foils of aluminum with a thin sheet of wax-impregnated paper between them. Since both the paper and the foil are flexible, the whole arrangement may be rolled up to form a small compact cylinder. From Eq. (35.6) it follows that the thinner the layer between the conducting plates, the greater the capacitance. However, there is a practical limitation to how thin the insulating separator may be, because if it is too thin a

FIGURE 35.5
Parallel-plate capacitor with variable capacitance.

spark may jump through it. The maximum potential difference which an insulating layer can stand may be computed from a knowledge of the thickness and of the *dielectric strength* of the material. *The dielectric strength is the potential gradient at which electrical breakdown occurs.*

Among the materials which are used as insulators in capacitors are impregnated papers, mica, plastics, ceramic materials, glass, and oils. Air is used in the variable capacitor of Figure 35.5; because of the low dielectric constant, air capacitors have relatively small capacitance for a given area.

In the circuit diagrams of radios and other electric circuits, capacitors are commonly represented by the symbols of Figure 35.6. An arrow drawn through the capacitor symbol indicates that it is variable; when no arrow is shown, it is implied that the capacitor has a fixed value.

A common and very inexpensive form of capacitor is the electrolytic capacitor. Such a capacitor has one plate of aluminum. The dielectric is a very thin coating of aluminum oxide on the surface of the plate, and the other conductor is a conducting solution. In such a capacitor d is exceedingly small, and therefore a relatively large capacitance can be provided in a rather small space. However, these capacitors break down at relatively low voltages; furthermore, it is important that the aluminum terminal be made positive, since the aluminum oxide layer conducts if the aluminum is negative.

35.8 Energy Stored in a Capacitor

In charging a capacitor, it is necessary to do work to carry the electric charge from one conductor to the other. At the beginning, the two conductors of the capacitor are at the same potential. As charge is transferred from one plate to the other, the difference of potential between the two increases. Suppose that the final potential difference V between the terminals of the capacitor is attained after Q coulombs of electricity have been transferred from one conductor to the other. At the beginning of the charging, the potential difference is zero; at the end, the difference is V. The average potential difference during the

(a)   (b)

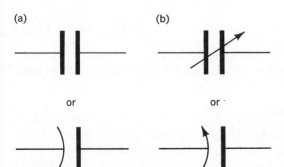

or   or

FIGURE 35.6

Symbols for (*a*) fixed, and (*b*) variable capacitors.

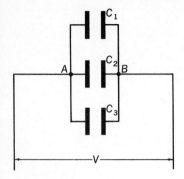

FIGURE 35.7
Capacitors connected in parallel.

charging is $V/2$. The work done is equal to the product of the average difference of potential and the quantity of electricity transferred. The energy $\mathcal{W}$ stored in the capacitor is given by

$$\mathcal{W} = \tfrac{1}{2}QV \qquad\qquad 35.7$$

This energy is released when the capacitor is discharged. If the capacitor is allowed to discharge through a wire, the energy is converted to heat in the wire.

Example A capacitor having a capacitance of 2 μF is charged with 10^{-3} coulomb of electricity. How much energy is stored in it?

$$\text{Energy} = \frac{1}{2}QV = \frac{1}{2}\frac{Q^2}{C}$$

$$= \frac{1}{2} \times \frac{10^{-3} \times 10^{-3}}{2 \times 10^{-6}}$$

$$= 0.25 \text{ joule}$$

35.9 Capacitors in Parallel

When two or more capacitors are connected in such a way that all the positive conductors are at the same potential V^+, and all the negative conductors at potential V^-, the capacitors are said to be connected *in parallel*. If a number of capacitors (Fig. 35.7) are connected in parallel, the system has a capacitance C equal to the sum of the separate capacitances. This result can be proved as follows:

The capacitors are all charged to the same difference of potential. Let V denote this difference of potential, and let Q_1, Q_2, and Q_3 be the charges on capacitors C_1, C_2, and C_3, respectively. Let Q be the total charge on all the capacitors. Then

$$Q = Q_1 + Q_2 + Q_3$$
$$Q_1 = C_1 V \qquad Q_2 = C_2 V \qquad Q_3 = C_3 V$$

and

$$Q = CV$$

Substituting yields

$$CV = C_1 V + C_2 V + C_3 V$$

Dividing by V gives

$$\boxed{C = C_1 + C_2 + C_3} \quad \textit{parallel} \qquad 35.8$$

Hence, to find the equivalent capacitance of a number of capacitors connected in parallel, it is only necessary to add together the separate capacitances.

35.10 Capacitors in Series

FIGURE 35.8
Capacitors connected in series.

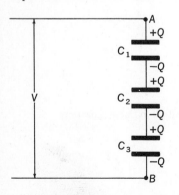

Two or more capacitors are said to be *in series* when they are connected as shown in Figure 35.8. If a potential difference V is applied between points A and B, a charge $+Q$ appears on the positive plate of C_1, and a corresponding charge $-Q$ on the negative plate of C_1. The electrons which produce the negative charge on C_1 must come from the plate of C_2 and leave it with a charge $+Q$. The negative plate of capacitor C_2 has a charge $-Q$ which comes from the positive plate of capacitor C_3, which is left with a charge $+Q$. Finally, the negative plate of C_3 bears a charge $-Q$. Thus, *when capacitors are charged in series, the same charge is stored on each capacitor.* The potential difference across the combination of capacitors in series is equal to the sum of the potential differences of the individual capacitors.

Let Q be the charge on each capacitor, C the equivalent capacitance of the capacitors when joined in series, and V_1, V_2, and V_3 the differences of potential between the terminals of C_1, C_2, and C_3, respectively. Since the total difference of potential is equal to the sum of the separate differences of potential,

$$V = V_1 + V_2 + V_3$$

If we divide both sides of this equation by Q, we obtain

$$\frac{V}{Q} = \frac{V_1}{Q} + \frac{V_2}{Q} + \frac{V_3}{Q}$$

Since $Q = Q_1 = Q_2 = Q_3$, we have

$$\frac{V}{Q} = \frac{V_1}{Q_1} + \frac{V_2}{Q_2} + \frac{V_3}{Q_3}$$

Since V/Q is the reciprocal of the capacitance,

$$\frac{1}{C} = \frac{1}{C_1} + \frac{1}{C_2} + \frac{1}{C_3} \qquad series! \qquad \text{35.9}$$

When capacitors are connected in series, the reciprocal of the resultant capacitance is the sum of the reciprocals of the individual capacitances.

Example   A capacitance of 4 μF is connected in series with one of 5 μF. What is the equivalent capacitance of the combination? If 100 volts is the potential difference across the combination, find the potential difference across the 4-μF capacitor.

$$\frac{1}{C} = \frac{1}{C_1} + \frac{1}{C_2} = \frac{1}{4} + \frac{1}{5} = \frac{9}{20}$$

$$C = {}^{20}\!/_9 = 2.22 \ \mu\text{F}$$

$$Q = CV = 2.22 \times 100 = 222 \ \mu\text{coulombs}$$

$$V_4 = \frac{Q}{C} = \frac{222 \ \mu\text{coulombs}}{4 \ \mu\text{F}} = 55.5 \text{ volts}$$

35.11 Groups of Capacitors

When several capacitors are connected in such a way that some are connected in parallel and others in series (Fig. 35.9), one may replace any parallel group with the equivalent single capacitor of value given

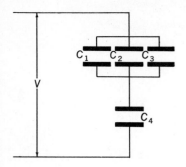

FIGURE 35.9

Three capacitors in parallel are connected in series with a single capacitor.

FIGURE 35.10

Series circuit results when the three parallel capacitors of Figure 35.9 are replaced with one equivalent 24-μF capacitor.

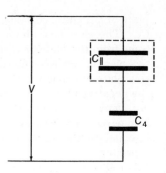

by Eq. (35.8). Once this is done for the parallel group (or groups), one is left with a problem in series capacitors.

Example   The four capacitors of Figure 35.9 are 6, 8, 10, and 12 μF, respectively. They are charged to a potential difference V of 120 volts. Find the charge and potential difference for each capacitor.

The capacitance of the three parallel capacitors is given by $C_{\parallel} = 6 + 8 + 10 = 24$ μF. If we replace these capacitors with their equivalent, our circuit reduces to that of Figure 35.10. The capacitance of a 24- and a 12-μF capacitor in series is C_S, where

$$\frac{1}{C_S} = \frac{1}{24} + \frac{1}{12} = \frac{1}{8} \qquad \text{or} \qquad C_S = 8 \ \mu\text{F}$$

The charge on each capacitor of Figure 35.10 is therefore given by $Q = C_S V = 8 \times 120 = 960$ μcoulombs. $V_{24} = {}^{960}\!/_{24} = 40$ volts, and $V_{12} = {}^{960}\!/_{12} = 80$ volts. Note that these potential differences add to 120 volts. The 24-μF capacitor, which is equivalent to the 6-, 8-, and 10-μF capacitors in parallel, has a potential difference of 40 volts, and so must the three individually. The charges are given as follows: $Q_6 = 6 \times 40 = 240$ μcoulombs, $Q_8 = 8 \times 40 = 320$ μcoulombs, and $Q_{10} = 10 \times 40 = 400$ μcoulombs. Note that these charges add to 960 μcoulombs.

Questions

1. Two parallel metal plates are separated by a 5-mm air gap. The plates are given equal but opposite charges. If a sheet of glass is placed between the plates, what happens to the potential difference between them? Why? What happens to the potential gradient? To the electric field intensity?

2. What determines the maximum potential difference which can safely be applied to a capacitor?

3. Is the condition of a dielectric in a capacitor different when the capacitor is charged than when it is uncharged?

4. What is piezoelectricity? Where is it used?

5. Two identical capacitors are connected in parallel and charged to a potential difference of 100 volts. If they are now removed from the circuit and the positive conductor of one capacitor is connected to the negative conductor of the second, what is the resulting potential difference?   (Some voltage multipliers actually operate in this way.)

6. Explain why the dielectric constant of the medium outside the two spheres makes no difference in the development of Eq. (35.5).

Problems

1. A charge of 0.004 coulomb is stored in a capacitor at a potential of 800 volts.   What is the capacitance of the capacitor?   What is the energy stored in the capacitor?
Ans. 5 μF; 1.6 joule

2. What is the difference of potential between the terminals of a capacitor that has a capacitance of 15 μF when the charge on the capacitor is 7.5×10^{-4} coulomb?   Find the energy stored in the capacitor.

3. The potential difference between two clouds is 7 million volts.   How much electrical energy is dissipated if a lightning stroke involving 60 coulombs leaps from one cloud to the other?   Assume that the potential difference between the clouds decreases to zero, and that the system behaves as though the clouds were the plates of a capacitor.
Ans. 210 million joules

4. What is the capacitance of a sphere of radius 1 m?   If the dielectric strength for air is 3×10^6 volt/m, what is the largest charge which ideally could be placed on this sphere?

5. What is the joint capacitance of three capacitors of 10, 15, and 30 μF when they are connected in series?   In parallel?   *Ans.* 5 μF; 55 μF

6. Capacitors of 12, 6, and 4 μF are arranged so that they may be connected in series or in parallel.   What capacitance is obtained in each case?

7. Find the capacitance of the earth if it is approximately a sphere of 6,400 km radius. If the electric intensity over the entire surface of the earth were 120 volts/m directed downward, what charge would the earth have to have?   What would the surface charge density be?   *Ans.* 711 μF; -5.5×10^5 coulomb; -1.06×10^{-9} coulomb/m^2

8. A 3-μF capacitor is charged to a potential of 120 volts.   Find the charge on the capacitor plates and the energy stored.

9. A parallel-plate capacitor has a capacitance of 5 $\mu\mu$F (or picofarads, abbreviated pF) with air between the plates, and a capacitance of 30 $\mu\mu$F with glass between the plates. What is the dielectric constant of the glass in question?   If a charge of 3×10^{-10} coulomb is placed on the plates with glass between them, what is the energy stored?   If the glass is removed without affecting the charge, what energy is stored?   What is the source of the added energy?
Ans. 6; 1.5×10^{-9} joule; 9×10^{-9} joule; work done in pulling out glass

10. A capacitor whose insulation can withstand an applied potential of 8,000 volts has a capacitance of 2.5 μF.   What is the maximum energy the capacitor can store?   The maximum charge?

11. Two capacitors, of capacitances 12 and 6 μF, are connected in series across a 60-volt battery.   Find the charge, the potential difference, and the energy stored for the 6-μF capacitor.   *Ans.* 240 μC; 40 volts; 4.8×10^{-3} joule

12. Two capacitors, of capacitances 8 and 4 μF, are connected in series across a potential difference of 150 volts. Find the charge, potential difference, and energy stored for the 8-μF capacitor.

13. Three capacitors, of capacitances 5, 7, and 23 μF, are connected in parallel across a 110-volt potential difference. Find the total capacitance and the charge on the 5-μF capacitor.   *Ans.* 35 μF; 550 μC

14. A 15-μF capacitor is connected in parallel with a 5-μF capacitor across a 300-volt potential difference. Find the charge on each capacitor and the total energy stored.

15. A capacitor is made of two sheets of tin foil in contact with a plate of glass of dielectric constant 6.5. If the area of each sheet of tin foil is 80 cm^2, and the thickness of the glass is 0.2 cm, what is the capacitance of the capacitor?   *Ans.* 230 $\mu\mu$F

16. A parallel-plate capacitor consists of two sheets of aluminum, each of area 0.5 m^2, separated by a thin layer of plastic insulation of dielectric constant 3 and thickness 0.1 mm. Find the capacitance and the charge stored when this capacitor is charged to a potential difference of 200 volts.

17. A capacitor is made up of 200 sheets of tin foil, each 30 by 20 cm. These sheets are separated by sheets of paraffined paper which are 0.15 mm thick and which have a dielectric constant of 2.5. What is the capacitance of the capacitor when alternate sheets of tin foil are joined together?   *Ans.* 1.76 μF

18. A parallel-plate capacitor using mica as the dielectric is to have a capacitance of 20 $\mu\mu$F and be able to withstand a potential difference of 8,000 volts. What is the minimum thickness of mica required? What is the minimum area the plates of the capacitor may have if the dielectric constant is 6?

19. Three capacitors are connected as shown in the accompanying figure. If the potential difference between A and B is 150 volts, and if C_1, C_2, and C_3 are, respectively, 6, 7, and 5 μF, find the capacitance of the combination, the charge on C_1, and the potential difference across C_2.   *Ans.* 4 μF; 600 μC; 50 volts

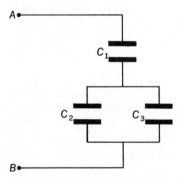

PROBS. 19 AND 20

20. Three capacitors are connected as shown in the accompanying figure to a source of unknown potential difference V between A and B. If C_1 is a 12-μF capacitor charged to a potential difference of 60 volts, find V and the charges on C_2 and C_3, which have capacitances of 30 and 20 μF, respectively.

21. When a capacitor that has a capacitance of 15 μF and a charge of 0.0045 coulomb is connected in parallel with an uncharged capacitor, the resulting potential difference is 100 volts. Find the capacitance of the second capacitor.   *Ans.* 30 μF

22. A 24-μF capacitor is charged to a potential difference of 150 volts. It is then disconnected from the source, but not discharged. Find the new potential difference if this capacitor is connected in parallel with an uncharged 36-μF capacitor.

23. Two identical air-dielectric parallel-plate capacitors with $C = 12$ $\mu\mu$F are charged in parallel to a potential difference of 100 volts and then disconnected from the charging source. A glass plate of dielectric constant 5 is inserted between the plates of one of the capacitors, filling the space completely. Find the new potential difference between the plates and the charge transferred from one capacitor to the other.

Ans. 33.3 volts; 800 $\mu\mu$C

24. Find the capacitance of the system of the accompanying figure and the charge on capacitor C_2 if C_1, C_2, C_3, and C_4 are, respectively, 30, 20, 9, and 12 μF, and the potential difference between A and B is 120 volts.

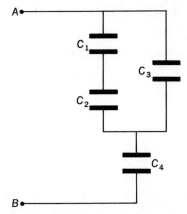

PROB. 24

25. Capacitor $C_1 = 10$ μF is charged to a potential difference of 50 volts, capacitor $C_2 = 15$ μF to a potential difference of 80 volts, and capacitor $C_3 = 20$ μF to a potential difference of 40 volts. They are then connected as shown in the accompanying figure. Find the charge on C_3 after the key is closed. Ans. 15.4 μC

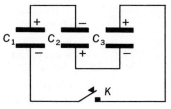

PROB. 25

CHAPTER 36 *Thus far in electricity we have confined our attention to electrostatics, the science dealing with electric charges at rest.   However most common applications of electricity involve charges in motion.   A flow of charges constitutes an electric current and exists whenever bodies at different potentials are connected by a conducting path.   In this chapter we discuss the factors which determine the value of the current which passes along a given conducting path.*

Electric Current and Resistance

36.1 Currents and Their Effects

If two metallic spheres, one charged positively and the other negatively, are connected by a copper wire, electrons flow until there is no longer a potential difference between the two spheres.   Such a flow of charge is called an electric *current*.   The magnitude of the current I is the charge per unit of time that passes any cross section of the wire.

$$I = \frac{Q}{t} \qquad\qquad \textbf{36.1}$$

Current is commonly measured in coulombs per second or *amperes*, named for the French physicist André Marie Ampère.   *The ampere is the current when one coulomb per second passes any cross section of a conductor.*

Electric currents are of great practical importance because of the many ways in which we can use the three principal effects they produce: (1) heating, (2) chemical, and (3) magnetic effects.

Heating by electric currents is utilized in making the filaments of incandescent lamps luminous, in operating electric stoves, and in hundreds of other ways.   There are cheaper ways to obtain thermal energy, but none is easier to control and handle than electrical energy.

The electroplating industry is based on the chemical effects of electric currents.   We depend on electric currents to produce aluminum, to charge batteries in automobiles, and to purify many metals.

The magnetic effects of currents are used in giant electromagnets and in tiny electrical relays in telephone circuits.   The interaction between currents and magnetic fields is fundamental to electric motors and to "drawing" the picture on a television receiver.

36.2 The Direction of a Current

The charges which are primarily responsible for the current in metallic conductors are negative electrons.   However, early in the nineteenth century there was no way to know whether it was negative or positive charges (or both) which were in motion. About 1820 Ampère introduced the *convention* that the *direction of the current is the direction in which a positive charge would move under the influence of the electric field.* This convention is still in use by the vast majority of physicists and engineers. By definition then, the *conventional* current in a wire flows from a point at higher potential to a point at lower potential, as though the current represented a movement of positive charge. Actually, *in metallic conductors* the positive nuclei are not free to move, and the transfer of charge results from a flow of electrons in a direction opposite that of the conventional current. In liquid and gaseous conductors, both positive and negative ions are in motion. In some of the modern high-energy accelerators, such as Van de Graaff generators and cyclotrons, the current may be a movement of positive charges. Obviously no convention could be most convenient for handling every possible situation.

When a constant potential difference is maintained between two points in a conductor, a constant flow of charge results. The current is always in the same direction and is said to be a *direct current.* On the other hand, when the flow of charges is first in one direction and then in the opposite direction, the flow of charge is called an *alternating current.* In the next five chapters, discussion is confined to direct currents.

36.3 Ohm's Law for a Resistor

To produce a steady current through a conductor, such as the filament of a lamp, it is necessary that an electric field be established in the conductor. Since the natural flow of charges in a conductor is always such as to eliminate the electric field, a *steady* current can result *only* if some device such as a battery or generator maintains the field. In this agency, called a source of *electromotive force* (emf), some other form of energy is converted into the electrical energy needed to keep the charges flowing. Various sources of emf are discussed in the chapters which follow.

Consider a conductor across which a constant potential difference is maintained by a battery, as indicated in Figure 36.1. In this figure the symbol A represents an ammeter, an instrument for measuring electric currents, while V represents a voltmeter, an instrument for measuring potential differences. The common forms of ammeters and voltmeters depend on the magnetic effects of electric currents for their operation. These effects are discussed in Chap. 39. In use, the two terminals of the voltmeter are connected to the two points between which one wishes to know the potential difference, while the ammeter is connected so that all the charges which pass through the device in which the current is to be measured also pass through the ammeter. (In Figure 36.1 the ammeter passes not only the current through the wire, but also the current through the voltmeter; the latter is assumed to be negligible in this case. It is not always negligible.) Let the current through the conductor be I_1 amperes (amp) when the potential difference across it is V_1 volts. If the battery is replaced by a different one,

FIGURE 36.1
Current, read by ammeter A, is produced in a resistor R (represented by the sawtooth symbol) by the application of a potential difference, read by voltmeter V.

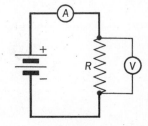

the potential difference and current may again be read and found to be V_2 and I_2. If V_2 is twice V_1, I_2 is twice I_1. Indeed, so long as the temperature of the wire is constant, the ratio of the potential difference to the current is constant. The ratio

$$R = \frac{V}{I} = \frac{V_1}{I_1} = \frac{V_2}{I_2} \qquad\qquad \textbf{36.2}$$

is called the *resistance* of the wire. The resistance is commonly expressed in *ohms*. *One ohm is that resistance in which a potential difference of one volt produces a current of one ampere.* This unit is named in honor of Georg S. Ohm, who discovered (1825) that the current in a wire is proportional to the potential difference between the ends. Much of our knowledge about resistance is due to the pioneering work of Ohm, who made his own batteries, wires, and meters in the early nineteenth century and used them to discover much of the information presented in this chapter. The symbol Ω (Greek capital omega) is often used as an abbreviation for ohms.

The relation

$$I = \frac{V}{R} \qquad\qquad \textbf{36.2}a$$

is *Ohm's law for a single resistor.* Ohm's law is obeyed within wide limits for metallic conductors. For many nonmetallic conductors the current is *not* proportional to the potential difference.

36.4 Joule's Law of Heating

When a potential difference V produces a current I through a conductor of resistance R, electrical energy is converted into thermal energy. The potential difference V represents the energy per unit charge converted from electrical to thermal energy in the conductor. The charge Q transported through the conductor in time t is It, by Eq. (36.1). Hence the total energy $\mathcal{W}$ dissipated in the conductor in time t is

$$\mathcal{W} = VQ = VIt \qquad\qquad \textbf{36.3}$$

If Ohm's law is obeyed for this conductor, $V = IR$, and

$$\mathcal{W} = I^2Rt \qquad\qquad \textbf{36.3}a$$

The fact that the amount of thermal energy produced by an electric current in a conductor is proportional to the square of the current, to the resistance, and to the time was reported by Joule, and relation [Eq. (36.3a)] is known as *Joule's law of heating.* Clearly, this formula gives energy in joules when I is in amperes and R in ohms. (If one wishes to obtain the energy in calories, one may use the relation 4.186 joules = 1 cal.)

Power is defined as the ratio $\mathcal{W}/t$; thus the power is equal to VI. The power is given in watts when the current is in amperes and the potential difference is in volts (volt-amperes = joules per coulomb × coulombs per second = joules per second = watts). With the aid of Ohm's law, we may express the power in the forms

$$P = VI = I^2R = \frac{V^2}{R} \qquad\qquad 36.4$$

< It is desirable to have some sort of device to protect electrical machines and appliances from excessive currents. One method of furnishing this protection is by means of fuses. A typical fuse consists essentially of a wire that has a low melting point. When an excessive current passes through this fuse wire, the heat generated is sufficient to melt the wire, and the circuit in which the wire was inserted is opened. The size of the fuse is so chosen that it melts when the current becomes greater than a preselected amount.

36.5 Resistivity

In his studies of resistance Ohm made wires of various materials, lengths, and areas. He was able to show that for a wire of given material at constant temperature *the resistance is directly proportional to the length and inversely proportional to the cross-sectional area.* This fact may be expressed by the equation

$$R = \rho \frac{l}{A} \qquad\qquad 36.5$$

where ρ is called the *resistivity* (or *specific resistance*) of the material. The resistivity depends on the material in question and on its temperature. In the metric system the resistivity of a material is numerically equal to the resistance of a piece of the material one meter in length and one square meter in cross-sectional area. The resistivities of several materials are recorded in Table 36.1.

< In the British engineering system the *resistivity* of a material is numerically equal to the resistance of a piece of the material one foot

TABLE 36.1 *Resistivities and Temperature Coefficients of Resistance (Approximate values at 20° C)*

Material	Resistivity,* ohm-meters	Temperature coefficient, per C°
Aluminum	2.6×10^{-8}	0.0040
Carbon	$3,500 \times 10^{-8}$	-0.0005
Constantan	49×10^{-8}	0.000002
Copper	1.7×10^{-8}	0.00393
Iron	9.7×10^{-8}	0.0058
Manganin	48×10^{-8}	0.0
Silver	1.6×10^{-8}	0.0038
Tungsten	5.5×10^{-8}	0.0047
Glass	Approx. 10^{13}	
Quartz	Approx. 10^{17}	

* To obtain ρ in ohms per mil-foot, multiply ρ in ohm-meters by 6×10^8.

long and one circular mil in area. A circular mil is defined as the area of a circle one one-thousandth of an inch in diameter. The units are usually written as *ohms per (circular) mil-foot,* which is dimensionally incorrect and misleading. The British engineering unit has an advantage of convenience for circular conductors in that the area of a wire d thousandths of an inch in diameter is d^2 cir mils.

36.6 Temperature Coefficient of Resistance

The resistance of most conductors increases as the temperature is increased. Figure 36.2 shows how the resistivity of platinum varies with temperature. For a few materials, such as carbon, the resistance decreases as the temperature is increased. In almost every case the change in the resistance of a conductor is roughly proportional to the change in the temperature and to the original resistance R:

$$\Delta R = \alpha R \, \Delta t \qquad\qquad\qquad 36.6$$

where ΔR represents the change in resistance, and Δt the change in temperature. The proportionality constant α is called the *temperature coefficient of resistance* and is defined as the change in resistance divided by the product of the original resistance and the change in temperature. If R_0 represents the resistance at $0°\text{C}$, and α_0 the temperature coefficient at $0°\text{C}$, the resistance R_t at temperature t may be written in the form

$$R_t = R_0(1 + \alpha_0 t) \qquad\qquad\qquad 36.7$$

since in this case $\Delta R = R_t - R_0$, and $\Delta t = t$. Approximate values of α for several conductors are listed in Table 36.1. The temperature coefficient of resistance is negative for materials which show a decrease in resistance as the temperature is raised.

For most pure metals the temperature coefficient of resistance is in the neighborhood of 0.004 per C° for small temperature changes near

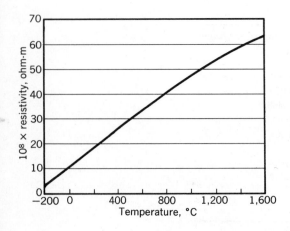

FIGURE 36.2
The resistivity (or specific resistance) of platinum rises with temperature.

0°C. Resistance is only approximately a linear function of temperature; if we define α as the slope of the curve showing resistivity as a function of temperature, pure metals behave much like platinum (Fig. 36.2), with α roughly proportional to the reciprocal of the absolute temperature. For most alloys α is much smaller than for metals. Indeed, for constantan and manganin, the temperature coefficients of resistance are very near zero. For this reason these two alloys are often used for resistors when it is desirable that the resistance be independent of temperature.

Since the resistance of a wire changes with the temperature, it is possible to infer the change in temperature from observations on the change of resistance. A resistance thermometer using platinum wire can be used to determine temperatures over a wide range up to the melting point of platinum. When properly calibrated, such a thermometer gives high precision in the measurement of temperatures. Figure 36.3 shows the essential components of a resistance thermometer.

Example   A resistance thermometer is made of platinum wire. Its resistance in a mixture of ice and water at 0°C was found to be 10 ohms; in a furnace of unknown temperature it was found to be 50 ohms. If the temperature coefficient of resistance of platinum has an average value of 0.0036 per C° over this range, what was the temperature of the furnace?

$$\text{Temperature of furnace} = t = \frac{R_t - R_0}{\alpha R_0}$$

$$= \frac{50 - 10}{0.0036 \times 10} = \frac{40}{0.036}$$

$$= 1100°\text{C}$$

36.7 Superconductivity

At very low temperatures the resistivities of all metals are very much smaller than at room temperature, but the resistivities of some materials drop suddenly to an immeasurably small value. The drop in resistance occurs over an exceedingly small temperature range, as is shown in Figure 36.4. Metals in which the resistance has vanished at very low temperatures are called *superconductors* and are said to be in the *superconducting* state. Not all metals become superconducting as the temperature approaches absolute zero. Metals such as gold, platinum, copper, sodium, and iron have resistivities which show no such abrupt changes. Among the elements which become superconductors are niobium, mercury, lead, tin, indium, and aluminum.

Comparison leads   Resistance coil

FIGURE 36.3

Resistance thermometer registers changes in its resistance as temperature changes.

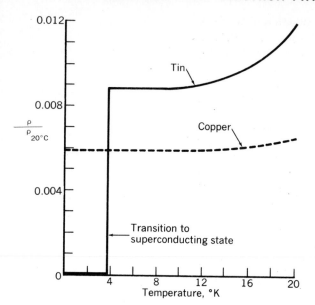

FIGURE 36.4
Resistivity-ratio curves for ordinary tin and copper, showing how tin becomes superconductive and loses all resistance below 3.74°K. Ratios are of resistivities at low temperatures to those at 20°C.

36.8 Qualitative Considerations in Conduction

In general, metals have low resistivities and high temperature coefficients of resistance; on the other hand, alloys ordinarily have higher resistivities and lower temperature coefficients. In a crude qualitative way these facts can be explained as follows: The atoms in a pure metal are arranged in a crystal, and there is an abundant supply of free electrons. Ideally, the resistance of a perfect crystal lattice should be zero, if there is no movement of the atoms. It is the energy lost by electrons in collisions with atoms which shows up as the Joule heat discussed in the Sec. 36.4. As the temperature of the metal is increased, movements of the atoms become greater; the chances of an electron colliding with an atom increase, and so does the resistance. In alloys, on the other hand, one may assume that the crystal array is less favorable for free movement of electrons; consequently, the resistivity is greater, especially at very low temperatures. However, as the temperature increases, the thermal vibrations of the atoms in the alloy are almost as likely to move a given atom out of the way of a moving electron as to move it into the way. Consequently, the resistance is considerably less temperature-sensitive than it is in the case of a pure metal.

Most nonmetallic solids are poor electrical conductors; some are excellent insulators. In general, the temperature coefficient of resistance of a nonmetallic substance is negative. For example, glasses which are good insulators at room temperature are conductors at higher temperatures. At room temperature insulators have practically no free electrons or mobile charged atoms (ions) available to carry current. When such materials are heated, the atoms have more internal energy. This increased thermal energy gives rise to a larger number of free electrons or conducting ions. For ordinary glass free positive sodium ions play an important role in conduction at elevated temperatures. On the other hand, copper oxide has a resistivity at 70°C which is only one-tenth its resistivity at 20°C, due to the rapid increase in the number of free electrons with temperature.

Carbon is one of the few nonmetals which has been widely used as an electrical conductor. It has a negative temperature coefficient of resistance because the number of free electrons available for conduction increases with temperature. The coefficient of thermal conductivity also increases with temperature, and for the same reason; both the electrical and thermal conductivities of *good* conductors are associated primarily with free electrons. It is a well-known fact that good conductors of electricity are also good conductors of heat, and that nonconductors of electricity are poor conductors of heat. The Wiedemann-Franz law states that the ratio of the thermal conductivity to the electrical conductivity of metals and alloys is proportional to the absolute temperature. That the Wiedemann-Franz law is approximately true for certain alloys is evident from Figure 36.5.

Materials which have resistivities at room temperature of the order of 10^{-4} to 10^7 ohm-m, intermediate between metallic conductors ($\rho \sim 10^{-7}$ ohm-m) and good insulators ($\rho \sim 10^{16}$ ohm-m and above), are known as *semiconductors*. The number of free electrons or other charge carriers increases rapidly with temperature for a typical semiconductor, with a resulting drop in resistance. In the past decade there has been a dramatic expansion of the use of semiconductors in electronic circuits. Among the more common semiconductors are

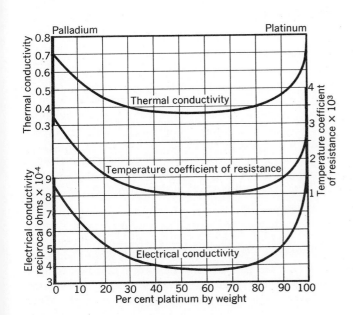

FIGURE 36.5

Relationship between electrical and thermal conductivities for palladium-platinum alloys.

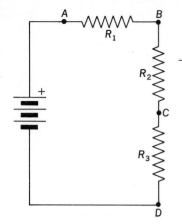

FIGURE 36.6

Three resistors connected in series.

silicon, germanium, selenium, cuprous oxide, and lead sulfide. The physical characteristics of semiconductors, as well as those of metals and insulators, are discussed further in Secs. 50.8 to 50.12.

36.9 Resistors in Series

The battery and the resistors of Figure 36.6 are connected *in series*. Two circuit elements are in series whenever all the charge passing through one of the elements passes through the second. Every electron which passes through the battery of Figure 36.6 passes through R_1, through R_2, and through R_3 and returns to the battery. The current through each resistor is the same. The current I is the same in all series resistors.

The work necessary to move a coulomb from A to D is the work necessary to move it from A to B plus the work necessary to move it from B to C plus the work from C to D. Thus, the potential difference across the combination of resistors in series is the sum of the potential differences across the individual resistors:

$$V = V_1 + V_2 + V_3$$

The resistance of the combination is, by definition, the ratio of the potential difference V across the combination to the current I:

$$R = \frac{V}{I} = \frac{V_1 + V_2 + V_3}{I} = R_1 + R_2 + R_3 \qquad \textbf{36.8}$$

Thus, *the resistance of any combination of resistors connected in series is equal to the sum of the individual resistances.*

36.10 Resistors in Parallel

The resistors of Figure 36.7 are connected *in parallel*. When several conductors are connected between two points so that the current divides between them and then rejoins, they are said to be *in parallel*. An electron in going from B to A of the figure may pass through R_1, R_2, or R_3. The potential difference across each resistor is the same, because the work required to move a charge from A to B is independent of the path chosen. If V is the potential difference between A and B, and V_1, V_2, and V_3 are the potential differences across R_1, R_2, and R_3, respectively, then $V = V_1 = V_2 = V_3$. The current I splits at point A, a part going through each of the parallel resistors. The total charge reaching B each second is equal to that leaving A each second. Therefore,

$$I = I_1 + I_2 + I_3$$

The resistance between A and B is, by definition, the ratio of V to I:

$$R = \frac{V}{I} = \frac{V}{I_1 + I_2 + I_3}$$

FIGURE 36.7

Three resistors connected in parallel.

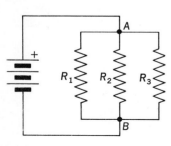

or

$$\frac{1}{R} = \frac{I}{V} = \frac{I_1 + I_2 + I_3}{V} = \frac{I_1}{V_1} + \frac{I_2}{V_2} + \frac{I_3}{V_3}$$

and

$$\frac{1}{R} = \frac{1}{R_1} + \frac{1}{R_2} + \frac{1}{R_3}$$ **36.9**

When resistors are connected in parallel, the reciprocal of the total resistance is equal to the sum of the reciprocals of the individual resistances.

Questions

1. What is meant by a negative temperature coefficient of resistance? Explain why some materials have negative temperature coefficients.

2. In what ways is the current in a conductor analogous to the flow of water through a pipe? At what points does the analogy fail?

3. What do we mean when we say that two circuit elements are in series? What must be the same for both?

4. What do we mean when we say that several circuit elements are in parallel? What is the same for all the elements? Why?

5. What are the advantages and disadvantages of strings of Christmas-tree lights in series? In parallel?

6. Why is the variation of resistance with temperature so different for a pure metal than for a semiconductor?

Problems

1. A potential difference of 40 volts is applied across a resistance of 8 ohms for a period of 2 min. What current is drawn? Calculate the charge which passes through the resistor. How many joules of energy does each coulomb lose in the resistor? What power is dissipated in the resistor? *Ans.* 5 amp; 600 coulombs; 40; 200 watts

2. A transmission line with a resistance of 4 ohms carries a current of 50 amp. What is the potential difference between the ends of the line? How much power is dissipated in the line? What charge is transferred each minute?

3. A 60-watt incandescent lamp operates at 120 volts. What current is drawn? What is the resistance of the lamp? How much charge passes through the filament each minute? How many electrons pass through each second?
Ans. 0.5 amp; 240 Ω; 30 coulombs; 3.1 $\times$ 10^{18}

4. Find the current drawn by, and the resistance of, a 660-watt, 110-volt toaster. If electrical energy costs 3 cents per kW-hr, how much does it cost to keep the toaster in steady operation for 30 min?

5. An electric heater element is designed to dissipate 720 watts when connected to a 120-volt line. Find the current drawn, the resistance of the heater, the charge which passes through the heater in 40 sec, and the energy transformed to heat in 40 sec.
Ans. 6 amp; 20 Ω; 240 coulombs; 28,800 joules

6. A silver wire of resistance 5 Ω is drawn through a die so that its length is tripled and its cross section is reduced to one-third of its previous value. Find the new resistance.

7. A copper bus bar is 2 cm thick, 4 cm wide, and 1 m long. Find its resistance and the potential difference between its ends when it bears a current of 2,000 amp.

Ans. 2.13 $\times$ 10^{-5} Ω; 0.043 volts

8. If 1 g of copper and 1 g of aluminum are used to make uniform wires each 10 m long, find the resistances of both wires. What is the ratio of the resistance of the copper wire to that of the aluminum wire? What would be the ratio of the resistance of a copper wire to that of an aluminum wire of the same dimensions?

9. A ribbon of silver, 5 cm long and 1 mm wide, is to be made into a resistance of 0.12 Ω. How thick must it be?   *Ans.* 6.7 μ

10. The field coil of an electric motor has a resistance of 36.225 Ω at 40°C, and 32.000 Ω at 0°C. What is its temperature coefficient of resistance?

11. If a lamp filament made of tungsten wire with a cross-sectional area of 5 $\times$ 10^{-9} m^2 is to have a resistance of 6 ohms at 20°C, how long must it be? If the temperature coefficient of resistance is 0.0047 per C°, find the resistance of this filament at 2,020°C.

Ans. 0.545 m; 62.4 Ω

12. A platinum resistance thermometer is used to determine the temperature of an oven. If the average temperature coefficient of resistance of platinum is 0.0037 per C°, and the resistance of the platinum coil is 80 Ω at 0°C, find the temperature when the coil has a resistance of 320 Ω.

13. The field coil of a motor draws a current of 2 amp from a 110-volt line when the motor is started and the coil is at 0°C. What is the resistance of the coil at 0°C? If the potential difference across the coil does not change, what current is drawn by the copper field coil at its normal operating temperature of 60°C?   *Ans.* 55 Ω; 1.6 amp

14. The electric resistance of a tantalum wire is 30 Ω at 20°C, and 40.8 Ω at 120°C. What is its resistance at 220°C if the resistance of tantalum varies linearly with temperature?

15. An oven requires 8 amp to heat it to the desired temperature when the applied voltage is 110 volts. How much resistance must be inserted in series with the oven in order to keep it at the same temperature if the potential difference is increased to 120 volts? How much power is dissipated in this resistor?   *Ans.* 1.25 Ω; 80 watts

16. An ammeter in series with a battery and a resistance R reads 5 amp. When an additional resistance of 6 Ω is inserted in series with the first, the reading of the ammeter is reduced to 3 amp. Find the resistance R. The resistances of battery and ammeter are negligible.

17. The belt of a Van de Graaff generator is 0.6 m wide and moves 30 m/sec. If half the charges sprayed on the belt reach the high-potential electrode, how many coulombs must be sprayed onto the belt each second to give a total current to the electrode of 2 mA? Find the charge sprayed on the belt per unit area.

Ans. 0.004 coulomb/sec; 2.2 $\times$ 10^{-4} coulomb/m^2

18. A 5,000-watt heating unit in a hot-water heater works 3 hr per day. If electrical energy costs 3 cents per kW-hr, how much does hot water cost each 30-day month? How many kilograms of water would be heated from 10° to 70°C each day if all the heat dissipated in the heater is effective in warming the water?

19. An airplane de-icer operates from a 24-volt battery and is capable of melting 0.1 kg of ice per minute.   Find the resistance and current when the de-icer is in operation.

Ans. 23.2 amp; 1.03 Ω

20. An electric iron of 1.2 kg mass has an average specific heat of 0.10 kcal/(kg)(C°). The heating unit takes 6 amp from a 110-volt line.   If half the heat is lost by radiation, how long will it take to bring the iron to a temperature of 150°C when it is at 20°C originally?

21. Calculate the resistance between points A and B in the accompanying figure if $R_1 = 12$ Ω, $R_2 = 4$ Ω, $R_3 = 7$ Ω, $R_4 = 6$ Ω, $R_5 = 3$ Ω, and $R_6 = 2$ Ω.

Ans. 11 Ω

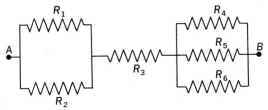

PROBS. 21 AND 22

22. Calculate the resistance between points A and B of the accompanying figure if $R_1 = 30$ Ω, $R_2 = 20$ Ω, $R_3 = 25$ Ω, $R_4 = 24$ Ω, $R_5 = 8$ Ω, and $R_6 = 6$ Ω.

23. Four 120-volt 30-watt electric lights are connected in parallel.   The group is then connected in series with a coil of 90 ohms resistance.   How much power is dissipated in each lamp and in the coil of wire when the combination is connected across a 180-volt battery?

Ans. 22 watts; 66 watts

24. When the light switch on a car is turned on, two headlights, two tail lamps, and a dash light are connected in parallel with a 12-volt battery of negligible internal resistance.   If each headlight has a resistance of 3 ohms, each tail lamp a resistance of 15 ohms, and the dash light a resistance of 20 ohms, find the current through the battery.

25. Find the resistance between A and B of the accompanying figure if $R_1 = 20$ Ω, $R_2 = 30$ Ω, $R_3 = 8$ Ω, $R_4 = 18$ Ω, and $R_5 = 36$ Ω.

Ans. 32 Ω

26. Find the resistance between A and B of the accompanying figure if $R_1 = 7$ Ω, $R_2 = 4$ Ω, $R_3 = 8$ Ω, $R_4 = 5$ Ω, and $R_5 = 20$ Ω.

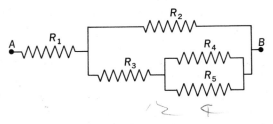

PROBS. 25 AND 26

CHAPTER 37 *In the preceding chapter we found that the current I through a conductor was given by the ratio of the potential difference V across the conductor to its resistance R.   To maintain a steady current in a conductor of fixed resistance, we must provide a constant potential difference.   How this can be done is the first topic of this chapter.   We clearly need some device which can convert some other kind of energy to electrical energy—a device known by the clumsy name "source of electromotive force" or by the abbreviation emf.   How can we find the current in each part of a complex circuit involving several resistors and emfs?   We learn that this question can be answered by applying two of the great conservation laws of physics—conservation of charge and conservation of energy.*

Electric Circuits

37.1 Electromotive Force

To maintain a steady current in a conductor, it is necessary to maintain a steady potential difference across the conductor. This potential difference can be supplied only if some device changes some other form of energy into electrical energy. Such a device is called a *source of electromotive force* (abbreviated *emf*).

There are many kinds of emf. In batteries chemical reactions occur, and chemical energy is converted into electrical energy. In the giant generators of our electric power plants mechanical energy is converted into electrical energy. In a thermocouple it is heat energy, while in the photoelectric cell it is radiant energy which is transformed.

When a charge q receives an energy $\mathcal{W}$ in passing through a battery or some other source of electrical energy, the emf $\mathcal{E}$ is given by

$$\mathcal{E} = \frac{\mathcal{W}}{q}$$

37.1

When $\mathcal{W}$ is in joules and q in coulombs, the emf is in joules per coulomb, or volts.

When a charge of one coulomb receives one joule of energy upon passing through a source, the source is said to have an electromotive force of one volt. A 12-volt battery delivers 12 joules of energy to each coulomb which passes through it. Electromotive force and potential difference are measured in the same units. An emf is a particular kind of potential difference, namely, one which arises through the transformation of some other form of energy into electrical energy.

In a source of emf not only may some other form of energy be transformed into electrical energy, but the reverse process may also occur—electrical energy may be converted into another form. For example, in charging a battery, charges are forced through the battery in a direction opposite that in which they go when the battery is discharging; these charges deliver electrical energy to the battery, where it is converted into and stored as chemical energy.

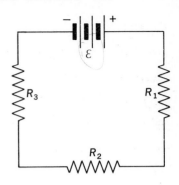

FIGURE 37.1
A coulomb gains an amount of energy in passing through the battery equal to the energy it loses in three resistors as it goes around the complete circuit.

37.2 The Conservation of Energy in a Simple Circuit

Consider the circuit of Figure 37.1 in which a battery is connected in series with three resistors. A charge q which passes through the battery gains an amount of energy $\mathcal{E}q$ joules. In passing through the resistance R_1, this charge loses energy V_1q joules. In passing through resistors R_2 and R_3 this charge loses amounts of energy V_2q and V_3q, respectively. In going once around the complete circuit, the charge loses exactly the same amount of energy as it gains. Therefore,

$$\mathcal{E}q = V_1q + V_2q + V_3q \qquad \text{37.2}$$
$$\mathcal{E} = V_1 + V_2 + V_3$$

or

$$\mathcal{E} = IR_1 + IR_2 + IR_3 \qquad \text{37.3}$$

If Eq. (37.3) is solved for I, we obtain

$$I = \frac{\mathcal{E}}{R_1 + R_2 + R_3} \qquad \text{37.4}$$

In a simple series circuit the current is equal to the ratio of the emf to the sum of the resistances in the circuit. This statement represents a simplified form of *Ohm's law for a complete circuit.*

37.3 The Resistances of Sources of Electromotive Force

Any source of emf, such as a battery or electrical generator, has some internal resistance. As a consequence, a current through a battery produces some heating. When the battery is being discharged, the total energy given to a charge q is $\mathcal{E}q$, but a portion of this energy is converted into heat within the battery. If the internal resistance is r, the potential drop in the battery resistance is Ir. The net potential gain V_t is the potential difference between the terminals of the battery.

$$V_t = \mathcal{E} - Ir \qquad \text{37.5}$$

The terminal potential difference is $\mathcal{E}$ only when no current is being drawn.

The decrease in the terminal potential difference of a battery when the current drawn is changed is illustrated by the dimming of automobile headlights when the starter is activated. The starter draws a large current from the battery. As a consequence of the increased Ir

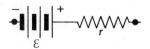

FIGURE 37.2

A real battery may be treated as an ideal resistanceless battery and a series resistor r.

drop within the battery, the terminal potential is reduced, and the potential difference across the lamps of the car is lower. For an automobile battery of emf about 12 volts, the internal resistance may be about 0.005 ohm. The current drawn by the lights is approximately 6 amp; thus, when current is being drawn only for the lights, the terminal potential difference of the battery is only a few hundredths of a volt less than the emf. If the current drawn from the battery is increased to 150 amp by operating the starter motor, V_t becomes $12 - 0.75$ or 11.25 volts. The brightness of the lamps is reduced by such a decrease in terminal potential difference.

For practical purposes we may assume that the real battery is made up of a pure emf and a series resistor, as suggested in Figure 37.2. Ohm's law for a complete circuit is applicable, but the internal resistance of the battery must be included in the total resistance.

Example A 45-volt battery has an internal resistance of 0.6 ohm. It is connected in a circuit as indicated in Figure 37.3. Find the current in each resistor.

First, the series equivalent of the two parallel resistors must be found.

$$\frac{1}{R_{\parallel}} = \frac{1}{12} + \frac{1}{8} = \frac{5}{24}$$

$$R_{\parallel} = 4.8 \text{ ohms}$$

Now applying Ohm's law for the complete circuit yields

$$I = \frac{E}{R} = \frac{45}{0.6 + 20 + 4.8 + 7} = \frac{45}{32.4} = 1.39 \text{ amp}$$

This is the current through the battery and the 20- and 7-ohm resistors. The potential difference across the parallel resistors is $1.39 \times 4.8 = 6.67$ volts. Therefore, the current in the 8-ohm resistor is $6.67/8 = 0.83$ amp, while that through the 12-ohm resistor is $6.67/12 = 0.56$ amp. Note that the sum of these currents is 1.39 amp.

FIGURE 37.3

Battery with four resistors, including two in parallel.

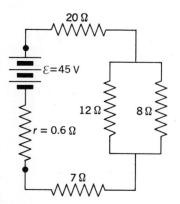

37.4 Charging a Battery

The terminal potential difference of a battery as it is discharged is given by $\mathcal{E} - Ir$. While the battery is being charged, the terminal potential difference is greater than the emf by an amount Ir, as can be seen from consideration of the energy transformations. In charging the battery, electrical energy is converted into chemical energy; the energy per unit charge is $\mathcal{E}$. The charging current produces heat in the battery, and the energy per unit charge required to produce this heating effect is Ir. Thus, the total electrical energy which must be delivered to the battery per unit charge is

$$V_t = \mathcal{E} + Ir \tag{37.6}$$

Regardless of the direction of the current through a cell or other source of emf, Joule heat is always produced.

37.5 Cells in Series

When two or more sources of emf are connected in series, the net emf is the algebraic sum of the individual emfs. If two cells are connected in series in such a way that both would produce a current in the same direction, the emf is the sum of the two emfs; on the other hand, if the two are connected in series in such a way that they would send currents in opposite directions, the net emf is the difference between the two. In the first case the cells are said to be connected in *series aiding,* in the second case in *series opposing.* When a battery is to be charged, it must be connected in series opposing with some other source of emf which supplies electrical energy to be transformed into chemical energy.

When several identical cells are connected in series, the total emf is equal to the number of cells multiplied by the emf of a single cell, while the resistance of the battery is equal to the resistance of an individual cell times the number of cells. The type of cell used in ordinary automobile batteries has an emf of approximately 2 volts; in order to obtain an emf of 6 volts, three cells are connected in series; for 12 volts, six cells are required.

37.6 Ohm's Law for a Complete Circuit

In Figure 37.4 several batteries of negligible resistance are connected in series with a number of resistors. For this circuit one may again apply the fundamental principle that the total energy gained by a charge in going around the complete circuit is equal to the total energy lost.

If a unit charge is carried clockwise around the circuit of Figure 37.4, the net change in potential energy for the complete circuit is zero, or

$$\mathcal{E}_1 - IR_1 - \mathcal{E}_2 - IR_2 + \mathcal{E}_3 - IR_3 = 0 \qquad \qquad 37.7$$

It is often convenient to mark plus and minus signs at the appropriate ends of all resistors and batteries. The potential change may be considered positive when the test charge is moved from the minus terminal of a circuit element to the positive one, and negative when the charge goes from plus to minus. It is not necessary that the charge be carried around the circuit in the direction in which the current flows. Indeed, if the direction of motion is reversed, all signs in Eq. (37.7) are changed, but the sum is still zero. In the circuit of Figure 37.4, battery 2 is being charged by the other batteries.

The total current, which is the same in all parts of the circuit, may be obtained by solving Eq. (37.7) to obtain

$$I = \frac{\mathcal{E}_1 - \mathcal{E}_2 + \mathcal{E}_3}{R_1 + R_2 + R_3} = \frac{\Sigma \mathcal{E}}{\Sigma R} \qquad \qquad 37.8$$

This equation represents Ohm's law for a complete series circuit, which may be stated as follows:

The current in any series circuit is given by the ratio of the algebraic sum of the emfs to the total series resistance of the circuit.

FIGURE 37.4

Series circuit containing three sources of emf.

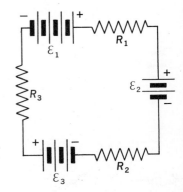

< Ohm's law for a complete circuit is to be distinguished from Ohm's law for a single resistor. The law for a single resistor involves only the potential difference across the resistor, while the law for the complete circuit involves the algebraic sum of the emfs in the circuit and the total resistance of the series circuit. In a series circuit the algebraic sum of the emfs is equal to the sum of the IR drops in the resistors. This follows directly from the law of conservation of energy.

When one applies Ohm's law to a complete circuit in which there are parallel resistors, each group of parallel resistors is first replaced with the equivalent series resistor. Then Ohm's law for the circuit is applied directly.

Example A battery of emf 20 volts and internal resistance 1 ohm is connected in series with a 5-ohm resistor, a second battery of emf 8 volts and internal resistance 2 ohms which is in series opposing, and a group of three resistors of 12, 6, and 4 ohms resistance in parallel as shown in Figure 37.5. Find the current in each resistor and the terminal potential difference of each battery.

We first replace the three parallel resistors with the equivalent single resistor: $R_\| = 2$ ohms from $1/R_\| = \frac{1}{12} + \frac{1}{6} + \frac{1}{4}$. We next apply Ohm's law for the circuit, which gives

$$I = \frac{20 - 8}{1 + 5 + 2 + 2} = \frac{12}{10} = 1.2 \text{ amp}$$

for the current in each battery and in the 5-ohm resistor. The potential drop across $R_\|$ is given by $IR_\| = 1.2 \times 2 = 2.4$ volts, which remains unchanged if we replace $R_\|$ with the original three resistors. The currents in these resistors are given by V/R as follows: $I_{12} = 2.4/12 = 0.2$ amp, $I_6 = 2.4/6 = 0.4$ amp, and $I_4 = 2.4/4 = 0.6$ amp. Note that the sum is 1.2 amp, the current in the main circuit.

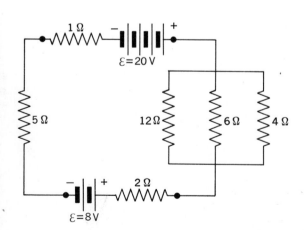

FIGURE 37.5
Circuit with two opposing batteries connected in series.

The terminal potential difference for the 20-volt battery is $\mathcal{E} - Ir = 20 - 1.2 \times 1 = 18.8$ volts, while the terminal potential difference for the 8-volt battery which is being charged is $\mathcal{E} + Ir = 8 + (1.2 \times 2) = 10.4$ volts.

37.7 Kirchhoff's Laws

Circuits ranging from the simplest to very complex networks with many branches and many emfs can be handled by application of two fundamental principles known as *Kirchhoff's laws*. These laws, which apply once a steady state has been reached, have been used in previous discussions, although they have not been specifically named. Kirchhoff's two laws are:

1. *The sum of all currents arriving at any point in a circuit is equal to the sum of the currents leaving that point.*

2. *Around any closed loop, the sum of the potential rises is equal to the sum of the potential drops.*

The first law must apply if we are to avoid an accumulation of charge at any point in the circuit or a continuing disappearance of charge at that point. If Kirchhoff's first law were not true, and the sum of the currents reaching a point exceeded the currents leaving it, the charge would build up at this point, and the potential of the point would change continuously.

Kirchhoff's second law is a special statement of the law of conservation of energy. If a charge gained more energy in going around a closed path than it lost, it would be able to gain more and more energy by repeated traversing of this path. This is obviously not permissible. Once the charge returns to its starting point, its potential energy must be exactly the same as when it started.

If a man takes a hike in the mountains and eventually returns to his starting point, we know that he has climbed up exactly as many feet as he has descended, since he ends at the same altitude at which he started. Kirchhoff's second law is the electrical analogue of this mechanical illustration.

In applying Kirchhoff's laws to a problem, it is convenient to carry out the following steps in order:

1. *Assign a direction and a symbol to the current in each independent branch of the circuit.* It is not necessary to worry about which direction to assign the current in a given branch, since if the incorrect assignment is made, the current will turn out to be negative.

2. *Place appropriate plus and minus signs at the terminals of every source of emf and every resistor in the circuit.* Remember that in a resistor the current is from the plus to the minus terminal; thus the choices of current directions in the first step determine the signs of the terminals of all resistors.

3. *Apply Kirchhoff's first law at enough junctions so that each current appears in an equation.* Be sure that each junction equation contains at least one current which has not appeared in earlier equations.

4. *Apply Kirchhoff's second law to closed loops until once again every current has been included in at least one equation.* When we go through a circuit element from minus to plus, potential is gained; from plus to minus it is lost. Once again be sure that every new loop equation involves at least one current which has not appeared in a previous loop equation.

5. *Solve the equations for the desired unknowns.*

A familiarity with the use of Kirchhoff's laws is best obtained by studying one or more examples and then by practice on additional problems.

Example Find the current in all branches of the circuit of Figure 37.6.

1. Let us designate the currents by I_1, I_2, and I_3 and assume them to be in the directions indicated by the arrows.

2. We place a + on the higher-potential end of each circuit component, and a − on the lower-potential end.

3. At point A, $I_1 + I_2 = I_3$, by Kirchhoff's first law.

4. If we start at point A and apply Kirchhoff's second law to the left loop going clockwise, we obtain

$$-15 + 2I_2 + 7I_2 - 3I_1 - I_1 + 40 = 0$$

By going clockwise from A around the right loop, we obtain

$$-8I_3 - 7I_2 - 2I_2 + 15 = 0$$

5. We now have the equations

$$I_1 + I_2 - I_3 = 0$$
$$4I_1 - 9I_2 = 25$$
$$9I_2 + 8I_3 = 15$$

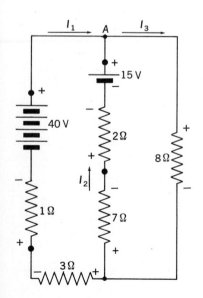

FIGURE 37.6
Circuit in which there are three branches, each with a different current.

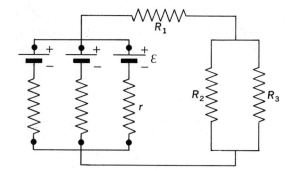

FIGURE 37.7
Circuit with three identical cells in parallel.

The solutions are $I_1 = 4$ amp, $I_2 = -1$ amp, and $I_3 = 3$ amp. The fact that I_2 is negative means that the current I_2 is in the direction opposite that assumed. The 15-volt battery is being charged.

When several identical sources of emf are connected in parallel, the emf of the combination is the emf of a single source. The net resistance of this combination is equal to the resistance of a single cell divided by the number of cells, since, effectively, all the resistances are in parallel. Cells which are not identical are seldom connected in parallel. Although Kirchhoff's laws are valid in any situation in which we have steady currents, it is easier to solve circuits such as that of Figure 37.7 by the method illustrated below. Note that this method leads to correct results only when the cells are identical, having the same emf, the same internal resistance, and the same lead resistances connecting the sources to the external circuit.

Example Three identical dry cells with $\mathcal{E} = 1.5$ volts and $r = 0.12$ ohms are connected in parallel to the circuit of Figure 37.7. Find the current in each cell and in each resistor if $R_1 = 5$ ohms, $R_2 = 30$ ohms, and $R_3 = 60$ ohms.

The emf of the three identical cells in parallel is 1.5 volts, and the resistance of the combination is 0.04 ohm (three 0.12-ohm resistors in parallel). The resistance of the 30- and 60-ohm parallel combination is 20 ohms. Application of Ohm's circuit law yields

$$I = \frac{1.5}{0.04 + 5 + 20} = \frac{1.5}{25.04} = 0.060 \text{ amp}$$

The potential drop across the 30- and 60-ohm resistors is 20×0.060, or 1.2 volts. Therefore, $I_{30} = 1.2/30 = 0.04$ amp, and $I_{60} = 1.2/60 = 0.02$ amp. The current through each of the three identical cells is one-third of 0.06 amp, or 0.02 amp.

FIGURE 37.8
Wheatstone bridge.

37.8 The Wheatstone Bridge

An accurate and simple method of measuring resistances employs the Wheatstone bridge. The circuit for this bridge is shown in Figure 37.8. A and B are fixed resistors, the values of which are known. The

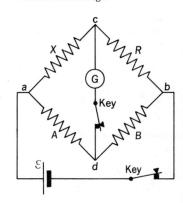

resistance X whose value is to be determined is connected in the third arm of the bridge, while a variable resistance R is connected in the fourth arm. The resistance R is varied until there is no current between c and d as indicated by the galvanometer G, an instrument for detecting small currents. When the galvanometer shows no current between c and d, the bridge is said to be *balanced*.

If there is no current in the galvanometer, the potential difference between points c and d must be zero. For this to be true, the potential drop across resistor A must be equal to the potential drop across X, since one end of each of these resistors is at the potential of point a. If I_A is the current in A, and I_X the current in X, the condition for no current in the galvanometer is that $V_{ac} = V_{ad}$ or $I_X X = I_A A$. Similarly, the fall of potential from c to b must be equal to the drop in potential from d to b, which gives $I_R R = I_B B$. The current in R and in X is the same when no current flows through the galvanometer. Similarly, the current in A is the same as that in B. Therefore $I_X X / I_R R = I_A A / I_B B$, or

$$\frac{X}{R} = \frac{A}{B} \qquad\qquad 37.9$$

In the slide-wire Wheatstone bridge the resistors A and B are segments of a wire of uniform cross section and resistivity. The ratio A/B is determined by the position of the movable contact along this wire. In high-quality commercial Wheatstone bridges, the ratio of A to B can be set at one of several values and the final balance made by varying R.

37.9 The Potentiometer

The potentiometer occupies an important place in electrical measurements because it can be used to measure potential differences with great accuracy and *without drawing any current*. This feature is of great importance in working with sources of emf of high internal resistance and low current capabilities.

A schematic diagram of a potentiometer is shown in Figure 37.9. The wire ab, which is of uniform cross section, carries a current maintained constant by the working battery B. There is a progressive drop in potential along the wire from a to b, directly proportional to the distance from a. To measure an emf whose value $\mathcal{E}_x$ is unknown, this emf is placed in series with a galvanometer and connected as shown in Figure 37.9, in which point c represents a movable contact. It is important that the emf $\mathcal{E}_x$ oppose the current which the working battery B would produce if $\mathcal{E}_x$ were zero. If the potential difference between a and b is greater than $\mathcal{E}_x$, there is some point c at which the potential difference across ac is equal to $\mathcal{E}_x$. This point can be found by moving the sliding contact until the current through the galvanometer is zero. The potentiometer is then *balanced*.

In the usual application of the potentiometer a standard cell of known emf $\mathcal{E}_s$ is first used in place of $\mathcal{E}_x$, and the balance point is

FIGURE 37.9

Simple potentiometer circuit.

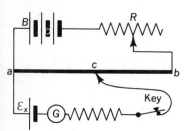

found at some point d. The unknown emf $\mathcal{E}_x$ is substituted for $\mathcal{E}_s$, and the balance point c is found. Then $\mathcal{E}_x$ can be calculated from the relation

$$\frac{\mathcal{E}_x}{\mathcal{E}_s} = \frac{ac}{ad}$$

where ac and ad represent the length of conductor from a to c and from a to d, respectively.

Questions

1. What are the advantages of connecting identical cells in parallel? What are the disadvantages?

2. Why are batteries which are not identical seldom connected in parallel?

3. Why is a voltmeter rated at 20,000 ohms/volt usually more desirable and more expensive than one of the same range rated 5,000 ohms/volt?

4. Draw a Wheatstone bridge, and derive the relationship among the resistances when the bridge is balanced.

5. Does interchanging the galvanometer and battery in a Wheatstone bridge affect the balance? Justify your answer with equations.

6. Draw a potentiometer circuit, and explain how it operates. How could the potentiometer be used to calibrate an ammeter with a standard resistor? Draw a suitable circuit.

Problems

1. A battery of emf 6 volts and internal resistance 0.2 Ω is connected in series with two resistors, one of 4.8 Ω and another of 15 Ω. Find the current, the potential difference across each resistor, and the terminal potential difference of the battery.

Ans. 0.3 amp; 1.44 volts; 4.5 volts; 5.94 volts

2. Three cells of a storage battery, each with a resistance of 0.02 Ω and an emf of 2.1 volts, are connected in series with a coil having a resistance of 4.14 Ω. Find the current and the terminal potential difference of the battery.

3. In the circuit of the accompanying figure, find the current in R_1 and the charge stored on the capacitor if $\mathcal{E} = 12$ volts, $r = 1\ \Omega$, $R_1 = 8\ \Omega$, $R_2 = 15\ \Omega$, and $C = 10\ \mu F$.

Ans. 0.5 amp; 75 μC

4. In the circuit of the accompanying figure, find the current in R_1 and the charge stored on the capacitor if $\mathcal{E} = 5$ volts, $r = 0.5\ \Omega$, $R_1 = 4.5\ \Omega$, $R_2 = 20\ \Omega$, and $C = 40\ \mu F$.

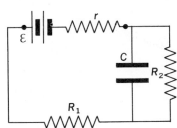

PROBS. 3 AND 4

5. A 15-Ω resistor bears a current of 0.4 amp when it is connected in parallel with two other resistors of 50 Ω and 24 Ω. Find the current in each of these two resistors.

Ans. 0.12 and 0.25 amp

6. A circuit has three parallel branches with resistances of 75, 60, and 150 Ω. When a current of 0.8 amp is flowing in the 75-Ω branch, how much current is flowing in each of the other branches?

7. When an external resistance of 18 Ω is connected to the terminals of a battery, the current is found to be 0.3 amp. When this resistance is increased to 48 Ω, the current drops to 0.12 amp. Find the emf and internal resistance of the battery.

Ans. 6 volts; 2 Ω

8. A battery having an internal resistance of 0.2 Ω and an emf of 12 volts is used to send a current through a 3-Ω resistance connected in series with two resistances, one of 1 Ω and the other of 4 Ω, in parallel. Find the current in each of the resistances.

9. A 48-volt battery with an internal resistance of 1 Ω is to be charged at the rate of 9 amp from a 120-volt source. What resistance must be connected in series with the battery? What will be the terminal potential difference of the battery during the charging process? Assuming that the emf arises entirely from the conversion of chemical to electrical energy, find the rate at which electrical energy is converted into chemical energy. At what rate is electrical energy converted into heat in the battery? In the series resistor?

Ans. 7 Ω; 57 volts; 432 watts; 81 watts; 567 watts

10. A storage battery having an emf of 36 volts and an internal resistance of 1.5 Ω is to be charged by connecting it to a 110-volt generator. What resistance must be introduced in series with it in order that the charging current may be 10 amp? What is the terminal potential difference of the battery?

11. Find the current through the batteries and through R_4 of the accompanying figure if $\mathscr{E}_1 = 30$ volts, $r_1 = 1$ Ω, $\mathscr{E}_2 = 10$ volts, $r_2 = 2$ Ω, $R_1 = 8$ Ω, $R_2 = 10$ Ω, $R_3 = 12$ Ω, and $R_4 = 6$ Ω. Find the terminal potential differences of the batteries and the potential difference between A and B.   *Ans.* 1.6 and 1.07 amp; 28.4 volts; 6.8 volts; 0.4 volts

12. Find the current through the batteries and through R_3 of the accompanying figure if $\mathscr{E}_1 = 45$ volts, $r_1 = 1$ Ω, $\mathscr{E}_2 = 15$ volts, $r_2 = 1$ Ω, $R_1 = 9$ Ω, $R_2 = 7$ Ω, $R_3 = 30$ Ω, and $R_4 = 20$ Ω.

13. In the accompanying figure, R_4 is 12 Ω and bears a current of 2 amp. If $R_3 = 8$ Ω, what current does R_3 carry? If $\mathscr{E}_1 = 24$ volts, $r_1 = r_2 = 1$ Ω, $R_1 = 4$ Ω, and $R_2 = 2$ Ω, find $\mathscr{E}_2$.   *Ans.* 3 amp; 40 volts

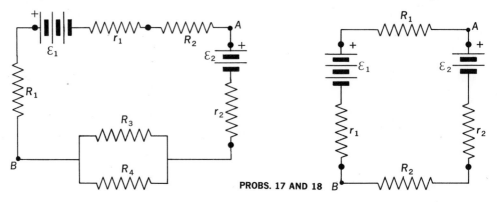

PROBS. 11 TO 13   PROBS. 17 AND 18

14. Four storage batteries, each having six cells with an emf of 2 volts and an internal resistance of 0.015 ohm per cell, are to be charged in series at the rate of 10 amp from a 110-volt line. How much resistance must be inserted in series with the batteries?

15. Twelve identical cells, each with an internal resistance of 1.2 Ω, are connected so as to have three parallel groups of four cells in series. The combination sends a 2 amp through an external resistance of 2.6 Ω. What is the emf of each cell? *Ans.* 2.1 volts

16. Six identical cells, each with an internal resistance of 0.12 Ω, are connected in parallel to send a current through an external resistance of 0.28 ohm. How much current will be obtained in the external resistance if each cell has an emf of 1.2 volts?

17. In the accompanying figure, $\mathcal{E}_1 = 12$ volts, $r_1 = 1\,\Omega$, $\mathcal{E}_2 = 6$ volts, $r_2 = 2\,\Omega$, $R_1 = 3\,\Omega$, and $R_2 = 4\,\Omega$. Find the current, the terminal potential difference of each battery, and the potential difference between points A and B.
Ans. 0.6 amp; 11.4 volts; 7.2 volts; 9.6 volts

18. In the accompanying figure, $\mathcal{E}_1 = 20$ volts, $r_1 = 1\,\Omega$, $\mathcal{E}_2 = 10$ volts, $r_2 = 2\,\Omega$, $R_1 = 8\,\Omega$, and $R_2 = 14\,\Omega$. Find the current, the terminal potential difference of each battery, and the potential difference between points A and B.

19. In the accompanying figure, $I_1 = 6$ amp, and $I_2 = 2$ amp. What is I_3? If $\mathcal{E}_1 = 52$ volts, $r_1 = 2\,\Omega$, $\mathcal{E}_2 = 4$ volts, $r_2 = 1\,\Omega$, $R_2 = 5\,\Omega$, and $R_4 = 2\,\Omega$, find R_1 and R_3.
Ans. 4 amp; 4 Ω; 2 Ω

20. In the accompanying figure, $I_2 = 3$ amp, and $I_3 = 4$ amp. If $R_1 = 4\,\Omega$, $r_1 = 2\,\Omega$, $R_2 = 5\,\Omega$, $r_2 = 1\,\Omega$, $R_3 = 6\,\Omega$, and $R_4 = 8\,\Omega$, find $\mathcal{E}_1$ and $\mathcal{E}_2$.

21. In the accompanying figure, $\mathcal{E}_1 = 50$ volts, $r_1 = 1\,\Omega$, $R_1 = 4\,\Omega$, $\mathcal{E}_2 = 40$ volts, $r_2 = 2\,\Omega$, $R_2 = 8\,\Omega$, and $R_3 = 6\,\Omega$. Find the current in each element in the circuit.
Ans. 4 amp; 1 amp; 5 amp

22. In the accompanying figure, $\mathcal{E}_1 = 47$ volts, $r_1 = 0.5\,\Omega$, $R_1 = 2\,\Omega$, $\mathcal{E}_2 = 82$ volts, $r_2 = 1\,\Omega$, $R_2 = 9\,\Omega$, and $R_3 = 7\,\Omega$. Find the current in each element in the circuit.

23. The current in any element of a network (such as we have been considering) as the result of the simultaneous action of a number of emfs in the network is the sum of the currents which would exist in this element if each source of emf were considered separately, with all other sources of emf being replaced by their internal resistances.

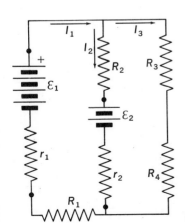

PROBS. 19 AND 20

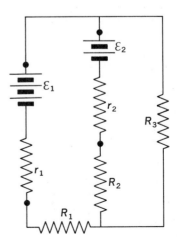

PROBS. 21 AND 22

This is a statement of the *superposition theorem*. Find the currents in the circuit of Figure 37.6 by applying this theorem.   *Ans.* 4 amp; −1 amp; 3 amp

24. A battery has an emf of 60 volts and an internal resistance of 4 Ω. Find the power dissipated in a variable external series resistor set, successively, at the values 2, 3, 4, 5, and 6 ohms. Plot a rough curve of power dissipated in the load as a function of load resistance to confirm the fact that maximum power is supplied to the load when the load resistance is equal to the internal resistance of the source.

CHAPTER 38 *In Chap. 37 we made use of the fact that batteries convert chemical energy to electrical energy, but we made no effort to explain how this energy transformation was accomplished. We now treat some of the basic facts of electrochemistry, in terms of which the functioning of simple batteries can be understood. But batteries are not the only sources of emf in which we are interested. In this chapter we also discuss thermocouples, which convert thermal energy to electrical energy.*

Chemical and Thermal Electromotive Forces

38.1 Electrolysis

If two copper plates are inserted into a beaker filled with water and connected to the terminals of a battery (Fig. 38.1), an ammeter in the circuit shows no current. However, if a little copper sulfate ($CuSO_4$) is poured into the beaker, there is a current through the solution. When the copper sulfate dissolves in water, many of the molecules split (or dissociate) into two charged particles called *ions*. One is a copper atom from which two electrons are missing, and the second is a sulfate (SO_4^{--}) ion with two excess electrons. The net charge in atomic units carried by an ion is called the *valence* of the ion. Thus the valence of the Cu^{++} ion is 2, while that of the sulfate ion is -2. In the solution the positively charged copper ions migrate to the negatively charged plate; the negatively charged sulfate ions, to the positive plate.

After a current has passed between the two copper electrodes for some time, the *cathode* (the electrode by which the conventional current leaves) has gained weight and is bright. The *anode* (by which current enters) has lost weight.   There has not only been a transfer of electricity through the solution, but copper has been carried from one plate to the other. The Cu^{++} ions which reach the cathode obtain two electrons there and are deposited as neutral copper atoms, while each sulfate ion which goes to the anode gives it the two excess electrons and joins with an atom of copper. The copper sulfate so formed goes into solution, thus keeping the amount of $CuSO_4$ constant. The net effect is a gain of copper by the cathode and a loss of copper by the anode.

The addition of any acid, base, or salt to the pure water in the beaker makes it conducting, provided the solute dissociates into ions. When a current is passed between two platinum electrodes in a dilute solution of sulfuric acid in water (Fig. 38.2), hydrogen is released

FIGURE 38.1

Electrolysis of copper sulfate results in copper ions migrating to the cathode, and sulfate ions to the anode.

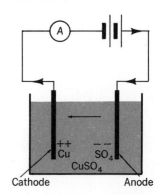

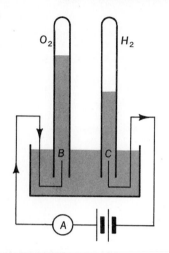

FIGURE 38.2
Electrolysis of water.

at the negative electrode, and oxygen at the positive electrode. The water is decomposed into its constituents. The volume of hydrogen released is twice that of oxygen. A simplified explanation of the process by which the water is decomposed is as follows: A sulfuric acid molecule in solution splits into one SO_4^{--} and two H^+ ions. (These hydrogen ions become attached to water molecules, forming H_3O^+ ions, but this is a complication which we need not consider further.) The hydrogen ions are attracted to the cathode, where they receive electrons to form neutral hydrogen atoms. Two atoms promptly form a hydrogen molecule which rises to the top of the collecting tube. The SO_4^{--} ions give up two electrons at the positive terminal and then unite with two atoms of hydrogen to form sulfuric acid. These atoms of hydrogen are taken from the water, and oxygen is set free. Two atoms of oxygen unite to form a molecule of oxygen gas. The sulfuric acid formed at the anode goes into solution; consequently, the amount of sulfuric acid in the water does not change.

38.2 Faraday's Laws of Electrolysis

To understand the quantitative laws of electrolysis, consider a number of electrolytic cells connected in series (Fig. 38.3) with a battery so that the same current passes through each cell for the same time. Suppose cell A contains a solution of silver nitrate with silver electrodes, B a solution of sulfuric acid with platinum electrodes, C a solution of copper sulfate with copper electrodes, and D a solution of nickel chloride with nickel electrodes. Passage of a charge through the cells liberates, at the respective cathodes, silver, hydrogen, copper, and nickel. By determining the amount of substance liberated at each cathode as a function of the charge transported, it is possible to confirm two laws of electrolysis, which were discovered by Michael Faraday.

1. *The mass of any substance liberated is proportional to the charge which passes through the cell.* Hence, the mass liberated is proportional to the product of the current and the time.

2. *The masses of different elements liberated by a given charge are proportional to the ratios of atomic weight to valence.*

Suppose that in cell B the current exists until 1.008 g of hydrogen is liberated. Then, in cell A, 107.9 g of silver is deposited; in cell C, 31.77 g of copper; in cell D, 29.35 g of nickel. Whatever current is chosen, and whatever the length of time it exists, the masses deposited

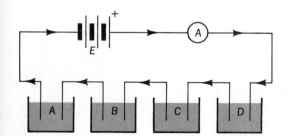

FIGURE 38.3
Four electrolysis cells connected in series.

at these cathodes always bear the same ratio to each other and are proportional to the quotient obtained by dividing the atomic weight by the valence. The ratio of the atomic weight to the valence of an element is called the *chemical equivalent,* or *combining weight.* When an element is monovalent, the chemical equivalent is equal to the atomic weight. If the element is divalent, the chemical equivalent is equal to one-half the atomic weight.

It requires 96,487 coulombs to deposit 1 g-equivalent wt of any element, and 9.65×10^7 coulombs to deposit 1 kg-equivalent wt. A charge of 96,487 coulombs is called one *faraday.* Faraday's two laws of electrolysis can be summarized by the relation

$$m = \frac{Q}{9.65 \times 10^7} \frac{A}{v} \qquad \textbf{38.1}$$

where m is the mass of the element liberated in kilograms, Q is the total charge in coulombs, A is the atomic weight of the element, and v is its valence.

The mass deposited is directly proportional to the charge. *The electrochemical equivalent of any substance is defined as the ratio of the mass of the substance deposited to the charge transferred.* It is denoted by the symbol Z. From Eq. (38.1),

$$Z = \frac{m}{Q} = \frac{1}{9.65 \times 10^7} \frac{A}{v} \qquad \textbf{38.2}$$

One of the most accurate methods we have for measuring the electric charge which passes through a circuit is to insert in the circuit an electrolytic cell containing a solution of silver nitrate. The mass of silver deposited is a measure of the total quantity of charge passed. Indeed, for many years the ampere was defined as that current which would deposit 0.001118 g/sec from a standard solution of silver nitrate. Since 1948 the ampere has been defined in terms of the interaction between two current-carrying conductors (Sec. 39.8).

38.3 Applications of Electrolysis

Electrolysis is of great commercial importance. The chromium plating of automobile parts and the silver plating of tableware are examples of the wide variety of commercial plating operations. Practically all our aluminum is produced by the electrolysis of aluminum oxide from a molten mixture. It takes 10 kW-hr of electrical energy to produce a single pound of aluminum. Chlorine and many other commercially important elements are obtained by electrolytic processes.

By no means are all electrolytic processes desirable. Electrolysis is an important factor in limiting the life of underground pipes. When a steel pipe is laid near an electrified railroad, the current may find its way into the pipe instead of traveling from the generator to the motors directly through the track. At certain points the water pipe may be eaten away, as is the anode in the electrolysis of copper sulfate. The electrochemical action is complex, but, as part of the process, iron is removed from the pipe in regions where it serves as anode.

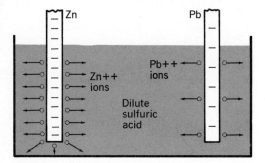

FIGURE 38.4
Diffusion of ions in a zinc–lead–sulfuric-acid cell.

38.4 Chemical Electromotive Forces

Electrical energy used to send electric current through a solution can produce chemical reactions such as the liberation of hydrogen and oxygen from water. The reverse process, i.e., chemical reactions providing electrical energy, also occurs. This fact was discovered about 1800 by the Italian physicist Volta, who built the first batteries.

Most batteries are composed of several cells connected in series. In each cell a chemical reaction converts chemical energy into electrical energy. A cell easily analyzed is one in which a zinc plate and a lead plate are immersed in a dilute solution of sulfuric acid (Fig. 38.4). Zinc ions leave the metal and go into solution. Each zinc ion bears two units of positive charge, having left two electrons with the metal. Thus, the zinc metal becomes negatively charged. As it becomes more negative, it attracts positive zinc ions in the solution. Eventually an equilibrium is reached in which the rate of loss of zinc ions is equal to the rate of return. When this occurs, the potential of the zinc is lower than the potential of the solution.

Similarly, lead ions leave the lead plate and go into solution. They bear two unit positive charges and leave the lead plate negative relative to the solution. However, equilibrium for the lead ions is established when the lead is less negative than the zinc. There is now a potential difference between the zinc plate and the lead plate, as shown in Figure 38.5a. If a wire is connected between the zinc and lead plates, electrons flow through the wire from the zinc to the

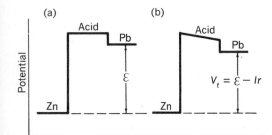

FIGURE 38.5
How potential varies in a zinc–lead–sulfuric-acid cell (a) when there is no current, and (b) when a current is drawn.

lead. When there is a current through the cell, there is a potential drop in the solution, owing to its resistance (Fig. 38.5b).

As electrons leave the zinc plate, it becomes less negative; the equilibrium is disturbed, so that more zinc ions go into solution. At the same time the lead plate becomes more negative, and positive ions are attracted back.

Chemical cells can be made from a large number of different materials. The emf depends on the particular materials involved. Generally speaking, the most active chemical metal forms the negative terminal. Table 38.1 shows the electromotive series of metals. It indicates the potentials of various metals relative to a hydrogen electrode formed by bubbling hydrogen gas over a spongy platinum conductor. The values in the table are for standard ion concentrations.

An *ideal* cell utilizing any two of these elements as electrodes has an emf given by the difference between the potential differences listed in Table 38.1 for the elements in question. For example, the potential of the copper-zinc cell can be predicted by observing that zinc, relative to hydrogen, has a potential of -0.76, while copper has a potential of $+0.34$. A copper-zinc cell has an emf of approximately 1.10 volts.

The emf of a cell is determined primarily by the energy released in the chemical reactions per coulomb of charge transferred through the cell. However, it would be erroneous to assume that the only energy transformations occurring in a cell are between chemical and electrical energy. When some cells are discharged, part of the chemical energy is transformed into heat; when such cells are charged, this heat is retransformed to chemical energy. Other cells transform heat energy into electrical energy during discharge, and electrical energy into heat energy when they are being charged.

TABLE 38.1   *The Electromotive (or Electrochemical) Series (All potential differences are referred to a standard hydrogen electrode taken as zero and are for a temperature of 25° C)*

Element	Potential difference, volts	Element	Potential difference, volts
Li	-2.96	Cd	-0.40
Rb	-2.93	Ni	-0.23
K	-2.92	Sn	-0.14
Ca	-2.76	Pb	-0.12
Na	-2.71	H	0
Mg	-2.40	Cu	0.34
Al	-1.70	Ag	0.80
Zn	-0.76	Hg	0.80
Fe	-0.44	Au	1.5

38.5 Polarization of Cells

If a zinc strip and a copper strip are inserted into a juicy lemon, the juice serves as electrolyte, and a potential difference can be observed between the zinc and the copper. Another simple cell can be made by immersing a zinc plate and a copper plate in a dilute solution of some acid such as H_2SO_4. Neither of these zinc-acid-copper cells performs very satisfactorily as a source of emf because, as current is drawn, hydrogen ions are deposited on the copper. This reduces the emf, since the positive electrode is now essentially hydrogen, rather than copper. Further, hydrogen bubbles on the surface of the plate form an insulating layer and greatly increase the resistance of the cell. This is an example of an effect called *polarization*. (This should not be confused with polarization of a dielectric.) Polarization can occur in many ways in a cell, but its net effect is to reduce the observed emf to a value below that which would be expected on the basis of the electrochemical series. This occurs because one or both of the terminals is coated with some less effective material.

38.6 Primary and Secondary Batteries

A few of the many possible kinds of chemical reactions which may be used for batteries are reversible. In most cases the chemical reaction cannot be reversed by changing the direction of the current. A cell in which the chemical reaction is irreversible is a *primary* cell, while one which can be charged and discharged repeatedly is known as a *secondary* cell. The simple zinc-acid-copper cell mentioned above is a primary cell. If one attempts to reverse the chemical process by making the zinc electrode positive, the zinc ions do not plate out. Rather, copper and hydrogen ions are deposited, and the zinc stays in solution. The reaction is not reversible.

There are, however, a number of reversible cells which are useful for batteries. Prominent among them are the lead storage cell and the Edison cell (Sec. 38.7), which can be charged and recharged many times.

< 38.7 Composition of Common Cells

The chemical reactions which take place in several kinds of cells of practical or historical importance are discussed below.

The Daniell Cell. One of the earliest practical sources of emf was the Daniell cell. It consists of a copper electrode submerged in copper sulfate and a zinc electrode in zinc sulfate. A porous partition separates the zinc sulfate from the copper sulfate such that charges can pass through but the chemicals do not mix readily. In such a cell the zinc electrode becomes negative, and the copper plate positive. When the plates of the Daniell cell are connected through a resistance, electrons flowing through the wire reduce the negative charge on the zinc terminal and permit more zinc to go into solution. The potential of the copper electrode is reduced, and copper ions are deposited from the solution. The net effect of the reaction is to convert zinc and copper sulfate into zinc sulfate plus copper. In this reaction chemical energy is transformed into electrical energy.

In the early days of telegraphy the Daniell cell was the standard source of emf. Its output is about 1.1 volts, but the terminal potential difference of a cell is somewhat less when current is drawn. The *volt* as the practical unit of potential difference originated with the use of Daniell cells in early telegraph circuits, when the "voltage" was just the number of Daniell cells connected in series.

The Dry Cell. The Leclanché cell is a primary cell of interest because a later modification, known as the *dry cell,* is widely used. This cell consists of a zinc rod which dips into a solution of ammonium chloride. The other electrode of the cell is a carbon rod. The ammonium chloride in the electrolyte dissociates into NH_4^+ and Cl^-. The interaction of the Cl^- ions with the zinc leaves the zinc plate negative. When the plates are connected externally, electrons flow to the carbon rod. The NH_4^+ ions go to the carbon and there give up their charge, breaking down into NH_3 and hydrogen. Hydrogen collects on the electrode, and the NH_3 is absorbed by the water. If the hydrogen remained on the electrode, the cell would soon be polarized. To prevent this, the carbon electrode is surrounded by a cup filled with manganese dioxide and graphite. The MnO_2 reacts chemically with the hydrogen to produce water and thus acts as a *depolarizer.* The graphite serves to keep the material in the cup conducting. Since the action of the depolarizer is slow, the cell is adapted to work in which it is used for a short time and then allowed to stand. This type of cell has an emf of about 1.5 volts.

The dry cell (Fig. 38.6) differs from the Leclanché cell only in that the electrolyte is in the form of a paste of ammonium chloride instead of a solution. The negative electrode is the zinc can that contains the carbon and paste. The zinc on the inside of the can is covered with several layers of blotting paper, and the space around the carbon rod that forms the positive electrode is filled with a mixture of carbon, manganese dioxide, and sawdust saturated with a solution of ammonium chloride. The top is sealed with wax to prevent evaporation of the moisture in the paste. (When a dry cell is really dry, its conductance is so low that it is useless.)

Lead Storage Cell. In the lead storage cell, both the positive and negative plates are made of heavy lead grids full of holes or grooves filled with the active material. The positive plates contain lead peroxide, and the negative plates spongy lead. A cell is usually formed of a number of such plates, alternately negative and positive, covered with sulfuric acid. The negative plates are connected together and act as one terminal of the battery, and the positive plates are connected together to form the other terminal. It is customary to have one more negative plate than positive so that every positive plate lies between two negative ones. In this way, both sides of a positive plate are charged or discharged. During the process of recharging, there is a restoration of the peroxide accompanied by an increase in volume, causing a swelling of the plate. Since this swelling takes place equally

FIGURE 38.6
Dry cell.

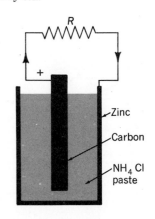

Zinc

Carbon

NH_4 Cl
paste

on both sides of a positive plate, there is little tendency for the plates to warp. If the plates are close together and if, through the use of a large number of plates, the area is large, the cell has a small internal resistance. By increasing the number of plates and making the areas larger, the current capacity of the cell is increased.

When a lead storage cell is delivering a current, both the lead peroxide on the positive electrode and the spongy lead on the negative electrode are converted to lead sulfate. As this occurs, the emf of the cell gradually decreases, as shown in Figure 38.7. In order to charge the battery and make it ready for further use, it is only necessary to maintain an electric current in it in a direction opposite that in which the current flows when the cell is in use. During this process the lead sulfate on the negative plate is reduced to spongy lead, while the lead sulfate on the positive plate is reconverted to lead peroxide. After a sufficient charging time, the original condition of the battery is restored. The chemical action taking place during the process of charging and discharging may be represented by the following equations:

Discharging:

| At positive plate, | $PbO_2 + H_2SO_4 + H_2 \rightarrow PbSO_4 + 2H_2O$ |
| At negative plate, | $Pb + SO_4 \rightarrow PbSO_4$ |

Charging:

| At positive plate, | $PbSO_4 + SO_4 + 2H_2O \rightarrow PbO_2 + 2H_2SO_4$ |
| At negative plate, | $PbSO_4 + H_2 \rightarrow Pb + H_2SO_4$ |

It is seen from these equations that, during the process of charging, sulfuric acid is formed. Since the specific gravity of H_2SO_4 is greater than that of water, the density of the electrolyte rises when a battery is being charged. During discharge, sulfuric acid disappears and water is formed. For this reason, the density of the electrolyte decreases during discharge (Figure 38.7). By measuring the density of the electrolyte, it is possible to find the state of charge of the battery.

Edison Storage Cell. A storage battery composed of Edison cells is lighter, more rugged, and longer-lived than a lead storage battery. In the Edison cell the negative plate is a nickel-plated steel grid with a large number of pockets filled with powdered iron and iron oxide

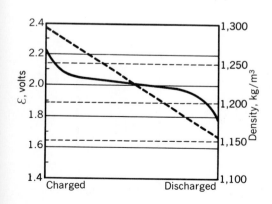

FIGURE 38.7

How the electromotive force (solid line) of a lead cell and the density (dashed line) of sulfuric acid vary with the state of charge.

(FeO). The positive plate is a nickel-plated steel grid with perforated steel tubes filled with alternate layers of nickel oxides and flaked nickel. The electrolyte is a solution of potassium hydroxide. When the cell is discharging, the nickel oxides are reduced to lower oxides, and the iron is oxidized. When the cell is being charged, the reaction is reversed. The electrolyte enters into intermediate reactions. Its effect in charging and discharging is to transfer oxygen from one plate of the cell to the other. The density changes only slightly during the reactions. The normal emf of an Edison cell is about 1.2 volts, varying from 1.4 volts to 0.9 volt as the cell discharges. This variation of emf and the relatively high cost are major disadvantages of Edison cells.

Weston Standard Cell. Standard cells offer a means of obtaining definite, known, and constant potential differences. The most widely used of these standard cells is the cadmium or Weston cell (Fig. 38.8). Its emf changes very little with temperature, which is one of the reasons the Weston cell is considered the best standard available. At 20°C its emf is 1.0183 volts, and the emf decreases about 4×10^{-5} volt for each centigrade degree of temperature increase.

38.8 Fuel Cells

In a battery chemical energy may be converted into electrical energy until one or more of the active materials is used up, at which point the battery is ready for discard or, possibly, recharge. In a fuel cell active materials are supplied, and the reaction products removed, continuously; thus the fuel cell can operate as long as the required materials are supplied.

In one type of fuel cell hydrogen gas and oxygen are supplied, and energy is released by the oxidation of hydrogen to form water; the process is the reverse of that which occurs in the electrolysis of water. In other kinds of fuel cells chemical energy from the oxidation of various hydrocarbons is converted into electrical energy. A major advantage of the fuel cell is its high efficiency—vastly greater than that available when the fuel is burned in a heat engine and then converted to electrical energy, chiefly because of the low Carnot efficiency (Sec. 23.6). A hydrogen-oxygen fuel cell at 25°C has a theoretical peak efficiency of 83 per cent; other fuel cells have still higher theoretical

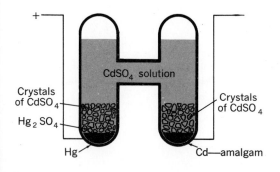

Crystals of CdSO$_4$

Hg$_2$SO$_4$

CdSO$_4$ solution

Crystals of CdSO$_4$

Hg

Cd—amalgam

FIGURE 38.8
Weston standard cell.

efficiencies, and practical fuel cells can convert 60 to 70 per cent of chemical energy to electrical energy.

Although Grove produced the first successful fuel cell in 1839, it is only recently that fuel cells have been developed to the point of economic significance.

38.9 Thermoelectricity: The Seebeck Effect

When two different materials are in contact, there is ordinarily a potential difference between them. In electrostatics this phenomenon permits us to produce charges by contact and separation. In batteries the potential differences between metals and solutions give rise to the emfs. When two metals are placed in contact, the potential difference between them depends on the metals and on the temperature of the junction.

When two wires of dissimilar metals (e.g., copper and iron) are joined together at the ends to form a closed circuit and one of the junctions thus formed is maintained at a temperature different from that of the other (Fig. 38.9), an electric current is established in the circuit. This effect was discovered in 1821 by Seebeck. The magnitude of the emf producing the current depends on the two kinds of wire and on the temperatures of the two junctions. If the junctions are at the same temperature, the emfs established are exactly equal and opposite, so that there is no net emf.

Consider first a thermocouple made of iron and copper (Fig. 38.9). If one of the junctions is kept at 0°C while the other is heated, a net thermoelectromotive force is produced. When the temperature of the hot junction is raised, the thermal emf first increases at a nearly uniform rate (Fig. 38.10). As the temperature is raised further, the rate of increase becomes less. When the temperature of the hot junction becomes 260°C, a further increase in temperature results in a decrease in the thermal emf. The temperature at which the emf reaches its maximum is the *neutral temperature,* so named because there is neither increase nor decrease of thermal emf with temperature. When the temperature of the hot junction is raised above the neutral temperature, the thermal emf decreases and finally becomes zero at approximately 520°C. If the temperature of the hot junction is still

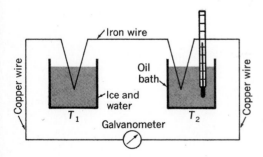

FIGURE 38.9

Thermal emf exists when the temperatures of the two copper-iron junctions are different.

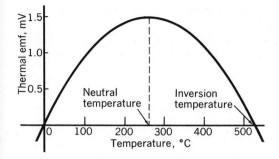

FIGURE 38.10

Thermal emf of a copper-iron thermocouple as a function of the temperature of the hot junction when the cold junction is at 0°C. The neutral temperature and the peak emf depend on the purity of the metals.

further increased, the current in the circuit reverses direction. The temperature at which the thermal emf passes through zero is called the *inversion temperature*. The curve obtained by plotting thermo-electromotive force as a function of the temperature of one junction (with the second junction kept at constant temperature) has the shape of a parabola.

For some materials, such as chromel and alumel, the emf increases continuously as the temperature of the hot junction is raised. For these materials the neutral temperature and the inversion temperature are reached by cooling the variable-temperature junction rather than by warming it.

Thermocouples are convenient for measuring temperatures, since the emf depends on the temperature difference between the junctions in a known way. Ordinarily, one junction is kept at a constant temperature, usually in an ice bath at 0°C. The hot junction need not be anywhere near the cold junction. It may be installed at some inaccessible point, where it would be impossible to place and read a standard mercury thermometer. Thermocouples can be used for measuring temperatures roughly up to the melting points of the materials involved, which may be as high as 2900°F for some couples. Further, they can be made much smaller than glass or metal expansion thermometers, so that they can be used to measure the temperatures of very small objects, such as insects or twigs of trees.

It is likely that one would want to make connection to a galvanometer by means of copper wires fastened to the ends of the thermocouple elements. Adding other materials in the circuit has *no effect so long as the junctions of the other metals are all at the same temperature.* Electromotive forces exist at the new junctions, but the algebraic sum of the emfs in the circuit remains the same. The lengths of the wires have no effect on the emf (although they do influence the resistance of the circuit).

The emfs involved in the Seebeck effect are ordinarily very small, usually of the order of millivolts. To obtain higher emfs, we may connect a number of thermocouples in series, thus producing a *thermopile.* Thermopiles are often used for measuring radiant energy.

38.10 The Peltier and Thomson Effects

We have seen that when two dissimilar metals are placed in contact, electrons diffuse from one metal to the other, and an emf exists between the surfaces. This potential difference is called the *Peltier emf*. It depends on the metals in contact and upon the temperature of the junction.

If the two ends of a wire of any material are at different temperatures, electrons are likely to diffuse more rapidly in one direction than in the other. This unequal diffusion produces a potential difference called the *Thomson emf*. The Seebeck effect, discussed in Sec. 38.9, arises as the result of Thomson emfs between opposite ends of wires of the same material which are at different temperatures and Peltier emfs at the junctions of the metals. Usually the Peltier emfs greatly exceed the Thomson emfs.

When a current is passed through a thermocouple by a battery in the circuit, the Peltier emf at one junction aids the battery, while the Peltier emf at the second junction is in series opposing. At the junction where the Peltier emf is in opposition, heat is evolved not only because of the Joule heating effect, but also because of the work done against the emf. At the other junction thermal energy is absorbed and converted into electrical energy. The temperature of this junction may be reduced substantially. When a current is passed through a thermocouple made of bismuth and antimony, one junction is heated and the other is cooled. Heat is developed at one junction and absorbed at the other. This is known as the *Peltier effect*.

Questions

1. What factors determine the electromotive force of a battery?

2. What is the source of the electrical energy supplied by a chemical cell?

3. Why aren't thermocouples more widely used as practical generators of electrical energy?

4. A chromel-alumel thermocouple is connected to a galvanometer by copper wires. Under what conditions does the presence of the copper wires change the net emf in the circuit?

5. What happens to the various metallic impurities in the electrolytic purification of copper?

Problems

1. A copper plate of 108.962 g mass is placed in an electroplating bath. A steady current is sent through the bath for 20 min, and the mass of the plate is increased to 110.243 g. What was the current in amperes, assuming copper is divalent?

Ans. 3.24 amp

2. A current of 5 amp flows for 2 hr through a series of cells containing nickel nitrate, copper sulfate ($CuSO_4$), and silver nitrate. Find the masses of nickel (valence 2), copper (valence 2), and silver (valence 1) deposited.

3. An electrolytic cell containing a solution of silver nitrate is connected in series with a cell containing copper sulfate. What mass of Ag^+ ions is deposited on the cathode of the first cell by a charge which deposits 2 g of Cu^{++} ions on the cathode of the second cell? What charge has passed through the two cells? *Ans.* 6.78 g; 6,070 coulombs

4. How long a time will be required for a current of 8 amp to plate 1.9 g of silver on a knife?

5. Find the volumes of hydrogen and oxygen released under standard conditions by the electrolysis of acidulated water for a period of 20 min with a current of 0.5 amp.
Ans. 69.6 cm^3; 34.8 cm^3

6. An object that has a surface of 15 cm^2 is to be plated with silver. What will be the average thickness of the silver if a current of 0.2 amp flows for 8 hr?

7. Find the electrochemical equivalent of gold if a current of 0.4 amp deposits 1.170 g in 24 min. *Ans.* 2.04 × 10^{-6} kg/coulomb

8. Find the electrochemical equivalent of chlorine, which is monovalent.

CHAPTER 39 *Electric charges at rest exert forces on one another through Coulomb interaction. Charges in motion also interact with one another, through magnetic fields. Currents, of course, are charges in motion, and so magnetic interactions are of great importance whenever we deal with currents. Most of our meters, our electric motors, and the great generators of our electric companies depend on magnetic interactions for their operation. Before we can study the physics underlying these devices, we must gain some knowledge of magnetism and magnetic fields.*

Magnetic Fields of Currents

39.1 Magnets

The mineral lodestone (Fe_3O_4) has the ability to attract other pieces of the same mineral or small pieces of iron. This fact was known in the seventh century B.C. How much earlier it had been discovered we do not know. Lodestones turn with the same side toward the north when they are suspended from cords or floated on corks in water. This property led to the invention of the mariner's compass before the twelfth century.

When a steel knitting needle is stroked from one end to the other with a piece of lodestone, the needle may acquire the property of attracting iron filings and of setting itself along a north-south line when suspended by a string. Such a needle is said to be *magnetized* and is commonly called a *magnet*. Most materials cannot be magnetized in this way; relatively few show attraction for a lodestone or a small magnet. Iron and some of its alloys are by far the best known of magnetic materials; cobalt, nickel, and a number of alloys also exhibit prominent magnetic properties.

One end of a magnetized needle, suspended by a cord so that it is free to rotate in any direction, normally points in a northerly direction. This end of the needle is commonly called the *north pole* (N pole), an abbreviation for the more fully descriptive *north-seeking pole*. The opposite end of the needle is called the *south pole* (S pole).

If this magnetized needle is dipped into soft-iron filings, the filings cling tenaciously to the ends; relatively few stick to the middle. It is often convenient to think of the magnetic properties of the needle as being concentrated in the two ends or poles, although this is an oversimplification.

When two magnetized needles are brought near one another, the two north poles repel one another, as do the two south poles. On the other hand, there is an attractive force between the north pole of one magnet and the south pole of the other. Such observations lead to the conclusion that *like poles repel, unlike poles attract.*

39.2 Interactions of Currents and Magnets

In 1819 Oersted discovered that a magnet in the neighborhood of a current-bearing wire undergoes a deflection. A magnetized needle held above a straight wire carrying a current is deflected as shown in Figure 39.1. If the magnet is held below the wire, the N pole is deflected in the opposite direction. The direction in which a north pole points may always be found by the application of a simple rule, illustrated in Figure 39.2:

If the right thumb is pointed in the direction of the conventional current and the fingers are allowed to curl, the direction in which the fingers point is the direction in which the north pole of the needle is deflected by the current.

If current is passed through a long cylindrical coil of wire (called a *solenoid*) produced by winding fine wire on a matchstick, the solenoid behaves like a small magnet of the same shape. While current is passing through the solenoid, it will pick up small iron filings. It has a north and a south "pole," which exert forces on other poles. The fact that a current-bearing solenoid behaves like a magnet of the same dimensions led Ampère to suggest in 1820 that the forces between iron magnets arise from electric currents in the iron. This point of view has been substantiated by later research and is discussed in Chap. 40.

Magnetic interactions occur among moving charges, whether they be currents in wires, a beam of electrons in a television tube, or the electrons in magnetic materials. The forces so produced are of tremendous practical importance. Electric motors depend on them, as do most of our meters for measuring electric currents and potential differences.

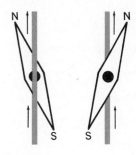

FIGURE 39.1

Current deflecting a compass needle.

FIGURE 39.2

Pointing the right thumb in the direction of the conventional current and curling the fingers in the direction of the magnetic field, which is the direction of the force on the N pole of a magnetic needle.

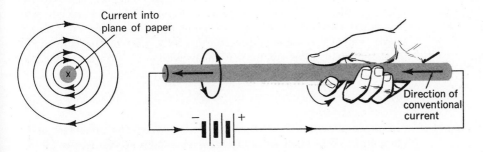

(a)

(b)

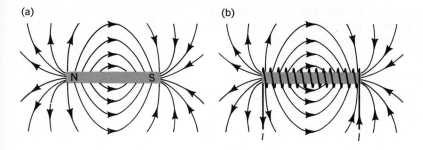

FIGURE 39.3

Magnetic fields are similar around (a) a bar magnet, and (b) a current-bearing solenoid.

39.3 The Magnetic Field

A magnetic field is any region in which forces may be observed to act on small magnets or on small current-bearing elements. *The direction of the magnetic field at any point is the direction of the force experienced by the north-seeking pole of a small test magnet when the test magnet is placed at the point.* A small current-bearing solenoid could be substituted for the test magnet.

One may readily explore the magnetic field associated with a large bar magnet by using a small compass needle to find the direction in which the N pole points at various places in the field. A plot of the magnetic field associated with a magnet is shown in Figure 39.3a. In discussing magnetic fields, it is convenient to make use of magnetic lines of force, defined as lines whose tangents give the direction of the magnetic field at every point. It is customary to draw the lines close together where the field is strong, farther apart where the field becomes weaker. The lines of force for a bar magnet are similar to those for a suitably chosen current-bearing solenoid (Fig. 39.3b). The magnetic field associated with a straight current-bearing conductor is shown in Figure 39.2. The lines of force in this case are circles concentric with the wire.

The magnetic field at any point is characterized not only by a direction, but also by a strength. The vector which describes the field at a point is called the *magnetic induction, magnetic flux density,* or *magnetic intensity*. It is represented by the symbol **B**. To measure **B,** we make use of the fact that there is a force on a current element in a magnetic field.

Consider first the special case of the uniform magnetic field between the pole pieces of the large magnet of Figure 39.4. If a straight wire bearing a current I is placed perpendicular to the lines of magnetic force, and if l represents the length of the part of the wire in the magnetic field, there is a force **F** on the wire in the direction indicated. We define the magnetic intensity **B** with the equation

$$B = \frac{F}{Il}$$

39.1

In practical units **F** is measured in newtons, I in amperes, and l in meters. Then **B** has the dimensions newtons per ampere-meter.

FIGURE 39.4

A current-bearing conductor lying perpendicular to a uniform magnetic field experiences a force which is perpendicular to both the magnetic field and its own length. (**B** is directed downward.)

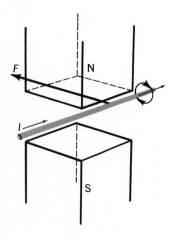

In the preceding discussion we stated that the wire must be perpendicular to the direction of the magnetic field. This is very important; indeed, if the wire lies along the lines of force, there is no force at all. If the wire makes an angle θ with the field, the force is given by

$$F = IlB \sin \theta \qquad\qquad \textbf{39.2}$$

Many magnetic fields are not uniform, but vary from point to point. The field intensity **B** at any point is the limit of the ratio $\Delta F / I \, \Delta l$ then, as Δl is made smaller and smaller. Here ΔF represents the small force on a small element of length Δl. The result of using any finite length l of wire is to measure the average intensity over the region covered by l. In actual practice it is often difficult to determine the force on a small element of a current-bearing conductor; therefore other means are ordinarily used to measure **B**.

The direction of the force on a current-bearing wire is perpendicular both to the length of the wire and to the magnetic field. For the particular situation of Figure 39.4 the direction of this force may be found as follows: The lines of flux associated with the current are concentric circles, as indicated. The magnetic field due to the current in the wire exerts a force on the N pole of the magnet in the direction opposite that indicated by **F**. Similarly, the force on the S pole due to the current is out of the paper (opposite to **F**). Since the current in the wire pushes outward on the magnet, the magnet exerts a force inward on the current-bearing wire in accordance with Newton's third law.

The origin of some magnetic fields, such as that of the earth, may not be obvious. In such a case one can find the direction of the force on the wire by observing that on one side of the wire the magnetic field due to the current (Fig. 39.5) reinforces the field already present, while on the other side of the wire the two fields are opposite in direction. The force on the wire is directed from the stronger field toward the weaker one, or from the side on which the two fields reinforce to the side on which the two fields oppose.

39.4 Magnetic Force on a Moving Charge

The force exerted on a current-bearing conductor in a magnetic field is the resultant of the forces which act on individual moving charges in the conductor. Let us consider a conductor in which there are n charged particles per unit length, each with charge $+q$ and velocity v perpendicular to a magnetic induction B (Fig. 39.6). The current through the plane PP' is the charge passing per second, which is

$$I = qnv$$

The force on a length l of wire is out of the plane of the paper and is given by $IlB = qnlvB$. Since the number of charges in the length l is nl, the force on each particle is

$$F = qvB \qquad\qquad \textbf{39.3}$$

Equation (39.3) gives the force on a single charged particle moving with a velocity v perpendicular to a magnetic field of intensity B.

FIGURE 39.5

The force on a current-bearing conductor in a magnetic field is from the stronger toward the weaker resultant field.

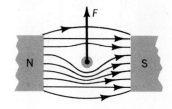

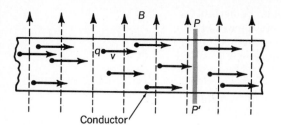

FIGURE 39.6

The force on a current-bearing conductor in a magnetic field results from the forces acting on the individual moving charges.

But what is the force if the particle is not moving at right angles to **B?** In this case we resolve the velocity **v** into components $v \sin \theta$ perpendicular to **B** and $v \cos \theta$ parallel to **B,** where θ is the angle between **v** and **B.** There is no force exerted by a magnetic field on a charge moving parallel to the field; only the component of the velocity perpendicular to **B** contributes to the resulting force, which is given by

$$F = qvB \sin \theta \qquad \textbf{39.3}a$$

The force is perpendicular to the plane defined by **B** and **v.** Equation (39.3a) is one of the basic equations of charged-particle physics.

The deflection of charged particles by magnetic fields has many uses. The electron beam which sketches the pictures on a television tube is usually directed by magnetic forces. In cyclotrons, betatrons, and synchrotrons, accelerated charged particles are restrained to roughly circular paths by magnetic fields. Electron microscopes and mass spectrographs use magnetic forces to control beams of charged particles. Some of these important instruments are described in later chapters.

39.5 The Magnetic Moment of a Coil

FIGURE 39.7

A rectangular loop of wire bearing a current is subject to a torque in a magnetic field unless its plane is perpendicular to the magnetic lines of force.

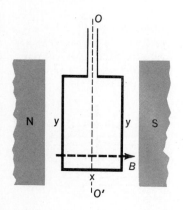

Consider a single rectangular loop of wire, bearing a current I, placed in a uniform magnetic field of intensity B with one side of the rectangle perpendicular to the field and another side lying along the field (Fig. 39.7). Let y represent the length of the side perpendicular to the magnetic field, and x the length of the side parallel to the magnetic field. Under these circumstances there are no forces on the sides marked x, but the force on each of the wires perpendicular to the field is given by $F = BIy$. The lever arm about the axis OO' for one of the vertical sides is $x/2$, and the torque L on this one side is given by $L = BIyx/2$. The net torque acting to rotate the loop is twice this, or $BIyx$. The product yx is equal to the area A of the rectangle. The torque L on the loop is thus

$$\boxed{L = BIA} \qquad \textbf{39.4}$$

Current-bearing coils and magnetized materials in various shapes also experience torques in a magnetic field. The concept of magnetic moment, which we introduce now, is applicable to any object which is subject to a torque when it is placed in a uniform magnetic field. *The magnetic moment M of any object is the ratio of the torque experienced*

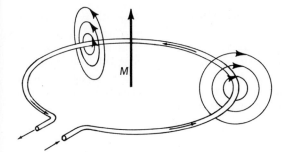

FIGURE 39.8

Magnetic field and magnetic moment associated with a current-bearing loop.

by the object when it is placed in a uniform magnetic field B in such a position that the torque takes on its maximum value to the magnetic induction B; thus, $M = L_{max}/B$.

For the coil of Figure 39.7 the torque, maximum when the plane of the coil is parallel to the magnetic field B, is BIA, and hence the magnetic moment is IA. By use of calculus it can be shown that Eq. (39.4) is applicable to a loop of any shape.

The magnetic moment M of a current-bearing loop is the product of the current I and the area A of the loop. The magnetic moment is a vector perpendicular to the plane of the coil in the direction in which a right-handed screw would advance if turned in the direction of the current I. It has the dimensions amp-m². The magnetic moment associated with a current-bearing loop is shown in Figure 39.8. The torque L on a loop of magnetic moment M is given by BM when M is perpendicular to B. When M and B are parallel, the torque is zero. In general, if the angle between M and B is θ, the torque is given by

$$L = BM \sin \theta \tag{39.5}$$

If there is no opposing torque, the loop (Fig. 39.7) rotates under the influence of the magnetic field until the magnetic moment is aligned in the direction of the field.

Thus far we have been discussing single loops. If a coil made by winding N turns in series bears a current I, each turn has a magnetic moment of magnitude IA, and the resultant magnetic moment is N times that of a single loop. Thus, for a coil of N turns, $M = NIA$.

39.6 The Moving-coil Galvanometer

If a coil such as that of Figure 39.9 is suspended between the poles of a permanent magnet and a small current is passed through the coil, the coil rotates until the restoring torque exerted by the suspension is equal to the torque due to the interaction of the current and the magnetic field. This latter torque is proportional to the current. Therefore, the angular deflection of the coil is proportional to the current, provided the restoring torque is proportional to the angular displacement and the magnetic field is perpendicular to **M** for all displacements. This latter condition is reasonably well satisfied for angles up to 30°

FIGURE 39.9

Moving-coil galvanometer.

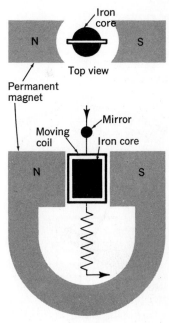

Side view

for the magnet of Figure 39.9. Thus, a single loop of wire suspended by an elastic suspension in a magnetic field can be used to detect and measure currents. The sensitivity of the instrument can be changed by adding turns to the coil. Such a coil, suspended in a magnetic field, is called a *galvanometer* when it is used to detect and measure small currents. A light pointer or mirror attached to the coil is ordinarily used to measure the angular deflection.

39.7 Ammeters and Voltmeters

When a galvanometer and its scale are so adjusted that the scale readings indicate the current passing through some portion of a circuit in amperes, the meter is called an *ammeter*. A common form of ammeter is shown in Figure 39.10. It consists of a coil of fine copper wire wound on a light frame which is mounted on jeweled bearings between the poles of a permanent magnet. When a current exists in the coil, it rotates between the poles of the magnet. Two spiral springs, one at the top and the other at the bottom, carry the current into and out of the coil and provide a restoring torque proportional to the angular displacement.

Since a very small fraction of an ampere through the coil of an ordinary ammeter produces a full-scale deflection, it is necessary to use a low-resistance *shunt* to carry a large fraction of the current which passes through the ammeter. (A shunt is a resistance connected in parallel with a circuit element.) Because the current flowing in the movable coil is always a constant fraction of the full current entering the instrument, the scale can be calibrated so that the pointer indicates the entire current. Any galvanometer can be made to operate as an ammeter by use of a suitable shunt. By choice of some other shunt, the galvanometer can be made into an ammeter of different range.

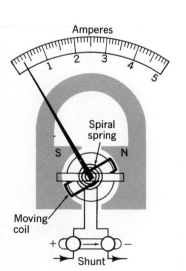

FIGURE 39.10

An ammeter registers the effect of variations in current through a coil in a magnetic field.

FIGURE 39.11

Two-scale voltmeter.

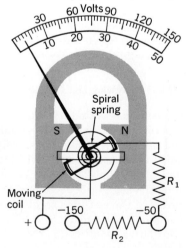

A galvanometer can also be made into a *voltmeter* by the proper application of an additional resistance (Fig. 39.11). A voltmeter, as its name implies, is an instrument used to measure potential difference. By connecting a high resistance in series with the galvanometer coil, the current passing through the coil can be limited to a value which will not exceed full-scale deflection. Since for a given resistance the current is directly proportional to the potential difference across the instrument, the deflection of the pointer is proportional to the potential difference, and the scale may be calibrated to read potential difference directly in volts. By suitable choice of the series resistance one can make a voltmeter which gives full-scale deflection for any desired potential difference across its terminals.

Example A galvanometer requires 0.00015 amp to produce a full-scale deflection. The coil has a resistance of 60 ohms. What shunt resistance is needed to convert this galvanometer into an ammeter reading 2 amp full scale?

Of the 2 amp which enter the ammeter for a full-scale deflection, 0.00015 amp must pass through the galvanometer, and the remainder $(2 - 0.00015 = 1.99985$ amp$)$ through the shunt. Since the shunt and galvanometer are in parallel, their potential differences are the same.

$$V_G = V_S \quad \text{and} \quad I_G R_G = I_S R_S$$
$$0.00015 \times 60 = 1.99985 R_S$$
$$R_S = \frac{0.009}{1.99985} = 0.0045 \text{ ohm}$$

Example What series resistance R is needed to convert the galvanometer of the preceding example into a voltmeter reading 6 volts full scale?

When 6 volts is impressed across the voltmeter, a current of 0.00015 amp must pass through the coil and the series resistance if the deflection is to be full scale. The total resistance of the voltmeter must be

$$R_V = \frac{6}{0.00015} = 40{,}000 \text{ ohms}$$

But R_V is equal to R plus the resistance of the galvanometer; therefore

$$R = 40{,}000 - 60 = 39{,}940 \text{ ohms}$$

39.8 The Magnetic Field of a Long Straight Wire

In Sec. 39.2 it is shown that a long straight wire carrying a current has a magnetic field associated with it. The lines of force are concentric circles about the wire. When the wire lies in air (or some other nonmagnetic material), the magnetic intensity **B** at any point is proportional to the current I and inversely proportional to the distance r

from the wire. It can be shown that $B = 2\kappa I/r$, where κ is a constant which has the value 10^{-7} newton/amp². The magnetic field strength B at a distance r from a long straight wire carrying a current I is given by

$$B = \frac{2I}{10^7 r} \hspace{3cm} \textbf{39.6}$$

When two long wires parallel to one another bear currents I_1 and I_2 in the same direction, there is an attractive force between them. If the wires are separated by a distance r, the magnetic field at the first wire due to the current in the second is given by $2I_2/10^7 r$. Therefore, the force on a length l of the first wire is given by

$$F = I_1 l B = \frac{2I_1 I_2 l}{10^7 r} \hspace{2.5cm} \textbf{39.7}$$

The force per unit length is $2I_1 I_2/10^7 r$. That the force is attractive can be seen by studying Figure 39.12. If the directions of the currents in the two wires are opposite, the force between the wires is repulsive. In this figure we make use of the common practice of representing a current out of the paper with a dot (point of an arrow moving toward you) and a current into the paper with cross feathers (tail of an arrow moving away from you).

Although Eq. (39.7) has been derived for long straight wires, there is an attractive force between any two neighboring conductors which are carrying currents in the same direction. One of the most accurate methods of measuring current involves the determination, in an instrument known as the "current balance," of the attractive force between two precisely made, parallel coils carrying the same current. In the absolute system of units, officially adopted by the United States (*National Bureau of Standards Circular* C 459, 1947), the ampere is defined in terms of measurements made with a current balance. The coulomb is then derived from the ampere as the charge which is carried by a current of one ampere in one second. (For pedagogical reasons we have introduced the coulomb first and then defined the ampere; our units are consistent with those adopted by the National Bureau of Standards.)

When coils carry an alternating current, neighboring turns are attracted to one another by forces which change as the alternating

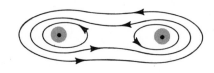
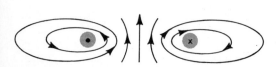

FIGURE 39.12

Two parallel wires attract one another when they bear currents in the same direction, and repel one another when the currents are in opposite directions.

current increases and decreases. The turns may vibrate, moving together and then apart. This leads to the familiar and annoying hum associated with many coils carrying alternating currents.

39.9 The Magnetic Fields of Other Current Configurations

The magnetic field due to any current configuration is the vector sum of the contributions due to the current in each minute element of length Δl. The contribution ΔB to the magnetic field due to the current in a small element of length Δl (Fig. 39.13) is given by

$$\Delta B = \frac{\kappa I \, \Delta l \sin \theta}{r^2}$$ **39.8**

where θ is the angle between the element Δl and the vector $\mathbf{r}$ connecting Δl to the point at which ΔB is to be measured, and κ is 10^{-7} newton/amp². This equation is an expression of a fundamental rule known as *Ampère's law.* Equation (39.8) is applicable only if the wire is in a nonmagnetic medium. It should be emphasized that the contribution ΔB from each element of length Δl is a vector which must be added vectorially to all the other ΔB's if one wishes to find the resultant magnetic intensity.

The magnetic field at the center of a circular loop of wire (Fig. 39.8) of radius a is readily computed by use of Eq. (39.8). Since the contributions ΔB of the tiny elements of length Δl are all in the same direction and are equal in size, addition of the components gives $B = Il/10^7 a^2$. The length of the wire l is $2\pi a$, so that this equation reduces to

$$B = \frac{2\pi I}{10^7 a}$$

If the circular loop is replaced by a circular coil having N turns, the contributions of these turns are all in the same direction. Accordingly, at the center of the circular coil the magnetic intensity $\mathbf{B}$ is given by

$$B = \frac{2\pi N I}{10^7 a}$$ **39.9**

One of the common current configurations in magnetic circuits is that of the solenoid, often used for windings on electromagnets. The solenoid provides a uniform field over its entire central section. If it is long compared with its diameter, the magnetic field is almost the same at all points inside the solenoid, except at distances less than one diameter from the ends. At the ends the field falls off. In the central section of the solenoid the magnetic field $\mathbf{B}$ is given by the relation

$$B = \frac{4\pi n I}{10^7}$$ **39.10**

where n is the number of turns per meter. It is important to note that n represents the *number of turns per unit length,* while N is used to represent the total number of turns; $n = N/l$, where l is the length of the solenoid. Equation (39.10) is applicable no matter what the cross-

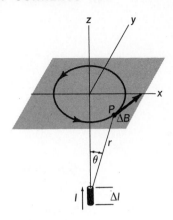

FIGURE 39.13
Ampère's law gives the contribution ΔB to the magnetic field at point P of the current-bearing element of length Δl.

sectional shape of the solenoid may be. Solenoids with square or rectangular cross section are common.

The magnetic fields of a solenoid, a loop, and a single straight wire are shown in Figures 39.3*b*, 39.8, and 39.2, respectively. In every case *magnetic lines of flux are continuous. They never begin or end;* rather they follow closed curves which encircle the current-bearing conductors. In this respect magnetic lines of force are different from electrical lines of force, which begin and end on electric charges.

Questions

1. Can lines of magnetic flux ever cross? Explain.

2. A long helical brass spring hangs vertically with its lower end just making contact with a pool of mercury. If a large current is passed through the mercury and the spring, what will occur? Why? Will the motion of the end of the spring be simple harmonic?

3. How can you convert a galvanometer into an ammeter of specified full-scale reading? Into a voltmeter?

4. A stream of electrons is moving toward the east. If the stream passes through a uniform magnetic field directed upward, in what direction is the electron beam deflected?

5. How much work is done by a magnetic field on a stream of free electrons moving through it? Justify your answer. Prove that a constant magnetic field does no work on a charged particle passing through it.

Problems

1. Find the force on and the acceleration of an electron moving 5×10^7 m/sec at right angles to a magnetic field of intensity 0.0008 newton/amp-m in a television picture tube. The mass of the electron is 9.1×10^{-31} kg.

Ans. 6.4×10^{-15} newton; 7.04×10^{15} m/sec^2

2. An electron is moving perpendicular to a magnetic field with a speed of 8×10^6 m/sec. If the intensity of the magnetic field is 0.075 newton/amp-m, what force acts on the electron? What is its acceleration?

3. Find the force on 7 cm of conductor bearing a current of 6 amp if it lies perpendicular to a magnetic field of intensity 1.2 newton/amp-m. What would the force be if the wire made an angle of 60° with the magnetic field? *Ans.* 0.504 and 0.436 newton

4. A long wire bearing a current of 9 amp lies perpendicular to a uniform magnetic field between the poles of a large magnet. If 12 cm of the wire lies in the field, and if the force on this length is 0.045 newton, find the magnetic intensity B.

5. A coil of magnetic moment 4.5×10^{-8} amp-m^2 experiences a torque of 9×10^{-9} newton-m when it is placed in a magnetic field with the magnetic moment normal to the field. Find the magnetic intensity. If the coil has 10 turns and an area of 1.5 cm^2, what current does it bear? *Ans.* 0.2 newton/amp-m; 3×10^{-5} amp

6. A coil of 15 turns of wire has an area of 4 cm^2. It carries a current of 3×10^{-6} amp. Find the magnetic moment of the coil. If the magnetic moment is perpendicular to a magnetic field of intensity 1.1 newton/amp-m, what is the torque on the coil?

7. A rectangular galvanometer coil is 1.5 cm high, 1 cm long, and has 40 turns of wire. Find its magnetic moment when it bears a current of 10^{-4} amp. What torque is exerted on this coil in a uniform magnetic field of intensity 0.8 newton/amp-m when the plane of the coil (a) is parallel to the field, (b) is perpendicular to the field, and (c) makes an angle of 30° with the field?

> *Ans.* 6×10^{-7} amp-m²; (a) 4.8×10^{-7}, (b) 0, and (c) 4.15×10^{-7} newton-m

8. Find the magnetic intensity at the center of a circular coil of 50 turns of 3 cm radius when the coil bears a current of 8 amp. What is the magnetic moment of the coil?

9. A current in a circular loop of wire with a diameter of 10 cm produces a field strength of 4×10^{-5} newton/amp-m at the center of the loop. What is the current? Find the magnetic moment of the loop. *Ans.* 3.18 amp; 0.025 amp-m²

10. Find the magnetic intensity a distance of 4 cm from a long straight wire bearing a current of 12 amp.

11. Two straight, long, parallel wires are 10 cm apart. A current of 6 amp passes through one wire, and a current of 5 amp through the other. If the two currents are in the same direction, what is the magnetic intensity at a point midway between the wires? Find the attractive force per meter of length between the wires.

> *Ans.* 4×10^{-6} newton/amp-m; 6×10^{-5} newton/m

12. Find the force on the current loop of the accompanying figure if $I_1 = 25$ amp, $I_2 = 3$ amp, $a = 20$ cm, $b = 8$ cm, and $d = 2$ cm.

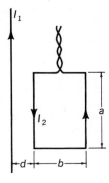

PROBS. 12 AND 13

13. Find the force on the current loop of the accompanying figure if I_1 and I_2 are 10 and 8 amp, respectively, while a, b, and d are 15, 6, and 4 cm, respectively.

> *Ans.* 3.6×10^{-5} newton to the right

14. A solenoid of 400 turns is wound on a cylinder 60 cm long and 3 cm in diameter. What is the magnetic field intensity near the center when the current is 0.25 amp?

15. How many turns of wire must there be in a solenoid 1.1 m long in order that a current of 3.5 amp may produce a magnetic field of 0.005 newton/amp-m at its center?

> *Ans.* 1,250

16. A cylindrical solenoid of 2,400 turns, 12 cm in diameter and 1.5 m long, is placed with its axis parallel to the lines of the earth's magnetic field. If the latter has an intensity of 2×10^{-5} newton/amp-m, what current must flow through the coil in order to make the magnetic field at its center zero?

17. In two concentric solenoids the currents flow in opposite directions. The inner one has 50 turns per centimeter, and the outer one 20 turns per centimeter. What current in the outer coil will be necessary in order to have the field at the center zero when the inner coil is carrying 2.4 amp? If no current passes through the outer coil, what is the magnetic intensity at the center? *Ans.* 6 amp; 0.0151 newton/amp-m

18. Find the contribution to the magnetic induction at a, b, and c due to the current I in a short length Δl of conductor (see accompanying figure) if I is 5 amp and Δl is 2 cm. The angle between Δl and the line to b is 37°.

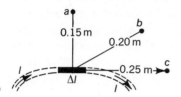

PROBS. 18 AND 19

19. Find the contribution to the magnetic induction at a, b, and c due to the current I in a short length Δl of conductor (see accompanying figure) if I is 40 amp and Δl is 0.5 cm. The angle between Δl and the line to b is 37°.

Ans. 8.9×10^{-7}, 3×10^{-7}, and 0 newton/amp-m

20. A meter movement is a galvanometer with a resistance of 5 Ω, and it requires 0.003 amp for full-scale deflection. Find the resistance required to convert this galvanometer to (*a*) a voltmeter reading 3 volts full scale and (*b*) an ammeter reading 0.5 amp full scale.

21. A galvanometer of 10 Ω resistance requires a current of 0.0012 amp to produce full-scale deflection. What resistance is required to convert this galvanometer to an ammeter reading 2 amp full scale? To a voltmeter reading 30 volts full scale?

Ans. 0.012/1.9988 Ω; 24,990 Ω

22. A two-scale voltmeter is wired as shown in Figure 39.11, where the galvanometer has a resistance of 30 Ω and requires a current of 2.0×10^{-3} amp for full-scale deflection. Find R_1 and R_2 if the voltmeter is to read full scale for 50 and 150 volts.

23. A current I of 10 amp passes through a long straight wire which makes a semicircular bend of radius r about point C of the accompanying figure. If $r = 4$ cm, find the magnetic intensity B at C and at point P far from the bend.

Ans. 1.29×10^{-4} and 1×10^{-4} newton/amp-m

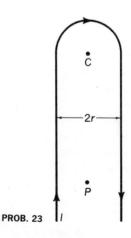

PROB. 23

24. A galvanometer has a moving coil with a resistance of 120 Ω and a sensitivity of 1 mm deflection for 2×10^{-7} amp. What shunt will be needed to produce a 5-cm deflection for 0.001 amp in the main circuit?

25. A long horizontal wire is bent to include a circular loop of $r = 10$ cm (see accompanying figure). If a current of 5 amp exists in this wire, what is the magnetic induction B at the center C of the loop? If the loop is twisted about the axis AA' so its plane is vertical, what is the magnitude of B at the center of the loop?

Ans. 2.14×10^{-5} and 3.3×10^{-5} newton/amp-m

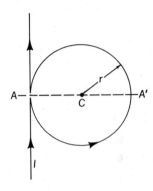

PROB. 25

CHAPTER 40 *We now know what a magnetic field is and how magnetic fields are associated with certain current distributions, but we have said little indeed about the magnets of simple compasses and the familiar bar magnets with which children play. What are the origin and nature of their magnetic fields? And why does a compass needle point roughly north? These are questions which we discuss in this chapter.*

Magnets

40.1 The Magnetic Moment of a Magnet

In Chap. 39 we saw that a coil placed in a magnetic field of strength **B** with its magnetic moment **M** perpendicular to the field experiences a torque equal to BM. Similarly, a current-bearing solenoid placed in a magnetic field with its axis perpendicular to the field experiences a torque equal to the resultant of the torques acting on each of the turns of the solenoid. These turns can be regarded as a series of individual coaxial coils. The resulting magnetic moment of the solenoid is NIA, where N is the total number of turns, I the current, and A the cross-sectional area of the solenoid.

If we place a small bar magnet (magnetic needle) with its axis perpendicular to a magnetic field (Fig. 40.1), it experiences a torque in a direction such as to align the axis of the magnet with the direction of **B**. As defined in Sec. 39.5, the magnetic moment **M** is the ratio of the torque **L** to the field strength **B**. Since the *apparent* magnetic properties of the magnet are associated with the poles at the ends, it is often convenient to think of the torque as arising from the forces acting on the north and south poles, which are separated by a distance equal roughly to the length of the magnet l. Let us define the pole strength p of this magnetic needle as the ratio of the magnetic moment to the length.

$$p = \frac{M}{l} \tag{40.1}$$

Since the dimensions of the magnetic moment are amp-m², the dimensions of pole strength are ampere-meters. The force **F** on a pole p placed in a magnetic field of strength **B** is given by

$$F = Bp \tag{40.2}$$

A pole has a strength of one ampere-meter if the force acting on it is one newton when the pole is placed in a magnetic field of intensity one newton per ampere-meter. Observe that the force on the north pole

FIGURE 40.1

A bar magnet with axis perpendicular to a uniform magnetic field experiences a torque which tends to align the magnet with the field.

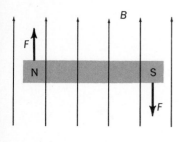

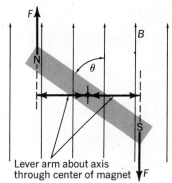

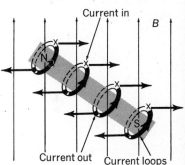

of the magnet is in the direction of **B,** while the force on the south pole is opposite to **B.**

If the axis of the magnet makes an angle θ with the magnetic field, the torque is less than if the magnet were perpendicular to the field. In general, the torque **L** is given by

$$L = BM \sin \theta = Bpl \sin \theta \qquad \text{40.3}$$

as can be seen from Figure 40.2.

In many problems regarding magnets it is convenient to consider the forces and torques on the magnet as arising from the interaction between magnetic field and point poles. However, it should be remembered that the pole picture is a simplification of the more general point of view that there are forces on current elements in magnetic fields. The torque on the magnet of Figure 40.2 can be explained in terms of torques acting on elementary current loops. The magnetic moment **M** of the magnet is just that which would be produced by a current $I = M/A$ (where A is the cross-sectional area of the magnet) flowing as a current sheet around the magnet. The point of view of the current loops is rigorous and universally acceptable, but for many problems the force-on-pole concept is simpler and more convenient.

Magnets never have single poles. The magnetic field arises from currents and, as we have seen in Chap. 39, magnetic lines of force are always continuous. The pole of a magnet is a region where a large fraction of lines of force enters or leaves the magnet. Since every line of force which enters a magnet also leaves, it is clear that no magnet can have a single pole.

40.2 Coulomb's Law

When the poles of bar magnets are brought close to one another, they interact. *Like poles repel one another, and unlike poles attract.* Coulomb studied the interaction between magnetic needles with small torsion balances and found that the force between two poles varies as the product of the pole strengths and inversely as the square of the distance between the poles:

$$F = \kappa \frac{p_1 p_2}{r^2} \qquad \text{40.4}$$

When the force is in newtons, pole strengths in ampere-meters, and r in meters, κ is 10^{-7} newton/amp^2, the same constant which appears in Ampère's law.

Coulomb's law is applicable whenever one can regard the magnetic properties of the needle as concentrated in point poles. This, in turn, requires that the distance between the two magnets be substantially greater than the thickness of either magnet, since otherwise a pole of a magnet cannot be correctly approximated by a point pole. If one wishes to calculate the force which one magnetic needle exerts on another, it is ordinarily necessary to calculate not only the forces between nearest poles, but also the forces between the other poles. The

Lever arm about axis through center of magnet

Current in

Current out   Current loops

FIGURE 40.2

The torque on a bar magnet whose axis makes an angle θ with a uniform magnetic field is the resultant of all the torques exerted on current loops of infinitesimally small dimensions.

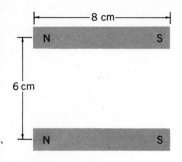

FIGURE 40.3

One small magnet can be floated above another.

N pole of one magnet exerts forces on both the N and S poles of the second magnet; similarly the S pole exerts forces on both poles of the other magnet. Therefore, to calculate the total force exerted on one magnet by another, it is necessary to compute four forces and add them vectorially.

Example Two small identical magnets are 8 cm long and have pole strengths of 60 amp-m. When they are restrained so they cannot rotate, it is possible to make one "float" 6 cm above the other (Fig. 40.3). Find the force which the lower magnet exerts on the upper one (which is the weight of the upper magnet, of course).

$$F_{NN} = \kappa \frac{p_1 p_2}{r^2} = 10^{-7} \frac{60 \times 60}{(0.06)^2} = 0.100 \text{ newton}$$

$$F_{NS} = 10^{-7} \frac{60 \times 60}{(0.1)^2} = 0.036 \text{ newton}$$

Similarly $F_{SS} = 0.100$ newton, and $F_{SN} = 0.036$ newton. The vertical component of F_{NS} is $0.036 \times 0.6 = 0.0216$ newton, and the horizontal component is $0.036 \times 0.8 = 0.0288$ newton. The horizontal component of F_{SN} exactly balances the horizontal component of F_{NS}. If we take the upward direction as positive, the vertical force on the upper magnet is given by

$$F = 0.100 + 0.100 - 0.0216 - 0.0216 = 0.1568 \text{ newton or 16 g-wt}$$

Any pole or group of poles has a magnetic field associated with it. To determine the field intensity **B** at any point, we may imagine that we bring a test pole p_t to the point in question and measure the force **F** on this pole. The intensity **B** is given by $\mathbf{F}/p_t$. To calculate the magnetic intensity due to any group of poles, we find the magnetic intensity which each pole would produce by itself and add all these fields together vectorially. The magnetic field due to one pole p can be calculated readily by Coulomb's law. The force on a test pole p_t at a distance r from the pole p is given by $F = pp_t/10^7 r^2$, and

$$B = \frac{F}{p_t} = \frac{p}{10^7 r^2} \qquad \textbf{40.5}$$

FIGURE 40.4

The magnetic intensity at any point P is the resultant of the fields of the two poles of the magnet.

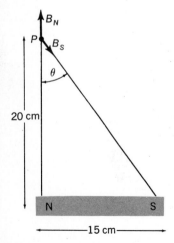

Example A magnet 15 cm long with poles of strength 250 amp-m lies on a table. Find the magnitude of the magnetic intensity B at a point P 20 cm directly above the N pole of the magnet (Fig. 40.4).

The magnetic fields are given by

$$B_N = \frac{p_N}{10^7 r^2} = \frac{250}{10^7 (0.2)^2} = 6.25 \times 10^{-4} \text{ newton/amp-m}$$

$$B_S = \frac{p_S}{10^7 r^2} = \frac{250}{10^7 (0.25)^2} = 4.00 \times 10^{-4} \text{ newton/amp-m}$$

The vertical component of B_S is $B_S \cos \theta = 3.2 \times 10^{-4}$ newton/amp-m, and the horizontal component is $B_S \sin \theta = 2.4 \times 10^{-4}$ newton/amp-m. The vertical component of the resultant intensity is

$(6.25 - 3.2) \times 10^{-4} = 3.05 \times 10^{-4}$, and the horizontal component is 2.4×10^{-4}. The resultant B is

$$\sqrt{(3.05)^2 + (2.4)^2} \times 10^{-4} = 3.9 \times 10^{-4} \text{ newton/amp-m}$$

40.3 The Magnetic Field of the Earth

The usefulness of the compass as a device for determining direction arises from the fact that the earth has a magnetic field which aligns the compass needle.   At points high above the earth's surface this field is approximately that which would be produced by a tremendous bar magnet (Fig. 40.5) near, but not at, the center of the earth with its axis making an angle of 11° with the earth's rotational axis, its south-seeking pole at 78.5° north latitude, 69° west longitude, and its north-seeking pole at 78.5° south latitude, 111° east longitude. At the surface of the earth this field is grossly distorted by magnetic materials of the earth's crust, with the result that in 1960 the magnetic poles of the earth as defined by vertical lines of force were located at 76° north latitude, 102° west longitude and 72° south latitude, 140° east longitude.

In view of the fact that the earth's magnetic axis does not coincide with its axis of rotation, a compass needle points to true north at relatively few regions on the earth's surface.   The angle between a free horizontal compass needle and true north is called the *angle of declination*.   Figure 40.6 shows the declination at various places in the United States.   A line on the earth's surface along which a compass

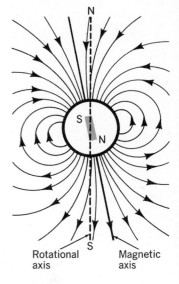

FIGURE 40.5

Earth's magnetic field.

FIGURE 40.6

Geomagnetic declination (solid lines) and inclination (dashed lines) for the United States.

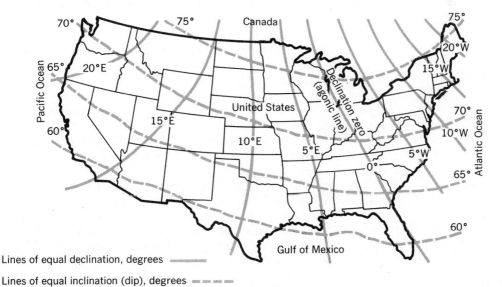

Lines of equal declination, degrees ⎯⎯⎯

Lines of equal inclination (dip), degrees ⎯ ⎯ ⎯

needle points to true north is called an *agonic line*. At points east of the agonic line in the United States, the declination is west; at points west of the agonic line, the declination is east. In New York City the declination is about 11.5° west, while in San Francisco it is roughly 18° east.

When a compass needle is free to orient itself along the lines of magnetic force, the needle points downward as well as to the north. The angle between the free magnetic needle and the horizontal plane is called the *inclination* or *angle of dip*. Figure 40.6 also shows lines of constant dip, which are called *isoclinic* lines. The inclination in various parts of the United States varies from about 50 to 80°.

< The earth's magnetic field is a relatively weak one. The horizontal component varies approximately from 25×10^{-6} newton/amp-m in the southern part of the United States to 15×10^{-6} newton/amp-m in the northern part. The vertical component varies similarly from about 40×10^{-6} to 55×10^{-6} newton/amp-m as one goes from south to north.

The magnetic isogonic and isoclinic lines, shown in Figure 40.6 as smooth regular lines, actually have many local irregularities and variations. One would expect the magnetic lines of the earth to be significantly altered by large deposits of iron ores and other magnetic materials, and indeed they are. One method of prospecting involves the careful measurement of the earth's magnetic field over large areas. The vertical component of the earth's field sometimes increases sharply above a body of magnetic ore and is often weaker than normal above an oil deposit.

The earth's magnetic field is not static. Over a period of years the declination at a given point changes substantially. Since 1580 it has varied between 11° east and 24° west at London. To explain the origin of such variations we invoke the "dynamo theory," according to which motions of parts of the earth's fluid core relative to other parts set up currents, which in turn modify the motions. A detailed study of the changes in magnetic field at the surface of the earth suggests that the average speed of the magnetic core material is about one meter per hour. The magnetic field at the earth's surface is a weak clue to the vastly stronger fields in the core.

Roughly 99 per cent of the earth's field is due to phenomena in the earth itself; the remainder has its origin in external currents in the ionosphere. In disturbed regions of the solar atmosphere, strong magnetic fields are accompanied by the emission of a tenuous stream of matter, chiefly protons and electrons. When the earth passes through such a stream, the moving charges interact with the earth's magnetic field and its ionosphere, producing a fluctuation in the field at the earth's surface. Magnetic storms of this kind can be partially correlated with sunspots and solar flares, as well as with northern lights (*aurora borealis*) and phenomena of a similar nature on the earth.

40.4 Magnetic Materials

Relatively few materials possess strong magnetic properties. Iron, nickel, and cobalt are the only common elements which ordinarily interact appreciably with a small magnet. Gadolinium and liquid oxygen are also strongly magnetic; so are a substantial number of alloys. All materials which interact strongly with magnets are classed as *ferromagnetic*.

For the vast majority of materials magnetic effects are exceedingly small. However, when carefully studied in a strong nonuniform magnetic field, each material falls into one of two classes. Some become very feebly magnetized in the direction of the field. If a needle of such a material is placed in the field, it aligns itself with the field and is called *paramagnetic* (*para* means "parallel"). Examples are palladium, manganese, and many metallic salts. Other materials become very feebly magnetized in the direction opposite the field. A needle of bismuth aligns itself at right angles to a strong nonuniform magnetic field. Such a material is called *diamagnetic* (*dia* means "across"). Most elements and chemical compounds are slightly diamagnetic. Bismuth is the most diamagnetic element.

For most practical purposes paramagnetic and diamagnetic materials can be regarded as magnetically inactive. They are not useful for magnets. Ferromagnetic materials are of very great practical importance and utility. They are vital for transformers, electric motors, electric generators, and electromagnets.

40.5 Origin of Ferromagnetism

Why some materials are magnetic and others are not is a complex question. However, a qualitative answer can be given in fairly simple terms. Magnetic effects are always associated with moving electric charges. As long ago as 1820, Ampère suggested that within magnetized iron there are circulating currents. It is obvious that these currents cannot be due to a flow of charges around the circumference of the iron core, since such currents would necessarily dissipate heat in the iron as a result of the resistance. Instead, the currents are due to the motions of the atomic electrons. The electrons associated with any given atom are in constant motion, and a moving charge produces a magnetic field.

An electron may establish a magnetic field in two ways. First, we may picture the electron as traveling around the nucleus of the atom in an orbit analogous to the orbit in which the earth revolves about the sun. Second, the electron may be thought of as rotating about its own axis, much as the earth rotates once each day about its axis. A single electron may establish a magnetic field by virtue of its orbital and its spin motions. In almost all atoms the *net* effect of the magnetic fields set up by various electrons is exceedingly small or zero, because the magnetic field set up by one electron counterbalances the fields set up by other electrons. However, in iron, nickel, and cobalt the magnetic fields due to the spinning of the electrons do not cancel for certain of the electrons in an unfilled (M) shell. In these metals, individual atoms act as tiny magnets.

It must be emphasized that, although magnetic properties are associated with individual atoms of iron, not all materials containing iron are magnetic. In the chemical combination, the sharing of electrons may give rise to a situation in which the magnetic fields add to zero. Whereas many of the compounds and alloys of iron are magnetic, a number, including stainless steel, are not. On the other hand, the Heusler alloys, containing aluminum, copper, and manganese, are ferromagnetic, although none of the component elements are.

40.6 Magnetization by Induction

In a ferromagnetic material, sometimes individual atoms are the elementary magnets, sometimes combinations or groups of atoms. Although the net magnetic field outside a piece of unmagnetized soft iron is zero, over small volumes of the order of 10^{-6} cm^3 most of the elementary magnets are aligned with their N poles in the same direction. There is no field outside the iron because these tiny *domains* are oriented at random. If this iron is placed in a magnetic field, it is magnetized *by induction*. This magnetization occurs through two processes: (1) Domains which are magnetized in the direction of the inducing field grow at the expense of neighboring domains which are magnetized in less favorable directions. (2) The direction of magnetization of an entire domain may be shifted by the simultaneous rotation of the elementary magnets which make up the domain.

Further evidence confirming that the nature of the magnetizing process is the alignment of elementary magnets are the following observations:

1. When a piece of soft iron lies in a weak field, its magnetization is increased by tapping. Tapping the iron gives the elementary magnets a better chance to align themselves with the magnetizing field. On the other hand, if a piece of magnetized material is not in a field, tapping usually disturbs the alignment of some of the domains and thereby reduces the strength of the magnet.

2. Increasing the temperature of the magnet tends to demagnetize it, because adding kinetic energy to the molecules by thermal agitation produces the same effects as tapping or dropping the magnet. Iron heated above 760°C loses its magnetic properties. Indeed, all magnetic materials have a temperature above which they lose their magnetism. The temperature at which the magnetic properties of a given material disappear is called the *Curie point* of that material.

3. If a long permanent magnet is cut into two equal shorter pieces, the magnetized domains remain aligned. There are now two magnets, each half as long as the original. The pole strength of each new magnet is roughly equal to that of the original magnet. It is easy to understand why magnetic effects seem to be concentrated at the ends or poles when one remembers that throughout the body of the magnet the arrangement of elementary magnets leaves a N pole close to each

S pole, so that their effects cancel one another. At one end of the magnet there is a concentration of elementary N poles, and at the other end of S poles. Consequently, the magnetic effects are strong at the ends.

When the N pole of a bar magnet is brought near an unmagnetized needle, the elementary magnets in the needle align themselves in the field. Thus, a S pole is produced near the N pole of the bar magnet. Since the attractive force between the S pole of the needle and the N pole of the bar magnet is greater than the repulsive force between the two N poles, there is a net attractive force. It should be noted that *this attractive force arises only in a nonuniform magnetic field.* In a uniform field the forces on opposite poles are equal and opposite.

While most common magnets have two poles, it is entirely possible for a magnet to have three or more. For example, if the middle of a piece of soft iron is brought up to the strong N pole of an electromagnet, it develops a N pole at each end and a stronger S pole at the middle. When steel gas or water pipes are explored with a small compass needle, several N and S poles are often found along a few feet of the pipe. Such poles are called *consequent* poles.

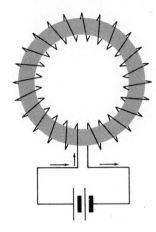

FIGURE 40.7

Magnetic lines of force exist within a toroid or ring solenoid; there is no external field.

40.7 Permeability and the Magnetizing Field

If a long solenoid is bent in the form of a circle until the two ends touch (Fig. 40.7), it becomes a *ring solenoid* or *toroid*. Consider a toroid which has n turns per meter of length and bears a current I. Bending a long solenoid to form a toroid does not change the magnetic field inside; thus the magnetic field in a toroid is given by $B = 4\pi nI/10^7$, according to Eq. (39.10).

Suppose the entire core of the toroid is now filled with iron, and a current I is sent through the windings. How is the value of **B** inside the toroid affected by this iron? A measurement[1] of **B** shows that it is now several hundred times greater than it was before the iron was added.

The magnetic field in the iron may be written

$$B = \frac{4\pi K_m nI}{10^7} \qquad\qquad \textbf{40.6}$$

where K_m is called the *relative permeability*. For any material K_m is the ratio of magnetic intensity in the material to magnetic intensity in vacuum. If we fill the toroid with some other material, such as bismuth, silver, wood, or nickel, and measure the magnetic intensity for a given current in the windings, we can determine its relative permeability (Table 40.1). Those materials with relative permeabilities less than unity are diamagnetic, those with permeabilities slightly greater

---

[1] The measurement of **B** in the solid material may be made without disturbing the material in any way by wrapping a few turns of wire around the solenoid as indicated in Figure 41.3 and observing the induced emf as the field is changed. The operation of such a measuring device, known as a fluxmeter, is described in Chap. 41.

TABLE 40.1 *Relative Permeabilities of Various Substances*
(Vacuum = 1.000 by definition)

Material	Relative permeability	Material	Maximum relative permeability
Bismuth	0.99983	Cobalt	250
Silver	0.99998	Nickel	600
Copper	0.99999	Mild steel	2,000
Water	0.99999	Iron (0.2% impurity)	5,000
Air	1.0000004	Silicon iron*	7,000
Aluminum	1.00002	Permalloy	100,000
		Supermalloy	1,000,000

* Used in power transformers.

than unity are paramagnetic, and those with permeabilities much larger than unity are ferromagnetic.

The magnetic intensity in a toroid depends on two factors: (1) the properties of the medium in the toroid and (2) the influences which are inducing the magnetization of the medium. In this case the inducing field is provided by the current through the turns of the toroid. In other situations it may be provided by magnetic poles or other kinds of current distributions. It is called the *magnetizing field* and is represented by **H.** In the special case of the uniformly filled toroid we have continuous magnetization and no poles; the magnetizing force is the product of the current and the number of turns per unit length. Thus we have

$$H = nI \qquad\qquad \textbf{40.7}$$

If nI is replaced by H in Eq. (40.6), we obtain

$$B = \frac{4\pi}{10^7} K_m H = \mu H \qquad\qquad \textbf{40.8}$$

Here μ stands for $4\pi K_m/10^7$ newtons/amp^2 and is called the *absolute permeability* of the material. Since the relative permeability K_m of a vacuum is unity, the absolute permeability is $4\pi/10^7$ for a vacuum (and for air for practical purposes). It is usually represented by μ_0 and called the *permeability of free space.*

B is different inside the toroid when it is filled with iron because of the magnetization of the iron which occurs when we apply the magnetizing field. We have seen (Sec. 40.1) that the magnetic moment M of a bar magnet of cross-sectional area A and length l is that which would exist if there were a current M/A flowing around the surface, i.e., a surface current M/lA per unit length. The ratio M/lA is the magnetic moment per unit valume, which we shall indicate with M_v. With magnetic material in the toroid the total magnetic intensity **B** comes from two contributions: $\mu_0\textbf{H}$ due to the conduction currents in the windings and $\mu_0 \mathbf{M}_v$ due to the internal currents in the magnetic material.

$$\mathbf{B} = \mu_0(\mathbf{H} + \mathbf{M}_v) \qquad\qquad 40.9$$

In an *ideal* magnetic material $\mathbf{M}_v$ is proportional to the magnetizing field $\mathbf{H}$. From the equation $\mathbf{B} = \mu\mathbf{H} = \mu_0(\mathbf{H} + \mathbf{M}_v)$, we obtain the relation

$$\mu = \mu_0 \left(1 + \frac{M_v}{H} \right) = \mu_0 K_m \qquad\qquad 40.10$$

Example A toroid of mean circumference 0.5 m has 500 turns, each bearing a current of 0.15 amp. (*a*) Find H and B if the toroid has an air core. (*b*) Find B and M_v if the core is filled with iron of relative permeability 5,000. (*c*) Find the average magnetic moment per iron atom if the density of iron is 7,850 kg/m³.

(*a*) By Eq. (40.7),

$$H = \frac{500 \text{ turns}}{0.5 \text{ m}} \times 0.15 \text{ amp} = 150 \text{ amp/m}$$

$$\begin{aligned} B &= 4\pi \times 10^{-7} \text{ newton/amp}^2 \times 150 \text{ amp/m} \\ &= 1.88 \times 10^{-4} \text{ newton/amp-m} \end{aligned}$$

(*b*) For iron with $K_m = 5,000$, by Eq. (40.8),

$$\begin{aligned} B &= 4\pi \times 10^{-7} \times 5,000 \times 150 \text{ newtons/amp-m} \\ &= 0.94 \text{ newton/amp-m} \end{aligned}$$

By Eq. (40.9),

$$0.94 \text{ newton/amp-m} = 4\pi \times 10^{-7} \text{ newton/amp}^2 \times (150 + M_v)$$
$$M_v = 7.5 \times 10^5 \text{ amp/m (or amp-m}^2/\text{m}^3)$$

(*c*) One kilogram-atomic weight (55.85 kg) of iron has 6.02×10^{26} atoms. Therefore in 1 m³ there are $7,850 \times 6.02 \times 10^{26}/55.85$ atoms. Hence there are 8.48×10^{28} atoms in 1 m³ of iron, which has a magnetic moment M_v of 7.5×10^5 amp-m²/m³. The average magnetic moment per iron atom is 8.9×10^{-24} amp-m².

For a material such as permalloy, which has a K_m of the order of 100,000, Eq. (40.10) shows that $\mathbf{M}_v$, the magnetic moment per unit volume due to the "internal currents," is about 99,999 times as great as the magnetizing field due to currents in the external windings.

Only when $\mathbf{M}_v$ is proportional to $\mathbf{H}$ is the permeability μ a constant. We shall see in Sec. 40.8 that for ferromagnetic materials μ is not constant over any large range of values of $\mathbf{H}$.

If we solve Eq. (40.9) for $\mathbf{H}$, we obtain

$$\mathbf{H} = \frac{\mathbf{B}}{\mu_0} - \mathbf{M}_v \qquad\qquad 40.11$$

This is the defining equation[1] for $\mathbf{H}$ in the general case.

---

[1] $\mathbf{B}$, $\mathbf{H}$, and $\mathbf{M}_v$ are vectors and do not always have the same direction.

40.8 The Magnetization Curve

If a toroid is wound around an iron core and a fluxmeter provided to measure changes in magnetic intensity in the core, we can measure **B** as a function of **H** by starting with an unmagnetized core and no current in the windings and increasing the current in the windings step by step. If this is done, we obtain a so-called "magnetization curve" in which the magnetic intensity B is plotted as a function of the magnetizing field $H = nI$. For a typical iron sample, a curve similar to that of Figure 40.8a is obtained.

The permeability μ is the ratio of B to H, by definition. Figure 40.8b shows how μ varies with H for the particular magnetization curve of Figure 40.8a. Observe that the permeability is not constant for a ferromagnetic substance, as it is for an ideal magnetic material. Rather it varies over a considerable range. It is not difficult to understand qualitatively why this is true. The iron core is composed of a large number of magnetic domains originally oriented at random. When a tiny current is passed through the windings, the magnetizing field H has a small effect on these domains compared with the influence of neighboring domains; therefore relatively small changes in magnetization occur. As the current is increased, the more favorably aligned domains grow at the expense of the others. The number of elementary magnetic dipoles oriented in the direction of· the magnetizing field increases rapidly, as is shown by the steep portion of the magnetization curve. Once most of the elementary magnets are aligned, the region of "hard magnetization" begins. Here the magnetizations of the unaligned domains undergo rotations which bring them into more exact alignment with the applied field. When essentially all the elementary magnets are aligned, the iron is said to be *saturated*. From this point on, increases in H result in small increases in B. When the iron is saturated, the permeability (B/H) falls off rapidly as H is increased.

If one observes a portion of the magnetization curve with instruments of great sensitivity, he finds that the curve is not perfectly smooth, but that it is made up of a number of tiny jumps, called *Barkhausen steps,* owing to the fact that a large number of neighboring elementary

(a)

(b)

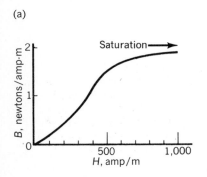

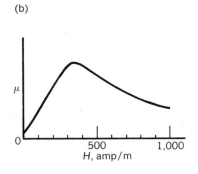

FIGURE 40.8
How (a) the magnetic intensity and (b) the permeability of a sample initially unmagnetized vary with the magnetizing field.

magnets along a domain boundary align themselves with the applied field simultaneously, thereby producing sharp little jumps in the magnetization.

Although this picture of magnetism is a simplified one, it does present the qualitative features in reasonable perspective. During magnetization the sizes of domains change, and domains are reoriented. There may even be an observable change in the length of the magnet. Such a change in length magnetization is known as *magnetostriction.* Magnetostriction oscillators are used to produce sound waves of very high frequency, particularly in liquid mediums.

40.9 Hysteresis

When an iron core is saturated and the magnetizing field is removed, the magnetization does not fall to zero, because the magnetic domains have been aligned by the magnetization process and help to keep one another aligned. To demagnetize the specimen completely, a magnetizing field in the opposite direction must be applied. If a specimen is magnetized first in one direction and then in another, the relationship between B and H is as shown in the curves of Figure 40.9 which are called *hysteresis curves.*

A material which makes a good permanent magnet has a very broad hysteresis loop, since this indicates a high retention of magnetism when the magnetizing field is removed. Such a material would not be good for an electromagnet, which should lose its magnetic properties when the magnetizing field is eliminated. In a-c transformers, motors, etc., one ordinarily desires a magnetic material with a hysteresis loop of small area, because it takes energy to reverse the direction of the magnetization. The area of the hysteresis loop is a measure of the energy lost per cycle per unit volume of the material. A transformer made of steel with a broad hysteresis loop would be unsatisfactory because of the large amounts of energy which would be lost in magnetizing and demagnetizing it many times each second.

Soft iron demagnetizes rapidly when the magnetizing field is removed, so it is desirable for electromagnets and transformers. On the other hand, the alloy *alnico,* made of aluminum, nickel, and cobalt steel, is particularly high in retentivity and therefore makes a fine permanent magnet.

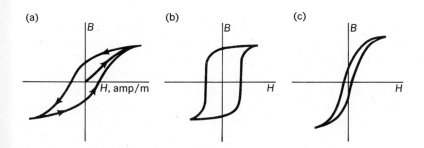

FIGURE 40.9

Hysteresis curves (a) for a piece of soft iron, (b) for an alloy which may be made into a permanent magnet, and (c) for an alloy suitable for use in a power transformer.

$<$ **40.10 Applications of Electromagnets**

If a solenoid is wound around a soft-iron core, the iron becomes strongly magnetized when a current is passed through the solenoid and loses most of its magnetism when the current is stopped. There are many uses for such electromagnets. Large ones can pick up rails and operate switches on railroads, as well as lift and move scrap iron and other magnetic materials. Small electromagnets have been developed for extracting particles of iron from the eye and for opening and closing switches in telephone and automobile circuits.

A common use of electromagnetism is in the doorbell. Here a soft-iron vane is attracted by the electromagnet when the switch is closed. When the iron moves toward the poles of the electromagnet, the clapper strikes the bell, and the electrical connection is broken by the movement of the iron vane. The current ceases, and spring action moves the vane back toward its original position. Contact is reestablished, the electromagnet is activated once more, and another cycle begins. The same basic idea is also utilized in the electric horn, except that a diaphragm is set into vibration instead of a clapper. The loudspeakers of many radios, record players, and television receivers (Sec. 45.8) utilize electromagnets as fundamental components.

Questions

1. If a small permanent magnet is placed in a nonuniform magnetic field, is there any net force on the magnet? Why?

2. One of two initially identical steel bars is magnetized and retains part of its magnetic moment. How can it be distinguished from the unmagnetized bar in a region in which there is no magnetic field due to the earth or other magnets?

3. What is meant by "the demagnetizing effect of poles"? Explain why a good permanent magnet usually has a "keeper" of soft iron placed between its poles when it is not in use?

4. A steel post is driven into the ground in the United States. Is it likely to be magnetized? Why? At which end is the N pole likely to be?

5. If a substantial quantity of magnetic ore lay beneath the earth's surface, how would the magnetic field of the earth be affected nearby? Consider both horizontal and vertical components.

Problems

1. Find the magnetizing field H and the magnetic flux density B at (a) a point 10 cm from a long straight wire bearing a current of 15 amp and (b) the center of a 2,000-turn solenoid which is 25 cm long and bears a current of 2 amp.
Ans. (a) 23.9 amp/m; 3×10^{-5} newton/amp-m; (b) 16,000 amp/m; 0.020 newton/amp-m

2. The magnetic declination in northern California is 18° east. How far from a true-north course would a flier be after traveling 100 miles following the compass without making a correction for declination? Would he be east or west of his course?

3. A magnet has a pole strength of 40 amp-m. It is placed at right angles to the earth's magnetic field of 2×10^{-5} newton/amp-m, and a torque of 6×10^{-5} newton-m acts on it. Find the magnetic moment of the magnet and the distance between the poles. What would the torque be if the magnet were rotated so its axis made an angle of 30° with the field? *Ans.* 3 amp-m^2; 7.5 cm; 3×10^{-5} newton-m

4. What torque is necessary to hold the axis of a magnet at an angle of 50° to the magnetic meridian where the horizontal component of the earth's magnetic field is 2×10^{-5} newton/amp-m? The length of the magnet is 15 cm, and its pole strength is 60 amp-m.

5. A small test magnet has poles of 50 amp-m strength separated by 2 cm. Find the force on each pole when this magnet is placed at the center of a circular loop with a radius of 25 cm in which a current of 10 amp is flowing. (Assume the magnetic intensity is uniform over the volume occupied by the magnet.) What is the resultant force on the magnet? Find the torque on the magnet if its axis is perpendicular to the magnetic field. *Ans.* 1.26×10^{-3} newton; zero; 2.51×10^{-5} newton-m

6. A magnet with poles of 60 amp-m strength separated by a distance of 4 cm is placed in the uniform field inside a solenoid with its axis at right angles to the lines of force. If the solenoid is 40 cm long and has 300 turns bearing a current of 2 amp, what torque does the field exert on the magnet?

7. An electromagnet has a solenoidal winding 30 cm long with a total of 600 turns. What is the magnetizing field H near the center of the winding and far from any poles if the current is 0.7 amp? What is the magnetic induction B at this point if the iron has a relative permeability of 400? *Ans.* 1,400 amp/m; 0.704 newton/amp-m

8. An iron ring has a cross section of 0.8 cm^2 and an average diameter of 20 cm. It is wound with 600 turns of copper wire. If the iron in the core has a relative permeability of 550, what is the magnetic intensity in the iron when a current of 3 amp flows through the windings?

9. The axes of two magnets are colinear. One has poles of strength 60 amp-m separated by 10 cm, and the second has a magnetic moment of 8 amp-m^2 with poles of strength 100 amp-m. Find the attractive force between the magnets if the N pole of one is 5 cm from the S pole of the second. *Ans.* 0.189 newton

10. Identical magnets 12 cm long with poles of 270 amp-m strength lie 9 cm apart with axes parallel (Fig. 40.3). Find the attractive force between the magnets if the N pole of one is opposite the S pole of the other.

11. Find the magnetic induction at a point 12 cm from the center of a magnet on the perpendicular bisector of the line joining the poles if the magnet is 10 cm long and its pole strength is 250 amp-m. *Ans.* 1.14×10^{-3} newton/amp-m parallel to axis

12. A N pole of 30 amp-m strength is placed 15 cm from a S pole of 90 amp-m strength. How far from the N pole, on a line drawn through the two poles, will the resultant field due to these poles be zero?

13. A bar magnet is 20 cm long, and each pole has a strength of 50 amp-m. Find the magnitude of the intensity of the magnetic field at a point 15 cm from the S pole, measured at right angles to the axis of the magnet.

Ans. 1.85×10^{-4} newton/amp-m

14. The poles of a magnet are 20 cm apart, and each has a strength of 50 amp-m.

What is the magnitude of the magnetic intensity at a point 16 cm from one pole and 12 cm from the other?

15. A bar magnet 15 cm long with a pole strength of 8 amp-m is horizontal, at right angles to the earth's magnetic field, with its N pole pointing west. Find the intensity of the magnetic field in a horizontal plane at a point 20 cm west of the N pole. Take the horizontal component of the earth's magnetic field as 2×10^{-5} newton/amp-m.

Ans. 2.41×10^{-5} newton/amp-m 34°W of N

16. At a place where the horizontal component of the earth's magnetic field is 2×10^{-5} newton/amp-m, a bar magnet 15 cm long with a pole strength of 3 amp-m is horizontal, at right angles to the earth's field, with its N pole pointing toward the west. Find the direction and intensity of the field in a horizontal plane at a point 10 cm west of the N pole of the magnet.

17. An iron anchor ring is wound with 700 turns. If the current in this toroidal solenoid is 0.6 amp and the relative permeability of the iron core is 250, what is the magnetic induction B, assuming that the toroid has a mean circumference of 40 cm? What is the magnetizing force H? Find the magnetic moment per unit volume of iron and the average contribution to this magnetization per iron atom.

Ans. 0.33 newton/amp-m; 1,050 amp/m; 2.61×10^5 amp/m; 3.08×10^{-24} amp-m²

18. A solenoid that is 50 cm long is wound with 1,400 turns of copper wire. An iron rod having a relative permeability of 450 is placed along the axis of the solenoid. What is the magnetic intensity in the rod when a current of 0.5 amp flows through the wire? What are the magnetizing field and the magnetic moment per unit volume of the iron. Find the average contribution per iron atom to the magnetization.

19. A toroid with 1,200 turns is wound on an iron ring, 4 cm² in cross-sectional area, of 80 cm mean circumference and of 5,000 relative permeability. If the windings carry 0.06 amp, find (*a*) the magnetizing field H, (*b*) the product of H and the length, called the *magnetomotive force,* (*c*) the magnetic induction B, (*d*) the product of B and the cross-sectional area of the ring, called the *flux,* and (*e*) the ratio of magnetomotive force to flux, called the *reluctance* of the circuit.

Ans. (*a*) 90 amp/m; (*b*) 72 amp; (*c*) 0.565 newton/amp-m; (*d*) 2.26×10^{-4} newton-m/amp (or weber); (*e*) 3.18×10^5 amp²/newton-m (or amp/weber)

CHAPTER 41 *In our discussion of electric circuits thus far, we have used batteries and thermocouples as sources of emf. Electrical energy from either of these sources is relatively expensive. Now that we have learned some facts about magnetic phenomena, we are ready to develop the fundamental physics upon which depends the economic conversion of mechanical energy to electrical energy. We recall that when an electric current is sent through a conductor, a magnetic field appears near the wire. If a current always produces a magnetic field, is there some way in which a magnetic field can produce a current? There is, and its discovery made economically feasible the broad use of electrical energy in our daily lives.*

Induced Electromotive Forces

41.1 The Discovery of Induced Emfs

The discovery by Oersted in 1819 that a current has an associated magnetic field led a number of physicists to search for some means by which a magnetic field might produce a current. The first observation of such a phenomenon was made in 1830 by Joseph Henry. He used a horseshoe-shaped electromagnet around which he wound a second coil, the terminals of which were connected to a galvanometer (Fig. 41.1). Henry found that when the current through the electromagnet is changed, either increased or decreased, there is a deflection of the galvanometer coil. When the current in the electromagnet is steady, there is no current through the galvanometer. When the current in the magnet is turned on, the deflection of the galvanometer is in one direction; when the current is stopped, the deflection is in the opposite direction.

Several months later Michael Faraday independently discovered the deflection of a galvanometer connected to one coil when the current in an adjacent coil was started or stopped. Faraday published his findings first and is therefore usually credited with the discovery.

Faraday made a thorough study of the phenomenon. He found that the galvanometer in series with the second coil deflected not only when the current in the first coil was started and stopped, but also when the first coil carried a steady current and was moved nearer to or farther from the second. He brought a magnet near the second coil and then withdrew it. The galvanometer needle deflected during the motion of the magnet. When the north pole of a magnet was brought near the coil, the current flowed in one direction. When this pole was

FIGURE 41.1
Apparatus used by Henry when he discovered electromagnetic induction.

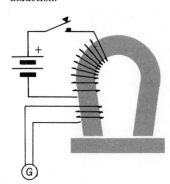

withdrawn, the current flowed in the opposite direction. If a south pole was brought toward the coil, the deflection was in the same direction as when the north pole was withdrawn. Whenever the magnetic lines of force linking the second coil were changed, there was an induced emf which produced a current through the galvanometer. This phenomenon is called *electromagnetic induction*. To develop quantitative relations between change in magnetic field and induced emf, we must become familiar with the meaning of the term *magnetic flux*.

41.2 Magnetic Flux: The Weber

Consider an area A (Fig. 41.2*a*) with its plane perpendicular to a uniform magnetic field of intensity **B**. The magnetic flux Φ through this area is defined as the product of **B** and A:

$$\Phi = BA \qquad\qquad 41.1$$

The flux Φ is given in *webers* when B is in newtons per ampere-meter and A is in square meters. The weber is thus dimensionally equivalent to the newton-meter per ampere. It is named in honor of W. E. Weber (1804–1891), German physicist.

In many situations it is easier to measure the flux through a coil than it is to measure **B** directly. If Φ and the area are known, the average value of **B** is given by Φ/A webers/m². (The weber per square meter and the newton per ampere-meter are equivalent units.)

If **B** is not perpendicular to the plane of the area through which the flux is desired, $\Phi = BA \cos\theta$, where θ is the angle between **B** and the normal to the area (Fig. 41.2*b*). When **B** is not constant over the area, Eq. (41.1) is applicable if we take the *average* flux density for **B**.

An alternative point of view toward flux was developed by Faraday. We saw in Sec. 39.3 that a magnetic field may be represented by lines of force. If we draw many lines of force in regions where the field is strong, and correspondingly fewer where the field is weak, we have a plot which shows not only the direction of the magnetic field at various points, but also its intensity. If we agree to limit the number of lines of force so that we draw one line per square meter where **B** is 1 weber/m², two lines per square meter where **B** is 2 webers/m², etc., the number of lines through any large area is just equal to the magnetic flux through that area. Let us call lines drawn according to this convention "lines of flux" to distinguish them from lines of *force*, which give only the direction of the field. In terms of this physical picture, the *flux* through any area is equal to the number of *flux lines* which pass through the area.

41.3 Faraday's Law of Electromagnetic Induction

Faraday found experimentally that the magnitude of the induced emf in a single loop was directly proportional to the rate at which the flux linking the loop changed.

$$e = -\frac{\Delta\Phi}{\Delta t} \qquad\qquad 41.2$$

FIGURE 41.2

The magnetic flux linking an area is the product of the area and the component of the magnetic intensity perpendicular to the area; $\Phi = AB \cos\theta$.

(a)

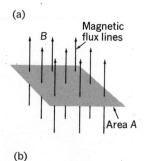

Magnetic flux lines

B

Area A

(b)

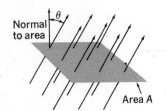

Normal to area

θ

Area A

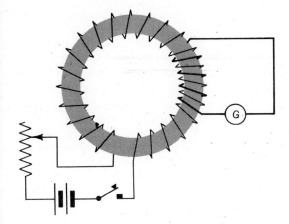

FIGURE 41.3
Iron-core toroid with a fluxmeter that measures changes in the magnetic flux.

where $\Delta\Phi$ is the change in flux occurring in the time Δt. The emf e†
is given in volts when $\Delta\Phi/\Delta t$ is in webers per second. An emf $\Delta\Phi/\Delta t$
is induced in each turn of a coil. If N turns are connected in series,
the total emf in the coil is N times that induced in a single loop. The
significance of the minus sign is discussed in Sec. 41.5.

41.4 The Fluxmeter

In Sec. 40.7 it was assumed that we can measure **B** inside a toroid without
cutting any holes in the material. We are now in a position to see
how this can be done. Consider the iron-filled toroid shown in Figure
41.3. Assume the iron is originally unmagnetized and the current in
the winding is zero. If N turns of wire are wound around this toroid
and connected to a suitable galvanometer, we can measure **B** as
follows: We pass a small current through the toroid windings. This
changes the magnetic intensity in the iron from zero to some value **B.**
If A is the cross-sectional area of the iron core, the flux in the
iron goes from zero to BA in a time t. According to Faraday's law of
induction, there is, in the fluxmeter windings, an induced emf e given by

$$e = \frac{-N\Delta\Phi}{\Delta t} = \frac{-NAB}{t}.$$

There is a current in the fluxmeter given by $i = e/R = NAB/Rt$.
Now $it = NAB/R$ is equal to the charge q passing through the fluxmeter. If we use a suitable galvanometer, we obtain a deflection proportional to this charge. If we know q, N, and A, we can calculate **B.**

41.5 Lenz's Law

The direction of the induced emf is readily predicted by application of
a rule due to Lenz. *The direction of an induced emf is always such*

† Note that we have used e rather than $\mathscr{E}$ to indicate the induced emf in
this case. In general, we use $\mathscr{E}$ and I to represent constant values, and the lowercase letters e and i to indicate emfs and currents which vary in time.

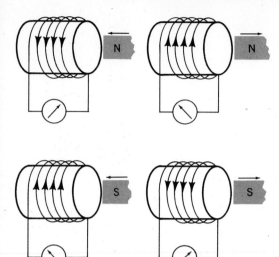

FIGURE 41.4

The act of inducing emf is opposed by the magnetic field of the resulting current.

that any current it produces opposes, through its magnetic effects, the change inducing the emf.

To illustrate Lenz's law, consider an N pole that is being pushed (Fig. 41.4) toward a coil. The current induced in the coil is in such a direction that its magnetic field opposes the motion of the magnet. In this case, it is directed toward the north pole of the magnet, which requires that the current be counterclockwise. When the N pole is withdrawn, the directions of induced emf and current reverse, since the induced magnetic effect opposes the act which creates it.

Actually, Lenz's law represents one of the many forms in which conservation of energy appears in physics. That this law follows from the conservation of energy may be seen by this reasoning: Changing a magnetic field induces an emf and a corresponding current if there is a conducting path. Thus, electrical energy appears as the result of this act. It is the work done against the opposing magnetic field which is transformed into electrical energy.

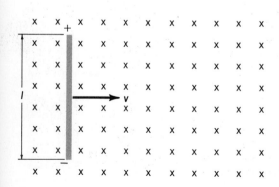

FIGURE 41.5

Motional emf is induced by moving a wire across a magnetic field; in this case, **B** is into the page, and the upper end of the wire is positive.

41.6 Motional Electromotive Force

If a wire of length **l** is moved with a velocity **v** perpendicular to a magnetic field of flux density **B** (Fig. 41.5), there is induced in this wire an emf

$$\mathcal{E} = vBl \qquad\qquad 41.3$$

The origin of this emf is in the force exerted on each individual charge moving through the magnetic field. This force, as we saw in Sec. 39.4, is qvB. The electric field strength $E = F/q = vB$. The potential difference across a wire of length l is given by the product of the field strength and the length. Therefore, $\mathcal{E} = El = vBl$. (In the event that **B, v,** and **l** are not mutually perpendicular, $\mathcal{E}$ is numerically equal to the volume of a parallelepiped with sides in the directions of **B, v,** and **l** and lengths proportional to the magnitudes of the respective quantities.)

In many electric generators the emf is induced by moving wires through a magnetic field at high speed. The direction of the induced emf is such that the force on the resulting current opposes the movement of the wire across the field. From this it follows immediately that the magnetic field of the current produced by the induced emf strengthens the field on the side toward which the wire is moving and weakens it on the opposite side. Once we know the direction of the magnetic field associated with the induced current, we can let the fingers of the right hand curve along the lines of force; the right thumb then points in the direction of the induced emf (see Sec. 39.2). In the situation shown in Figure 41.6, the induced emf produces a current into the paper when the wire is moved as indicated.

41.7 The EMF in a Rotating Loop

When a rectangular loop of wire rotates in a uniform magnetic field (Fig. 41.7), the conductors move through the field, and a motional emf is induced. The conductors ab and cd cut across the flux lines, while conductors ad and bc do not. In conductor ab there is induced an instantaneous emf

$$e_1 = vBl \sin \theta$$

where θ is the angle between the velocity **v** of the wire and **B**. The direction of the induced emf is from b toward a as ab moves downward. At the same time, in side cd there exists an emf of equal magnitude directed from d to c. The emfs in ab and cd are in series, and the net emf in the loop $badc$ is

$$e = 2vBl \sin \theta = \mathcal{E}_{max} \sin \theta \qquad\qquad 41.4$$

where $\mathcal{E}_{max}$ is the maximum emf induced in the coil.

The instantaneous emf induced in the coil varies as θ changes. It is zero when the plane of the coil is vertical, since in this position the wires in the coil move parallel to the magnetic intensity **B,** and $\sin \theta = 0$. When the plane of the coil is horizontal, the wires move

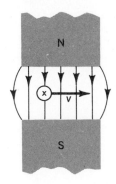

FIGURE 41.6

By moving the wire to the right, an emf is induced which results in a current into the page.

FIGURE 41.7

Emf is induced in a rectangular loop rotating in a uniform magnetic field with constant angular velocity.

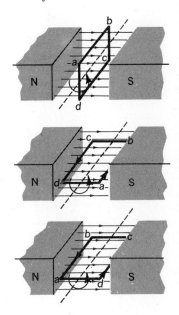

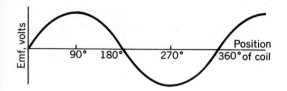

FIGURE 41.8

How emf induced in the loop of Figure 41.7 varies with the angle through which the coil rotates.

perpendicular to the lines of flux, $\sin \theta = 1$, and the induced emf is maximum. The relation between the position of the coil and the induced emf is evident from Figure 41.8. As the curve shows, the emf generated rises from zero to a maximum value at 90°, decreases to zero again at 180°, reverses its direction to reach its largest negative value at 270°, and returns to zero when the rotation is completed. An *alternating emf* is induced in the coil. If such an emf is applied to a circuit, the current alternates with the same frequency as the emf (Chap. 43).

41.8 Mutual Inductance

Consider the neighboring circuits of Figure 41.9. When the key is pressed, the current in coil A rises, and the associated magnetic lines of flux produce a change in the magnetic flux linking coil B. As a consequence, there is an induced emf and a resulting current in coil B. The current in B lasts only as long as the current in A is changing. In such a circuit, coil A is called the *primary,* and coil B the *secondary.* When the current in the primary is increasing, the induced emf in the secondary produces a current which, by its magnetic effect, opposes the rise of current in the primary. Note that it is always the *change in current in the primary* which is opposed, not the current itself. Thus, when the current is at its maximum value and is being reduced, the magnetic effect due to the induced current in coil B is such as to keep the primary current at its previous value. The effect which results in an emf being produced in one circuit due to a changing current in another circuit is called *mutual induction.*

FIGURE 41.9

Mutual inductance between two circuits occurs when magnetic flux from circuit A links circuit B so that current changes in A induce an emf in B.

The emf e_2 induced in the secondary coil is directly proportional to the rate of change of current in the primary:

$$e_2 = M \frac{\Delta i_1}{\Delta t} \qquad \textbf{41.5}$$

where the constant M is called the *coefficient of mutual inductance.*

The coefficient of mutual inductance between two circuits is the ratio of the emf induced in the second circuit to the rate of change of current with time in the first circuit. When an emf of 1 volt is induced in a secondary coil by a current change of 1 amp/sec in the primary, the coefficient of mutual inductance is said to be 1 *henry.*

Example The mutual inductance between two circuits is 0.4 henry. Find the emf induced in the secondary at an instant when the current is changing at the rate of 90 amp/sec in the primary.

$$e_2 = M \frac{\Delta i_1}{\Delta t} = 0.4 \times 90 = 36 \text{ volts}$$

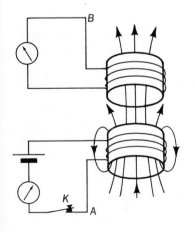

41.9 The Transformer

If an iron core (Fig. 41.10) is wound with two separate coils, and if an alternating current is maintained in one of them, an alternating emf of the same frequency is induced in the other. Such a device is known as a *transformer*. The first coil is called the *primary,* and the other the *secondary*. Power is transferred from the primary to the secondary by *mutual inductance*.

The change from one a-c potential difference to another can be made very efficiently at low frequency by means of a transformer. For example, at 60 cycles/sec the efficiency of a large transformer may be 99 per cent, while smaller transformers may be 90 per cent efficient. Some power is dissipated in hysteresis and eddy currents induced in the iron by the changing magnetic flux. Also, there is some Joule heating (I^2R) in the windings, but in a well-designed transformer the power delivered to the secondary is almost equal to the power supplied to the primary. If V_p and V_s are the primary and secondary potential differences,[1] and I_p and I_s are the corresponding currents,

$$V_pI_p \simeq V_sI_s \qquad\qquad 41.6$$

Further, for this well-designed transformer the same magnetic flux links both the primary and the secondary windings. Consequently, the ratio of the emf induced in the secondary to that applied to the primary is equal to the ratio of the number of turns in the secondary N_s to the number in the primary N_p:

$$\frac{\mathcal{E}_s}{\mathcal{E}_p} = \frac{N_s}{N_p} \qquad\qquad 41.7$$

In an ideal transformer there are no losses, and the induced emfs in the primary and secondary are equal to the corresponding terminal potentials V_p and V_s. From $\mathcal{E}_p = V_p$, $\mathcal{E}_s = V_s$, and Eqs. (41.6) and (41.7), we can write

$$\frac{V_s}{V_p} = \frac{\mathcal{E}_s}{\mathcal{E}_p} = \frac{N_s}{N_p} = \frac{I_p}{I_s} \qquad\qquad 41.8$$

Where the emf is large, the current is small; where the emf is small, the current is large. By means of a transformer, a small emf and a large current may be transformed into a large emf and a small current, or vice versa.

<   In small transformers, where the ratio of transformation is not large, economy of construction and efficiency of operation are obtained by using the same coil for both primary and secondary. Such a transformer is known as an *autotransformer*. The arrangement and connections of the coil are shown in Figure 41.11. The entire coil AC is the primary of the transformer, and the part between B and C is the secondary. Equation (41.8) is applicable to autotransformers as well as to other types, provided always that heat losses are negligible.

[1] Here we may regard the values of the V's and I's to be either the maximum values attained during the cycle or the "effective" values as defined in Sec. 43.2.

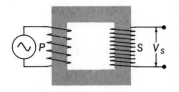

FIGURE 41.10

Transformer designed to step up the primary potential difference.

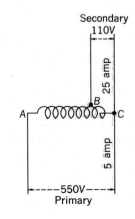

FIGURE 41.11

Autotransformer designed to step down the potential difference from 550 to 110 volts.

At higher frequencies eddy-current and hysteresis losses in iron become prohibitive, so no iron is used. In such an air-core transformer only a fraction of the magnetic flux from the primary links each turn of the secondary, and the efficiency is low. Under these conditions the transformer equations above are no longer good approximations.

41.10 The Induction Coil

An illustration of mutual inductance is found in the induction coil, which is constructed as shown in Figure 41.12. A primary coil made of a few turns of heavy copper wire is wound around an iron core. Insulated from this primary coil is the secondary coil, which is wound on the outside of the primary. The secondary contains a large number of turns of fine, well-insulated wire. By making or breaking the current in the primary at D, an emf is induced in the secondary. In order to make and break the current in the primary, an interrupter similar to that of the doorbell (Sec. 40.10) is connected in the circuit.

When the primary circuit is broken, the current is rapidly reduced to zero, and an emf is induced in the secondary. This emf is large, because the number of turns in the secondary is very large and the time in which the primary current is stopped is short. To get the greatest induced emf, the primary current must be stopped as quickly as possible. To effect this, a capacitor C is connected across the gap in the primary. It acts as a storage place into which the charge surges when the circuit is broken. Without this capacitor an arc would be established at the contacts when the circuit was opened. Such an arc pits the contacts and results in a slower stopping of primary current. There is also an emf induced in the secondary when the primary current is rising. This emf is much smaller, because the time required for the current to build up to its maximum value is long compared with the time required to stop the current. The primary current and the induced emf in the secondary are plotted as a function of time in Figure 41.13.

The spark coil of an automobile is an induction coil similar to the one just described, except that, instead of a mechanical vibrator opening and closing the primary circuit, a cam on the distributor shaft opens the "points" at the instant a high potential is needed to make a

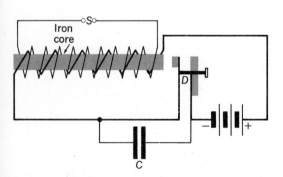

FIGURE 41.12
Induction coil.

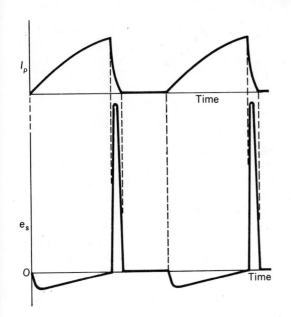

FIGURE 41.13
How the current I_p in the primary of an induction coil and the emf e_s induced in the secondary vary with time.

spark between the terminals of a spark plug. The secondary potential is many thousand volts, although only 12 volts are available in the primary.

41.11 Self-inductance

When the current through a circuit such as that in Figure 41.14 is changing, the magnetic flux linking this circuit is also changing. So long as B is proportional to H, the flux Φ linking the circuit is directly proportional to the instantaneous current i; thus

$$\Phi = Li \qquad \text{41.9}$$

where L is a constant known as the *coefficient of self-inductance*. If, in a time Δt, the current changes by an amount Δi, the flux changes by $\Delta\Phi$ and there is, by Eq. (41.2), an induced emf

$$e = -\frac{\Delta\Phi}{\Delta t} = -L\frac{\Delta i}{\Delta t} \qquad \text{41.10}$$

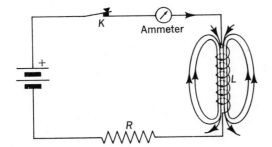

FIGURE 41.14
The flux linking the inductor L changes when the current changes, thereby inducing an emf.

The negative sign appears in Eq. (41.10) because, by Lenz's law, the direction of the induced emf is always such as to oppose the change in current.

Self-inductance is ordinarily measured in henrys. *The self-inductance of a circuit or component is one henry when there is induced an emf of one volt in that circuit or component at an instant when the current is changing at the rate of one ampere per second.*

The self-inductances of many d-c circuits are negligibly small, but a coil with many turns, a large solenoid, or an electromagnet may have a large self-inductance. In a-c circuits inductance is of great practical importance, since the current is constantly changing. The emf resulting from self-inductance always opposes the *change of current;* it operates to hold down the current when it is rising and to maintain the current when it is decreasing.

Consider the circuit of Figure 41.15a. When the key K is closed, the current in the circuit begins to rise. If we apply Kirchhoff's second law to the circuit at any instant, we obtain

$$\mathcal{E} - Ri - L\frac{\Delta i}{\Delta t} = 0 \qquad\qquad \textbf{41.11}$$

At the instant the switch is closed, i is zero, and $\mathcal{E} = L\,\Delta i/\Delta t$. As time goes on, i increases and eventually the value $I = \mathcal{E}/R$ (Fig. 41.15b).

If the battery in Figure 41.15 is suddenly shorted out of the circuit by closing the key S, the emf of self-induction keeps a current passing through the circuit until all the energy stored in the magnetic field of the inductor is dissipated. The current in the circuit is shown as a function of time after closing S in the right half of Figure 41.15b.

When a current I passes through an inductor L, the energy $\mathcal{W}$ stored in the magnetic field is given by

$$\mathcal{W} = \frac{1}{2}LI^2 \qquad\qquad \textbf{41.12}$$

as can readily be shown by the application of integral calculus (see Derivations in Appendix). The energy calculated from Eq. (41.12) is expressed in joules when L is in henrys and I in amperes.

FIGURE 41.15

Inductor circuit (*a*) produces rise and decay in current (*b*).

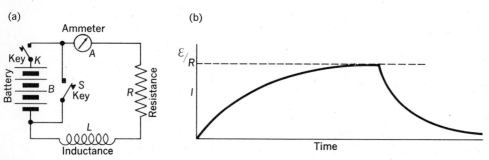

(a)

(b)

Questions

1. A closed conducting plane loop is moved perpendicular to a uniform magnetic field. Is there an induced emf when the plane of the loop is (*a*) parallel to the motion and (*b*) perpendicular to the motion? Discuss the proposal that the ground speed of an airplane be measured by determining the emf induced in a horizontal loop fixed in the plane by the vertical component of the earth's magnetic field.

2. What factors determine the mutual inductance of two coils?

3. How can a wire-wound resistor be made so it is essentially noninductive?

4. What happens to the work done against the back emf of an inductor in establishing a current?

5. A d-c series circuit includes an inductor and a switch. If 10 amp passes through the circuit, is there any limitation on how quickly the current can be reduced to zero by opening the switch? Explain why there is often a spark across the terminals of a switch in a d-c circuit when the switch is opened?

6. How does one obtain the thousands of volts needed for the spark in the cylinder of an automobile when one starts with 12 volts from a battery?

Problems

1. The magnetic induction B in the core of a spark coil changes from 1.6 to 0.1 weber/m^2 in 2×10^{-4} sec. If the cross-sectional area of the core is 4 cm^2, find the original flux through the core. What is the average emf induced in the secondary coil if it has 6,000 turns? *Ans.* 6.4×10^{-4} weber; 18,000 volts

2. The secondary of an induction coil has 20,000 turns. If the flux linking the coil changes from 7.5×10^{-4} to 5×10^{-5} weber in 1.5×10^{-4} sec, how great is the in- duced emf?

3. A coil of 240 turns with an area of 350 cm^2 is placed with its plane perpendicular to the earth's field and is rotated in 0.015 sec through a quarter turn, so that its plane is parallel to the earth's field. What is the average emf induced if the earth's field has an intensity of 8×10^{-5} weber/m^2 (newton/amp-m)? *Ans.* 0.0448 volt

4. A small "search" coil with an area of 1.6 cm^2 has 50 turns of very fine wire. This coil is placed between the pole pieces of a small magnet and then suddenly jerked out. If the average induced emf is 0.2 volt when the coil is pulled to a field-free region in 0.04 sec, what is the magnetic intensity between the poles?

5. A jet aircraft is flying due south at 300 m/sec at a place where the vertical compo- nent of the earth's magnetic field is 8×10^{-5} weber/m^2 (newton/amp-m). Find the po- tential difference between wing tips if they are 25 m apart. Which tip has the higher potential? *Ans.* 0.6 volt; left

6. A horizontal wire 0.5 m long is falling at a speed of 4 m/sec perpendicular to a uni- form magnetic field of 1.2 webers/m^2 (newton/amp-m) which is directed from west to east. Calculate the magnitude of the induced emf. Is the north or south end of the wire positive?

7. An emf of 6 volts is obtained by moving a wire 1.5 m long at a rate of 10 m/sec perpendicular to a uniform magnetic field. What is the intensity of the field?

Ans. 0.4 weber/m^2 (newton/amp-m)

8. An axle of a truck is 2.5 m long. If the truck is moving due north at 24 m/sec at a place where the vertical component of the earth's magnetic field is 9×10^{-5} weber/m^2, find the potential difference between the two ends of the axle. Which end is positive?

9. Two circuits have a coefficient of mutual inductance of 0.09 henry. What average emf is introduced in the secondary by a change from 0 to 20 amp in 0.006 sec in the primary?

Ans. 300 volts

10. The coefficient of mutual inductance between two coils is 0.07 henry. What emf is induced in the second coil if the current is changing at the rate of 3,000 amp/sec in the first coil?

11. When the current in the primary of a small transformer is changing at the rate of 400 amp/sec, the induced emf in the secondary is 12 volts. What is the coefficient of mutual inductance?

Ans. 0.03 henry

12. The secondary of a transformer has 250 times as many turns as the primary. It is used in a 110-volt circuit. What is the voltage across the secondary?

13. A transformer has 1,000 turns on the primary and 50 turns on the secondary. What is the maximum output potential difference if the maximum input voltage is 3,000? If the transformer is assumed to have an efficiency of 100 per cent, what maximum primary current is required if a maximum current of 2 amp is drawn from the secondary?

Ans. 150 volts; 0.1 amp

14. The current in a circuit changes from 15 amp to zero in 0.003 sec. If the average induced emf is 360 volts, what is the coefficient of self-inductance of the circuit?

15. What back emf is induced in a coil of self-inductance 0.007 henry when the current in the coil is changing at the rate of 120 amp/sec? What energy is stored in the inductor when the current is 4 amp?

Ans. 0.84 volt; 0.056 joule

16. An electromagnet has a self-inductance of 5 henrys. How much energy is stored in the magnetic field when a current of 6 amp exists in the coil? What average emf is induced if the current is reduced to zero in 0.015 sec?

17. A ballistic galvanometer with a resistance of 200 Ω gives a full-scale deflection for 7×10^{-4} coulomb of electricity. A coil of 300 turns and 100 Ω resistance is to be constructed to study fields up to 1.4 webers/m^2 by observing deflections produced when the coil is suddenly removed from the field. What is the maximum area allowable for the coil?

Ans. 5 cm^2

18. A coil of 100 turns with a radius of 5 mm and a resistance of 40 Ω is placed between the poles of an electromagnet and suddenly removed. A charge of 8×10^{-6} coulomb is sent through a ballistic galvanometer connected to the coil. The resistance of the galvanometer is 160 Ω. What is the intensity of the magnetic field?

19. A toroid of 0.5 m circumference and 4 cm^2 cross-sectional area has 2,500 turns bearing a current of 0.3 amp. It is wound on an iron ring with relative permeability 800. Find the magnetizing field H, the magnetic induction B, the flux Φ, the coefficient of self-inductance L, and the energy stored in the magnetic field.

Ans. 1,500 amp/m; 1.51 webers/m^2; 6.04×10^{-4} weber; 0.002 henry; 9×10^{-5} joule

20. The circuit of Figure 41.14 consists of a 20-volt battery, a 10-Ω resistor, a 0.04-henry inductor, and a key. Find the rate at which current begins to rise when the key is closed, the current at the instant the rate of change of current is 100 amp/sec, and the final steady current.

21. A constant potential difference of 60 volts is suddenly applied to a coil which has a resistance of 15 Ω and a self-inductance of 0.0075 henry. At what rate does the current begin to rise? What is the current at the instant the rate of change of current is 600 amp/sec? What is the final current?　　　　*Ans.* 8,000 amp/sec; 3.7 amp; 4 amp

CHAPTER 42 *Mechanical energy can be converted to electrical energy through the processes described in Chap. 41. In this chapter we are interested in how practical arrangements for generating substantial emfs can be achieved. Some generators which convert mechanical energy to electrical energy can also transform electrical energy to mechanical energy. Electric motors perform this latter conversion.*

Generators and Motors

42.1 Instantaneous Electromotive Force

When a single loop of wire is rotated at constant angular velocity in a uniform magnetic field (Fig. 42.1), the instantaneous emf induced in the loop varies sinusoidally in time (Sec. 41.7). One full cycle is completed each rotation. If ν represents the frequency (or number of cycles completed in unit time), the emf e at any instant is, by Eq. (41.4),

$$e = \mathcal{E}_{\max} \sin \theta = \mathcal{E}_{\max} \sin 2\pi\nu t \qquad \textbf{42.1}$$

Both the angle θ and the time t are measured from the instant the plane of the coil is perpendicular to the magnetic intensity B. In this equation and subsequent ones we use lowercase letters to represent the instantaneous values of quantities which vary in time, and capital letters to indicate quantities which are constant.

42.2 Collecting Rings

If the loop of Figure 42.1 is opened at the axis and an outside circuit is connected to the two leads, the induced emf may be applied to the external circuit. To make continuous connection to the outside circuit, the ends of the wire forming the coil are fastened to rings (Fig. 42.2a) mounted on the axis of the rotating loop, and sliding connectors, called "brushes," complete the circuit. The slip rings rotate with the loop, while the nonrotating brushes are pressed against the slip rings.

When an alternating emf is applied to a circuit which has resistance R only (no appreciable inductance or capacitance), the current i at any instant is simply the ratio of the applied potential difference to the resistance:

$$i = \frac{e}{R} = \frac{\mathcal{E}_{\max} \sin 2\pi\nu t}{R} = I_{\max} \sin 2\pi\nu t \qquad \textbf{42.2}$$

The current and the emf reach their maximum values at the same

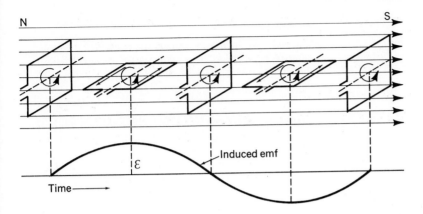

FIGURE 42.1
Motional emf induced in the loop is greatest when the effective conductors are moving perpendicular to the magnetic intensity.

instant and pass through their zeros together. The current is an alternating one and is said to be "in phase" with the emf, since the phase (the argument of the sine function) is the same for both at any time.

42.3 The Commutator

We have seen that the emf induced in a loop rotating in a magnetic field is an alternating one. To obtain a current which is always in the same direction through the external circuit, the terminals of the rotating loop are joined to a *commutator*, which is a ring divided into two segments, as shown in Figure 42.2*b*. Against this divided ring press two brushes which are connected to the external circuit and so placed that they slip from one segment of the commutator to the other at the instant the emf of the revolving coil passes through zero.

If the loop of Figure 42.2*b* is rotating counterclockwise, the wire *ab* which is moving downward has an emf in the direction of the arrow, while the current in the wire *cd* is in the opposite direction. Hence, current leaves the brush *S* and passes through the external circuit in

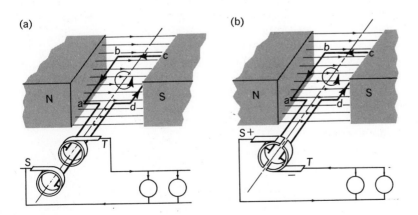

FIGURE 42.2
Connecting rings for generators are (*a*) slip or collection rings, which provide continuous connection to the external a-c circuit, and (*b*) split-ring commutator, which delivers unidirectional current to the external circuit.

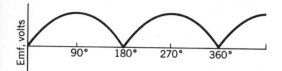

FIGURE 42.3

The potential difference between the brushes of the commutator of Figure 42.2*b* as a function of the angular position of the coil.

the direction of the arrow from *S* to *T*. When the loop has made one-half revolution, the segment of the commutator which was in contact with brush *T* makes contact with brush *S*, and the other segment makes contact with brush *T*. The wire *ab* is now moving upward, and current in it is reversed. The wire *cd* is moving down, and the current in it is also reversed. However, the segments of the commutator have reversed their positions. The current still leaves by brush *S* and flows through the external circuit in the direction in which it flowed originally. In the revolving coil the current alternates; in the external circuit the current is pulsating but *unidirectional*. The potential difference between the brushes is shown in Figure 42.3.

42.4 Practical Generators

In most practical generators of both alternating and direct current, several coils are rotated simultaneously in a magnetic field. These several coils are connected in such a way as to give the desired emf and current capacity.

Consider a d-c generator with two coils whose planes are mutually perpendicular (Fig. 42.4). If the coils are connected in series through a suitable commutator arrangement, the fluctuation in the output emf is much smaller than are the fluctuations in output of each coil separately, as is shown in Figure 42.5. By adding more coils, the resultant output can be made constant except for small fluctuations known as the *commutator ripple*.

The wires which rotate past the poles of a generator are ordinarily embedded in slots in an iron core. The rotating system involving the iron core and the wires is known as the *armature*. The purpose of the iron core is to increase the magnetic intensity **B** and thereby to increase the emf induced. There are emfs induced, not only in the copper wires of the armature, but in any material which moves in the magnetic field, including the iron of the armature. If the armature were a solid piece of iron, these induced emfs would lead to large currents circulating in the iron, and much energy would be dissipated as heat by these current whirlpools which are called *eddy currents*. To reduce the eddy currents, the iron core is constructed from thin sheets or *laminations* separated by thin insulating layers to make the resistance high.

Not only does the practical generator have several coils mounted on the same armature, but these coils often pass several magnetic poles during each revolution. Four- and six-pole generators are common; in some applications as many as twenty-four poles are passed in a single

FIGURE 42.4

Generator with two mutually perpendicular coils.

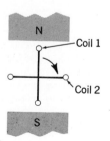

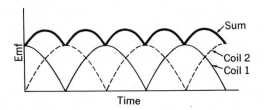

FIGURE 42.5
Connecting the commutated outputs of the two coils of
Figure 42.4 in series leads to a steadier output emf than
either coil produces alone.

revolution. In a six-pole generator one complete cycle is induced for
each third of a revolution, or three cycles in each revolution.

An emf may equally well be induced in a stationary coil by the
varying of a magnetic field.

42.5 Excitation of the Fields of Generators

Generators and motors are sometimes classified with regard to the
manner in which their magnetic fields are produced. In the simplest
type of generator the magnetic field may be due to a permanent magnet.
An example of such a generator is the *magneto,* shown in Fig. 42.6.

Most large generators have fields which are produced by electromagnets. Such generators may be classified as self-excited or separately
excited, depending on whether the generator produces its own magnetic
field or uses some other source to excite the electromagnet. Self-
excited generators may be divided into series-, shunt-, and compound-
wound generators.

In the series-wound generator (Fig. 42.7a) the current to the external
circuit goes through the field coil, which consists of a few turns of
heavy wire. When the generator is not delivering current, the only
magnetic field is that due to residual magnetism. The greater the
current drawn by the external circuit, the greater is the current in the
field coils, and therefore the greater the magnetic field in which
the armature rotates. When the generator is operated at constant
speed, the greater the current, the greater the emf generated. Series-
wound generators are relatively uncommon because one does not ordi-

FIGURE 42.6
Distribution of the magnetic
flux in a magneto.

narily desire an emf which increases rapidly as the current drawn is increased.

In the shunt-wound generator the field coils are in parallel with the external circuit (Fig. 42.7b). When such a generator is operated at constant speed, if the current in the external circuit is increased, the terminal potential difference V_t of the generator decreases for the following reason: The terminal potential is the induced emf $\mathscr{E}$ minus Ir, where r is the resistance of the armature, and I the armature current. As I increases, the terminal potential decreases, and so does the current in the field coils (given by V_t divided by the resistance of the field coils). This reduces the magnetic field and the induced emf. Therefore, a shunt-wound generator provides a potential which decreases as the current drawn is increased. Such a current-voltage response is not commonly desired.

When the terminal potential supplied by a generator is to be essentially independent of the current load, a compound-wound generator (Fig. 42.7c) is used. Such a generator has field coils which are composed of a series-wound part and a shunt-wound part. The characteristic of a series-wound field (increased emf with increasing current demand) and the characteristic of a shunt-wound generator (terminal potential decreasing with load current) may be combined to yield a generator with almost any desired variation of terminal potential with load current.

42.6 The Efficiency of Generators

The efficiency of a generator is defined as the ratio of the electrical energy output of the generator to the energy input, or, alternatively, as the ratio of the electric power output to the power input. The power output of the generator is the product of the terminal potential and the current to the external circuit. The power input is greater, of

FIGURE 42.7

Generators may be (a) series wound, (b) shunt wound, or (c) compound wound.

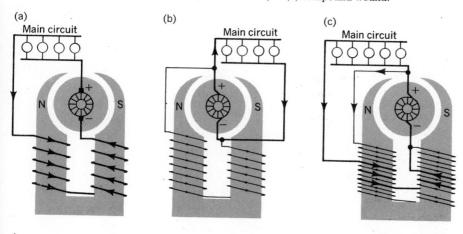

course; it is equal to the power output plus the various losses, such as the I^2R heat loss in the armature and the field coils, hysteresis losses, eddy-current losses, and frictional losses.

42.7 Electric Motor

When a wire bearing an electric current I is placed in a magnetic field **B** so that the length **l** of the wire is perpendicular to the field, the wire experiences a force $F = IlB$ [Eq. (39.2)]. This force is perpendicular to both the magnetic field and the length of the wire. On one side of the wire, the magnetic field due to the current in the wire adds to the field due to the external magnetic circuit, while on the opposite side the two fields oppose. The force on the wire is from the stronger toward the weaker field. If the current is reversed, the force is reversed.

Figure 42.8 shows the cross section of a single current-bearing loop of wire in a uniform magnetic field. Assume that the current enters at a and leaves at b. There results a force downward on wire a and upward on wire b. Thus, there is a torque in a direction such as to produce a counterclockwise rotation about the axis of the coil. In an electric motor there are ordinarily many conductors bearing currents perpendicular to a magnetic field. The resulting torque produces rotation of the armature.

There are many kinds of electric motors. That is, there are many ways to convert electrical energy to mechanical energy. The underlying principle in most motors is that of a current-bearing conductor experiencing a force in a magnetic field.

42.8 Back EMF in a Motor

When the conductors in the armature of a motor rotate in a magnetic field, an emf is induced which opposes the current in the conductors. For this reason it is called a *back emf*, or a *counter emf*.

If an incandescent lamp is connected in series with a small shunt-wound motor while the armature is held stationary, the lamp glows as if the motor were absent, since the armature resistance is small. When

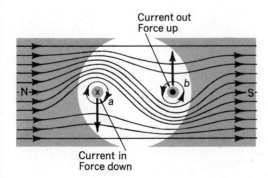

FIGURE 42.8
Torque on a current-bearing coil.

the armature is allowed to revolve, the lamp becomes dim. This is because the emf generated in the armature opposes the impressed emf and thereby reduces the current in the circuit. In a constant magnetic field, the faster the armature revolves, the greater is the back emf, and the smaller the armature current.

For shunt-wound motors the potential difference across the armature is the potential V_t applied to its terminals. The terminal potential of the armature is equal to the back emf plus the potential drop across the armature resistance r_a due to the armature current I_a:

$$V_t = \mathcal{E}_b + I_a r_a \qquad\qquad 42.3$$

A motor is analogous to a battery under charge, except that electrical energy is transformed into mechanical energy rather than to chemical energy. If Eq. (42.3) is solved for the armature current, it yields

$$I_a = \frac{V_t - \mathcal{E}_b}{r_a} \qquad\qquad 42.3a$$

The electrical work done against the back emf appears as mechanical energy output of the motor. Indeed, the mechanical power output P of the motor is equal to the product of the back emf $\mathcal{E}_b$ and the armature current:

$$P = \mathcal{E}_b I_a \qquad\qquad 42.4$$

This follows directly from the fact that $\mathcal{E}_b$ is the electrical work per unit charge performed to produce motion of the conductors, while I_a is the charge per second passing through the conductors.

$<$ Since the armature current of a motor depends on the difference between the terminal potential and the back emf, the current is largest when the armature is at rest, for in this case the back emf is zero. In order to keep the current in a large motor from being excessive at the start, it is customary to introduce a series resistor that reduces the current flowing in the circuit. As the speed of the motor increases and the back emf becomes appreciable, this resistance is removed from the circuit. Such a resistance is called a "starting resistance" or a "starting box."

42.9 Series-wound and Shunt-wound Motors

If large starting torques are required, motors having field coils which are in series with the armature are used. In such a series-wound motor the back emf is small when the motor is starting and the current drawn is large. Since this same current passes through the series field coils, the magnetic field is also large. The starting torque is proportional to IlB, the force on an individual conductor. As the motor gains speed, the back emf increases, and both armature current and field strength decrease. Therefore, the torque is much smaller at high speeds. Series-wound motors are often used for rock crushers and other machines in which particularly large starting torques are desired.

In shunt-wound motors the field coils are in parallel with the armature coils. For a constant applied potential difference, the field strength is constant, and the torque is directly proportional to the armature current, whereas in the series-wound motor the torque is more nearly proportional to the square of the current. Most common small electric motors are shunt wound.

The efficiency of a motor may be obtained by dividing the mechanical power output of the motor by the electrical power input. The difference between the input and output power is dissipated in heating, air friction, etc.

42.10 Dynamos

The fundamental components of many motors are identical with those of generators. The single term *dynamo* describes an electrical device which can function as either motor or generator. When a dynamo is supplied with a potential difference and energy by an electrical source and does mechanical work, it is a motor. When it is driven by a mechanical torque, it develops electrical energy and acts as a generator. Not every motor can be operated as a generator, but many can.

There are many applications for a dynamo operating part-time as a motor and the rest of the time as a generator. An example is the dynamo used in diesel-electric locomotives. When the train is set in motion, diesel engines drive generators to supply current to the dynamos on the axles of the driving wheels. These dynamos exert large torques on the wheels and put the locomotive in motion. When it is desired to reduce the speed of the train, the dynamo may be disconnected from its power supply, leaving the armature rotating in a magnetic field as long as the wheels turn. An emf is induced in the armature; if the terminals are connected to a resistor, a current flows. The dynamo is now operating as a generator, converting kinetic energy of the train into electrical energy, and thus braking the train. In diesel-electric locomotives the electrical energy is dissipated in heat, but in electric locomotives it may be fed back into the power lines.

42.11 Watt-hour Meter

The Thomson form of recording watt-hour meter (Fig. 42.9) consists of a little shunt motor whose armature turns at a speed which is proportional to the power supplied to it. The armature is geared to dials which record the energy in kilowatt-hours. The stationary field coils L and M are connected in series with the generator supplying the current to the external circuit. The field strength of the motor is therefore proportional to the current to the load. The armature is connected across the line, as a voltmeter would be connected. The potential difference across the armature is the potential supplied to the load, and the armature current is proportional to this potential. The torque which turns the motor is proportional to the product of the current in

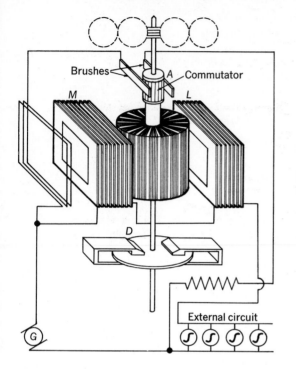

FIGURE 42.9
Watt-hour meter.

the armature and the magnetic field in which the armature turns. Hence, the torque which turns the armature is proportional to the product of the current supplied to the load and the potential at which it is supplied, i.e., to the power received.

In order that the motor does not run too fast, and in order that it may stop as soon as the current ceases to flow, an electromagnetic brake D is attached to it. This brake consists of an aluminum disk rotating between the poles of a permanent magnet. The eddy currents induced in the disk by its rotation between the poles of the magnet retard its motion and cause it to stop as soon as the current ceases to flow. This type of watt-hour meter can be used with either direct or alternating current.

Questions

1. Why are series-wound motors used when very high starting torques are desired?

2. How could you make a generator which would have an emf constant in magnitude and direction?

3. What is the response of a shunt-wound generator to an increase in load current? Of a series-wound generator? Of a compound-wound generator?

4. Does reversing the connections on a d-c shunt-wound motor reverse the direction of rotation? Why? If it does not, how can the rotation direction be reversed?

5. Why does a d-c generator ordinarily have many commutator segments, rather than only two?

Problems

1. A rectangular loop of wire 10 by 12 cm bears a current of 5 amp. The plane of the coil is parallel to a uniform magnetic field of 1.4 webers/m², with its 12-cm length perpendicular to the lines of flux. Find the force on each side of the loop. Using this force, find the torque on the loop. Find the magnetic moment of the loop, and use its value to check the value of the torque.   *Ans.* 0.84 newton; zero; 0.084 newton-m; 0.06 amp-m²

2. Find the torque on a rectangular loop of wire bearing a current of 6 amp when its plane is parallel to the magnetic lines of a field with an intensity of 1.2 newtons/amp-m. The dimensions of the loop are 15 cm parallel to the flux and 20 cm at right angles to it.

3. The flux density between the poles of a certain motor is 1.1 webers/m². A conductor carrying 6 amp lies in this magnetic field so that it is perpendicular to the field. Find the force on it if 0.1 m of the conductor is in the field. If the wire moves 5 cm perpendicular to the field in 0.01 sec, and if the field is uniform over this distance, find the work done on the wire. Show that the same work is predicted by finding the induced back emf and multiplying it by the charge transferred in the 0.01 sec.

Ans. 0.66 newton; 0.033 joule; 0.55 volt

4. Part of the windings of an electric motor is a segment of wire 15 cm long which lies perpendicular to the magnetic field of 1.2 newtons/amp-m. Find the force on this segment when it bears a current of 8 amp.

5. The armature of a generator has a resistance of 0.15 Ω. When the current through the armature is 8 amp, the terminal potential is 224 volts. What will be the terminal potential when the current is 40 amp, assuming that the field strength and the speed remain unchanged? What is the emf induced?   *Ans.* 219.2 volts; 225.2 volts

6. A separately excited, constant-speed generator that develops 124 volts at no load furnishes only 116 volts when a current of 40 amp is drawn. What is the resistance of the armature?

7. The armature of a separately excited generator has a resistance of 0.16 Ω. When run at its rated speed, it yields 125 volts on open circuit and 117 volts on full load. What is the current at full load? How much power is delivered to the external circuit? What horsepower is needed to drive the generator if its over-all efficiency is 90 per cent?

Ans. 50 amp; 5.85 kW; 9.34 hp

8. The brush potential of a separately excited generator, when it is delivering 5 amp, is 125 volts. When the generator delivers 20 amp, the potential difference across the brushes falls to 119 volts. What are the induced emf and the resistance of the armature?

9. A shunt-wound generator delivers 50 amp to an external load at a brush potential of 120 volts. The field coils have a resistance of 60 Ω, and the armature has a resistance of 0.12 Ω. If the stray-power loss is 500 watts, what is the efficiency of the generator?

Ans. 85 per cent

10. The armature of a shunt-wound generator has a resistance of 0.15 Ω. The terminal potential difference of the generator is 122 volts when the armature current is 50 amp. Find the emf of the generator and the power dissipated in heat in the armature.

11. A shunt motor takes a total current of 10.5 amp from 120-volt mains. The resistance of the armature is 1.6 Ω, and that of the field coils is 80 Ω. Find the current in the field coils and in the armature, the back emf induced, and the mechanical power output of the motor. *Ans.* 1.5 amp; 9 amp; 105.6 volts; 950 watts

12. A shunt-wound motor draws 5.5 amp from a 120-volt line. The field coils have a resistance of 240 Ω, and the armature resistance is 0.6 Ω. Find the armature current and the back emf. What is the mechanical power output of the motor? How much power is dissipated in I^2R heating in the motor?

13. A shunt-wound motor has an armature with a resistance of 0.3 Ω and operates from a 220-volt line. What starting resistance is required if the armature current must be limited to 20 amp? When the motor is operating normally with the starting resistor out, the armature draws 5 amp. Find the back emf and the mechanical power output. *Ans.* 10.7 Ω; 218.5 volts; 1,093 watts

14. A motor running at full load on a 120-volt line develops a back emf of 112 volts and draws a current of 5 amp through the armature. What is the mechanical power output of the motor, disregarding frictional losses? What is the armature resistance?

15. A shunt-wound motor with an armature resistance of 0.5 Ω operates on a 110-volt circuit. Find the resistance which must be temporarily connected in series with the armature to limit the starting current to 11 amp. Find the current drawn and the mechanical power output when the back emf generated is 106 volts. *Ans.* 9.5 Ω; 8 amp; 848 watts

16. The armature of a motor connected to a 220-volt line draws 40 amp at the instant the connection is made, when the motor is at rest. There is a starting resistance of 4 Ω in the circuit. What is the resistance of the armature? What is the counter emf when the current drawn is 10 amp (with the starting resistance shorted out)?

17. A series-wound motor has an armature with a resistance of 0.5 Ω and field coils with a resistance of 4.5 Ω. The motor draws 10 amp at 110 volts. Find the power supplied to the motor, the back emf induced in the armature, the power transformed into heat, and the mechanical power output. *Ans.* 1,100 watts; 60 volts; 500 watts; 600 watts

18. In the circuit of the accompanying figure, $\mathcal{E}_a = 80$ volts, $r_a = 2$ Ω, $R_2 = 5$ Ω, $\mathcal{E}_b = 24$ volts, $r_b = 0.5$ Ω, $R_3 = 15$ Ω, $R_4 = 10$ Ω, and the current through the generator is 2 amp. Find R_1 and the terminal potential differences of the generator and battery.

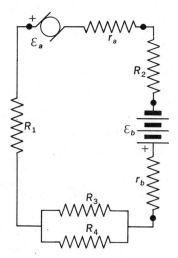

19. In the circuit of the accompanying figure, $\mathscr{E}_a = 60$ volts, $r_a = 1\ \Omega$, $R_1 = 6\ \Omega$, $R_2 = 4\ \Omega$, $\mathscr{E}_b = 15$ volts, $r_b = 0.5\ \Omega$, and $R_3 = R_4 = 7\ \Omega$. Find the current in the main circuit and the terminal potential differences of the generator and battery.

Ans. 3 amp; 57 volts; 16.5 volts

20. In the circuit of the accompanying figure, $\mathscr{E}_a$ is the back emf of a motor. It has a value of 20 volts. The armature resistance and the resistance of the battery are both $1\ \Omega$, and all other resistances are $4\ \Omega$. Find the emf of the battery if the motor draws 2 amp. What are the terminal potential and the mechanical power output of the motor?

21. In the circuit of the accompanying figure a battery of 50 volts emf and $1\ \Omega$ internal resistance is providing electrical energy to operate a motor which has an armature resistance of $0.5\ \Omega$. If $R_3 = R_4 = 5\ \Omega$, and $R_1 = R_2 = 3\ \Omega$, what is the back emf of the motor when the armature draws 3 amp? What is the mechanical power output of the motor?

Ans. 20 volts; 60 watts

CHAPTER 43 *When a coil is rotated in a uniform magnetic field, an alternating emf is generated. Because it is particularly easy to generate alternating emfs, and because transformers make it economically feasible to increase or decrease an alternating emf, most of the practical generation and distribution of electric power utilizes alternating currents. Many of the ideas we have treated for the simpler d-c circuits can be carried over to a-c circuits, but there are also many other factors which must be considered. In this chapter we discuss these factors.*

Alternating Currents

43.1 The Alternating EMF

If the armature of a generator is rotated in a uniform horizontal magnetic field, the instantaneous emf induced in a single loop can be represented by a sine curve (Fig. 43.1) in which the angle through which the coil has turned from a vertical plane is plotted on the horizontal axis, and the corresponding induced emf on the vertical axis (see Sec. 41.7). The instantaneous emf e is given by

$$e = \mathcal{E}_{max} \sin \theta = \mathcal{E}_{max} \sin 2\pi\nu t \qquad \textbf{43.1}$$

where $\mathcal{E}_{max}$ is the maximum emf induced, θ is the angle through which the coil has turned from the position in which the conductors are moving parallel to the magnetic field, ν is the frequency, and t is the time.

It is often convenient to think of the sine wave of Figure 43.1 as being generated by a vector of magnitude $\mathcal{E}_{max}$ rotating with frequency ν. The instantaneous emf is then represented by the vertical component of this vector, as shown in the figure.

The frequency ordinarily used in electric-power generation and distribution in the United States is 60 cycles/sec. In Europe 50 cycles/sec is a common frequency, while in aircraft and guided missiles 400 cycles/sec generators are widely used. In telephones and in the audio amplifiers of radio and television sets the frequencies involved are the acoustical frequencies themselves. The frequencies used for radio transmission in the standard broadcast band range from 525 to 1,600 kc/sec; there are other bands at higher and lower frequencies. Television, radar, and microwave transmission is carried out at much higher frequencies.

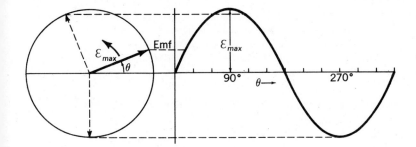

FIGURE 43.1

An alternating emf varies in time like the vertical component of a vector rotating at the same frequency.

43.2 Effective Value of Alternating Current

The power dissipated in heat in a resistor by a direct current is I^2R. For a direct current the maximum value, the average value, and the instantaneous value are all the same. For an alternating current, the average value of current over a whole cycle is zero; the current fluctuates between the maximum value in one direction and the same maximum value in the opposite direction. Nevertheless, an alternating current is effective in producing heat in a resistor. If the instantaneous value of the current is i, i^2 is always positive, even though i is negative during one-half of each cycle.

When an instantaneous potential difference $v = V_{\max} \sin 2\pi\nu t$ is applied across a pure resistor R, the instantaneous i is $(V_{\max} \sin 2\pi\nu t)/R = I_{\max} \sin 2\pi\nu t$ (Sec. 42.2). The current is in phase with the applied potential difference, and Ohm's law is directly applicable to instantaneous current and maximum current, provided the appropriate potential difference is used. Thus,

$$i = \frac{v}{R} \quad \text{and} \quad I_{\max} = \frac{V_{\max}}{R}$$

The power dissipated in a resistor R at any instant is vi, the product of the instantaneous values of potential difference and current (Fig. 43.2). Since $v = iR$, the instantaneous power is i^2R, and the average power dissipated over each cycle is $\overline{i^2}R$, where $\overline{i^2}$ is the average value of the square of the current. We call $I = \sqrt{\overline{i^2}}$ the *effective value* of the alternating current. *The effective value of an alternating current is the value of that direct current which would produce heat at the same rate as the alternating current in a given resistor.* An alternating current is said to have an effective value of 2 amp when it generates heat in a 1-ohm resistor at the rate of 4 watts —the same rate at which a direct current of 2 amp produces heat in a 1-ohm resistor. Since the heating effect depends on the square of the current, this is equivalent to saying that the average value of the square of the alternating current is the same as the square of the corresponding direct current. The effective value of an alternating current is found by taking the average of the square of the instantaneous current and then extracting its square root. Sometimes

FIGURE 43.2

Potential difference v, current i, and power dissipated in a resistor as a function of time for an alternating potential difference.

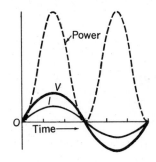

the effective value of the alternating current obtained in this way is called the *root-mean-square* (rms) current.

The effective value of a sine-wave current is given[1] by

$$I_{\text{eff}} = \frac{I_{\text{max}}}{\sqrt{2}} = 0.707 I_{\text{max}} \qquad\qquad \textbf{43.2}$$

where I_{max} is the maximum value of the current. Similarly, the effective value of an alternating potential difference is 0.707 times the maximum; i.e.,

$$V_{\text{eff}} = \frac{V_{\text{max}}}{\sqrt{2}} = 0.707 V_{\text{max}} \qquad\qquad \textbf{43.2}a$$

Ordinary a-c ammeters and voltmeters are calibrated to read effective values. When we speak of a 110-volt a-c circuit or of an alternating current of 5 amp, we are specifying effective values. Hereafter we use V and I without subscripts to denote effective values.

43.3 Advantages of A-C Transmission

One of the major reasons for the widespread use of alternating currents is that it is possible to change from one potential difference to another simply and efficiently by use of transformers (Sec. 41.9). This is highly desirable, since it is most economical to transmit electric power at potentials which are much too high to be used safely in a home or factory.

To illustrate why it is desirable to transmit power at high potentials, consider the following practical problem: A power company must deliver 1,100 kW to a distant city over a transmission line which has a resistance of 2 ohms. How much power is dissipated in the delivery line at 110,000 volts and at 1,100 volts? From $P = VI$ it is clear that the line must deliver 10 amp at 110,000 volts or 1,000 amp at 1,100 volts. The I^2R power loss in this line is 200 watts at 110,000 volts and 2,000,000 watts at 1,100 volts. In the latter case more power would be dissipated in the line than is delivered to the ultimate consumer!

If these arguments were the only ones involved, it would be desirable to transmit power at potentials of many million volts. However, as the potential increases, there are serious power losses due to corona, and the difficulties of insulation become severe. For these reasons high-voltage power transmission lines typically operate at potential differences of a few hundred thousand volts, although lines operating at about a million volts have been constructed.

43.4 Current in an Inductive Circuit

When an alternating potential of frequency ν is applied to a large inductor with negligible resistance (Fig. 43.3a), the current is limited by the inductance. This limitation is due to the fact that, as the current

---

[1] These relations and several others in this chapter can be obtained readily by use of calculus. The derivations may be found in the Appendix.

(a)   (b)

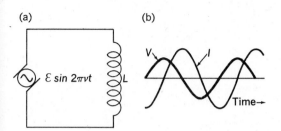

$\mathcal{E} \sin 2\pi vt$

FIGURE 43.3
A circuit (a) containing a source of alternating emf and an inductor of negligible resistance has (b) current i that lags behind the applied emf by 90°.

changes, a back emf is induced in the inductance. At every instant this emf opposes the *change in the current*. If we apply Kirchhoff's second law to this situation, we have

$$v = \mathcal{E}_{max} \sin 2\pi vt = L \frac{\Delta i}{\Delta t}$$

We note that $\Delta i/\Delta t$, the rate at which the current is changing with time, is greatest when v is maximal, and that when $v = 0$, $\Delta i/\Delta t$ is also zero, which means that the current is either maximal or minimal (Fig. 43.3b). Thus, when a potential difference is applied across a pure inductance, the current is not in phase with the potential difference. Rather it reaches its maximum value when the potential is passing through zero and is zero when the potential difference is at its maximum. The current lags 90° behind the potential difference. With calculus it can readily be shown that

$$i = -\frac{\mathcal{E}_{max}}{2\pi vL} \cos 2\pi vt = -I_{max} \cos 2\pi vt \qquad 43.3$$

The potential-difference and current curves of Figure 43.3b can be visualized as being generated by two mutually perpendicular vectors rotating together with the same frequency. The maximum current is $\mathcal{E}_{max}$ divided by the quantity $2\pi vL$, which is called the *inductive reactance* of the inductor and is indicated by X_L. The effective current is just $I = \mathcal{E}/2\pi vL = \mathcal{E}/X_L$. The dimensions of X_L are volts per ampere or ohms.

If a circuit (Fig. 43.4a) contains both resistance and inductance, the current lags behind the potential by some angle less than 90° (Fig. 43.4b). Kirchhoff's second law applied to the circuit yields

$$e = \mathcal{E}_{max} \sin 2\pi vt = Ri + L \frac{\Delta i}{\Delta t}$$

(a)   (b)

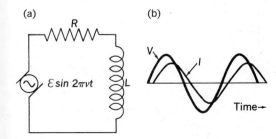

R

$\mathcal{E} \sin 2\pi vt$

FIGURE 43.4
A series circuit (a) containing a source of alternating emf, resistance, and inductance has (b) current i that lags behind the applied potential difference v by an angle θ given by $\tan \theta = 2\pi vL/R$.

It is shown in the Appendix that in this case

$$I = \frac{\mathscr{E}}{\sqrt{R^2 + (2\pi\nu L)^2}} \qquad \text{43.4}$$

and that the current lags behind the potential by an angle θ such that $\tan\theta = 2\pi\nu L/R$. The quantity by which $\mathscr{E}$ must be divided to get I is called the *impedance* of the circuit and is represented by Z. In this case $Z = \sqrt{R^2 + (2\pi\nu L)^2}$. It can be computed as the resultant of R and $2\pi\nu L$, where R and $2\pi\nu L$ are drawn as vectors at right angles to one another as shown in Figure 43.5a. The angle θ by which the current lags behind the emf is the angle between Z and R.

An a-c voltmeter connected across the resistor R would read IR. Connected across the inductor L, it would read IX_L. The arithmetical sum $IR + IX_L$ is not equal to the applied effective emf $\mathscr{E}$, since when the potential difference is maximal across the resistor, it is zero across the inductor. Rather, we must add the potentials vectorially, with IX_L 90° ahead of IR as shown in Figure 43.5b, to obtain $\mathscr{E}$. Obviously, the triangle in this figure is similar to the impedance triangle of Figure 43.5a; each side is just I times the corresponding side in the impedance diagram.

In an ordinary transformer, when no current is being drawn in the secondary, the current in the primary is limited by the inductive reactance of the primary. Since the primary of a large transformer ordinarily has a low resistance, the current is controlled almost entirely by the self-inductance when the secondary circuit is open, and by the self-inductance and the mutual inductance when there is a current in the secondary.

43.5 The Capacitive Circuit

If an alternating emf is applied across a capacitor, the current is zero when the applied emf is maximum, because the capacitor is charged to the maximum potential difference. As the potential decreases, the capacitor begins to discharge. The current increases and reaches its maximum value when the emf passes through zero. Thus, the current and the emf are out of phase. In the case of a *pure capacitance* there is a 90° phase difference between the two, with the current leading the emf. The effective current I is given by

$$I = \frac{\mathscr{E}}{1/2\pi\nu C} = \frac{\mathscr{E}}{X_C} \qquad \text{43.5}$$

(a)   (b)

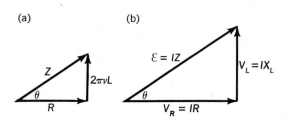

FIGURE 43.5

(*a*) Vector diagram for finding the angle by which current lags behind applied emf in an a-c series circuit containing inductance and resistance. (*b*) The vector sum of the potential differences IR and IX_L is equal to the applied emf.

(a)

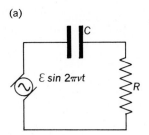

(b)

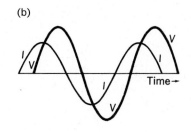

FIGURE 43.6

A series circuit (*a*) containing capacitance and resistance has (*b*) current which leads the applied emf.

where C is the capacitance, and the quantity $1/2\pi\nu C = X_C$ is called the *capacitive reactance*.

When a circuit (Fig. 43.6*a*) contains both capacitance and resistance, the current is given by

$$I = \frac{\mathcal{E}}{\sqrt{R^2 + (1/2\pi\nu C)^2}} \qquad 43.6$$

In this case the current leads the emf (Fig. 43.6*b*) by the angle θ ($\tan\theta = X_C/R$). The effective potential difference across the resistance is given by IR, while the effective potential difference across the capacitor is given by IX_C. The vector sum of IR and IX_C gives the applied emf $\mathcal{E}$.

43.6 Circuit Containing Inductance, Capacitance, and Resistance

In a series a-c circuit containing inductance, capacitance, and resistance (Fig. 43.7*a*), the current is given by

$$I = \frac{\mathcal{E}}{\sqrt{R^2 + (2\pi\nu L - 1/2\pi\nu C)^2}} = \frac{\mathcal{E}}{Z} \qquad 43.7$$

Note that the impedance may be considered as the *geometric sum* of the resistance, the inductive reactance, and the capacitive reactance with due regard given to the fact that the inductive reactance and the capacitive reactance shift the phase in opposite directions. The impedance can be computed by drawing a vector diagram such as the one in Figure 43.7*b*. The angle by which the current lags behind the emf

(a)   (b)

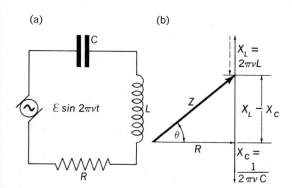

FIGURE 43.7

(*a*) Series circuit containing resistance, inductance, and capacitance, and (*b*) its impedance, or phasor, diagram.

is θ. Clearly, $\tan \theta = (X_L - X_C)/R$, $\sin \theta = (X_L - X_C)/Z$, $\cos \theta = R/Z$. When X_C is larger than X_L, θ is negative, and the current leads the applied emf.

> **Example** In the circuit of Figure 43.7a, $\mathcal{E} = 24$ volts, the total resistance $R = 10$ ohms, $L = 0.05$ henry, and $C = 10^{-4}$ farad. If the frequency is 60 cycles/sec, find the impedance of the circuit and the current. What would an a-c voltmeter connected across R read? Across L? Across C?

$$X_L = 2\pi\nu L = 6.28 \times 60 \times 0.05 = 18.9 \text{ ohms}$$
$$X_C = \frac{1}{2\pi\nu C} = \frac{1}{377 \times 10^{-4}} = 26.5 \text{ ohms}$$
$$Z = \sqrt{R^2 + (X_L - X_C)^2} = \sqrt{(10)^2 + (18.9 - 26.5)^2}$$
$$= \sqrt{100 + 57.8} = 12.5 \text{ ohms}$$
$$I = \frac{\mathcal{E}}{Z} = \frac{24 \text{ volts}}{12.5 \text{ ohms}} = 1.9 \text{ amp}$$
$$V_R = IR = 19 \text{ volts}$$
$$V_L = IX_L = 1.9 \times 18.9 = 36 \text{ volts}$$
$$V_C = IX_C = 1.9 \times 26.5 = 51 \text{ volts}$$

In this circuit the current leads the emf by an angle given by $\cos \theta = R/Z = 10/12.5 = 0.8$; $\theta = -37°$. (The minus sign means the current leads the emf.)

43.7 Resonance in Series Circuits

When $X_C = X_L$, the total reactance is zero, and the current is given by $I = \mathcal{E}/R$. In these circumstances the current is in phase with the applied emf, and the circuit is said to be *resonant*. When an emf of constant amplitude but increasing frequency is applied to a series circuit with both inductive and capacitive reactance, the current increases until it reaches a maximum at the resonance frequency. As the frequency rises further, the current becomes smaller. The frequency for which a circuit is resonant can be obtained readily from the requirement that $X_L = X_C$. This gives $2\pi\nu L = 1/2\pi\nu C$, or

$$\nu = \frac{1}{2\pi\sqrt{LC}} \qquad\qquad \textbf{43.8}$$

Physically, in a circuit at resonance, energy is stored during part of the cycle in the magnetic field of the inductor. A quarter cycle later this energy is stored in the electric field of the capacitor. In another quarter cycle it is once again stored in the magnetic field of the inductor. Thus energy is transferred back and forth between inductor and capacitor. The current is in phase with the applied emf because the effects of inductance and capacitance cancel one another. The only net energy supplied to the circuit is that dissipated as heat in the resistor.

43.8 Power in A-C Circuits

The power supplied at any instant in an a-c circuit is obtained by multiplying the instantaneous current by the emf at the same instant:

$$p = ei \qquad\qquad 43.9$$

where p is the instantaneous power, i the instantaneous current, and e the instantaneous emf. The power varies from instant to instant, since both the current i and the applied emf e change with time.

When the current and the potential difference are in phase, the average power dissipated over one or more cycles is the product of the effective current I and the effective potential difference V (Sec. 43.2). The power is always positive (Fig. 43.2), since the current and the potential difference always have the same sign. When the current and potential difference are out of phase, the power is no longer given by IV. When an emf is applied across a capacitor, the power is negative as much as it is positive, and there is no *net* supply of energy by the generator; the generator supplies energy to charge the capacitor, and then the capacitor returns the energy. For a circuit in which the reactance is primarily inductive, the power curve is similar to that in Figure 43.8. In this case, the instantaneous power is negative during part of the cycle, which means that some of the energy stored in the inductance is being returned to the power source. In the general case, the power dissipated in a series a-c circuit is given by the relation

$$P = \mathcal{E}I \cos\theta \qquad\qquad 43.10$$

where θ is the angle by which the current lags behind the applied emf. The vector diagram from which θ may be found is shown in Figure 43.7b. Cosine θ is called the *power factor* of the circuit.

Power companies are eager to have a power factor as near unity as possible, because in those cases in which the power factor is far different from unity, part of the energy supplied is returned each cycle. Since the power company has to provide the I^2R line losses which occur in delivering the power to the customer, this results in a disadvantageous situation. Most power companies charge higher rates for any consumer whose power factor is appreciably different from unity. By the suitable use of additional inductors or capacitors, it is possible to bring the power factors of most loads fairly close to unity.

43.9 Oscillatory Discharge

Consider the circuit of Figure 43.9a, in which we have a capacitor and an inductor. If we close key K_1, the capacitor is charged to a potential difference $\mathcal{E}$, and energy is stored in the capacitor. Let us now open K_1 and close K_2. The capacitor C begins to discharge, and a current is established through the inductor L. Energy is transferred from the electric field of the capacitor to the magnetic field of the inductor. When C is completely discharged, energy is stored in the inductor,

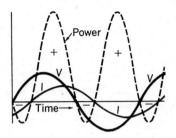

FIGURE 43.8
Power supplied to a circuit in which applied potential difference V and current I are not in phase.

(a)

(b)

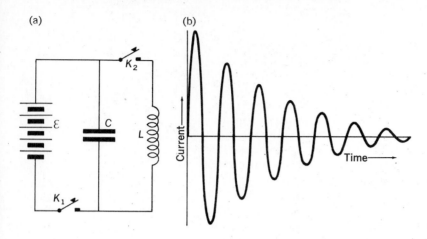

FIGURE 43.9
(*a*) Circuit for producing the oscillatory discharge of a capacitor through an inductor, and (*b*) graph of damped oscillations.

which sustains the current until the capacitor has been charged oppositely to its original condition. Now the capacitor discharges by a current in the opposite direction, thereby transferring energy to the inductor, which in turn uses this energy to recharge the capacitor to the condition in which it was when K_2 was closed.

If there were no resistance in this circuit, the capacitor would be charged to the potential difference with which it started. However, some of the energy is dissipated in heat in the inevitable resistance of the circuit; thus the potential difference does not attain the value $\mathcal{E}$. The capacitor discharges again and again. The current rises and falls, as shown in Figure 43.9*b*. After a number of oscillations, all the energy originally stored in the capacitor is dissipated.

The frequency of oscillation is the frequency to which the circuit is resonant. That is the frequency at which the inductive and capacitive reactances are equal, provided the resistance of the circuit is small compared with the reactances. By Eq. (43.8), the frequency of oscillation is given by

$$\nu = \frac{1}{2\pi\sqrt{LC}} \qquad\qquad \textbf{43.11}$$

Example   The oscillating circuit of a radio station has an inductance of 5×10^{-6} henry and a capacity of 0.01 μF. Neglecting the effect of resistance, find the natural (resonant) frequency and the wavelength of the electromagnetic waves.

$$\nu = \frac{1}{2\pi\sqrt{LC}} = \frac{1}{2\pi\sqrt{5 \times 10^{-6} \times 1 \times 10^{-8}}}$$

$$= 720{,}000 \text{ cycles/sec}$$

$$\text{Wavelength} = \frac{\text{velocity}}{\text{frequency}} = \frac{3 \times 10^8 \text{ m/sec}}{720{,}000/\text{sec}} = 417 \text{ m}$$

Questions

1. Could one define the ampere of alternating current in terms of chemical effects? Why is the heating effect particularly appropriate for defining the a-c ampere?

2. A good transformer automatically adjusts the primary current to take care of the load in the secondary circuit. How is this accomplished?

3. Why do almost all transformers for 60-cycle alternating current use iron cores, while transformers for frequencies in the megacycle range do not?

4. Why are a-c generators and transformers rated in kilovolt-amperes rather than kilowatts? What is the difference?

5. Why are ordinary d-c voltmeters and ammeters unsuitable for a-c circuits?

6. An a-c series circuit contains resistors, an inductor, and a variable capacitor. If the frequency is constant, will increasing the capacitance increase or decrease the current? Explain carefully.

7. Radios are ordinarily tuned to various stations by changing the capacitance of an air capacitor. This is done by varying the effective area of the plates. If one wishes to tune to a station with a higher frequency, must the effective area be increased or decreased?

8. The twelve standard TV channels are located in the 54 to 72, 76 to 78, and 174 to 216 Mc/sec bands, while the standard radio band is 550 to 1,600 kc/sec. With this in mind, give at least one reason why TV channels are switched by changing inductors while radio stations are switched by changing a single variable air capacitor.

Problems

1. A pure 50-Ω resistor is connected to a 60-cycle/sec power supply which has a 150-volt amplitude. Find the maximum current, the rms (or effective) current, the average current, and the power dissipation. *Ans.* 3 amp; 2.12 amp; zero; 225 watts

2. An alternating current passing through a resistance of 9 Ω produces heat at the rate of 144 watts. What is the effective value of the current? Of the potential difference? What are the maximum values?

3. An alternating emf has a frequency of 60 cycles/sec and an effective value of 110 volts. What is the maximum value of the emf? What is the instantaneous value of the emf at times 1/720, 1/360, 1/240, and 1/180 sec after it passes the zero value?
Ans. 156 volts; 78, 135, 156, and 135 volts

4. An alternating emf of frequency 400 cycles/sec has a peak value of 200 volts. Find the instantaneous value of the emf at the instants 1/360 and 1/240 sec after it passes through its zero value. What is the rms (or effective) value?

5. An a-c generating station generates 500 kW and transmits this power through a power line of 2 Ω total resistance. Find the power dissipated in the line if transmission is (*a*) at 250 kV and (*b*) at 2.5 kV. *Ans.* (*a*) 8 watts; (*b*) 80,000 watts

6. Find the reactance of a 0.08-henry inductor and of a 15-μF capacitor at 60 cycles/sec.

7. An iron-core coil bearing a 60-cycle/sec current of 2 amp dissipates heat at the rate of 120 watts. If it has an inductive reactance of 40 ohms, find the inductance, the resistance, and the impedance of the coil and the applied potential difference.

Ans. 0.106 henry; 30 Ω; 50 ohms; 100 volts

8. A pure inductance of 0.2 henry and a 50-Ω resistor are connected in series across a 110-volt, 60-cycle/sec source. Find the current and the angle by which it lags behind the source potential difference.

9. A coil has an inductance of 0.0398 henry and a resistance of 40 Ω. What are its reactance and its impedance at 120 cycles/sec? By what angle does the current in this coil lag behind the potential difference? What resistance must be connected in series with this coil to give a total impedance of 100 ohms? *Ans.* 30 ohms; 50 ohms; 37°; 55.4 Ω

10. At what frequency would a 20-μF capacitor have a reactance of 80 ohms? What inductance would have this same reactance at this frequency?

11. An inductor has a resistance of 15 Ω and an inductive reactance of 60 ohms at 60 cycles/sec. It is connected in series with an emf of 120 volts and a resistor of 65 Ω. Find the current, the potential difference across the inductor (do not forget its resistance), and the potential difference across the resistor. *Ans.* 1.2 amp; 74.2 volts; 78 volts

12. Find the reactance of a 0.3-μF capacitor at 10 cycles/sec, 10 kc/sec, 10 Mc/sec, and 1,000 Mc/sec. Note that a capacitor passes high frequencies readily and offers high reactance to low frequencies.

13. Find the capacitive reactance of a 15-μF capacitor at 2,000 cycles/sec. Compute the inductance required to produce series resonance with the capacitor at this frequency.

Ans. 5.3 ohms; 4.2 × 10⁻⁴ henry

14. A current of 0.6 amp is drawn from a 120-volt 60-cycle/sec line when a 100-Ω resistor is connected in series with a capacitor. Find the capacitance and the angle by which the current leads the potential difference.

15. A 7-μF capacitor and a 30-Ω resistor are connected in series with a 4-volt, 1,000-cycle/sec emf. Find the current, the angle by which the current leads the emf, and the power dissipated. *Ans.* 0.104 amp; 37°; 0.34 watt

16. Signals with a frequency of 1,200 kc/sec are sent out by a radio station. Find the wavelength. What capacitance is required to produce resonance at this frequency with an inductance of 0.002 henry?

17. A radio station broadcasts on an assigned frequency of 750 kc/sec. Find the wavelength of the radio waves sent out. What inductance must be connected in series with a capacitance of 15 $\mu\mu$F (or pF) for resonance at this frequency?

Ans. 400 m; 3.01 × 10⁻³ henry

18. What capacitance is required with an inductance of 1.5 μH to form a resonant circuit for a wavelength of 20 cm?

19. A television station operates at a frequency of 200 Mc/sec. What inductance is needed with a capacitance of 2 $\mu\mu$F to form a circuit resonant to this frequency? What is the wavelength of the radiation? *Ans.* 0.308 μH; 1.5 m

20. In the a-c circuit shown in Figure 43.7, the effective emf is 100 volts, the inductance is 0.08 henry, the resistance is 40 Ω, and the capacitance is 20 μF. The frequency is 500/π cycles/sec. (*a*) Find the inductive reactance, the capacitive reactance, and the impedance. (*b*) Find the current and the potential difference across each part of the system. (Note that it is the vector sum of the voltages which adds to 100. The voltage across an inductance or capacitance may exceed the applied voltage!) (c) Find the angle by which the current lags the emf. (d) Find the power dissipated in the circuit.

21. In the a-c circuit shown in Figure 43.7, the effective emf is 65 volts, the inductance is 0.225 henry, the resistance is 120 Ω, and the capacitance is 1 μF. The frequency is 1,000/π cycles/sec. (a) Find the inductive reactance, the capacitive reactance, and the impedance. (b) Find the current and the potential difference across each part of the system. (Note that it is the vector sum of the voltages which adds to 65. The voltage across an inductance or capacitance may exceed the applied voltage!) (c) Find the angle by which the current lags the emf. (d) Find the power dissipated in the circuit. *Ans.* (a) 450 Ω; 500 Ω; 130 Ω; (b) 0.5 amp; $V_R = 60$ volts; $V_b = 225$ volts; $V_c = 250$ volts; (c) $-22.6°$; (d) 30 watts

CHAPTER 44 *In the preceding eight chapters we have been examining d-c and a-c circuits, considering currents passing through solid or liquid conductors, and in general paying little attention to the motions of the individual charged particles. Now we shall examine the conduction of electricity through an ionized gas, or* plasma, *and the passage of individual ions through an evacuated region. Studies in these areas resulted in the discovery of X rays, contributed mightily to our understanding of atomic structure, and led to the development of the high-energy accelerators so important in nuclear physics.*

Electrons and Positive Ions

44.1 Gaseous Ionization

Molecules of air and other gases are normally electrically neutral. Un-ionized air is an excellent insulator, a fact demonstrated by the observation that the leaves of an electroscope may hold their charges many hours. However, an ionized gas is a good conductor. Indeed, if virtually every molecule of the gas has lost one or more electrons, the assemblage of positive ions and free electrons is an excellent conductor. A highly ionized gas is known as a *plasma*—sometimes called the fourth state of matter since it is not solid, liquid, or gas in the usual sense of these words. Actually the major portion of the matter in our universe is in the plasma phase, since this is the state of stars and most interstellar matter. On the earth, conditions of temperature and pressure are such that most matter is solid, liquid, or gaseous, but relatively little of the universe has anything similar to our terrestrial environment.

To ionize a gas molecule, one must provide the few electron volts of energy needed to free an electron. This may be accomplished in a variety of ways, of which collision with an energetic electron or ion is perhaps the most familiar. This is the dominant process in fluorescent lamps, neon tubes, and similar devices in which positive ions are accelerated toward a negative electrode (cathode), and negative ions, chiefly electrons, toward a positive electrode (anode). If the ions have enough energy when they collide with neutral molecules, additional ion pairs are produced.

Charged particles emitted by radioactive nuclei produce ionization in any gas through which they pass. Many devices for detecting and measuring the radiation from fallout or other nuclear disintegrations are fundamentally electroscopes depending on gaseous ionization for their readings.

When gamma rays, X rays, and ultraviolet radiation pass through gases, electrons are ejected from the atoms, thereby producing positive gas ions and free electrons. Gases drawn from a flame contain many ions. This ionization is greatly enhanced if the flame is fed with a salt such as sodium chloride, which readily breaks into ion pairs. Any gas can be ionized by raising the temperature sufficiently high. The temperature required for a specified fraction of ionized molecules depends on the gas involved. Even neutral molecules can ionize one another if they have enough kinetic energy.

Air at atmospheric pressure "breaks down" under electric fields of about 30,000 volts/cm. At reduced pressures the breakdown occurs at lower field strengths. The corona glow from a lightning rod is an example of ionization by a strong electric field. Once such ionization begins, other ions are produced by collisions, and a conducting path between two charged objects is created.

44.2 The Ionization Chamber

An ionization chamber is a device for measuring the number of ion pairs produced in a gas. A simple type of ionization chamber is shown in Figure 44.1a where two charged metal plates are used to collect ions produced by a beam of X rays. If the plates are connected through a sensitive galvanometer to the terminals of a battery, a current passes from one plate to another.

The current through the conducting gas is not proportional to the applied potential difference; hence, it does not follow Ohm's law. As the potential difference between the plates is increased, the current

FIGURE 44.1

(a) Circuit of primitive ionization chamber, and (b) graph of current in the chamber as a function of electrical intensity for a constant external source of ionization.

(a)

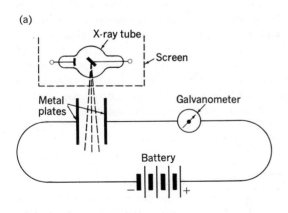

(b)

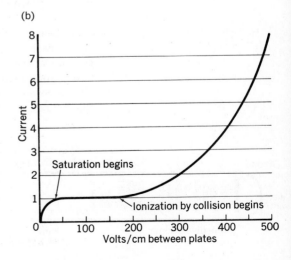

through the galvanometer increases as the electric intensity between the plates is made larger (Fig. 44.1*b*). If the potential gradient is only a few volts per centimeter, many of the ions recombine before they are collected by the plates. However, an electric field of the order of 25 volts/cm is ordinarily sufficient to collect virtually all the ions produced, at which point the *saturation current* is attained. Once saturation is reached, a further moderate increase in field gives no significant change in current.

If the potential gradient is increased far above the value required for saturation, the current increases again, at first slowly, then more rapidly as more and more ion pairs are produced by collisions. At a sufficiently high potential gradient the gas breaks down, and a discharge occurs between the plates.

44.3 Discharge in Gases at Low Pressures

When an electric discharge is maintained between two electrodes in a long glass tube filled with air (Fig. 44.2), some beautiful and interesting effects are observed as the air is pumped out of the tube. If the potential difference between the electrodes is not much greater than is necessary to maintain the discharge, sparks jump between the electrodes at atmospheric pressure. As the pressure in the tube is lowered, a narrow pink streamer appears between the electrodes. As the pressure is reduced further, the streamer expands until it fills almost the entire volume of the tube. By the time the pressure is reduced to 1 mm Hg, the entire gas glows.

As the pressure is reduced still further, one reaches the stage of discharge indicated in Figure 44.2. A velvety glow, known as the *cathode glow,* covers the surface of the negative electrode. Outside this glow is a region called the *Crookes dark space.* Beyond this is a luminous region known as the *negative glow,* and then a second dark region called the *Faraday dark space.* Then follows another luminous region, known as the *positive column,* which reaches to the positive electrode. The positive column is not perfectly continuous, but may show alternate light and dark layers called *striations* across the path of the discharge. If the distance between the electrodes is increased, the appearance of the cathode region is not much changed; the positive column increases in length to fill the added volume. Practically all the potential difference across the discharge tube occurs between the cathode and the negative edge of the positive column.

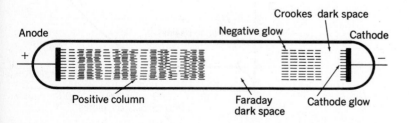

Anode

Crookes dark space

Negative glow

Cathode

Positive column

Faraday dark space

Cathode glow

FIGURE 44.2
Discharge of electricity through a gas at reduced pressure.

The potential difference required to maintain the discharge in a tube depends sensitively upon the pressure. When the air is at atmospheric pressure, a high potential difference is required. As the pressure is reduced, the potential difference required to maintain the discharge decreases steadily (Fig. 44.3). At some relatively low pressure, a minimum in the curve is reached; then, as the pressure is decreased still further, the potential difference required to maintain the discharge increases sharply. Practically all the ionization of the air in the discharge tube occurs as the result of impacts. At high pressure the few residual ions (which may be formed by cosmic rays or by radioactivity) are accelerated by the electric field in the tube, but they travel short distances between collisions and attain relatively low energies. In order to produce more ionization they must have a certain minimum energy. If an ion is to attain this minimum energy between collisions at high pressure, it is necessary that a high electric field be maintained. As the pressure is reduced, the distance an ion travels between collisions is increased, and the ion has a greater distance over which to acquire the energy needed to produce ionization by collision. Eventually the pressure becomes so low that ions may go all the way to the collecting electrode without colliding. Then a higher potential difference is required to maintain the discharge; the ions may eject electrons and other ions when they collide with the electrode. These *secondary ions* aid in supporting the discharge.

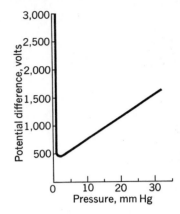

FIGURE 44.3
Potential difference required to maintain a discharge as it varies with pressure for a particular discharge tube.

44.4 Cathode Rays

As the pressure in a discharge tube is reduced beyond the stage pictured in Figure 44.2, the Faraday dark space lengthens, and the positive column shrinks. Eventually a greenish glow spreads over the entire tube. This is due to fluorescence of the glass as it is bombarded with high-speed electrons which, Crookes showed, have their origin at the cathode of the tube. These particles were named *cathode rays* before they were identified as electrons—indeed, before electrons were "discovered." Cathode rays have the following properties:

1. *The rays travel in straight lines in the absence of electric and magnetic fields.* This fact may be demonstrated by inserting some obstacle in the path of the rays and observing that the geometric shadow of the obstacle does not show fluorescence (Fig. 44.4).

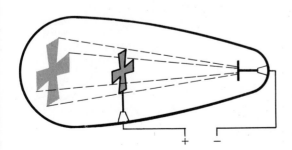

FIGURE 44.4
Sharp shadow shows that cathode rays travel in straight lines.

2. *The rays are deflected by an electric field* (Fig. 44.5).

3. *The rays are deflected by a magnetic field.*

4. *The rays carry negative electric charge.* The direction of the deflection in both electric and magnetic fields supports this conclusion. Further, by applying a suitable magnetic field in the arrangement of Figure 44.6, a cathode-ray beam can be deflected so that it enters the small cylindrical vessel at E which is connected to a galvanometer G. The galvanometer shows that negative charge is collected in E when cathode rays enter the cylinder.

5. *The rays emerge normally from the surface of the cathode.* If the cathode has a concave surface, the cathode rays come to a focus near its geometric center. If the anode of the discharge tube is shielded by some obstruction or is off at one side of the tube, the cathode rays strike at points which one would expect to be hit if the rays left perpendicularly from the surface of the cathode.

6. *The rays penetrate small thicknesses of matter.* If a thin window of aluminum is inserted in the tube, the cathode rays pass through the aluminum and make themselves evident by forming luminous streamers in the air beyond the window.

44.5 The Ratio of Electronic Charge to Mass

By using a tube similar to that in Figure 44.5, J. J. Thomson was able to measure the velocity of cathode rays (electrons). If the plate S of this cathode-ray tube is made positive, the beam is deflected downward.

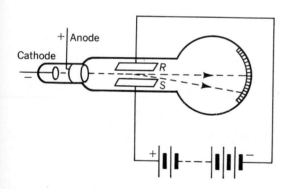

FIGURE 44.5
Cathode rays are deflected by an electric field.

FIGURE 44.6
Cathode rays are deflected by a magnetic field and bear negative charge.

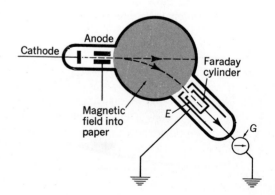

Now if a magnetic field uniform over the area between the plates R and S is applied out of the plane of the paper, it exerts an upward force on the moving electrons. It is possible to choose magnetic and electric fields in such a way that their effects exactly balance. The downward force due to the electric intensity E has a magnitude Ee, where e is the charge on an electron. The upward force due to the magnetic intensity B has magnitude evB if v is the speed of the electrons. When the beam is undeflected, $Ee = evB$, and

$$v = \frac{E}{B} \qquad\qquad\qquad \textbf{44.1}$$

Thomson found that electrons which had been accelerated through a potential difference of 25 kV had a speed of about 8×10^7 m/sec, over one-fourth the speed of light. From the deflection of the electrons by the electric field in the absence of a magnetic field and the speed of the electron, Thomson calculated e/m, the ratio of the charge of an electron to its mass.

Thomson's pioneering experiments in deflecting beams of high-speed electrons by electric and magnetic fields laid the foundation for modern cathode-ray oscilloscopes and television picture tubes.

A more direct way to determine e/m is by measuring the radius of curvature of the path of an electron moving with known velocity perpendicular to a uniform magnetic intensity B. The centripetal force mv^2/r required for the circular path is provided by the force evB exerted on the moving charge by the magnetic field. Therefore,

$$\frac{mv^2}{r} = evB \qquad\qquad\qquad \textbf{44.2}$$

or

$$\frac{e}{m} = \frac{v}{Br} \qquad\qquad\qquad \textbf{44.2a}$$

The result of many painstaking measurements is that

$$\frac{e}{m} = 1.759 \times 10^{11} \text{ coulomb/kg}$$

When this value is combined with Millikan's much later determination of $e = 1.602 \times 10^{19}$ coulomb, we find that the mass m of the electron is 9.11×10^{-31} kg.

In Chap. 38 we found that it requires 9.649×10^7 coulombs to deposit electrolytically 1 kg-equivalent mass of any element. In the case of hydrogen this corresponds to 1.008 kg. If the cathode rays in a discharge tube bear the same magnitude of charge as a monovalent ion, we can calculate the ratio of the mass M of a hydrogen atom to that of the electron. For the hydrogen atom $e/M = 9.649 \times 10^7$ coulombs/1.008 kg $= 9.575 \times 10^7$ coulombs/kg, from which we have

$$\frac{\text{Mass of hydrogen atom}}{\text{Mass of electron}} = \frac{M}{m} = \frac{1.759 \times 10^8}{9.575 \times 10^4} = 1{,}837$$

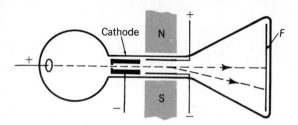

FIGURE 44.7
Positive ions passing through the hole in the cathode are deflected by both electric and magnetic fields.

44.6 Positive Ions

When a potential difference is applied between the terminals of a discharge tube, positive ions are accelerated as well as electrons. If a hole is drilled through the cathode (Fig. 44.7), some of the positive ions stream through the hole, giving a fine line of positive rays. J. J. Thomson used a tube similar to that of Figure 44.7 to deflect the positive rays by means of electric and magnetic fields, thereby determining the ratio of charge to mass for the various positive ions present. The beam of positive ions passing between the poles of an electromagnet (Fig. 44.8) is deflected horizontally. An electric field parallel to the magnetic flux produces a vertical deflection. As a result, positive ions of different charge-to-mass ratios were deflected to form different parabolic traces on a photographic film. Slow-moving ions of a given kind undergo larger deflections than higher-energy ions of the same kind, primarily because the slower ions spend more time in the deflecting fields.

From the shape and location of such parabolic traces on a photographic plate, the ratio of charge to mass can be determined. In this way Thomson showed in 1907 that neon is composed of atoms of two mass numbers, 20 and 22. This was the first proof that atoms of a given chemical element may have different masses. Atoms of the same element which have different masses are called *isotopes*.

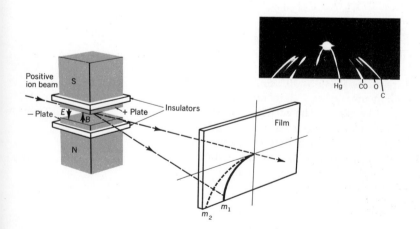

FIGURE 44.8
Parabolic trace on a film is formed by positive ions of the same charge-to-mass ratio but different velocities when deflected by parallel electric and magnetic fields. Reversal of the magnetic field produced the other half of the parabolas in the insert.

44.7 Mass Spectrometers

Several types of instruments have been developed for the accurate determination of the charge-to-mass ratios of isotopes and complex ions. Such instruments are known as *mass spectrometers* (or *mass spectrographs* if they provide photographic recordings). Figure 44.9 is a schematic digram of a Bainbridge mass spectrograph. Ions from a source are accelerated through a potential difference and pass through slits S_1 and S_2 into a region in which a uniform electric field E is provided by the plates P_1 and P_2; a uniform magnetic field B perpendicular to the plane of the paper is maintained by a magnet not shown. E and B are adjusted so that only ions having a desired velocity v pass through slit S_3. Ions with too low a speed are deflected toward the negative plate, and those with too high a speed toward the positive plate; only ions with $v = E/B$ are undeflected. An arrangement of crossed electric and magnetic fields of this kind is often called a *velocity selector*.

Once the ions have passed S_3 they are still in the magnetic field, but no longer in an electric field. Consequently the ions move in a circular path with

$$m\frac{v^2}{r} = qvB \qquad \text{44.2b}$$

From measurements of r, B, and E, a straightforward computation gives q/m for the positive ions. Figure 44.10 shows the circular paths of ion beams of three different masses in a mass spectrometer.

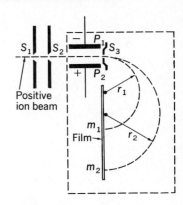

FIGURE 44.9

The uniform magnetic field in a Bainbridge-type mass spectrograph is out of the page over the region enclosed by the dashed rectangle.

FIGURE 44.10

Paths of atomic beams of three different masses in a mass spectrometer.

<   It is not necessary that a mass spectrometer include a velocity selector. If one is satisfied with a somewhat less uniform velocity for the incident ions, one can simply accelerate the ions through a potential difference V and make them incident directly on S_3. The work Vq done on each ion by the accelerating field is equal to the kinetic energy $\frac{1}{2}mv^2$ gained by the ion, or $v = \sqrt{2Vq/m}$. Simpler mass spectrometers of this kind have been widely used to separate isotopes of various elements.

With the mass spectrometer it is possible to determine directly the ratio of the charge on an ion to its mass. If we know the number of atomic charge units borne by the ion, we can calculate its mass. In obtaining a precise set of mass values for the hundreds of isotopes of the known elements, elaborate comparison measurements are made. This is important because, typically, one can determine the mass difference between two ions of nearly the same q/m with far greater precision than that with which one can determine the mass of either ion by itself.

44.8 Avogadro's Number and the Masses of Atoms

The mass spectrometer is by no means the only tool we have for estimating atomic masses. For example, in Chap. 38 we learned that it takes 9.649×10^7 coulombs to deposit electrolytically 1 kg-equivalent mass of any element. Let us now find Avogadro's number, the number of atoms in a kilogram-atomic weight. Since a monovalent atomic ion is a neutral atom with one electron missing, the charge on the ion is 1.602×10^{-19} coulomb. Therefore, Avogadro's number N_A is given by

$$N_A = \frac{9.649 \times 10^7 \text{ coulombs/kg-atomic wt}}{1.602 \times 10^{-19} \text{ coulomb/atom}}$$

$$= 6.023 \times 10^{26} \frac{\text{atoms}}{\text{kg-atomic wt}}$$

The atomic weight of chlorine is 35.5, and the average mass of chlorine atoms is given by $35.5/N_A = 5.89 \times 10^{-26}$ kg. This average mass does not, of course, necessarily represent the mass of every chlorine atom; chlorine has two stable isotopes, and roughly three-fourths of the atoms have a mass of 5.81×10^{-26} kg, while the other one-fourth have a mass of 6.14×10^{-26} kg. The average mass of any other atom can be found by dividing its atomic weight by N_A.

44.9 Charged-particle Accelerators

In both nuclear and atomic physics we use beams of high-energy ions (in particular, protons and deuterons) for studying the reactions induced in various targets. A variety of particle accelerators have been developed, many of which depend on magnetic fields to constrain the particle to move in a circular orbit while electric fields produce the accelerations. Although particle accelerators are basic tools of nuclear physics, the underlying principles are those which govern the interactions of ions with electric and magnetic fields.

The Cyclotron. The first major accelerator based on circular orbits in a magnetic field was the cyclotron, developed in 1932 by Lawrence and Livingston. The key parts of the cyclotron are a large electromagnet which provides a constant magnetic field over a large area and an oscillating electric field between two semicircular hollow elements, called *dees* because they have the shape of a D. Ions are produced at the center of the magnetic field between the two dees, as shown in Figure 44.11. A charged particle which is accelerated toward the lower dee gains energy as it crosses the gap between the dees. Once in the lower dee its path is circular, since

$$qvB = \frac{mv^2}{r} \qquad\qquad\qquad \textbf{44.2b}$$

Soon the particle finds itself in the region between the two dees once more. If now the upper dee is negative, and the lower dee positive, the particle is accelerated across the gap and enters the upper dee with a higher velocity, where it traverses a semicircular arc of greater radius. When it again reaches the gap between the dees, the electric field has reversed, and the particle is accelerated downward. At each passing of the gap it gains energy, and the radius of its path in the magnetic field becomes greater, until eventually the particle has a very high energy and its orbit approaches the circumference of the magnetic poles. It is then removed from the cyclotron and directed against a target. The time $T_{1/2}$ required for the particle to make the half circle in one of the dees is

$$T_{1/2} = \frac{\pi r}{v}$$

In this time the accelerating field should be reversed; therefore this is the time for one-half cycle of the alternating potential difference ap-

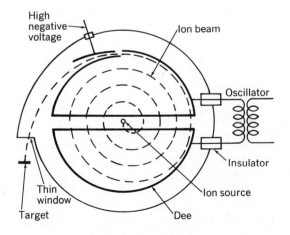

FIGURE 44.11
Cyclotron, showing the path of a charged particle in the vacuum chamber.

plied to the dees. The number of complete revolutions made per second is

$$\nu = \frac{v}{2\pi r} \qquad\qquad 44.3$$

Substituting the ratio v/r from Eq. 44.2b, we obtain

$$\nu = \frac{Bq}{2\pi m} \qquad\qquad 44.4$$

If we apply the constant frequency given by Eq. (44.4) to the dees, ions are accelerated each time they pass the gap.

< The time required for a charged particle to make half a revolution in the cyclotron is independent of radius only so long as the mass of the particle is constant. As we shall see in Sec. 46.8, the mass of any particle varies rapidly with velocity when v approaches c, the speed of light. If the cyclotron is used to accelerate a particle to a velocity which is more than a few per cent of the speed of light, the mass of the particle increases with time. By Eq. (44.4), the accelerating field can be kept in step with the particles only by decreasing the frequency as the mass increases. In very large cyclotrons the speed of the particles becomes great enough so that relativistic effects are important. Then the frequency of the cyclotron must be varied during an acceleration cycle. A cyclotron operated in such a way is said to be *frequency modulated* and is sometimes called a *synchrocyclotron*.

The Betatron. The betatron is used to produce high-speed electrons. It consists essentially of a large electromagnet between the poles of which is placed an evacuated tube in the form of a doughnut (Fig. 44.12). Alternating current is applied to the coils of the electromagnet, and the accelerating potential difference is induced by the changing magnetic field, which acts on the electrons in the vacuum tube as if the tube were the secondary of a transformer. The electrons previously injected into the tube are whirled around in circular

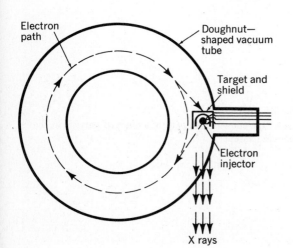

FIGURE 44.12
Doughnut-shaped vacuum tube of a betatron.

paths.   As the electrons gain energy, the magnetic field is increased at such a rate that it is just strong enough to keep the electrons rotating in the same circular path.   While the magnetic field builds up to its maximum value, the electrons travel around the vacuum tube many thousand times and acquire a velocity which closely approaches the speed of light.

The Synchrotron.   In a synchrotron particles are accelerated at essentially constant radius in a doughnut-shaped evacuated tube.   The acceleration is produced by a radio-frequency electric field applied across one or more gaps, as in the cyclotron.   The magnetic field serves to keep the particle traversing the same circular path as it goes around.   As the speed of the particle increases, the strength of the magnetic field must be increased so that the particle does not hit the walls of the doughnut.   The frequency applied across the gap is increased, so that each time the particle crosses the gap it is properly accelerated.   Synchrotrons ordinarily are designed to accelerate either protons or electrons.   Protons with energies of many billions of electron volts are currently available from synchrotrons (Fig. 44.13).

FIGURE 44.13
Tunnel of the 33-GeV alternating-gradient synchrotron where it joins the 50-MeV linear accelerator which injects protons into the "doughnut."   At the right is a small portion of the magnet ring providing the guide field for the ½-mile-circumference ring.

Questions

1. How does the conduction of electricity in a gas differ from conduction in a copper wire? Discuss the similarities and differences.

2. What are the properties of cathode rays?

3. What is "recombination" in electrical discharges? Why does it occur?

4. What is an electron volt? Why is the electron volt a convenient unit for measuring energies in atomic and nuclear physics?

5. How can beams of electrons be focused? What types of electron lenses can you suggest?

6. The gas between two parallel plates is ionized by a constant X-ray beam. If the potential difference between the plates is increased from zero to a very high value, what happens to the current? Explain carefully. Is Ohm's law obeyed?

7. How does a cyclotron give protons millions of electron volts of energy even though the highest potential difference involved is only a few kilovolts?

Problems

1. What is the current through a mercury discharge tube operated on a d-c potential difference if, each minute, 5×10^{20} electrons and 2×10^{18} singly charged mercury ions pass a given cross section of the tube? What fraction of the current is carried by Hg^+ ions?
Ans. 1.34 amp; 0.4 per cent

2. Two small spheres, equally charged with negative electricity and 1.5 cm apart, repel each other with a force of 2×10^{-4} newton. How many excess electrons does each sphere carry? What is the mass of these electrons?

3. An electron with an energy of 200 eV enters a uniform magnetic field of intensity 5×10^{-4} weber/m² which is perpendicular to the electron's velocity. Find the radius of the path of the electron and the energy of the electron after it has traveled 0.15 m in the magnetic field.
Ans. 9.55 cm; 200 eV

4. Find the mass of a fluorine atom and of a mercury atom if the atomic weight of fluorine is 19.0 and that of mercury is 200.

5. The velocity selector of a mass spectrometer utilizes crossed electric and magnetic fields. The deflection plates are 1.5 cm apart and have a potential difference of 4,500 volts between them, and the magnetic induction is 0.6 weber/m². Find the speed of protons which will pass through undeflected. How does this compare with the speed of electrons and of Na^+ ions which would pass through undeflected?
Ans. 5×10^5 m/sec; same

6. In determining the speed of electrons by Thomson's method it is found that a magnetic field of 7×10^{-3} newton/amp-m is just adequate to compensate for an electric field of 4×10^5 newtons/coulomb. Find the speed.

7. If the magnetic induction of the mass spectrograph of Figure 44.9 is 0.25 weber/m² and the electric intensity between the plates is 25,000 volts/m, find (*a*) the speed of ions passed by the velocity selector, (*b*) the radius of the path of $(Ne^{20})^+$ ions (atomic weight = 20) which reach the photographic plate, and (*c*) the distance between the line formed by $(Ne^{20})^+$ ions and that formed by $(Ne^{22})^+$ ions for the same velocity-selector setting. *Ans.* (*a*) 10^5 m/sec; (*b*) 8.3 cm; (*c*) 1.66 cm

8. Alpha particles (He^{++} ions) of the same energy are passing between two parallel charged plates in a field of electric intensity 3×10^5 newtons/coulomb. A magnetic field perpendicular to the velocity of the alpha particles and to the electric field is varied until the alpha particles are not deflected. At this point $B = 0.2$ weber/m². Find the force exerted on an alpha particle by the electric field and the speed of the particles.

9. A cyclotron has pole faces with a diameter of 1.6 m and operates at a frequency of 25 Mc/sec. Find the time required for a proton to traverse a semicircle in one dee, the magnetic field required to accelerate protons, and the maximum kinetic energy which protons can receive under these conditions.

Ans. 2×10^{-8} sec; 1.64 webers/m²; 82.5 MeV

10. A particle of mass m, charge q, and speed v is moving perpendicular to a magnetic induction B. Show that the momentum of the particle is qBr, where r is the radius of curvature of the path in which the particle moves.

11. Calculate the maximum energy of protons obtainable from a cyclotron of 1.2 m dee diameter and 1.5 webers/m² magnetic induction. At what frequency must the cyclotron be operated? If the average energy gain per dee passage is 50 keV, how many revolutions do the protons make? *Ans.* 39 MeV; 22.9 Mc/sec; 390

12. Calculate the maximum energy which the cyclotron of Prob. 11 can give alpha particles (He^{++} ions). At what frequency must the cyclotron be operated?

13. An alpha particle (He^{++} ion) with a speed of 4×10^7 m/sec is moving perpendicular to a uniform magnetic field of 1.4 webers/m² in a cyclotron. Find the force on the alpha particle and the radius of the circular path which it follows. What frequency must be applied to the dees to accelerate this alpha particle? If the radius of the cyclotron is 1.5 m, what is the maximum energy an alpha particle can be given in this cyclotron?

Ans. 1.8×10^{-11} newton; 0.594 m; 10.7 Mc/sec; 212 MeV

14. Show that in a cyclotron the maximum kinetic energy which can be given an ion is $q^2B^2r^2/2m$, where B is the magnetic intensity, and r the maximum allowable radius.

15. An ion of mass m bearing a charge q is accelerated through a potential difference V. It then enters a magnetic field of flux density B, moving perpendicular to the field. Find the velocity (assumed to be small compared to the speed of light) of the ion and the radius of its path in the magnetic field in terms of m, q, V, and B.

Ans. $\sqrt{2Vq/m}$; $(\sqrt{2mV/q})/B$

16. Show that if two ions of the same charge and energy but different mass are passing through a uniform magnetic field, the radii of the paths are proportional to the square roots of the masses.

CHAPTER 45 *Research in the passage of electrons through evacuated regions and their deflection by electric and magnetic fields gave us a knowledge of the mass and charge of the electron. But it did far more than this; it laid the foundations for radio and television and the vast electronics industry. In this chapter we consider the physics of simple vacuum tubes and their use for producing, amplifying, and detecting electromagnetic waves of radio and television frequencies.*

Electronics

45.1 Thermionic Emission

In 1883, when Thomas Edison was developing the incandescent lamp, he made an important discovery. He observed that if he had a third electrode (Fig. 45.1) in one of his lamps, there was a current to this electrode when it was *positive* relative to the incandescent filament, but not when it was *negative*. *When materials are heated to a high temperature, electrons are emitted.* In Edison's experiments these electrons were attracted to the positive electrode, and a current was registered. When the third electrode was negative, the electrons were repelled. The emission of electrons from heated surfaces is *thermionic emission;* it is sometimes called the *Edison effect*.

The qualitative explanation of thermionic emission is relatively simple. In every material there are some electrons which are less tightly bound than others. In metals, for instance, there are electrons which are free to move about, although they cannot leave the surface of the metal unless they are given additional energy. One way of providing this energy is by raising the temperature. As the temperature goes up, an occasional electron gets enough energy to escape. At higher temperature more electrons leave, some of which have not only enough energy to escape, but enough to have relatively high speeds after they break free of the material. Figure 45.2 shows schematically that both the number and the average speed of escaping electrons increase as the temperature is raised.

Thermionic emission is analogous in many ways to evaporation from the surface of a liquid. In both cases, particles which happen to obtain an unusually large amount of energy when they are at the surface may escape. The theoretical work of Richardson showed that the current density J (current I emitted per unit area A) from a heated surface should be given by the relation

$$J = \frac{I}{A} = aT^2 e^{-b/T} \qquad\qquad \textbf{45.1}$$

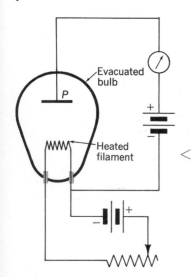

FIGURE 45.1

Hot wire emits electrons which go to electrode P when it is positive relative to the emitter.

where a and b are constants, T is the absolute temperature, and e is the base of the natural system of logarithms. The constant a is the same for all pure metals. The constant b varies from metal to metal and has particularly low values for those elements which are good thermionic emitters.

The number of electrons emitted per unit area per second increases rapidly as the temperature is increased (Fig. 45.3). In order that we be able to measure the total emitted current, it is necessary that the potential difference between the emitting surface and the positive collecting plate be fairly high. If it is not, there is a cloud of electrons around the emitting surface which repels additional electrons and drives many of them back to the filament. This electron cloud is called a *space charge* (Fig. 45.4). If the collecting plate is made only slightly positive, the current is limited by this space charge and bears no simple relation to the total number of electrons emitted from the filament. Figure 45.5 shows how the current collected by the plate depends on the potential for three temperatures of the filament. In each case the maximum current is determined by the rate at which electrons are emitted. When every electron emitted is collected, the current has reached its *saturation* value. As the temperature of the emitting surface is raised, the saturation current increases. At low plate potentials the current is *space-charge limited* and does not depend on the temperature so long as the temperature is sufficiently high. Clearly, the current to the collecting plate does not obey Ohm's law.

The oxides of barium and strontium are copious electron emitters at relatively low temperatures. Many radio tubes and other electronic devices which operate at low plate potentials use cathodes coated with such oxides. Where high potentials are required, the bombardment of the negative cathode by positive ions may destroy the oxide surface. If the potentials are not particularly high, a thoriated tungsten filament is commonly used as the emitter. It is produced by adding a small amount of thorium oxide to tungsten. When this material is heated, a layer of

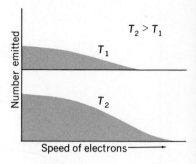

FIGURE 45.2
Increase in the number of electrons emitted and their average speed with increase in temperature.

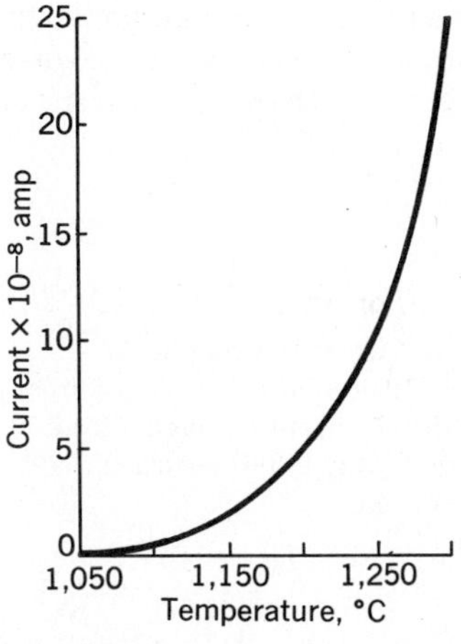

FIGURE 45.3
Thermionic emission increases rapidly with a rise in temperature.

FIGURE 45.4
The space charge of electrons near an emitter increases as the temperature is raised.

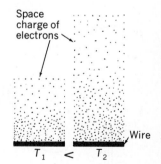

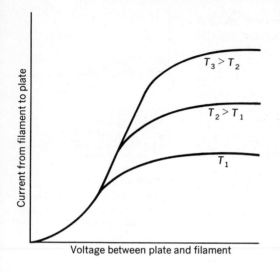

FIGURE 45.5

Current to a collecting plate as a function of the potential difference between filament and plate at three different temperatures.

thorium is formed on the surface of the tungsten and provides an excellent emitting surface. Where the filament is subject to bombardment by high-energy positive ions, thoriated tungsten fails, and pure tungsten emitters are used.

45.2 The Diode

A two-element vacuum tube containing an electron-emitting cathode and a plate is called a *diode*. Such a tube conducts electricity freely when the plate is positive, but not when the plate is negative. A diode is useful for changing an alternating current to a direct one. When it is used in this way, it is called a *rectifier*.

Suppose we wish to charge a battery, but we have available only an alternating potential difference. The direct application of an alternating potential difference to the battery results in no useful charging, since the electrical energy stored during one half cycle is returned during the second half cycle. However, if we provide a circuit similar to that of Figure 45.6a, there is a current through the battery only when the plate of the rectifier tube is positive. Thus there is a current in

(a)

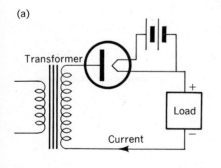

(b)

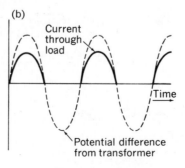

FIGURE 45.6

(*a*) Circuit showing diode rectifier used to give a unidirectional current through a load, and (*b*) graph of resulting current.

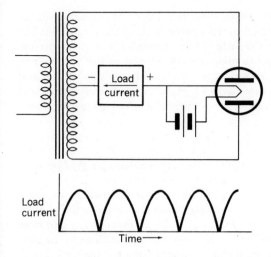

FIGURE 45.7

Full-wave rectification circuit used to provide the current shown below to the load.

the proper direction to charge the battery. Figure 45.6*b* shows the alternating potential difference provided for the circuit and the current. In this circuit current exists only during half a cycle. This is therefore called *half-wave rectification*.

The circuit shown in Figure 45.7 provides *full-wave rectification*. When the upper terminal of the a-c transformer is positive, electrons go from the cathode to the upper plate of the tube and then through the load. Conversely, when the lower end of the transformer is positive, electrons go to the lower plate. The current through the load is always in the same direction.

If it is desired to make the current steady, one can introduce a filter consisting of one or more capacitors in parallel with the load and one or more inductors (called *chokes* when used in this way) in series with the load (Fig. 45.8). By suitable choice of capacitors and inductors it

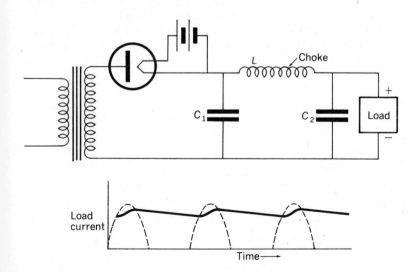

FIGURE 45.8

A filtered rectifier keeps the load current almost constant, in contrast to variations without the filter, shown by the dotted curve.

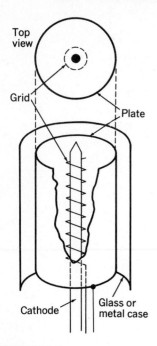

FIGURE 45.9
Simple triode.

is possible to provide almost any desired degree of constancy in the current. The general action of the capacitors is to store energy in the electrostatic field when the output from the tube is at its maximum and to release this energy to maintain the current as the output from the tube falls to zero. An inductor connected in series with the load stores energy in its magnetic field when the current is maximum and releases this energy to maintain the current as the current decreases.

45.3 The Triode

In 1907 De Forest had the brilliant idea of introducing a *grid* between the cathode and the plate of a diode to control the current to the plate. This grid consists of an open mesh or helix around the filament, as shown in Figure 45.9. By keeping the grid at a potential slightly negative relative to the cathode, it is possible to prevent the grid from collecting electrons (Fig. 45.10). Because the grid is close to the electron-emitting cathode, a small change in grid potential makes a significant change in the number of electrons which pass the grid and reach the plate.

If the plate potential of a triode is kept constant and the grid potential is varied, the plate current varies as a function of grid potential as shown in Figure 45.11. (Note that all potential differences are measured relative to the filament.) If the grid is made sufficiently negative, the current to the plate may be cut off entirely.

Figure 45.12 shows the plate current of a typical triode as a function of plate potential for three different values of the grid potential. Note that at points x and y in this figure the plate current is exactly the same. From x to y the grid potential decreases from -2 to -5 volts, while the plate potential increases from 90 to 140 volts. Thus, an increase in the plate potential of 50 volts has compensated for a decrease in grid potential of 3 volts. To put it another way, a reduction in the grid potential of 3 volts requires an increase of 50 volts in plate potential to keep the plate current constant. Under these conditions of operation, the grid is $^{5}\!\%$ or 16.7 times as effective in controlling the plate current as is the plate. We say that the *amplification factor* is 16.7.

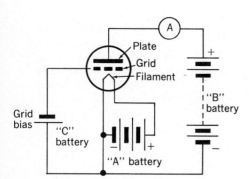

FIGURE 45.10
Circuit for measuring the static characteristics of a triode.

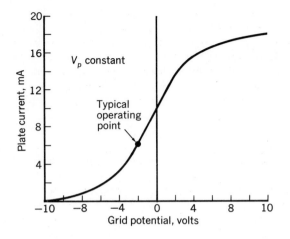

FIGURE 45.11

Relation between plate current and grid potential in a triode when plate potential is held constant.

If, when the grid potential of a triode is changed by a small amount $-\Delta V_g$, it requires a change in plate potential ΔV_p to keep the plate current constant, the amplification factor μ is defined as

$$\mu = \frac{\Delta V_p}{-\Delta V_g} \qquad I_p \text{ constant} \qquad\qquad \textbf{45.2}$$

45.4 The Triode as an Amplifier

The fact that small changes in the grid potential can produce large changes in the plate current in a triode permits us to obtain large potential variations in the plate circuit when the grid potential is changed by small amounts.   Consider the circuit shown in Figure 45.13.   If we apply a small alternating signal to the grid, the plate cur-

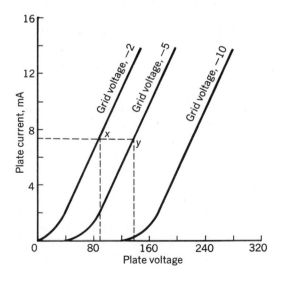

FIGURE 45.12

Plate current in a triode as a function of plate potential for three grid potentials.

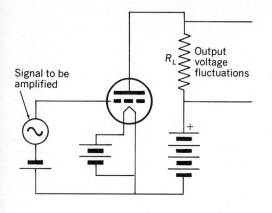

FIGURE 45.13

Circuit using a triode as an amplifier.

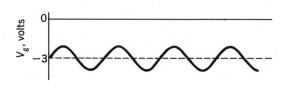

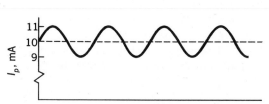

FIGURE 45.14

Variation of grid potential, plate current, and the potential difference across the load resistor R_L.

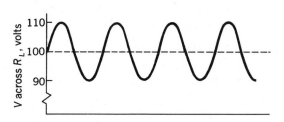

rent changes as indicated in Figure 45.14. As a result of this change in plate current, the potential difference across the plate load resistor R_L varies. For such a circuit we define the *voltage gain* as

$$\text{Voltage gain} = \frac{V_{\text{out}}}{V_{\text{in}}} = \frac{R_L \Delta i_p}{\Delta e_g} \qquad \text{45.3}$$

where R_L is the resistance of the plate resistor, and Δi_p and Δe_g are the variations in plate current and grid potential, respectively.

It is possible to apply the changes in potential across the plate (or load) resistor to the grid of a second amplifier tube. In this way signals may be amplified by a factor of many hundreds.

45.5 The Triode Oscillator

In Sec. 43.9 we learned that when a capacitor is discharged through an inductor of low resistance, damped oscillations occur with a frequency ν given by Eq. (43.8): $\nu = 1/2\pi \sqrt{LC}$. The oscillations are damped because energy is dissipated in heat and sent out as radiation, while no energy is supplied to the circuit. Steady oscillations of constant amplitude can be maintained in such a circuit provided energy is supplied to compensate for the losses. It is possible to use a triode to produce such stable oscillations by providing energy to the oscillating circuit from the plate potential supply of the triode. One of the ways in which this can be done is indicated in Figure 45.15. Here the condenser C_1 and the inductor L_1 form the oscillating circuit. The oscillations produce variations in the potential of the grid. This, in turn, results in variations of the plate current. The varying plate current passes through the inductor L_2 and induces, by mutual induction, an emf in the coil L_1, thereby supplying energy to the oscillating grid circuit. The energy is fed back into the grid circuit in such a way as to provide for the losses in this circuit. In this way oscillations of constant amplitude and of frequency determined by the grid-circuit elements are maintained.

If one wishes the oscillation frequency to remain very constant, one uses for C_1 a capacitor which has as dielectric between its plates a carefully cut crystal of quartz. In an oscillating electric field, such a crystal undergoes mechanical vibrations (see Sec. 35.3), the frequency of which depends on the thickness of the quartz. If the oscillating circuit and the crystal are resonant to essentially the same frequency, the oscillator assumes the frequency of the mechanical vibrations of the quartz. In such a case the oscillator is *crystal-controlled*.

45.6 The Radio Transmitter

In preceding sections we have seen how simple diode and triode vacuum tubes operate. We now consider how vacuum tubes may be used in simple radio circuits. Since the detailed operation of a radio transmitter or receiver involves many complexities, we emphasize only the basic physics of their operation.

All radio and television stations send out electromagnetic waves. The frequencies involved vary from many thousand to many million cycles per second. In principle, a simple oscillator such as that of

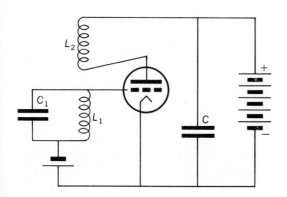

FIGURE 45.15
Simple oscillator using a triode.

Figure 45.15 could produce these oscillations; in practice, more sophisticated circuits are used. A primitive type of radio transmitter is shown in Figure 45.16. It consists of an oscillator, an antenna, and a *modulator*. The oscillator frequency is determined by the resonant grid circuit. For the standard radio band the frequencies range from 550 to 1,600 kc/sec. The oscillations in the grid circuit produce, through mutual induction, an oscillating current in the inductor L_3 which is part of the antenna circuit. The oscillator thus "drives" the antenna, setting up in it an alternating current of frequency characteristic of the oscillator. The current surging back and forth in the antenna produces the rapidly changing electromagnetic field which we know as radio waves and which can be detected at great distances from the transmitter.

To discuss the origin of the electromagnetic field sent out from an antenna, we must know a conclusion of electromagnetic theory which states that whenever charges are accelerated, an electric field is produced parallel to and proportional to the acceleration. Accompanying this electric field is a magnetic field in phase with and perpendicular to it. Figure 45.17 shows schematically the *radiation fields* associated with a charge performing simple harmonic oscillations in the y direction. These radiation fields propagate away from the accelerated charge with the speed of light, decreasing in amplitude as $1/r$, where r is the distance from the radiating charge. (The radiation fields exist in addition to the electrostatic field of the charge and the magnetic field due to the velocity of the charge.)

If a simple alternating current from an oscillator is used to drive an antenna, the transmitter sends out a constant-amplitude signal at a

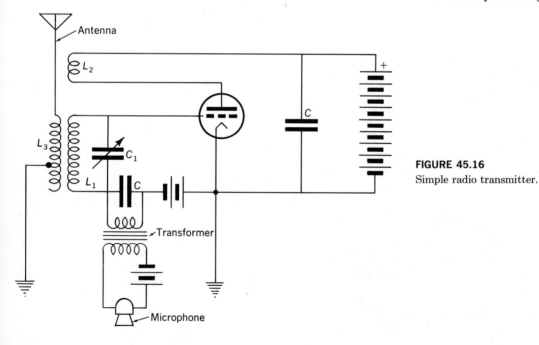

FIGURE 45.16
Simple radio transmitter.

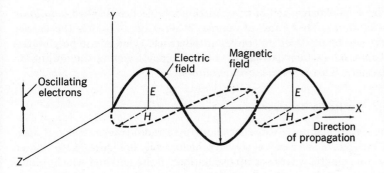

FIGURE 45.17

Electric and magnetic radiation fields some distance from an antenna in which the charges oscillate parallel to the *y* axis.

high frequency, called the *carrier frequency*. If we wish to convey intelligence by such a signal, we must interrupt it or modify it in some way. The most primitive method of doing this is to turn the oscillator on and off, thus sending a series of dots and dashes. However, it is also possible to send information which leads to accurate reproduction of sound waves. If we speak into the microphone of Figure 45.16, there are set up in the grid circuit additional small voltage fluctuations which vary the amplitude of the oscillations. If we wish to send a 1,000-cycle note over the transmitter, we "modulate" (i.e., vary) the amplitude of the carrier wave at a frequency of 1,000 times a second. Since the carrier frequency is many thousand times as high as the highest sound frequency we wish to transmit, the carrier wave makes many thousands of oscillations in each period of the sound wave. The general appearance of the unmodulated carrier wave, of the sound frequency with which we modulate this wave, and of the modulated wave which is sent out by the transmitter are all shown in Figure 45.18.

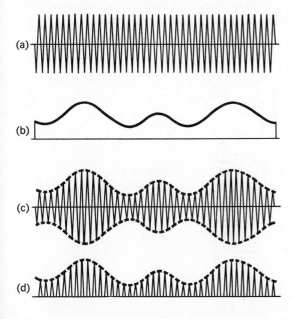

FIGURE 45.18

(*a*) Unmodulated carrier waves, (*b*) audio-frequency wave, (*c*) modulated carrier wave, and (*d*) rectified wave.

This particular method of transmitting intelligence is called *amplitude modulation.* There are, of course, other ways in which the carrier wave can be modified to convey intelligence. One of the possibilities is to introduce fluctuations in the frequency, keeping the amplitude constant. This is *frequency modulation.*

45.7 The Radio Receiver

The electromagnetic waves sent out by a radio transmitter fall upon the antenna of the receiver shown schematically in Figure 45.19. These electromagnetic waves set up oscillations in the antenna which induce small potential variations in the grid circuit of the receiver. There are many transmitters from which signals may be received. It is in the grid circuit L_2C_2 that the selection of the signal to be heard is made. By varying the capacitance C_2, the grid circuit L_2C_2 can be made resonant to any desired carrier frequency. Then oscillations in the antenna corresponding to that particular frequency establish changes in potential in the grid circuit, while oscillations of all other frequencies produce negligible effects because the impedance of the circuit is small for other frequencies.

The oscillations of potential across C_2 in the resonance circuit are applied to the grid of the triode in Figure 45.19. If this grid is made sufficiently negative, the plate current increases substantially when the grid potential changes in the positive direction, but decreases relatively little (or not at all) when the changes are in the negative direction. In this case the output of the plate circuit is similar to Figure 45.18d. The variations in plate current at radio frequency are such that the human ear cannot detect them; however, the average plate current over many carrier-wave oscillations fluctuates with the modulation frequency. Thus the current through the earphones oscillates with the modulation frequency, and sound is heard.

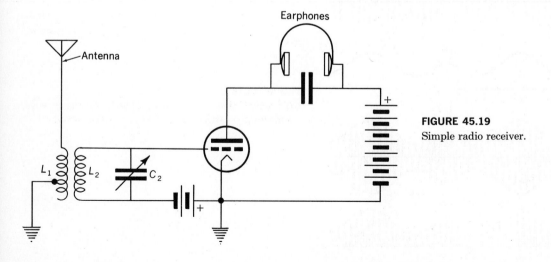

FIGURE 45.19
Simple radio receiver.

<   If one wishes to drive a loudspeaker, much more energy must be provided than can be expected from the output of a single triode of the type indicated. In a modern radio receiver several more tubes may be used to provide this additional power. The signal coming into the initial resonant circuit is amplified before the detection process is performed. Then the audio frequency may be amplified several times before it is finally supplied to a *power amplifier* which drives the loudspeaker.

45.8 The Loudspeaker

A loudspeaker is a device which transforms audio-frequency variations in electric current into sound waves. Figure 45.20 shows schematically the principal parts of a dynamic loudspeaker. A light thin coil of wire is attached to the apex of a light cone. The coil is placed in a magnetic field. Current from the power amplifier is fed to this coil; the fluctuating current produces fluctuating forces upon the coil, causing it to vibrate. The cone vibrates with the coil and produces waves in the surrounding air.

45.9 The Kennelly-Heaviside Layers

Radio reception from distant stations is usually superior at night. Sometimes reception is excellent at distances of several thousand miles when a receiving station only a few hundred miles away may not be able to detect the signal. In order to explain these phenomena it was

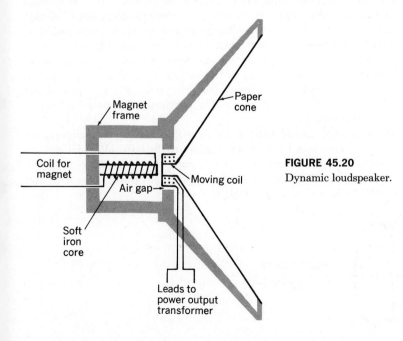

FIGURE 45.20
Dynamic loudspeaker.

suggested by Kennelly and by Heaviside that there are layers of ionized air in the upper atmosphere which act as refractors and reflectors of radio waves. Ions are produced in the outer layers by a variety of processes, chiefly by ultraviolet light from the sun. The height of the ionized layers changes from time to time; as a result, the transmission of electrical waves varies with time. In general, the ionizing layers form at different altitudes at different times of day, being higher and more uniform at night.

45.10 The Cathode-ray Oscilloscope

One of the most useful of all types of vacuum tubes is the so-called *cathode-ray tube*. A heated cathode (Fig. 45.21) emits electrons. These electrons are accelerated to a cylindrical anode, which has a hole in its center through which the cathode rays pass. The electron beam may be controlled by the grid. Beyond the anode is a beam of rapidly moving electrons of well-defined energy.

This beam passes between a pair of flat plates P_1 whose plane is horizontal. If a potential difference is applied between these plates, an electric field is created which may move the beam of electrons up or down. Next the beam passes between a pair of plates P_2 whose plane is vertical. If a potential difference is applied between these plates, the beam may be moved to the right or left. The beam of electrons strikes a screen coated with a fluorescent material that emits light where the electrons strike. The position of the point on the screen at which electrons strike may be controlled by the potentials applied to the deflecting plates.

In one common application of the oscilloscope the horizontal deflectors P_2 have applied to them a sawtooth potential variation which sweeps the beam at a constant rate from left to right and then suddenly switches the beam back to the left edge. If a sinusoidal potential difference is applied to the deflecting plates P_1, the beam traces a sine curve on the face of the oscilloscope. If some other type of potential variation is applied to the plates P_1, the picture on the oscilloscope screen reproduces the fluctuations in potential across the deflecting plates.

When a cathode-ray tube is combined with electronic circuits for amplifying signals and applying potentials to the horizontal and vertical deflecting plates, the unit is called a *cathode-ray oscilloscope*. The cathode-ray oscilloscope is one of the most convenient, versatile, and powerful tools of modern physics.

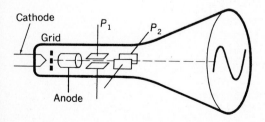

FIGURE 45.21
Cathode-ray tube.

< **45.11 Television**

In the television receiver a cathode-ray tube, in which horizontal and vertical deflections are usually produced by magnetic rather than electric fields, is used. The magnetic deflection is obtained through a pair of coils, one on each side of the picture tube, that produce a horizontal magnetic field, and another pair, one above and one below the neck of the tube, that produce a vertical field. By sending high-frequency alternating currents through these coils it is possible to make the cathode-ray beam move back and forth across the tube, producing the familiar lines of the television picture.

If one moved the cathode-ray beam across the face of the oscilloscope, then down a little and across the screen again, etc., there would be drawn on the face of the screen only a number of white lines. However, by controlling the intensity of the beam by means of the grid in the tube, it is possible to draw lines which vary in their lightness, depending on the potential applied to the grid at the particular instant the spot is drawing a given segment of the line. Thus the cathode-ray beam draws lines of varying brightness. There are 525 horizontal lines drawn to make a complete picture. In order to transmit pictures of moving objects, it is necessary that the picture be "redrawn" many times a second. In current television practice the even-numbered lines are drawn in $\frac{1}{60}$ sec and the odd-numbered lines in the next $\frac{1}{60}$ sec. Thus, 30 complete pictures or "frames" are drawn each second.

At the sending station the information transmitted is obtained in roughly the following way: An image of the picture to be transmitted is produced by lenses on the photosensitive screen of a tube known as an *image orthicon tube*. Each element of the sensitive surface emits photoelectrons, the number of which depends upon the intensity of the incident light. By a complex process the number of photoelectrons emitted from each of the tiny sensitive elements is determined and is converted into information which can be used to modulate the carrier wave. At the receiver this information is used to control the grid potential at the instant the corresponding element of the picture is to be reproduced on the receiving screen.

45.12 Radar

The wavelengths of ordinary radio waves are of the order of a thousand feet. Such waves bend readily around obstacles such as buildings or airplanes. If radio waves of much higher frequency, and therefore shorter wavelength, are produced, the waves are readily reflected by aircraft and other objects of comparable size. Further, these waves can be focused into sharp beams by a reasonably small antenna. If a sharply focused beam of high-frequency waves is used to scan the sky, it is reflected by airplanes or other objects in the sky. By measuring the time lapse between the transmission of a pulse and the reception of the reflected pulse, one can determine the distance of the object from the transmitter, since radio waves are transmitted with the speed of light.

It is possible to scan a relatively large area by means of a radar transmitter and show on an oscilloscope screen the areas from which there is substantial reflection and those from which the reflection is much smaller. In this way one can make a radar map of an area which is not visible because of clouds, fog, or darkness.

One of the earliest and simplest examples of the use of radio waves to measure distance is found in the radio altimeter. If a radio wave is sent down from an airplane, it is reflected by the earth. If this radiation is sent in pulses, and if it is possible to measure the time it takes the wave to travel to the earth and return, the altitude of the plane above the terrain can be calculated.

Questions

1. What is "space charge"? Discuss the importance of space charge in electron tubes.

2. How does one change stations in an ordinary radio? In a television receiver? Why the difference?

3. Why is the grid of a triode that is used as a detector biased more negatively than the same grid would be if the triode were used as an amplifier?

4. How does a triode act as an oscillator? From what source does the energy come to maintain the oscillations?

5. How is the picture drawn on the screen of a television tube?

6. How does a cathode-ray oscilloscope work? What are some of its uses?

7. Draw a circuit showing how a simple diode can be used as a rectifier to charge a battery.

8. Draw a diagram of a full-wave rectifier using a transformer as a power source to charge a battery.

9. Explain, with curves, how a triode can be used to amplify a small signal.

Problems

1. The current in the plate circuit of a vacuum tube is 40 mA. How many electrons are arriving at the plate each second?   *Ans.* 2.5×10^{17}

2. A device has been designed which measures a current of 60 electrons per second. What fraction of an ampere is this?

3. The signal available from an antenna has an amplitude of 8 μV. If this signal is passed through two stages of amplification, each with a voltage gain of 35, what is the amplitude of the potential fluctuations in the output circuit? Through how many more stages of the same voltage gain would the signal have to be passed to obtain an output voltage in excess of 2 volts?   *Ans.* 9.8 mV; 2

4. A vacuum tube has an amplification factor of 16. If the grid voltage is decreased 0.2 volt, how much must the plate potential be raised for the plate current to remain constant?

5. When an a-c signal of 0.4 volt amplitude is impressed on the grid of a triode which is biased at -3 volts, the plate current varies from 4 to 8 mA. If the resistance R_L in the plate circuit is 8,000 Ω, find the voltage amplification of the triode.   *Ans.* 40

6. The plate current of a vacuum tube is 5 mA when the grid potential is -2 volts and the plate potential is 150 volts. It is also 5 mA when the grid potential is -2.8 volts and the plate potential is 165 volts. What is the amplification factor?

7. A triode amplifier uses a plate resistor of 18,000 Ω. When no signal is applied to the grid, the plate current is 6 mA. If the voltage gain is 90, find the amplitude of the potential fluctuations across the plate resistor when a signal of amplitude 0.004 volt is applied to the grid. Between what limits does the plate current fluctuate?

Ans. 0.36 volt; 5.98 to 6.02 mA

8. A triode is used as an amplifier. If the grid is biased at -3 volts and a plate resistor R_L of 15,000 Ω is used, the plate current is 0.015 amp. If the grid potential is varied from -3.2 to -2.8 volts, the plate current varies from 14 to 16 mA. Find the maximum and minimum potential difference across the plate resistor and the voltage gain.

9. An electron is projected along the axis of a cathode-ray tube midway between two parallel plates with a velocity of 1.5×10^7 m/sec. The plates are 1.2 cm apart and 3 cm long and have a potential difference of 120 volts between them. Find (*a*) the angle the electron makes with the axis as it leaves the plates, (*b*) the distance of the electron from the axis as it leaves the plates, and (*c*) the distance from the axis at which the electron strikes a fluorescent screen 20 cm beyond the plates.

Ans. (*a*) 0.23 radian; (*b*) 0.35 cm; (*c*) 5.0 cm

10. A cathode-ray tube has electrostatic deflection plates 2 cm square with a separation of 0.5 cm, located 25 cm from the fluorescent screen of the tube. The electrons are accelerated through a potential difference of 1,500 volts between emitter and anode. Calculate the approximate deflection of the beam on the screen for each volt potential difference applied to the plates.

11. If the cathode-ray tube of Prob. 10 uses magnetic rather than electrostatic deflection, find the deflection produced by a magnetic field of 0.002 weber/m^2 which is assumed uniform over a length of 2 cm and zero elsewhere. *Ans.* 8 cm

12. Electrons in a television picture tube are accelerated through a potential difference of 10,000 volts. Find the speed of the electrons. (Your answer is about 2 per cent larger than the value given in Table 46.1 because you are not in a position to consider relativistic effects.)

PART VI   MODERN PHYSICS

CHAPTER 46 *The classical physics which we have been studying makes predictions in excellent agreement with observed results so long as we exclude from consideration objects of atomic dimensions and speeds which are comparable with the speed of light. In 1905 Einstein advanced his celebrated special theory of relativity, which linked space and time in a new way that resolved the dilemmas regarding the speed of light. The existence of this revolutionary theory has been widely publicized; in this chapter we develop several facets of Einstein's theory and its predictions.*

Relativity

46.1 Electromagnetic Waves and the Ether

Radio signals and visible light are transverse electromagnetic waves. Late in the nineteenth century physicists were speculating on the question "Through what medium are these waves propagated?" Such a question seemed most reasonable; after all, acoustic waves are transmitted through air, transverse waves are transmitted by the strings of a violin, and water waves are propagated at a water-air interface. There was no obvious medium to which one could assign electromagnetic waves, since they were known to pass through a vacuum. However, physicists believed that some medium was necessary for energy to be transmitted through a distance, and this medium was given the name *luminiferous ether*. Does such an ether exist? If it exists, how can one detect it and determine its characteristics? These, too, were questions which haunted physicists during the latter part of the nineteenth century.

Early speculations on the ether revealed that it must have remarkable properties. First of all, to sustain waves with the tremendous speed of light, a material of high rigidity was required. At the same time this rigidity raised problems about how the earth could move through the ether with no apparent retardation—or if one assumed the ether to be transported along with the earth, there was the problem of how the ether-atmospheres of the earth and the sun could be in relative motion without some evidence of shear forces.

46.2 An Acoustic Analogue

If a luminescent ether exists, the speed of light measured in a reference frame at rest with respect to this ether should be different from the speed determined in a reference frame moving with respect to the ether. Thus, the ether should provide an absolute reference frame to which the motions of all other frames and of all bodies in the universe could be referred. It was clear from the beginning that grave experimental difficulties would accompany any effort to resolve the question of how fast the earth moves relative to the ether or, indeed, to make any meaningful measurements whatever regarding the ether.

In order to see one way in which such measurements might be made, let us consider an experiment to determine whether the air through which sound waves are being propagated is moving relative to the earth. This is directly analogous to the problem of determining the ether "wind" associated with the motion of the earth through the ether. However, the acoustic experiment is vastly simpler than one involving light, because the speed of sound is modest, while the speed of light is great. Imagine two observers A and B a distance d apart. Let A send a signal to B when there is a wind blowing from A toward B with a velocity V (Fig. 46.1). The time required for the signal to go from A to B is $d/(c + V)$, where c is the speed of sound relative to air. The time required to transmit a signal from B back to A is $d/(c - V)$, since the propagation speed of the wave relative to B is $c - V$. For example, if $d = 330$ m, $V = 30.0$ m/sec, and the speed of sound in air $c = 330$ m/sec, the time required for a signal to go from A to B is $330/360 = 0.917$ sec, while the time required for the sound to go from B to A is $330/300 = 1.10$ sec. The total time for the traversal A to B and return is 2.017 sec. Clearly, this is different from the 2.000 sec which would be required in still air. While 0.017 sec is not a long time, it is easy with modern techniques to measure much shorter times.

Of course, there are simpler ways of telling whether the air is in motion between A and B, but ideally this type of experiment could establish whether A and B are moving or at rest *relative* to the air. In principle, by an experiment similar to this, the speed of the earth in its orbital motion about the sun might be measured relative to the ether, which for the moment we assume to be fixed in the solar system. However, a simple calculation shows that the time difference could not be measured directly by ordinary methods. To see this, we observe that the speed of the earth V in its orbital motion around the sun is 30 km/sec, roughly one ten-thousandth the speed of light c. If the apparatus were at rest relative to the ether, the time T_r for light to go a distance d from A to B and return to A would be $2d/c$. If the earth were moving with a speed V from A toward B through the ether, the time for the round trip T would be given

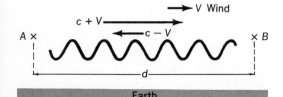

FIGURE 46.1

Transmission of a sound signal from A to B and back in a wind.

by $d/(c + V) + d/(c - V)$. The difference between these times $\Delta T = T - T_r$ is given by

$$\Delta T = T - T_r = \frac{d}{c + V} + \frac{d}{c - V} - \frac{2d}{c} = \frac{2d}{c}\frac{V^2}{c^2 - V^2}$$ **46.1**

Since $V = 10^{-4}c$, we have $\Delta T = 10^{-8}(2d/c) = 10^{-8}T_r$. Even if d were as great as 1,500 m (about a mile), ΔT would be only 10^{-13} sec—too short a time to measure directly, as Maxwell pointed out in a letter of 1880. However, in that time green light of $\lambda = 500$ mμ travels a distance of 60 wavelengths—a distance readily measurable with an interferometer. To detect the presumed motion of the earth through the ether, Michelson devised an ingenious experiment based on an interferometer (Sec. 30.5), which he invented for this purpose.

46.3 The Michelson-Morley Experiment

The ideas underlying Michelson's inspiration involve the following considerations: In the Michelson interferometer a beam of light is split into two parts which are sent by different paths and then recombined. Consider first the transit time of a light beam moving perpendicular to the velocity of the apparatus relative to the ether (Fig. 46.2). If the distance between the half-silvered plate P and the mirror is d, the light pulse travels a distance given by $cT_\perp = 2\sqrt{d^2 + (VT_\perp/2)^2}$, where $T_\perp$ is the time required for the light to go from P to M', and then to P'. Hence,

$$T_\perp = \frac{2d}{c\sqrt{1 - (V/c)^2}}$$ **46.2**

Let us now compare this time with that required for the portion of the wave which moves parallel to the motion, for which

$$T_\parallel = \frac{d}{c + V} + \frac{d}{c - V} = \frac{2cd}{c^2 - V^2} = \frac{2d}{c[1 - (V/c)^2]}$$ **46.3**

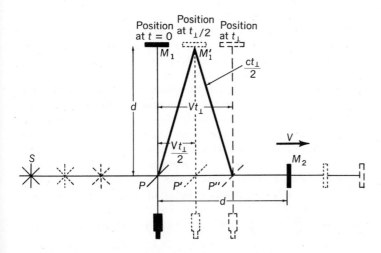

Position at $t = 0$ Position at $t_\perp/2$ Position at $t_\perp$

FIGURE 46.2

Signal takes longer to go from P to M_2 and return than from P to M_1 and return if the Michelson interferometer is moving with one arm parallel to a postulated ether wind. The position of the interferometer is shown dotted for time $\tfrac{1}{2}T_\perp$ when the light reaches M_1, and dashed for time $T_\perp$ when the light returns to P.

The round trip of the light takes slightly less time moving perpendicular to V that it does moving parallel to V. The difference $\Delta T = T_{\parallel} - T_{\perp}$ is small indeed. To a good approximation

$$\Delta T = T_{\parallel} - T_{\perp} = \frac{2d}{c} \frac{V^2}{2c^2}$$

46.4

This is only one-half the time difference of Eq. (46.1), but now the interferometer offers the possibility of a measurement.

In 1881 Michelson and Morley floated a large Michelson interferometer with $d = 11$ m on a pool of mercury. They watched the interference pattern as the interferometer was rotated, thereby interchanging the parallel and perpendicular paths. If the earth were moving through the ether, the interference fringes should have shifted through about 0.37 of a fringe as the interferometer was rotated. No such shift was detected!

Michelson and Morley performed this experiment repeatedly over a period of many months. No effect was observed which could be interpreted as showing a motion of the earth through the ether, in spite of the fact that they made measurements throughout the year, when the earth was moving in many different directions relative to the solar system. These results defied satisfactory explanation for 24 years. Michelson first interpreted the experiments as showing that the earth dragged some of the ether along with it, but a subsequent experiment by Lodge showed that a rapidly moving body could not possibly impart to the ether a speed in excess of 0.5 per cent of the speed of the body. The most important of the various proposed explanations was that of Lorentz and FitzGerald, who suggested that the arm of the interferometer moving in the direction of the earth's motion shrinks just enough to lead to the null result. As we shall see, this apparently tortured prediction is supported by Einstein's theory of relativity.

46.4 Postulates of the Special Theory of Relativity

In 1905 Einstein proposed an explanation of the Michelson-Morley dilemma which was amazing in its simplicity and genius. He argued that the reason there is no evidence of relative motion through the ether in any of a number of careful measurements is that any measurement of the speed of light will always yield a value independent of the velocity of the observer.

Einstein was keenly aware of the successes of classical mechanics, which predicted with great precision the motions of planets, aircraft, and baseballs. It was only when speeds were very great—comparable to that of light—that there was a problem. In classical physics we call a frame of reference in which Newton's laws of motion are valid an *inertial* frame. Any frame of reference which moves with constant velocity relative to an inertial frame is also an inertial frame. Thus, an airplane flying with a constant velocity of 600 mi/hr northward relative to an inertial frame provides the framework for another inertial system. Einstein proposed that if two postulates are accepted all the strange results which had been so difficult to interpret could be readily explained. These postulates of the special theory of relativity are:

1. The laws of physics are the same in all inertial frames.
2. The speed of light c is the same for every inertial frame.

An immediate implication of Einstein's postulates is that there exists no preferred frame in the universe; there is no ether relative to which everything can be measured. One inertial frame is equivalent to another so far as the speed of light is concerned. This idea requires, however, that the simple transformations used for centuries in going from one inertial frame to a second must be inadequate, although they work well for slowly moving bodies. The correct transformations must reduce to the classical ones for speeds small compared with the speed of light.

46.5 The Lorentz Transformations

Let us consider first the classical transformations from one inertial frame of reference to a second moving with constant velocity relative to the first. These are known as the *galilean* (or *newtonian*) *transformations*. Suppose we have two inertial frames: $OXYZ$, which we shall regard as at rest, and $O^*X^*Y^*Z^*$, which is moving with a velocity V along the X axis of the rest frame (Fig. 46.3). Let the origins of the two frames coincide at $t = 0$, and assume that time proceeds at the same rate in both frames. If at time t in the rest frame a body is located at a point P specified by (x,y,z), in the frame $O^*X^*Y^*Z^*$ the body is found at the point (x^*,y^*,z^*), where

$$x^* = x - Vt$$
$$y^* = y \qquad \text{galilean transformations} \qquad \textbf{46.5}$$
$$z^* = z$$

and

$$t^* = t$$

If a body has a velocity v in the frame $OXYZ$ with components v_x, v_y, v_z, the corresponding components in the $O^*X^*Y^*Z^*$ frame are

$$v_x^* = v_x - V \qquad v_y^* = v_y \qquad v_z^* = v_z \qquad \textbf{46.6}$$

These transformations predict that if a beam of light has a velocity c in the X direction of the rest frame, its velocity in the moving frame

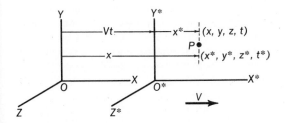

FIGURE 46.3

Reference frame $O^*X^*Y^*Z^*$ moving with constant velocity V in the X direction of reference frame $OXYZ$.

is $c - V$. But this is not consistent with the results of the Michelson-Morley experiment. Hence we need a new set of transformations which reduce to the galilean transformations for low velocities, but permit us to satisfy Einstein's second postulate for very high velocities. It was Einstein's good fortune that such transformations had already been derived by Lorentz. They are

$$x^* = \frac{x - Vt}{\sqrt{1 - V^2/c^2}}$$

$$y^* = y$$

$$z^* = z \qquad\qquad \text{Lorentz transformations} \qquad\qquad \textbf{46.7}$$

$$t^* = \frac{t - (V/c^2)x}{\sqrt{1 - V^2/c^2}}$$

When V is small compared with c, the Lorentz transformations reduce to the galilean transformations, but as v approaches the speed of light, they become different indeed.

46.6 The Lorentz Contraction and Time Dilation

Consider a measuring stick of length L^* extending from x_1^* to x_2^* in the moving frame of reference $O^*X^*Y^*Z^*$, so $L^* = x_2^* - x_1^*$ (Fig. 46.4). To an observer in the rest frame the rod has an apparent length $L = x_2 - x_1$, where x_2 and x_1 are measured at the same time t. By Eqs. (46.7), $x_2^* = (x_2 - Vt)/\sqrt{1 - V^2/c^2}$ and $x_1^* = (x_1 - Vt)/\sqrt{1 - V^2/c^2}$. When these are substituted in the expression for the apparent length L in the rest frame, we obtain

$$L^* = x_2^* - x_1^* = \frac{x_2 - Vt}{\sqrt{1 - V^2/c^2}} - \frac{x_1 - Vt}{\sqrt{1 - V^2/c^2}}$$

$$= \frac{x_2 - x_1}{\sqrt{1 - V^2/c^2}} = \frac{L}{\sqrt{1 - V^2/c^2}}$$

or

$$L = \sqrt{1 - \frac{V^2}{c^2}}\, L^* \qquad\qquad \textbf{46.8}$$

Thus, an object moving relative to an observer appears to be contracted in the direction of motion by the Lorentz factor $\sqrt{1 - V^2/c^2}$.

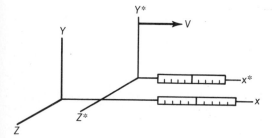

FIGURE 46.4

Frame $O^*X^*Y^*Z^*$, moving with velocity $0.5c$ parallel to the X axis of frame $OXYZ$, has in it a meter stick lying parallel to the X^* axis; this stick has a length of 0.87 m when measured by an observer at rest in $OXYZ$.

Example   A meter stick moving parallel to its length at a speed of $0.5c$ passes an observer at rest. What length would the observer find for this meter stick?

By Eq. (46.8),

$$L = \sqrt{1 - \frac{V^2}{c^2}} L^* = \sqrt{1 - 0.25} \times 1.00 \text{ m} = 0.87 \text{ m}$$

Next consider the effect of relative motion on a pendulum clock which is fixed at the origin of the rest frame $OXYZ$ and indicates intervals of time $T = t_2 - t_1$. To an observer in the frame $O^*X^*Y^*Z^*$ moving with velocity V past the clock, the period $T^* = t_2^* - t_1^*$. By Eqs. (46.7), since $x = 0$,

$$T^* = \frac{t_2 - t_1}{\sqrt{1 - V^2/c^2}} = \frac{T}{\sqrt{1 - V^2/c^2}} \qquad \textbf{46.9}$$

Thus, when an observer is moving relative to a clock (or the clock relative to the observer), the time interval as seen by this observer is longer than that seen by another observer at rest relative to the clock. To an observer at rest a moving clock runs slow.

Example   Muons are unstable particles which have an average lifetime of 2 μsec. If a beam of cosmic-ray muons has a speed of $0.98c$ relative to the earth, find the apparent average life and the distance traversed by the beam during this time.

In the frame in which the muons are at rest, T is 2×10^{-6} sec. Relative to the muons the earth is moving with a speed of $0.98c$. By Eq. (46.9),

$$T^* = \frac{T}{\sqrt{1 - V^2/c^2}} = \frac{2 \times 10^{-6} \text{ sec}}{\sqrt{1 - 0.96}} = \frac{2 \times 10^{-6} \text{ sec}}{\sqrt{1 - 0.96}} = 1 \times 10^{-5} \text{ sec}$$

In this time a muon travels

$$s^* = VT^* = 2.94 \times 10^8 \text{ m/sec} \times 1 \times 10^{-5} \text{ sec} = 2{,}940 \text{ m}$$

We now see how observers in fixed and moving frames can find the same speed for light. From the point of view of the observer in the fixed frame, the observer in the moving frame finds the same velocity because meter sticks are shortened and clocks run slow in the moving frame.

46.7 Velocity Transformation

Next consider the values observers in the frames $OXYZ$ and $O^*X^*Y^*Z^*$ would find for the velocity of a body moving along the X axis of the rest frame. By the definition of velocity, $v = \Delta x/\Delta t = (x_2 - x_1)/(t_2 - t_1)$. An observer in the moving frame would find $v^* = (x_2^* - x_1^*)/$

$(t_2^* - t_1^*)$, which, by the Lorentz transformations [Eqs. (46.7)], becomes

$$v^* = \frac{(x_2 - Vt_2) - (x_1 - Vt_1)}{(t_2 - Vx_2/c^2) - (t_1 - Vx_1/c^2)} = \frac{(x_2 - x_1)/(t_2 - t_1) - V}{1 - V(x_2 - x_1)/(t_2 - t_1)c^2}$$

or

$$v^* = \frac{v - V}{1 - Vv/c^2} \qquad\qquad \textbf{46.10}$$

This differs from the galilean velocity transformation by the term vV/c^2, which is negligible for ordinary velocities but becomes highly significant as v approaches c.

Example A beam of light moving with speed c along the X axis of frame $OXYZ$ (Fig. 46.3) passes an observer in frame $O^*X^*Y^*Z^*$, who determines its speed in his system. Show that he also obtains c, regardless of the value of V, the speed of $O^*X^*Y^*Z^*$ along the X axis of $OXYZ$.

By Eq. (46.10),

$$v^* = \frac{c - V}{1 - Vc/c^2} = c$$

Example A proton moving eastward with a speed of $0.60c$ in a nuclear-physics laboratory passes an electron moving westward with a speed of $0.90c$. Find the speed of the electron relative to a frame of reference riding with the proton.

If we call eastward the positive direction,

$$V = 0.60c \qquad \text{and} \qquad v = -0.90c$$

By Eq. 46.10,

$$v^* = \frac{-0.90c - 0.60c}{1 - (-0.90)(0.60)} = \frac{-1.50c}{1.54} = -0.97c$$

FIGURE 46.5

Ratio of the mass of a body in motion to its rest mass as a function of v/c.

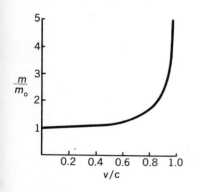

An important consequence of the theory of relativity is that according to its postulates no real body can move and no transfer of energy can occur with a speed which exceeds c, the speed of light in free space.

46.8 Relativistic Mass

If a constant force F acts on a mass m indefinitely, it is clear that Newton's second law $F = ma$ must break down as the speed of the body approaches the speed of light, since it follows directly from Eq. (46.10) that the speed of light represents an upper limit to velocities involving energy transfer. Thus, a constant force does not cause the body to accelerate forever. We may retain $F = ma$ if, as the speed approaches the speed of light, the mass of the body increases, rather than the velocity. Einstein showed by application of the law of conservation of momentum that if m_0 is the mass of a body when it is at rest, its mass m when moving with a velocity v is (Fig. 46.5)

$$m = \frac{m_0}{\sqrt{1 - v^2/c^2}} \qquad\qquad 46.11$$

In terms of this relation, the momentum of a body which has rest mass m_0 becomes

$$\text{Momentum} = mv = \frac{m_0 v}{\sqrt{1 - v^2/c^2}}$$

When a constant force acts on a body as its speed approaches the speed of light, the effect of doing work on the body, and thereby supplying it with energy, is to increase its mass rather than its speed. Einstein showed that this can be reconciled with conservation principles if mass is one of the forms of energy and if the additional energy given to the body is $\Delta \mathcal{W} = (m - m_0)c^2$. This idea may be extended so that a body of rest mass m_0 has a rest energy $m_0 c^2$; when its velocity is v and its mass m, its total energy $\mathcal{W}$ is mc^2. The kinetic energy (energy associated with motion) is

$$\text{Kinetic energy} = mc^2 - m_0 c^2 = \mathcal{W} - m_0 c^2 \qquad 46.12$$

$$= m_0 c^2 \left(\frac{1}{\sqrt{1 - v^2/c^2}} - 1 \right) \qquad 46.12a$$

If we expand this square root assuming that v^2/c^2 is small compared with 1, we obtain

$$\text{Kinetic energy} = m_0 c^2 \left[1 + \frac{1}{2} \frac{v^2}{c^2} + \frac{(-\frac{1}{2})(-\frac{3}{2})}{2!} \frac{v^4}{c^4} + \cdots - 1 \right]$$

$$= \frac{1}{2} m_0 v^2 \left(1 + \frac{3}{4} \frac{v^2}{c^2} + \cdots \right)$$

In the limiting case, where v/c is small compared with 1, we obtain the classical formula $\frac{1}{2}mv^2$ for the kinetic energy of a body. As v approaches c, we must turn to the relativistic relation for the kinetic energy as given in Eq. (46.12).

The revolutionary concept that mass is one of the forms of energy has proven to be a cornerstone of modern physics, permitting a new understanding of nuclear physics and leading to the development of nuclear fission as a practical energy source.

46.9 The Mass of the Electron

The first particle for which the relativistic change of mass with velocity was investigated was the electron, the least massive of charged particles. The experimental results are completely in accord with the predictions of the relativity theory. Since high-energy electrons are usually produced by accelerating them through a large potential difference, it is convenient to measure their energies in electron volts. *One electron volt is the energy attained by an electron in falling through a potential difference of one volt* (Sec. 34.8).

Table 46.1 shows how the ratios v/c and m/m_0 vary with the kinetic energy of an electron. In a modern synchrotron, in which electrons

TABLE 46.1

Kinetic energy of electron		$\dfrac{v}{c} = \dfrac{speed\ of\ electron}{speed\ of\ light}$	$\dfrac{m}{m_0}$
Electron volts	*Joules*		
0	0	0	1
10^2	1.6×10^{-17}	0.0205	1.0002
10^3	1.6×10^{-16}	0.0625	1.002
10^4	1.6×10^{-15}	0.195	1.02
10^5	1.6×10^{-14}	0.548	1.20
10^6	1.6×10^{-13}	0.941	2.96
10^7	1.6×10^{-12}	0.999	20.6
10^8	1.6×10^{-11}	1.000 −	197
10^9	1.6×10^{-10}	1.000 −	1,960

are given kinetic energies of over 1 billion eV, the mass of the moving electron is greater than the mass of the hydrogen atom at rest!

Example   A Van de Graaff generator accelerates electrons to a kinetic energy of 2 MeV. Find the mass of these electrons. Calculate the speed of the 2-MeV electrons.

$$2\ \text{MeV} = 2 \times 10^6\ \text{eV} \times 1.602 \times 10^{-19}\ \text{joule/eV}$$
$$= 3.2 \times 10^{-13}\ \text{joule}$$
$$3.2 \times 10^{-13}\ \text{joule} = (m - m_0)c^2 = (m - m_0)9 \times 10^{16}$$
$$m - m_0 = 35.6 \times 10^{-31}\ \text{kg}$$
$$m = (35.6 + 9.1) \times 10^{-31}\ \text{kg}$$
$$= 44.7 \times 10^{-31}\ \text{kg (almost 5 times the rest mass)}$$
$$44.7 \times 10^{-31} = \frac{9.11 \times 10^{-31}}{\sqrt{1 - v^2/c^2}} \qquad \text{by Eq. (46.11)}$$

Squaring both sides and transposing yields

$$2{,}000\left(1 - \frac{v^2}{c^2}\right) = 83$$
$$\frac{v^2}{c^2} = \frac{1{,}917}{2{,}000} = 0.959\ \frac{m^2}{\sec^2}$$
$$v = 0.98c = 2.94 \times 10^8\ \text{m/sec}$$

< **46.10 General Relativity**

In our discussion of relativity we have thus far confined our attention to inertial frames of reference. When this restriction applies, we are dealing with what is known as *special relativity*. If we consider frames of reference accelerated relative to an inertial frame, we are led to the *general theory* of relativity, also developed by Einstein. A simple example of an accelerated frame of reference is that of an elevator which is being accelerated upward. It is a well-known fact that an upward acceleration leads to an increase in the apparent weight of an object in the elevator. However, if an observer were isolated in an elevator on a strange planet, how could he untangle the gravitational contribution to the apparent weight from that associated with the acceleration of the elevator? Einstein concluded that there is no way to distinguish gravitational and acceleration effects in this situation. This conclusion, an important postulate of the general theory of relativity, is known as the *principle of equivalence*.

The special theory leads to most of the relativistic results which are of interest and applicability in modern physics, but the general theory leads to deeper insights and makes predictions which are not derivable from the special theory. We shall mention a few of these predictions.

1. Rays of light passing close to a star should be bent toward it. For example, a ray which just grazes the sun's surface on its way to the earth is deflected through about 1.75 seconds of arc. This observation was one of the first which tested the predictions of general relativity.

2. Physical processes should take place more slowly in regions of low gravitational potential than in regions of high gravitational potential. Thus, atomic vibrations on the sun should appear slowed down relative to their periods on the earth. This leads to the prediction that the spectral lines from atoms of the sun should be shifted very slightly toward the red end of the spectrum when compared with lines from the same elements on the earth.

3. The orbits of the planets should be slightly changed. This effect is important for the planet Mercury, which is closest to the sun. General relativity predicts that, aside from the precession of Mercury's orbit due to the perturbations of other planets, there should be an additional precession of about 43 sec per century. This precession had been known for many years, but its origin remained a mystery until Einstein developed his general theory.

Questions

1. What alternatives to the theory of relativity can you propose to explain the results of the Michelson-Morley experiment?

2. The objection has been raised to the theory of relativity that it violates "common sense." How could you refute this objection?

3. By what factor is the density of a body increased when it moves with speed v?

Problems

1. A river 4 miles wide has a current with a speed of 3 mi/hr. How much longer will it take a boat with a speed of 5 mi/hr to go upstream 4 miles and return than to go directly across the river and return to the same point?   *Ans.* 0.5 hr

2. A river 2 miles wide has a current of 3 mi/hr. How much longer will it take a motorboat with a speed relative to the water of 15 mi/hr to go 2 miles upstream and return than to go straight across the river and return to the same point?

3. Find the mass of an electron traveling at 0.6 times the speed of light. How many times as great as the rest mass is this value? *Ans.* 1.14×10^{-30} kg; 1.25

4. Find the work which must be done on an electron to increase its speed from $0.5c$ to $0.9c$, where c is the speed of light.

5. How many electron volts of energy must an electron gain to bring its mass to (*a*) $1.05 \, m_0$ and (*b*) $2 \, m_0$? In each case what is the speed of the electron?
Ans. (*a*) 25,500; 9.2×10^7 m/sec; (*b*) 511,000; 2.6×10^8 m/sec

6. Through what potential difference must protons be accelerated to achieve a speed of $0.600c$? What is the momentum of such a proton? The total energy?

7. An electron is accelerated to a kinetic energy of 51 MeV. Find the ratios m/m_0 and v/c. If an electron at rest can be assumed to be spherical, find the ratio of the longitudinal to the transverse diameter for the 51-MeV electron. *Ans.* 101; 0.99995; 0.0099

8. Find the speed of an electron when its mass is twenty times its rest mass.

9. A proton of rest mass 938 MeV (1.67×10^{-27} kg) is given a kinetic energy of 9.38×10^9 eV in a proton-synchrotron. Find the mass of the proton at this speed. What must be the radius of the orbit if the vertical magnetic field is 1.5 webers/m^2?
Ans. 1.84×10^{-26} kg; 23 m

10. Find the kinetic energy, total energy, mass, and momentum of an electron moving at a speed of 0.9 times that of light.

11. An arrow passes an observer with a speed 0.6 times that of light. If the rest length of the arrow is 0.75 m, find its apparent length as it passes the observer.
Ans. 0.6 m

12. The mean life of a muon (or μ meson) at rest is about 2×10^{-6} sec. If muons in cosmic rays have an average speed of $0.998c$, find their mean life and the approximate distance they move before decaying.

13. Imagine that you are at rest in a frame $O^* \, X^* \, Y^* \, Z^*$ which moves horizontally past an inertial frame $OXYZ$ at a speed of $0.6c$. A boy in the latter frame drops a ball which, according to your clock, falls for 0.5 sec. How long would the ball fall as timed by an observer at rest in the $OXYZ$ frame? *Ans.* 0.4 sec

14. Show that Eqs. (46.7) lead to the transformations $x = (x^* + Vt^*)/\sqrt{1 - V^2/c^2}$ and $t = (t^* + Vx^*/c^2)/\sqrt{1 - V^2/c^2}$.

15. An electron moving to the right with a speed of 2.5×10^8 m/sec passes an electron moving to the left with a speed of 2.8×10^8 m/sec. Find the speed of one electron relative to the other as predicted by (*a*) the newtonian-galilean transformation and (*b*) the relativistic transformation. *Ans.* (*a*) 5.3×10^8 m/sec; (*b*) 2.98×10^8 m/sec

16. An alpha particle moving east with a speed of $0.5c$ is passed by an electron moving west with a speed of $0.95c$. Find the speed of the electron relative to the alpha particle.

17. A synchrocyclotron has a magnetic field of 1.50 webers/m^2. Find the appropriate frequency for accelerating protons when the speed of the protons is (*a*) $0.0100c$ and (*b*) $0.500c$. *Ans.* (*a*) 22.9 Mc/sec; (*b*) 19.8 Mc/sec

18. A particle has a rest energy m_0c^2 and a total energy $\mathcal{W}$. Show that the velocity of this particle is $c\sqrt{1 - (m_0c^2/\mathcal{W})^2}$.

Ans 10 ① 0.66 MeV
② 1.17 MeV
③ 2.09×10^{-30} kgm
④ 5.64×10^{-22} kgm-m/sec

CHAPTER 47 *The failure of classical physics to solve the problems of atomic structure and spectra was a clear indication that some crucial ideas were missing. In 1901 Planck showed that the wavelength distribution of the radiation from a hot body could be predicted if one assumed that electromagnetic radiation comes in chunks, or* quanta, *rather than in continuously variable amounts. This idea proved to be extremely fruitful, as we shall see in this chapter.*

Quanta and X Rays

47.1 Planck's Quanta

At the end of the nineteenth century physics was faced with several dilemmas which suggested that the theories which had been so effective in treating the motions of macroscopic objects and in unifying the foundations of optics and electromagnetism could not be successfully extrapolated to (1) situations in which the speed of light was approached and (2) situations in which scientists were dealing with the structure of the atom and with objects of atomic size.

The brilliant insight of Einstein, sketchily treated in Chap. 46, gave us the theory of relativity, which resolved the first of these dilemmas. In 1901 Planck proposed a startling new idea which plays a vital role in our understanding of physics in atomic dimensions. Planck was endeavoring to develop an adequate theory for the wavelength distribution of black-body radiation (Fig. 22.6 and Sec. 22.5). He discovered that he could account quantitatively for black-body radiation curves if he assumed that energy is radiated in small packets which we call *photons* or *quanta*. The energy associated with each photon is given by

$$\text{Energy of photon} = \mathcal{W} = h\nu \qquad\qquad \textbf{47.1}$$

where ν is the frequency of the radiation, and h is a universal constant equal to 6.6256×10^{-34} joule-sec. In honor of its discoverer, h is called *Planck's constant.*

Planck's theory gave excellent agreement with experimental measurements on black-body radiation, but many regarded the agreement as fortuitous and considered the proposal that radiant energy comes in chunks or quanta as unacceptable. A theory such as Planck's, which utilizes some new or suspect assumption to explain a phenomenon, is called an *ad hoc* theory. Such theories are usually viewed with skepticism until the radical assumption is found to have wider application. The first of much supporting evidence for the validity of Planck's hypothesis came in 1905 when Einstein used it to explain the photoelectric effect—a phenomenon which had been a puzzle to physicists for more than a decade.

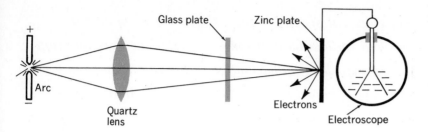

Glass plate   Zinc plate
Arc
Quartz
lens
Electrons
Electroscope

FIGURE 47.1

A zinc plate emits photo-electrons when ultraviolet light falls on it, but if a glass plate stops the ultraviolet, the photoemission ceases.

47.2 The Photoelectric Effect

In 1887 Hertz was doing pioneering work in the study of radio waves. In his experiments he used spark gaps, and he observed that when ultraviolet light fell on the electrodes of the gap, a spark passed at a substantially lower than usual potential difference. A little later it was found that a charged sheet of zinc exposed to ultraviolet radiation lost its charge when negative but retained its charge when positive. We now know that when ultraviolet light falls on a metallic surface, electrons are liberated from the metal. The energy required to eject an electron is provided by the incident electromagnetic radiation. When the metal is negatively charged, these "photoelectrons" are repelled. When the metal is positive, the photoelectrons are attracted back to the metal.

In the case of zinc, photoelectrons are emitted when ultraviolet radiation is incident, but not for visible light (Fig. 47.1). On the other hand, there are several elements from which light in the visible spectrum can remove photoelectrons. To explain these facts, Einstein adopted the hypothesis that radiant energy comes in photons of energy $h\nu$. Then, in order to eject a photoelectron from a surface, a photon must have enough energy to free the electron from the atom or material with which it is associated. If it requires an energy $\mathcal{W}$ to remove an electron from the metal, and if the photon imparts to it an energy $h\nu$ which is greater than $\mathcal{W}$, the difference in energy appears as kinetic energy of the ejected photoelectron. This explanation of the photoelectric effect in terms of quanta was made by Einstein in 1905 and was one of the early triumphs of the quantum idea. If we let $\mathcal{W}_{min}$ represent the smallest energy which can free an electron from the solid, the maximum kinetic energy of ejected electrons is given by Einstein's photoelectric relation:

$$\tfrac{1}{2}mv_{max}^2 = h\nu - \mathcal{W}_{min} \qquad \textbf{47.2}$$

FIGURE 47.2

The maximum kinetic energy of ejected photoelectrons depends on the frequency of the incident light.

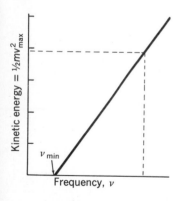

Many careful experiments have shown that the Einstein relationship is correct. If the frequency of the incident light is increased, the maximum kinetic energy of the ejected photoelectrons increases correspondingly (Fig. 47.2). Similarly, if the frequency of the incident photons is decreased, the energy of ejected photoelectrons decreases until the frequency $\nu_{min} = \mathcal{W}_{min}/h$ is reached. For any lower frequency, no photoelectrons are emitted.

If the frequency of the incident light is kept constant while the intensity is changed by increasing the number of photons incident, the number of photoelectrons emitted increases. For a given frequency of radiation the number of photoelectrons ejected per second is directly proportional to the intensity of the incident radiation.

Among the metals from which photoelectrons may be ejected by visible light are barium, cesium, lithium, potassium, sodium, and rubidium. These are elements from which it is particularly easy to remove an electron in chemical reactions. Both the chemical and photoelectric properties of electropositive elements depend on the ease with which an electron may be removed.

Example Light of wavelength 700 mμ is required to cause the emission of electrons from a potassium surface. What is the energy necessary to remove one of the least firmly bound electrons? Find the kinetic energy and velocity of such an electron if the potassium surface is bombarded with light of wavelength 500 mμ.

Energy of 700-mμ photon $= h\nu = \dfrac{hc}{\lambda}$

$$= 6.63 \times 10^{-34} \text{ joule-sec} \times \frac{3 \times 10^8 \text{ m/sec}}{700 \times 10^{-9} \text{ m}}$$

$$= 2.84 \times 10^{-19} \text{ joule}$$

Since this is the lowest-frequency photon which causes photoemission, $\mathcal{W}_{min} = 2.84 \times 10^{-19}$ joule.

Energy of 500-mμ photon $= 6.63 \times 10^{-34} \times \dfrac{3 \times 10^8}{500 \times 10^{-9}}$

$$= 3.98 \times 10^{-19} \text{ joule}$$

$\frac{1}{2}mv_{max}^2 = h\nu - \mathcal{W}_{min} = (3.98 - 2.84) \times 10^{-19}$ joule

$$= 1.14 \times 10^{-19} \text{ joule}$$

$\frac{1}{2}(9.1 \times 10^{-31})v_{max}^2 = 1.14 \times 10^{-19}$

$$v_{max}^2 = 24.8 \times 10^{10}$$

$$v_{max} = 5 \times 10^5 \text{ m/sec}$$

47.3 Photoelectric Cells

Devices which utilize the photoelectric effect have many important applications. One is the exposure meter used by the photographer. Here the rate of photoelectron ejection caused by the incident light is a measure of the illumination. Photocells are used to open store doors when people cut off a light beam, to sound burglar alarms, and to turn on street lights whenever the sun fails to provide adequate illumination. Photocells are used in physics, biology, and medicine for measuring the intensity of various kinds of electromagnetic radiation. In a television studio variations in light intensity on a photosensitive surface are used to convert the picture into electric signals in the image orthicon tube.

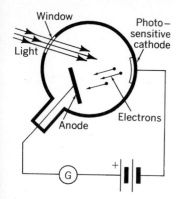

FIGURE 47.3
Photoelectric cell.

The sound track of motion-picture films permits varying amounts of light to pass through when the film is run between a light source and a photoelectric cell. The photoelectric cell converts the variations in light intensity into variations in electric current.

There are several different types of photoelectric cells. In some there are a light-sensitive surface which emits electrons and a second electrode, usually maintained at a fairly high positive potential, which collects the electrons. A circuit for such a photocell is shown in Figure 47.3 with a galvanometer to measure the relative light intensity.

A second type is the *photovoltaic* or *barrier layer* photocell in which incident light produces an emf between two terminals. A typical photovoltaic cell (Fig. 47.4) contains a thin metal disk *A* on which there is a film of light-sensitive material *B*. In contact with *B* is a conducting ring or layer *C*. In one common type *A* is an iron plate, and *B* is a thin film of selenium over which a thin gold coating is laid to serve as the conductor *C*. Another type of cell uses a copper plate as *A*, cuprous oxide as *B*, and a thin layer of silver as *C*. When the sensitive surface is illuminated, an emf is generated between the sensitive layer *B* and the metal disk *A*. Electrons are driven by the light from the layer *B* to the metal *A* across the thin insulating layer. This type of cell is used in exposure meters, since the light produces the emf required to deflect the galvanometer.

Solar cells, widely used to provide energy for satellites and space vehicles, are photovoltaic cells converting radiant energy into electrical energy. A familiar form uses a very perfect silicon crystal which is treated with trace impurities to introduce extra positive charges on one side of a thin wafer and extra negative charges on the other side (see Sec. 50.11). Radiant energy disturbs the electrical balance of the charges and thereby induces an emf which continues as long as light strikes the crystal. Such cells convert roughly 15 per cent of the incident radiant energy to electrical energy; efficiencies two or more times as great are theoretically possible.

A third type of photoelectric cell utilizes the photoconductivity effect. When photons are absorbed in a material, relatively few electrons leave the material. If a material which is normally an insulator or a poor conductor is irradiated, electrons originally bound to atoms are freed and become available for conduction through the material. The resistance of a piece of germanium, for example, decreases greatly when it is subjected to high illumination. The conductivity of a sele-

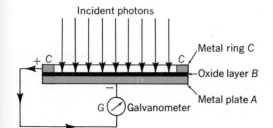

FIGURE 47.4

Electromotive force is produced by incident light in a barrier layer photovoltaic cell.

nium cell may be 25 or more times greater in bright light than in the dark. The conductivity of a thallium sulfide cell changes by an even larger factor.

47.4 The Discovery of X Rays

Another area of physics in which Planck's quantum hypothesis leads to predictions which agree with experiment is that of the continuous X-ray spectrum. Before we discuss this topic in Sec. 47.6, we introduce some background material on X rays.

In 1895 Röntgen was studying the conduction of electricity through partially evacuated tubes when he observed a mysterious radiation which was able to penetrate thin layers of material. He called this radiation *X rays*, with the "X" standing for "unknown." Röntgen promptly performed a broad series of experiments with X rays and learned many of the properties of this new kind of radiation. Among his findings were the following: X rays produce fluorescence in all kinds of materials. All substances are somewhat transparent to X rays, particularly those composed of light elements. Thus paper, wood, and aluminum are almost transparent, while lead and gold are relatively opaque. Photographic emulsions are sensitive to X rays, although the eye cannot see them. The rays are not deflected by either magnetic or electric fields and hence show no evidence of bearing electric charge. X rays are produced whenever a beam of high-energy electrons strikes matter. Röntgen was unable to concentrate X rays with lenses or mirrors and failed to find any evidence of interference or diffraction of X rays.

We now know that X rays are electromagnetic radiation similar to light and ultraviolet radiation, except that the wavelength is much shorter. Although the lines of demarcation between the various kinds of electromagnetic radiation are not sharp, we may think of X rays as including radiation of wavelengths shorter than about 100 Å.

Among the earliest X-ray photographs were pictures of the human hand and forearm. Soon pictures of this kind were utilized in studying fractures and similar abnormalities. Only three months after Röntgen's discovery, X rays were used in connection with a surgical operation.

The news that rays had been discovered which could take pictures through walls was tremendously exciting. X rays were front-page news all over the world in 1896. Grossly exaggerated claims and absurd statements made some people feel that privacy was lost forever. A London firm advertised the sale of X-ray-proof underclothing. A bill was introduced in one of the state legislatures "to prohibit the insertion of X rays, or any device for producing the same into, or their use in connection with, opera glasses, or similar aids to vision."

X rays have found many important applications. They have given the diagnostic methods of physicians, surgeons, and dentists an exactitude that formerly was impossible. X rays possess properties valuable in the treatment of certain diseases. Malignant cells are somewhat

FIGURE 47.5

Electrons accelerated in a gas-type X-ray tube come from ionization of the residual gas and from secondary emission of electrons when positive ions strike the cathode.

more readily killed by X rays than are normal ones. Under X-ray treatment inflamed glands shrink in size, and various morbid conditions of the blood and skin clear up. By means of X rays, the metallurgist determines the effect of heat treatment, tempering, rolling, and aging on metals and alloys. Hidden defects in objects and concealed cracks in metals may be revealed by X rays, which are a major tool in the nondestructive testing of materials.

47.5 The Production of X Rays

Electromagnetic radiation is emitted when electric charges are accelerated (Sec. 45.6). This radiation appears in the form of photons (Sec. 47.1), the energy of which is given by the product of Planck's constant h and the frequency ν. For a typical X-ray photon, λ may be 1 Å, and the corresponding energy 12,400 eV.

The most common means of producing X rays is to accelerate electrons through high potential differences in vacuum tubes and allow them to strike a target of some heavy element. In Röntgen's original experiments he applied a high potential difference between two elements in a partially evacuated tube. The electrons accelerated came from the ionization of the residual gas molecules and from secondary electrons ejected from the cathode by impact of positive ions. Gas tubes (Fig. 47.5) operating on this principle are still used for producing X rays.

In 1913 Coolidge developed an X-ray tube which was easier to control than the gas type. In the Coolidge tube (Fig. 47.6) the electrons are emitted from a heated filament F placed in a highly evacuated chamber. By varying the temperature of the filament, the number of electrons emitted can be controlled. These electrons are accelerated and strike a target T from which the X rays are emitted. The X rays go out in every direction, but those which travel into the target are absorbed.

47.6 The Continuous X-ray Spectrum

When a beam of high-energy electrons strikes a target, the wavelengths of the X rays emitted vary widely. (In Sec. 49.1 we shall describe

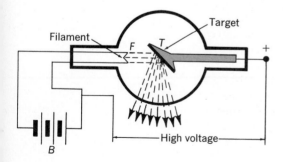

FIGURE 47.6

The hot filament is the source of electrons in a Coolidge X-ray tube.

how the wavelengths may be measured.) If the intensity associated with a given wavelength is plotted as a function of wavelength for different values of the applied potential across the tube, curves similar to those of Figure 47.7 are produced. Since every wavelength over a wide range is present, the spectra are *continuous*. Three features of these curves are immediately apparent:

1. The intensity radiated increases at all wavelengths when the potential difference across the tube is raised.

2. The shortest wavelength emitted at a given potential is sharply defined and decreases as the voltage across the tube increases.

3. As the potential difference across the tube is increased, the wavelength at which the maximum energy is radiated shifts toward shorter wavelengths.

We can understand why the spectrum is continuous and predict quantitatively the short-wavelength limit if we invoke the Planck hypothesis that electromagnetic radiation is emitted in photons of energy $h\nu$. X rays are produced when the kinetic energy of the incident electrons is transformed into electromagnetic radiation through collisions with atoms of the target. Most of the collisions are glancing ones in which only some moderate fraction of an electron's energy is radiated as a photon. Before being stopped, most electrons have several collisions and produce several photons of widely varying wavelengths. Occasionally an electron has a head-on collision in which it loses all its energy at once. Such collisions are relatively rare and are the ones which produce the X rays at the *short-wavelength limit*. Clearly, the most energy an electron can lose is all it has. This corresponds to Ve, where V is the potential difference across the tube, and e the electronic charge. If we equate this energy to that of the most energetic photon, we obtain

$$Ve = h\nu_{\max} = \frac{hc}{\lambda_{\min}} \qquad\qquad \textbf{47.3}$$

where c is the speed of light. Solving for $\lambda_{\min}$ yields

$$\lambda_{\min} = \frac{hc}{Ve} \qquad\qquad \textbf{47.3a}$$

This relationship is known as the *Duane-Hunt law*.

In many respects continuous X-ray emission is the inverse of the photoelectric effect. In the production of an X-ray photon the kinetic energy of the incident electron is converted into radiant energy; in the photoelectric effect the radiant energy of a photon is converted, at least in part, into kinetic energy of the electron.

The amount of energy available from each electron is increased as the potential difference across the tube is increased, and we should expect more energy to be radiated per electron. Thus the ordinates in Figure 47.7 increase as the potential difference across the tube is increased. The area under the curve is proportional to the amount of energy radiated in the form of X rays. The rest of the energy of the incident electrons appears as heat in the target.

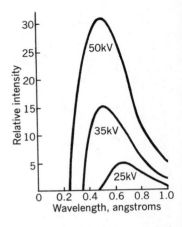

FIGURE 47.7
Wavelength distribution of the continuous X-ray spectrum from an aluminum target.

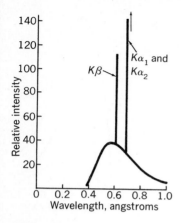

FIGURE 47.8

Wavelength distribution of X rays emitted from a molybdenum target operated at about 30 kV; at higher resolution, the characteristic lines rise far higher and show structure.

The shorter the wavelength of the X rays, the more penetrating they are. Increasing the potential difference across the tube results in a reduced average wavelength. X rays from a high-voltage tube are called *hard* X rays, while those emitted from a tube operating at low potentials are readily absorbed and are known as *soft* X rays.

47.7 Characteristic X-ray Spectra

If a molybdenum target replaces the aluminum target for which data are plotted in Figure 47.7, the curves for a given potential difference and tube current are similar except that (1) there is more energy radiated at every wavelength longer than λ_{min} and (2) at certain wavelengths large amounts of energy are radiated (Fig. 47.8). The first difference comes about as the result of the fact that the efficiency in producing the continuous X-ray spectrum is proportional to the atomic number of the target material. The second arises because we are now exciting the *characteristic* X-ray spectrum of molybdenum (Sec. 48.5). The positions of these sharp "lines" depend on the atomic number of the target element. For this reason they are called *characteristic lines*. No characteristic lines appear in the aluminum curves of Figure 47.7 because they are all at wavelengths greater than those shown.

47.8 The Detection and Measurement of High-energy Photons

There are three properties of high-energy photons which are ordinarily used to detect and measure the intensity of X rays, gamma rays, and photons of the far ultraviolet. These are:

1. *High-energy photons eject electrons from atoms and thereby produce ionization in a gas.* By collecting the ions in an ionization chamber (Fig. 47.9), one can determine the intensity. The ionization chamber may be made of a metal cylinder closed at both ends except for windows through which the rays pass. A metal collector AC is insulated from the cylinder and charged positively. When X rays pass through the chamber, electrons are collected by AC, and positive ions by the chamber itself. The current read by the galvanometer G is a measure of the intensity of the X-ray beam.

Ionization measurements are used to determine dosages of X rays and gamma rays. The unit dose, as adopted by the International Congress of Radiology, is called the *roentgen,* which may be defined as follows: *The roentgen is that quantity of X or gamma radiation which produces in dry air a total ionization of 3.33×10^{-10} coulomb per*

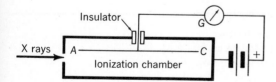

FIGURE 47.9

Ionization chamber used for measuring X rays and other ionizing radiations.

0.001293 *gram of air.* A dosage of about 400 *r* (*r* is the symbol for *roentgen*) over the entire body is fatal to about 50 per cent of a random sample of human beings. This quantity, called the *median lethal dose,* is of considerable interest in connection with atomic weapons. Dosages far smaller than the median lethal dose are dangerous; one should never expose oneself needlessly to substantial radiation doses.

2. *High-energy photons affect photographic emulsions.* Over a fairly wide range the blackening of a photographic plate is proportional to the amount of energy of a given wavelength absorbed in the emulsion.

3. *High-energy photons produce fluorescence.* In many materials this fluorescence is in the visible spectrum. In medical diagnostics the fluorescent screen is a widely used tool; for example, a fluorescent screen can be used to observe the movement of a mass of bismuth salt as it passes through the digestive tract of a patient. Materials which fluoresce in the ultraviolet when bombarded with high-energy photons are used in scintillation detectors and other devices for studying high-energy photons. When such photons fall on certain crystals, the fluorescence produced is a direct measure of the energy absorbed (Sec. 52.5).

Questions

1. What determines the energy of a photon? Can two photons have the same energy but different wavelengths in air?

2. Why can visible light remove photoelectrons from sodium but not from zinc?

3. How can electrons be removed from metals?

4. What factors determine the short-wavelength limit and general shape of the continuous X-ray spectrum as a function of wavelength?

5. Why are the very soft X rays absorbed out of a beam before the X rays are used to photograph a broken arm?

6. How is the short-wavelength limit of the continuous X-ray spectrum related to the photoelectric effect?

7. X-ray photographs are essentially shadowgraphs. What restrictions must be placed on the target area from which the X rays originate if the X-ray photograph is to have sharp definition?

Problems

1. A photon has an energy of 3 eV. Find its frequency and its wavelength in vacuum.
Ans. 7.24×10^{14}/sec; 4,140 Å

2. Determine the energy of a photon of mercury green radiation whose wavelength is 5,461 Å, both in joules and in electron volts.

3. The eye can detect about 5 photons/cm^2-sec of green light ($\lambda = 500$ mμ), while the ear can detect about 10^{-13} watt/m^2 under optimum conditions. As a power detector, which is more sensitive and by what factor? *Ans.* The eye; 5

4. On a clear day, about 2 cal of radiant energy from the sun strikes an area of 1 cm^2 each minute if that area is perpendicular to the direction of the sun. If this energy were all in the form of photons of green light of wavelength 5,000 Å, how many photons would arrive per square centimeter in 1 sec?

5. Electrons with a maximum energy of 2.2 eV are emitted from a surface radiated with light of $\lambda = 2,500$ Å. Find the energy of the incident photons and $\mathfrak{W}_{min}$, the smallest energy which can free an electron from the surface. *Ans.* 7.96 × 10^{-19} joule; 2.78 eV

6. It requires 5 × 10^{-19} joule to remove one of the least tightly bound electrons from a surface. Find the longest wavelength which will be effective in producing photoelectrons. What is the maximum energy of photoelectrons ejected from this surface by ultraviolet radiation of $\lambda = 2,000$ Å?

7. Find the maximum kinetic energy in electron volts of the photoelectrons ejected from a potassium photoemitter for wavelengths of 200, 300, 400, and 500 mμ if $\mathfrak{W}_{min} = 2.1$ eV. What is the longest wavelength which will eject photoelectrons?
Ans. 4.1; 2.0; 1.0; 0.4; 5,910 Å

8. A television tube operates at a potential difference of 10,000 volts. What is the short-wavelength limit of the X rays emitted?

9. Calculate the potential difference through which electrons must be accelerated to give the continuous X radiation a short-wavelength limit of 0.500 Å. *Ans.* 24,800 volts

10. A Coolidge X-ray tube is operating at 150,000 volts. With what velocity do the electrons strike the anode? (Relativity correction for the change of mass of electrons with speed must be made.) What is the short-wavelength limit of the X rays produced?

11. Calculate the short-wavelength limit for the radiation from (*a*) an X-ray tube operated at 30 kV, (*b*) a 20-MeV betatron, and (*c*) a 300-MeV synchrotron.
Ans. (*a*) 0.41 Å; (*b*) 6.2 × 10^{-14} m; (*c*) 4.10 × 10^{-15} m

CHAPTER 48 *The great success of Planck's quantum hypothesis in dealing with black-body radiation suggests that the same hypothesis might be useful for explaining the optical spectra of atoms. But a reasonable model of an atom is needed before we can make such an application. In this chapter we consider the Rutherford nuclear atom model and the Bohr model of the hydrogen atom.*

Atomic Energy Levels

48.1 The Balmer Series

Each chemical element emits its own unique spectrum when its electrons are excited in electrical discharges or in flames. As we saw in Sec. 32.1, the bright lines characteristic of any particular element offer a means of chemical identification of great simplicity and reliability. It was natural that scientists would endeavor to understand how these lines originate and what determines the particular array of lines associated with a given element.

For an atom which has a spectrum of the complexity of the iron spectrum (Fig. 32.4), the task of explaining quantitatively the origin of all the lines would be forbidding. On the other hand, the visible spectrum of hydrogen (Fig. 48.1) has a challenging regularity and apparent simplicity befitting the simplest and lightest of all atoms. This spectrum consists of an uncountable number of lines which become closer and closer together as the wavelength decreases, until finally at a certain minimum wavelength called the *series limit,* the lines cease. Many physicists had tried in vain to find a magic formula for this series before Balmer in 1885 showed that the wavelengths of these lines are predicted accurately by

$$\lambda = 3.6456 \times 10^{-7} \frac{m^2}{m^2 - 4} \qquad \lambda \text{ in meters}$$

where m is an integer taking the values 3, 4, 5, ... Thereafter this group of lines has been known as the *Balmer series.*

The Balmer formula is successful in giving us the wavelengths of the lines, but what is the physics which underlies this purely empirical relation? It was not until 1913 that this question could be answered in terms of an atom model which we now introduce.

48.2 The Rutherford Model of the Atom

To the early proponents of the atomic theory of matter, atoms were the fundamental building blocks of nature, each type of atom being indivisible (Sec. 33.2) and devoid of structure. However, evidence from the discharge of electricity through gases, from the photoelectric effect, and from thermionic emission suggests that atoms are not indivisible, but rather that the electron is one of the building blocks from which atoms are assembled. The fact that an atom is electrically neutral requires that it have equal amounts of positive and negative charge. Toward the end of the nineteenth century Thomson suggested that the positive electricity is distributed uniformly over a sphere which has the same radius as the atom (about 10^{-10} m). Inside this sphere he imagined a number of electrons which would correspond roughly to plums in a pudding. Photons, collisions with other atoms,

FIGURE 48.1

(*a*) The spectrum of atomic hydrogen consists of the Lyman series in the ultraviolet, the Balmer series in the visible, and several series in the infrared region. (*b*) The Balmer series in greater detail. (*c*) A portion of the spectrum of the star Zeta Tauri showing well over twenty lines of the Balmer series.

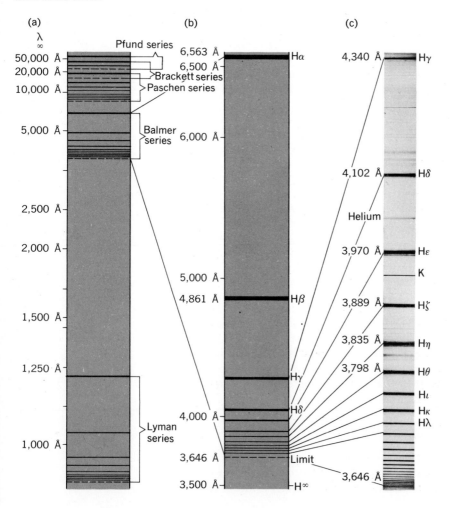

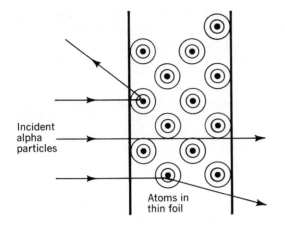

FIGURE 48.2
Alpha-particle scattering; very large repulsive forces are required to scatter particles backward.

Incident
alpha
particles

Atoms in
thin foil

and thermal collisions could eject electrons from such an atom. However, this model was not successful in explaining the origin of spectral lines; further, it soon became evident that atoms must be constructed very differently from Thomson's model.

In 1911 Rutherford fired alpha particles (He^{++} ions) from radioactive materials through thin metal foils and observed how they were deflected (Fig. 48.2). From the Thomson model one would expect only small deflections, because the positive and negative electricity in the atom, distributed over a relatively large volume, should exert no great forces to deflect the alpha particles. Rutherford's experiments showed that a surprisingly large number of alpha particles were scattered backward by the foil. The alpha particles which went through were given much larger changes in direction than could be explained on the basis of the Thomson model. Rutherford showed that such significant scattering at large angles was to be expected if all the positive electricity of the atom were concentrated at almost a point. He calculated how the number of alpha particles scattered should depend on angle for various kinds of foils and for alpha particles of different energies. His predictions were in excellent agreement with measurements made by Geiger and Marsden.

In the Rutherford model all the positive electricity is concentrated in a very small volume called the *nucleus*. Surrounding this core are the electrons, held to the nucleus by electrostatic attraction. The radius of even the largest nucleus is only about 10^{-14} m, while the radius of a typical atom is nearer to 10^{-10} m. Thus all the positive charge and almost all the mass of the atom are concentrated in about 10^{-12} the volume of the atom.

48.3 The Bohr Atom

In 1913 Niels Bohr made a great forward stride in explaining the structure of the atom. Bohr imagined that a hydrogen atom was composed of a nucleus called a *proton* and a single electron which revolves about the proton in a circular orbit (Fig. 48.3). The centripetal force required to keep the electron in this orbit is provided by the Coulomb electrostatic attraction between the proton and electron:

$$\frac{mv^2}{r} = \frac{1}{4\pi\epsilon_0}\frac{e^2}{r^2} \qquad\qquad \textbf{48.1}$$

where m, v, and e are the mass, velocity, and charge of the electron, and r is the radius of the orbit. Bohr further postulated that the only values which the angular momentum of the electron could have were integral multiples of $h/2\pi$, where h is Planck's constant.

$$mvr = n\frac{h}{2\pi} \qquad\qquad \textbf{48.2}$$

where n is an integer. This condition Bohr adopted from the radiation laws which Planck had developed several years earlier.

Solving Eqs. (48.1) and (48.2) simultaneously for r yields

$$r = \frac{\epsilon_0 n^2 h^2}{\pi m e^2} \qquad\qquad \textbf{48.3}$$

The smallest orbit in which the electron can exist is that given by $n = 1$. If $n = 1$ with the other constants given their proper values, $r_1 = 5.29 \times 10^{-11}$ m. This agrees well with measured values of the radius of the hydrogen atom. The next smallest allowed radius is four times as great, the third possible radius is $9r_1$, and so forth. Normally, the hydrogen electron is in the orbit corresponding to $n = 1$, but on occasions it may be "excited" to one of the larger orbits.

The total energy of the hydrogen electron is the sum of the kinetic and potential energies. The kinetic energy $mv^2/2$ is, by Eq. (48.1),

$$\text{Kinetic energy} = \tfrac{1}{2}mv^2 = \frac{e^2}{8\pi\epsilon_0 r}$$

while the potential energy, assumed to be zero when proton and electron are an infinite distance apart, is given by Eq. (34.1):

$$\text{Potential energy} = Ve = -\frac{e^2}{4\pi\epsilon_0 r}$$

from which

$$\text{Total energy} = \text{kinetic} + \text{potential energy} = -\frac{e^2}{8\pi\epsilon_0 r}$$

$$= -\frac{me^4}{8\epsilon_0{}^2 n^2 h^2} \qquad\qquad \textbf{48.4}$$

The minus sign means the electron is bound to the nucleus and cannot escape.

The hydrogen electron has its lowest possible energy when it is in the orbit characterized by $n = 1$. If the electron is in any other orbit, it may be expected to jump to an orbit of lower energy (Fig. 48.4). When it makes such a jump a photon of radiation is emitted. The energy of the emitted photon is $h\nu$, where ν is the frequency. It is equal to the energy lost by the electron as it goes from a level A characterized by the integer n_A to another level B characterized by n_B.

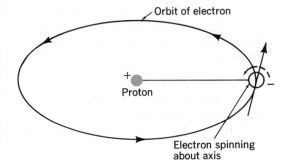

FIGURE 48.3

Bohr model of the hydrogen atom with electron spin added; sizes of nucleus and electron are exaggerated.

Energy radiated $= h\nu = \dfrac{me^4}{8\epsilon_0^2 h^2}\left(\dfrac{1}{n_B^2} - \dfrac{1}{n_A^2}\right)$ **48.5**

Combining Eq. (48.5) with the relation $c = \nu\lambda$, we obtain

$$\frac{1}{\lambda} = \frac{\nu}{c} = \frac{me^4}{8\epsilon_0^2 h^3 c}\left(\frac{1}{n_B^2} - \frac{1}{n_A^2}\right) = R\left(\frac{1}{n_B^2} - \frac{1}{n_A^2}\right) \qquad \textbf{48.6}$$

where R is called the Rydberg constant. It has the value 1.09737×10^7 m^{-1}.

48.4 Energy Levels of Hydrogen

According to Bohr's theory, an electron bound to a proton to form a hydrogen atom can exist only in certain orbits characterized by a total energy given by Eq. (48.4). Modern quantum mechanics does not support the assumption of well-defined electron orbits, but it does predict that the electron must be in one of the energy states (or levels) given by Eq. (48.4). In an electrical discharge through hydrogen, electrons are torn free from hydrogen atoms. Eventually the electrons and protons recombine; in this recombination the electron may be captured in

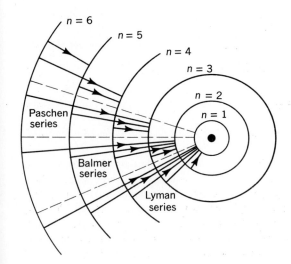

FIGURE 48.4

Bohr orbits and transitions for the hydrogen atom (not to scale).

one of the many possible energy levels (Fig. 48.5). Atoms with electrons in one of the higher states are said to be *excited*. The electron of an excited hydrogen atom normally makes successive transitions to lower states until it finally reaches the stable level corresponding to $n = 1$. When it jumps from one state to another, radiation is emitted.

The Balmer series arises when electrons from higher levels jump to the level with $n = 2$, as is shown schematically in Figures 48.4 and 48.5. According to Bohr's formula [Eq. (48.6)], the wavelengths of the series of lines emitted when electrons jump from higher states to that characterized by $n_B = 2$ are given by

$$\frac{1}{\lambda} = R\left(\frac{1}{4} - \frac{1}{n_A{}^2}\right)$$

or

$$\lambda = \frac{1}{R}\frac{4n_A{}^2}{n_A{}^2 - 4} = 3.65 \times 10^{-7}\frac{n_A{}^2}{n_A{}^2 - 4}$$

This agrees with Balmer's formula if we let $n_A = m$.

We expect electrons eventually to make transitions to the state with $n = 1$, since this is the normal state for the electron. For such a tran-

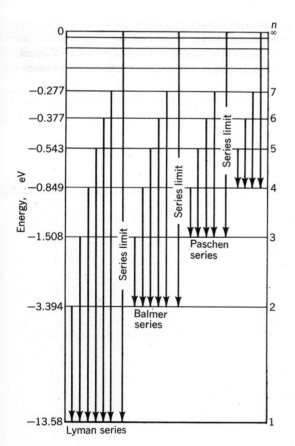

FIGURE 48.5

Energy-level diagram for hydrogen (not to scale).

sition Eq. (48.5) shows that the emitted frequencies should be in the ultraviolet region. Lyman studied the ultraviolet spectrum of hydrogen in 1906 and found, just as Bohr theory predicts, a series of lines corresponding to electron jumps from excited levels to the level $n = 1$. This series we call the *Lyman* series in honor of its discoverer.

What should happen if electrons in higher excited states make transitions to levels $n = 3$? Equation (48.5) predicts that the frequencies would be in the infrared region of the spectrum. In 1908 this series was discovered by Paschen. Later another series in the far infrared was discovered by Brackett. The wavelengths of the lines in these series are accurately given by Eq. (48.6) when $n_B = 3$ for the Paschen series and $n_B = 4$ for the Brackett series, while n_A takes on all larger integral values.

48.5 The Atomic Number and Characteristic X Rays

Consider an *ionized* helium atom. Here we have a nucleus with a charge of two fundamental units and a single electron. If we apply the Bohr theory to this system, the relations developed for hydrogen are applicable, provided we use $2e$ for the nuclear charge. The energies become four times as large in magnitude, and the predicted frequency of the line emitted for any given transition is four times that for hydrogen. Experiments reveal that this is indeed the case, except for very small shifts which can be explained.

In general, if we have a nucleus with positive charge Ze and a *single* electron, the force between electron and nucleus is $9 \times 10^9 Ze^2/r^2$, and the radius of an allowed circular orbit is found, by the method of Sec. 48.3, to be

$$r = \frac{\epsilon_0 n^2 h^2}{\pi m Z e^2} \qquad \textbf{48.3}a$$

while the energy is

$$\text{Total energy} = -\frac{mZ^2 e^4}{8\epsilon_0{}^2 n^2 h^2} \qquad \textbf{48.7}$$

Suppose that a single electron circling a nucleus of charge Ze in the orbit characterized by $n_A = 2$ were to make a transition to the $n_B = 1$ orbit. The Bohr theory predicts for such a transition that a photon of energy $\mathcal{W}$ should be emitted, where, by Eqs. (48.5) and (48.7),

$$\mathcal{W} = h\nu = \frac{mZ^2 e^4}{8\epsilon_0{}^2 h^2}\left(\frac{1}{n_B{}^2} - \frac{1}{n_A{}^2}\right) = \frac{mZ^2 e^4}{8\epsilon_0{}^2 h^2}\left(\frac{1}{1^2} - \frac{1}{2^2}\right) \qquad \textbf{48.8}$$

If this equation is solved for ν with the known values of h, m, and e inserted, we obtain

$$\nu = 2.46 \times 10^{15} Z^2 \text{ per sec} \qquad \textbf{48.9}$$

The English physicist Moseley found in the X-ray spectra of many elements a line of frequency given by the empirical relation

$$\nu = 2.52 \times 10^{15}(Z - 1.13)^2 \text{ per sec} \qquad \textbf{48.9}a$$

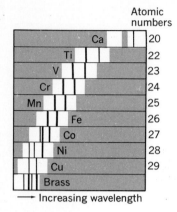

Atomic numbers

Ca	20
Ti	22
V	23
Cr	24
Mn	25
Fe	26
Co	27
Ni	28
Cu	29
Brass	

⟶ Increasing wavelength

FIGURE 48.6

Moseley photographs of K X-ray spectra.

This line is called $K\alpha$ and is the line at the right for each of the elements whose X-ray spectrum is shown in Figure 48.6. Subsequent work has shown that this line is indeed associated with the transition of an electron from a level with $n = 2$ to a level with $n = 1$. A plot of the square root of the frequency as a function of atomic number for this line is shown in Figure 48.7.

Moseley also observed a line called $K\beta$ associated with the transition $n_A = 3$ to $n_B = 1$. This line has a frequency which corresponds well with what one would expect if one placed $n_A = 3$ in Eq. (48.8). The square root of the frequency of $K\beta$ as a function of atomic number is also shown in Figure 48.7.

Both the slight difference between the constants of Eqs. (48.9) and (48.9a) and the correction to the atomic number in Eq. (48.9a) can be explained quantitatively as well as qualitatively in terms of effects due to other electrons. An orbit characterized by $n = 1$ is called a K orbit, and the associated electron a K electron. A K electron moves in a force field which is not very different from that of the nuclear charge Ze alone. The energy, however, is affected by the second K electron in particular and, to a smaller extent, by the other electrons. The net effect of all the other electrons is to make the effective nuclear charge appropriate to Eq. (48.8) about $Z - 1$ rather than Z.

The lines which Moseley studied have very short wavelengths and belong to the X-ray region of the electromagnetic spectrum. The frequencies are characteristic of the material which emits them and are, for this reason, called *characteristic X rays*. X rays involving an electronic transition from a state of higher n to the $n = 1$ level are called *K-series* lines. Other families of X-ray lines have also been observed. Those corresponding to transitions from higher n to the $n = 2$ level are called L lines (Fig. 48.8), and electrons with $n = 2$ are known as L electrons. Lines corresponding to transitions to levels characterized by $n = 3$ are called M lines, etc. Figure 48.9 shows the wavelengths at which the principal K, L, and M lines are found for various elements.

The X-ray spectra of elements permit us to make an unambiguous assignment of atomic number to every element. At one time there was uncertainty as to whether potassium or argon had the higher atomic

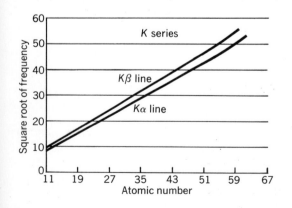

FIGURE 48.7

Moseley plots of the square roots of the frequencies of K lines as functions of the atomic number of the emitting element.

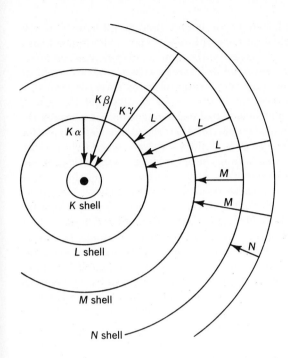

FIGURE 48.8

Transitions involved in the emission of characteristic X-ray lines in terms of the simplified Bohr model which ignores the fine structure of the shells.

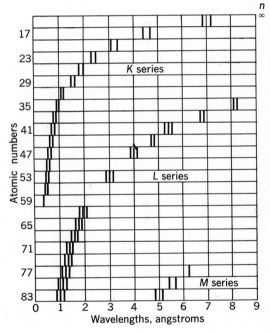

FIGURE 48.9

Wavelengths of the characteristic X-ray lines of the elements; only a small fraction of the L and M lines are shown.

number. Argon is heavier, but the chemical properties suggest potassium has the higher atomic number. X rays have shown clearly that argon has atomic number 18, while potassium has 19. X rays resolved a similar paradox in connection with cobalt and nickel.

48.6 Electron Spin

The $K\alpha$ X-ray lines observed by Moseley actually show up as double lines when examined under higher resolution. In 1925 Uhlenbeck and Goudsmit showed that these and many other features of atomic spectra could be explained by assuming that an electron not only revolves around a nucleus, but also rotates or "spins" about its own axis (see Fig. 48.3). A determination of the spin angular momentum about any axis always results in one of two values: either $+h/4\pi$ or $-h/4\pi$, where h is Planck's constant. For a single electron traversing an orbit, the total angular momentum is the vector resultant of the orbital angular momentum and the spin angular momentum. Essentially the spin either adds to or subtracts from the orbital angular momentum an amount $h/4\pi$. The energy is slightly different in the two cases for the following reason: The spinning charge produces a magnetic moment, so the spinning electron resembles a tiny magnet. From the point of view of the electron, the nucleus revolving about the electron produces a magnetic field; the energy of the electron-magnet depends on whether its magnetic moment is aligned with this field or opposed to it.

In the optical spectra of sodium and the other alkalies, the energy associated with a given orbit has two values, depending on whether the spin angular momentum of the excited electron is parallel or anti-parallel to the orbital angular momentum. Such a splitting of energy levels may give rise to series of double lines. The sodium D lines are examples of such a "doublet"; they have wavelengths of 5,890 and 5,896 Å.

48.7 Some Ideas of Quantum Mechanics

The brilliant success of the Bohr theory in explaining the spectra of hydrogen and the K-series X-ray lines makes it one of the great triumphs of modern physics. In spite of its success, the Bohr theory is not entirely correct. Indeed, one of its key postulates—that the angular momentum mvr of the electron in its orbit is $nh/2\pi$—is not true (Sec. 48.8). The Bohr theory is a magnificent contribution to physics, not because it is correct in detail, but because it opened the way for modern quantum mechanics. Although the formulation of quantum mechanics involves relatively advanced mathematics, some of the ideas can be discussed qualitatively.

One of the startling principles of quantum mechanics, advanced by Heisenberg in 1927, is that there is a basic uncertainty in nature which represents an ultimate limit to the precision with which processes can be described. One form of the Heisenberg *uncertainty principle* can be stated as follows:

In any experiment in which we endeavor to measure both the position and the momentum of a particle, there is an inherent indefiniteness in the results such that if Δx is the limit of uncertainty in the x coordinate of the position, and $\Delta(mv_x)$ is the uncertainty in the corresponding component of the momentum, the product of these uncertainties must be at least of the order of magnitude of Planck's constant h.

$$\Delta x \; \Delta(mv_x) \gtrless h \tag{48.10}$$

A similar indefiniteness accompanies any measurement of an energy.

If Δt is the time available for the energy measurement, there is an inherent uncertainty $\Delta \mathcal{W}$ in the energy such that

$$\Delta \mathcal{W} \, \Delta t \gtrless h \qquad\qquad\qquad 48.11$$

The constant h is so small that for macroscopic bodies these quantum indefinitenesses do not trouble us. However, when we deal with atomic sizes, the uncertainty principle is extremely important.

The uncertainty principle is a fundamental part of wave mechanics. It tells us that we cannot simultaneously know both the precise position and the exact velocity of a particle such as an electron. As a consequence, an atom model based on sharp orbits for electrons at precisely defined distances from a nucleus can only be a rough approximation. Actually there is a finite possibility of finding the electrons over a wide range of positions. For a hydrogen electron in its lowest energy state, wave mechanics predicts that the most probable distance of the electron from the nucleus is the Bohr radius, but there is a modest probability that the electron is as much as twice that distance away.

48.8 The Pauli Exclusion Principle

The energy states allowed to an atom having more than one electron can be described reasonably well if we think of each electron as existing in a hydrogenlike energy level and moving in the electric field of the nucleus and the other electrons with its own average orbit and its own orbital and spin angular momenta. Such a picture is an oversimplification, since each electron interacts constantly with other electrons. However, this picture gives a reasonable approximation in the sense that it represents a statistical "average" of the positions of the electrons. Figure 48.10 is a diagram, based on the orbital model, of an atom of copper with its 29 electrons.

The optical spectra of all atoms arise from the excitation of one or more electrons to a higher than normal energy level. Indeed, in the ground state of any atom each electron has the smallest energy it is allowed to have. Even for the most complicated atoms it is possible, by use of quantum mechanics, to calculate fairly accurately what energies electrons can have and what the wavelengths of the spectral lines are. The observed values agree well with predictions.

If we treat complex atoms from the point of view of hydrogenlike "orbits," we may specify the state of each electron in terms of four numbers, called *quantum numbers,* each of which has a physical significance. These quantum numbers are:

1. The principal quantum number n, which appears in Eq. (48.7) and is a rough measure of the average distance of the electron from the nucleus. The energy of a state depends strongly on n, which takes on integral values 1, 2, 3, 4, ...

2. The azimuthal quantum number l, which is a measure of the orbital angular momentum in units of $h/2\pi$. It takes on integral values $n - 1, n - 2, \ldots, 0$. Thus, when $n = 3$, l can be 2, 1, or 0.

FIGURE 48.10

Electron orbits of a copper atom, with nucleus and K orbits deleted.

3. The quantum number j, which measures the total angular momentum of the electron, spin plus orbital, in units of $h/2\pi$. Its values are limited to the positive half-integers $\frac{1}{2}$, $\frac{3}{2}$, . . ., $l - \frac{1}{2}$, $l + \frac{1}{2}$.

4. The quantum number m_j, which specifies how the total angular momentum is oriented in space relative to some direction prescribed by a magnetic field or some other kind of field. It takes on values j, $j - 1, j - 2, \ldots, -j$.

Now let us consider a copper atom with its 29 electrons. In its lowest energy state, are all these electrons in the $n = 1$ state? No, indeed—not any more than all the water molecules in a full pan are at the bottom. In the copper atom 2 electrons have $n = 1$, 8 have $n = 2$, 18 have $n = 3$, and 1 has $n = 4$. This is readily explained in terms of the *Pauli exclusion principle,* which tells us: *No two electrons associated with any given atom can have the same four quantum numbers.*

If $n = 1$, l is necessarily 0, and $j = \frac{1}{2}$, so m_j may have the values $-\frac{1}{2}$ and $+\frac{1}{2}$. Thus 2 electrons may have $n = 1$; these are the K electrons in X-ray notation. If $n = 2$, l may be 0 for two electrons and 1 for six electrons [for $j = \frac{1}{2}$, $m_j = -\frac{1}{2}$ and $\frac{1}{2}$ (two electrons); for $j = \frac{3}{2}$, $m_j = \frac{3}{2}$, $\frac{1}{2}$, $-\frac{1}{2}$, and $-\frac{3}{2}$ (four electrons)]. Thus, 8 electrons may have $n = 1$, or be in the L shell. Similarly, there can be at most 18 M electrons with $n = 3$. The maximum number of electrons which can have any given principal quantum number n is $2n^2$.

Normally the lowest energy states of the atom are filled. It takes a large amount of energy to eject an electron from one of these lowest levels and thereby excite the characteristic X-ray spectrum. An inner electron, displaced from its level, usually leaves the atom completely, since all but the high optical levels are filled. When a K ($n = 1$) electron is ejected, its vacancy is typically filled by an L electron, and a series of transitions occurs before the atom reaches its ground state once more.

48.9 The Periodic Table

The arrangement of atoms in the periodic table (inside back cover) can be explained in terms of the Pauli exclusion principle. Only two electrons in any atom can have $n = 1$; they form a "closed shell." The element lithium is characterized by three electrons. The third of these electrons cannot be in the $n = 1$ shell; it must seek an "orbit" with higher n. Of those available, the lowest energy corresponds to $n = 2$. A grand total of eight electrons can be added with $n = 2$. When we reach neon, both the $n = 1$ and $n = 2$ shells are completely filled, a total of 10 electrons. If we wish to add still another electron, it must go in an $n = 3$ level. The element sodium has 11 electrons; it represents the beginning of the filling of the third shell.

A single electron alone in a new shell (as in potassium, lithium, sodium, etc.) is relatively easy to detach from the atom. Potassium, rubidium, and cesium begin shells characterized by $n = 4$, 5, and 6, respectively. The outer electron of each of these elements is easily detachable. They are all electropositive elements, with similar chemical

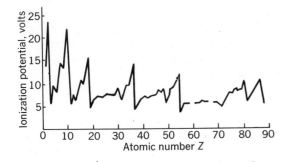

FIGURE 48.11

Ionization potentials of elements.

properties. In general, those elements whose atoms have the same number of electrons in an unfilled shell have similar chemical and physical properties.

After eight electrons have been added to the $n = 3$ shell, we reach the element *argon.* In the next element, *potassium,* the outer electron has $n = 4$, although several levels with $n = 3$ (but higher energy) remain empty. However, as we proceed up the periodic table, the $n = 3$ shell is quickly filled, and this gives rise to the first long period in the periodic table. The period is the principal quantum number n of the outermost electrons. A detailed explanation of why shells of higher n begin to fill before all the possible "orbits" of lower n are filled is beyond the scope of this text.

Many chemical and physical characteristics of the elements can be correlated with the way in which electrons are added to fill the various shells. One such characteristic is the ionization potential, or the energy required to remove one of the least tightly bound electrons from an atom, shown graphically in Figure 48.11. Note that for potassium, sodium, lithium, etc., the ionization potential is exceptionally low compared with that of neighboring atoms. This arises from the fact that in each case there is a single electron in a new outer shell. On the other hand, if there are eight electrons in any given outer shell, a peculiarly stable electronic configuration occurs in which the element is chemically inert. This is the case for the noble gases neon, argon, krypton, and xenon.

Many other properties show a similar periodicity. Among them are atomic diameter, compressibility, melting point, and coefficient of thermal expansion.

< **48.10 The Zeeman Effect**

When a source of light is placed between the poles of a powerful electromagnet, a single spectral line breaks up into several components (Fig. 48.12). This separation of a spectral line into components by the action of a magnetic field is known as the *Zeeman effect.* The number of components depends on the particular spectral line and is not the same when the light is viewed in the direction of the magnetic field as when the light is viewed at right angles to this direction. In some cases, a

FIGURE 48.12

A magnetic field splits a single spectral line (above) into several components (below). These lines were photographed after the light had passed through a polarizer which reduced the relative intensities of the outer lines.

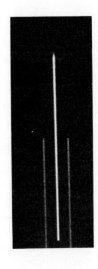

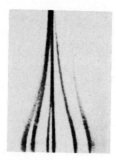

FIGURE 48.13

Stark effect for a line of the helium spectrum, showing splitting due to an electric field.

larger number of components is observed. Because of the interaction between the magnetic field due to the magnet and the magnetic fields due to the electrons in the atom, the energy levels in the atom are split up into a number of additional levels. Transitions between these new levels give rise to additional spectral lines.

48.11 The Stark Effect

An electric field may also cause the splitting up of spectral lines. In a sufficiently large electric field, a single spectral line is replaced by a number of components. The greater the electric field, the greater is the separation of these components. This separation of spectral lines into components by an electric field is known as the *Stark effect* after its discoverer. Figure 48.13 shows an example of the Stark effect in helium. The splitting of the spectral line varies from zero at the top of the figure, where there is no electric field, to its greatest value at the bottom, where the electric field is largest. Data on the amount of separation for different spectral lines give valuable information about the structure of the atoms emitting the lines.

Questions

1. What is a spectral series? What is a series limit?

2. What is the experimental evidence that all the positive charge and most of the mass of an atom are concentrated in a nucleus?

3. The atomic weight of argon is greater than that of potassium. Why do we believe potassium has the greater atomic number?

4. What is the Pauli exclusion principle? How does it help us understand the periodic table?

5. Is the gravitational attraction between the proton and the electron of a hydrogen atom significant compared with the Coulomb attraction? Find the ratio of Coulomb to gravitational attraction for an electron in the first Bohr orbit. Does this ratio change from orbit to orbit?

6. Physicists often use the rough approximation that the energy needed to remove a K electron from an atom of atomic number Z is $10Z^2$ eV. Why is this a better approximation for heavy elements than $13.6Z^2$ eV, which corresponds to Eq. (48.7)?

Problems

1. Find the orbital velocity of a hydrogen electron in the ground state on the basis of the Bohr theory. How many revolutions does it make each second?

Ans. 2.2×10^6 m/sec; 6.6×10^{15} rev/sec

2. The orbital electron of a singly ionized helium atom is attracted by the nucleus, which has a positive charge twice that of the electron. Find the radius of the first Bohr orbit of ionized helium and the speed of an electron in this orbit.

3. Calculate the wavelengths of the first two lines and of the series limit for the Balmer series of ionized helium.   *Ans.* 164, 122, and 91 mμ

4. Use the Balmer formula to calculate the wavelengths of the first four lines of the Balmer series of hydrogen.

5. The electron of a Bohr-model hydrogen atom revolves around the proton with a speed of 2.2×10^6 m/sec at a radius of 5.3×10^{-11} m. To what current does this correspond? Find the magnetic induction at the proton due to the motion of the electron. Compute the magnetic moment due to this orbital motion. (This magnetic moment is known as a *Bohr magneton.*)

Ans. 0.00105 amp; 12.5 webers/m²; 9.3×10^{-24} amp-m²

6. Compute the energies of the photons and the wavelengths of the longest and shortest spectral lines in the Lyman series.

7. Find the energy in electron volts required to strip a calcium atom ($Z = 20$) of its last electron, assuming the other 19 have been removed. How does this compare with the energy required to excite the K X-ray lines of calcium (about 3.7 keV)? Why the difference?   *Ans.* 5.4 keV; other electrons change potential

8. Find the energies of the photons and the wavelengths of the first three lines of the Paschen series for hydrogen.

9. Find the speed of an electron in a Bohr orbit of quantum number n.   *Ans.* $e^2/2\epsilon_0 nh$

10. Show that the ratio of the speed of an electron in the first Bohr orbit to the speed of light is $\alpha = e^2/2\epsilon_0 hc = 1/137$. This ratio is known as the *fine-structure constant.*

11. A mu-mesic atom consists of a nucleus of charge Z, a captured negative muon, and $Z - 1$ electrons. The smaller Bohr orbits of the muon are much closer to the nucleus than any of the Bohr orbits of the electrons. The muon has the same charge as an electron, but 207 times the mass. Assuming the electrons do not affect the muon significantly, find the radius of the first Bohr orbit for a muon captured by an aluminum nucleus ($Z = 13$). Find the energy of the muon in orbits characterized by $n = 1$ and $n = 2$ and the wavelength of the photon emitted when the muon makes the transition from the higher of these states to the lower.

Ans. 2×10^{-14} m; 4.76×10^5 eV; 1.19×10^5 eV; 3.5×10^{-12} m

12. (*a*) Show that the frequency of revolution of an electron in a circular Bohr orbit of hydrogen is given by $\nu = me^4/4\epsilon_0{}^2 n^3 h^3$. (*b*) Show that for large n the frequency of revolution is approximately equal to the frequency emitted according to Eq. (48.5) when the electrons make a transition from state n to state $n - 1$. (This problem is an example of *Bohr's correspondence principle,* which implies that when n is large, quantum physics makes the same predictions as classical physics.)

13. Show that, on the basis of the approximations which led to Eq. (48.9), the slope of the Moseley plot (Fig. 48.7) for $K\beta$ is expected to be $\sqrt{32/27}$ times that for $K\alpha$.

CHAPTER 49 *To the physicist of 1900 it seemed most reasonable to ask "Are X rays waves or particles?" To resolve this kind of question for any beam transferring energy from one place to another, he would perform certain experiments. Evidence of interference or diffraction established the wave nature of the beam. A confirming test for a beam of particles was to show that they exhibit rest mass or charge. The conclusions of 1900 were that electromagnetic radiation was clearly of wave nature, while cathode rays and positive rays were particles.*

In this chapter we shall examine some of the evidence for the modern view that "Is a beam composed of waves or particles?" is scarcely a proper question; we shall find that beams of cathode rays, for example, exhibit both wave and particle properties. *Which properties predominate depends on the particular experiment we perform. A beam of electromagnetic radiation exhibits wave properties in many situations, but in others the photons comprising the beam behave as particles. Particle properties are especially prominent for high-energy photons. In the sections which follow, we shall often use X rays as specific examples of high-energy photons, but the conclusions are equally valid for gamma-ray photons in the same energy range. The origin of the photon is unimportant—what counts is the energy hv which it bears.*

Waves and Particles

49.1 Wave Properties of X Rays

The early failure of Röntgen to observe interference and diffraction of X rays was associated with his apparatus and procedures. The first definite evidence of wave properties for X rays came out of an experiment devised by Laue in which a crystal played the role of a diffraction grating. When X rays fall on a body, the atoms scatter the incident radiation. In a crystalline substance the atoms are arranged in a regular way, and definite phase relationships exist between the scattered rays from neighboring atoms. If a narrow pencil of X rays falls on a crystal C (Fig. 49.1), the scattered rays reinforce one another

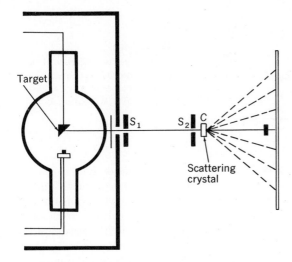

FIGURE 49.1
X-ray diffraction apparatus.

in certain directions by constructive interference. If a photographic plate is exposed, a series of spots is formed (Fig. 49.2) where constructive interference occurs. The theory of this interference was worked out by Laue. From the positions of these spots and the properties of the scattering crystal Laue calculated the range of wavelengths present in an X-ray beam.

The diffraction of X rays by crystals can be used to measure the wavelengths of the X rays. Consider a cubic crystal of sodium chloride (Fig. 49.3). If X rays are incident on a single plane of this crystal, each particle scatters the waves. By Huygens' principle the condition for constructive interference from every atom lying in this plane is

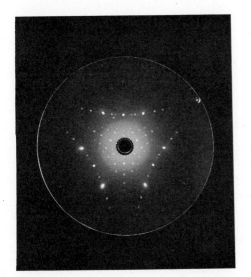

FIGURE 49.2
Laue photograph of tungsten.

FIGURE 49.3
Crystal lattice of rock salt (NaCl).

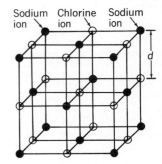

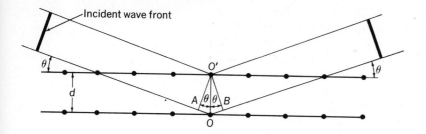

FIGURE 49.4
Constructive interference of the waves scattered from atoms in adjacent planes of a crystal occurs when $n\lambda = 2d \sin \theta$.

that the angle of incidence be equal to the angle of reflection. To form a Laue spot, it is necessary not only to have constructive interference of all scattered wavelets from a given plane of atoms, but also to have constructive interference of the radiation scattered from adjacent planes. In order that the radiation scattered by the second plane of Figure 49.4 interfere constructively with that scattered by the first plane, it is necessary that the path difference be an integral number of wavelengths. It can be seen from the figure that the difference in path is AOB. Let the distance between adjacent planes be d. Since $AO = OB = d \sin \theta$, it follows immediately that

$$n\lambda = 2d \sin \theta$$

49.1

where n is an integer, λ is the wavelength of the X rays, and θ is the glancing angle. Equation (49.1) is known as *Bragg's law*.

To measure the wavelengths of X rays, Bragg developed the X-ray spectrometer (Fig. 49.5), in which X rays are incident upon a crystal C

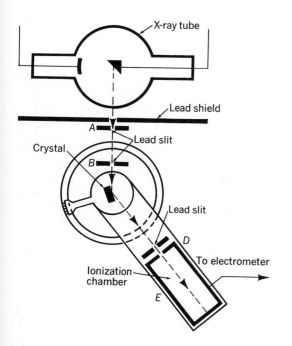

FIGURE 49.5
Spectrometer for measuring the wavelengths of X rays.

mounted on a rotating table such that the glancing angle θ can be varied. An ionization chamber is mounted on a movable arm and positioned in such a way that the angle of "reflection" is equal to the angle of incidence for the crystal face. The wavelength of the X rays which enter the chamber can be calculated from Eq. (49.1) if θ is measured and d is known.

Bragg calculated the grating space d for NaCl as follows: If M is the molecular weight of the NaCl, the number of atoms in a mass M is $2N_A$, where N_A is Avogadro's number. The number of atoms per kilogram is $2N_A/M$. To obtain the number of atoms per cubic meter, we multiply by the density ρ to obtain

$$\text{Number of atoms per cubic meter} = \frac{2N_A\rho}{M}$$

The volume per atom is therefore $M/2N_A\rho$. For a cubic crystal we can think of each atom as occupying a cube of length d on a side; thus $d^3 = M/2N_A\rho$, or

$$d = \sqrt[3]{\frac{M}{2N_A\rho}} \qquad \text{for a cubic crystal} \qquad \text{49.2}$$

The molecular weight of NaCl is 58.45, and the density is 2,160 kg/m^3. Since $N_A = 6.02 \times 10^{26}$, $d = 2.81 \times 10^{-10}$ m $= 2.81$ Å.

Bragg measured the wavelengths of many X-ray lines, using sodium chloride crystals. Once the wavelengths of lines are known, it is possible by Bragg's equation to determine the separations between planes (i.e., the grating spaces) for crystals of more complicated structure.

Example With an X-ray spectrometer using a rock-salt crystal, the glancing angle for the first reinforcement ($n = 1$) for the Cu $K\alpha$ line is found to be 15.8°. If the distance between the crystal planes is 2.81 Å, find the wavelength of this line.

$$n\lambda = 2d \sin \theta$$
$$n = 1 \quad \text{and} \quad d = 2.81 \text{ Å}$$
$$\sin \theta = 0.273$$
$$\lambda = 2 \times 2.81 \times 0.273 = 1.54 \text{ Å}$$

49.2 Absorption of High-energy Photons

If a sheet of any substance is placed in the path of a beam of high-energy photons such as X rays, the intensity of the beam is diminished. Let I_0 be the initial intensity of a homogeneous beam, and I its intensity after passing through a thickness z of the material. Then

$$I = I_0 e^{-\mu z} \qquad \text{49.3}$$

where μ is the *absorption coefficient* of the material for the particular wavelength, and e is the base of the natural logarithms. The absorption coefficient varies with the wavelength of the photons, usually increasing as the wavelength increases. It is found experimentally that the absorption depends only on the number and kinds of atoms present in the absorbing layer; it is independent of their physical or chemical state.

A thickness of absorber which is adequate to cut the intensity to one-half is called the *half-value layer*. When a beam of homogeneous X rays falls on an absorber just thick enough to remove half the beam, a second absorber of the same thickness removes half of what is left, so that one-fourth the initial intensity is transmitted. However, if a nonhomogeneous beam is incident, the second absorber removes less than half of what was transmitted by the first. The half-value layer removes more than half of the less penetrating and less than half of the more penetrating wavelengths of a nonhomogeneous beam. Therefore, the radiation which strikes the second absorber is more penetrating on the average than that which struck the first. Thin layers of copper or aluminum are used to remove the softer components of X rays. If the X rays were being used to treat a deep tumor, these soft X rays would only produce burns near the skin.

Photons with energies ranging from a few hundred up to a million electron volts are absorbed or removed from a beam primarily by photoelectric absorption and by scattering. Photons with energies above 1.02 MeV may be absorbed by pair production (Sec. 49.5) as well. We shall invoke the quantum hypothesis to achieve a quantitative understanding of these processes. In one type of scattering we find particularly convincing evidence of the particle properties of electromagnetic radiation; another type of scattering is readily explained in terms of wave properties.

49.3 Scattering and the Compton Effect

When a beam of X rays passes through matter, some energy is scattered out of the beam. According to the classical theory of J. J. Thomson, the atomic electrons are driven to perform simple harmonic motion by the electric intensity E of the incident waves (see Fig. 45.17). Since these electrons are accelerated, they radiate a frequency equal to that of the incident waves. Thus the electrons remove energy from the passing wave and reradiate this energy in other directions. Scattering of waves with the frequency of the incident radiation is observed over the entire electromagnetic spectrum; however, it is weak at high frequencies. This unmodified scattering can be treated satisfactorily in terms of classical waves.

In 1923 Compton published the results of careful measurements of the X-ray frequencies scattered by carbon atoms upon which monochromatic X rays were incident (Fig. 49.6). He found that the scattered beam contained two frequencies, one the same as that of the incident beam, and the second somewhat lower. Figure 49.6 shows the wavelength distribution of the radiation scattered at various angles. At each angle radiation is scattered not only at the wavelength of the incident beam, but also at a longer wavelength whose value depends on the scattering angle θ (the angle between the propagation directions of the incident and scattered radiation).

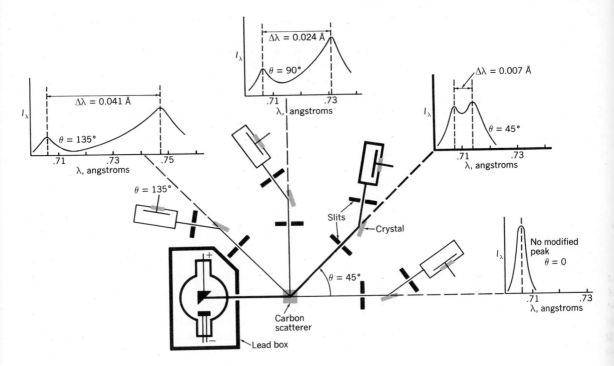

FIGURE 49.6

The scattering of Mo $K\alpha$ X rays ($\lambda = 0.707$ Å) at an angle θ produces two peaks in the scattered radiation, one at the wavelength of the incident radiation and the second at a wavelength greater by $\Delta\lambda = 0.024\,(1 - \cos\theta)$ Å.

Compton's measurements showed that the change in wavelength $\Delta\lambda$ is independent of the scattering material, but depends on the scattering angle θ according to the relation

$$\Delta\lambda = 0.024\,(1 - \cos\theta) \qquad \text{angstroms} \qquad \textbf{49.4}$$

Compton explained the wavelength shift in the scattering of X rays by assuming that the incident beam of X rays consists of a stream of photons of energy $h\nu_0$. These photons possess momentum $h\nu_0/c$ as well as energy. Their collisions with electrons (Fig. 49.7) may be described in terms of the laws of conservation of momentum and conservation of energy. Applying these laws to a collision, we obtain, for a nonrelativistic case in which the electron is initially at rest,

Conservation of energy: $\qquad h\nu_0 = h\nu + \tfrac{1}{2}mv^2 \qquad \textbf{49.5}$

Conservation of momentum:

x component: $\qquad \dfrac{h\nu_0}{c} = \dfrac{h\nu}{c}\cos\theta + mv\cos\phi \qquad \textbf{49.6}$

y component: $\qquad 0 = \dfrac{h\nu}{c}\sin\theta - mv\sin\phi \qquad \textbf{49.7}$

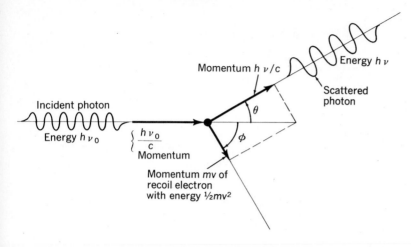

Momentum $h\nu/c$

Energy $h\nu$

Scattered photon

Incident photon

Energy $h\nu_0$

$\dfrac{h\nu_0}{c}$ Momentum

Momentum mv of recoil electron with energy $\frac{1}{2}mv^2$

FIGURE 49.7

Elastic collision of a photon with a free electron initially at rest.

where m and v are the mass and final speed of the electron, θ is the angle through which the photon is scattered, and ϕ is the angle between v and the direction in which the photon was incident. With considerable effort these equations may be solved to find the change in wavelength $\Delta\lambda = c/\nu - c/\nu_0$. The result is that

$$\Delta\lambda = \frac{h}{mc}(1 - \cos\theta) = 0.02426(1 - \cos\theta) \qquad \text{angstroms} \qquad \textbf{49.4}a$$

Compton's experiments were a clear indication that electromagnetic radiation has particle as well as wave properties. The Compton effect is convincing evidence that radiation in the X-ray region comes in photons or quanta which behave like particles in collisions with electrons.

49.4 Photoelectric Absorption

Many incident X-ray photons eject electrons from the atoms of the absorbing material by a process known as *photoelectric absorption*. For penetrating X rays the probability of ejecting a K electron is far greater than that of ejecting any one of the other electrons. As the wavelength of the incident radiation is increased, the absorption increases rapidly up to the point at which the photons no longer have enough energy to eject K electrons. At this point the absorption drops sharply (Fig. 49.8), although electrons continue to be ejected from the L, M, and other shells. As the wavelength is increased still further, the absorption again increases rapidly until three absorption discontinuities for the L shell are reached. At still longer wavelengths there are five absorption "edges" associated with the M shell, and seven with the N shell.

The photoelectric absorption of high-energy photons is further confirmation of Planck's quantum hypothesis. The maximum kinetic energies for the photoelectrons from any shell are predicted by the

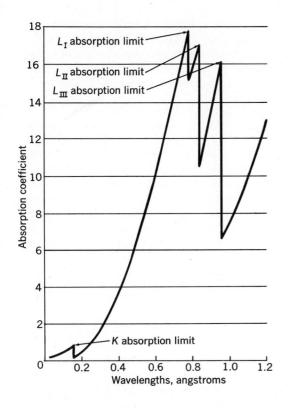

FIGURE 49.8
How the photoelectric absorption coefficient varies with wavelength, in this case for lead.

Einstein relation (Eq. 47.2): (kinetic energy)$_{max}$ = $h\nu$ − $\mathcal{W}$, where $\mathcal{W}$ is now the energy required to liberate an electron from the shell in question.

49.5 Pair Production and the Positron

When photons with energies greater than 1.02 MeV pass through matter, a third absorption process, called *pair production,* takes place. In this process the photon interacts with the nucleus of the atom and is transformed into two particles, an *electron* and a *positron*. A *positron* is a particle identical with an electron, except that it bears a positive charge. The higher the energy of a photon, the more probable pair production becomes. It requires a minimum energy of 1.02 MeV to provide the mass of the electron and the positron. The positron and electron share whatever energy is left over from the energy of the incident photon. Thus, if pairs are produced by a 4.02-MeV photon, the electron and positron each have 1.5 MeV of kinetic energy.

Positrons exist for a very short time. As they move through matter, they lose energy rapidly. As soon as they are stopped, an electron and a positron interact to annihilate each other. Two electron masses vanish, and 1.02 MeV of energy is released. This usually appears in the form of two 0.51-MeV photons moving in opposite directions. The two photons are formed rather than a single 1.02-MeV photon because it is not possible to conserve both energy and momentum for a single photon (unless some additional particle is involved). Both in pair production and in pair annihilation the particle properties of photons are in evidence.

49.6 De Broglie's Hypothesis

In 1924 de Broglie suggested that if electromagnetic waves showed particle properties, it was possible that particles would exhibit wave properties. His principal argument was based on the fact that nature reveals many symmetries. Another possible symmetry was that both electromagnetic radiation and classical particles have both particle and wave properties. If particles have wave properties, how can one predict the wavelengths? Here de Broglie argued that the Compton effect showed that photons had momentum $h\nu/c$, or simply h/λ. Hence one should assign a wavelength $\lambda = h/(\text{momentum})$ to photons, and perhaps to particles as well. For a particle of mass m and velocity v, the resulting *de Broglie wavelength* is

$$\lambda = \frac{h}{mv} \qquad\qquad \textbf{49.8}$$

whether the particle be an airplane or an electron. For macroscopic bodies this wavelength is so tiny that we have no practical means of measuring it. However, for electrons and other atomic particles, wavelengths of measurable magnitude are available. Measurements on such particles confirm the de Broglie hypothesis.

   Example   What is the de Broglie wavelength of an electron traveling at a speed of 10^7 m/sec? Through what potential difference must an electron fall to achieve this speed?

$$\lambda = \frac{h}{mv} = \frac{6.63 \times 10^{-34} \text{ joule-sec}}{9.1 \times 10^{-31} \text{ kg} \times 10^7 \text{ m/sec}}$$
$$= 7 \times 10^{-11} \text{ m} = 0.7 \text{ Å}$$
$$Ve = \frac{1}{2}mv^2$$
$$V \times 1.60 \times 10^{-19} \text{ coulomb} = \frac{1}{2} \times 9.1 \times 10^{-31} \times 10^{14} \text{ joule}$$
$$V = 280 \text{ joules/coulomb} = 280 \text{ volts}$$

49.7 Wave Properties of Electrons

The first experimental confirmation of de Broglie's hypothesis was made by Davisson and Germer in 1927. They bombarded a single crystal of nickel with a narrow pencil of low-voltage electrons incident perpendicular to the crystal face, and determined the intensity of the "reflected" electrons as a function of the angle at which they bounced off the crystal. There were striking maxima and mimima in this angular distribution which could be quantitatively explained if the electrons had the wavelengths predicted by Eq. (49.8).

An entirely different experiment by G. P. Thomson also supported the de Broglie hypothesis and emphasized the similarity between electrons and X rays of the same wavelength. If a pencil of monochromatic X rays passes through a *powdered* crystalline substance placed at C in Figure 49.1, the X rays produce a diffraction pattern on the photographic plate. This pattern consists of a series of concentric circular fringes produced by interference of the scattered X rays (Fig. 49.9a). If a stream of electrons, all of the same velocity, passes through a thin film of metal, a similar set of rings is produced (Fig. 49.9b). In both cases one can compute the positions of the observed fringes on the assumption that the incident beams consist of waves of appropriate wavelength—for the electrons, the de Broglie wavelength $\lambda = h/mv$.

(a)

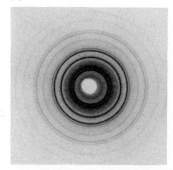

(b)

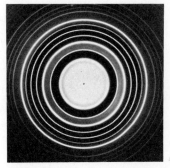

< 49.8 The Electron Microscope

The resolving power of an optical microscope is limited by the wavelength of the light used. In order that two neighboring particles be separable, light of very short wavelength must be used if the particles are very close together. Unfortunately we do not have lenses which can focus X rays and thereby permit us to build an X-ray microscope. However, when electrons are accelerated through a potential difference in the neighborhood of 10^5 volts, their wavelengths are only a few hundredths of an angstrom. With such wavelengths, particles that are as close as 10^{-9} m can be separated and photographed by an electron microscope. The electrons can be controlled and focused by electric and magnetic fields.

FIGURE 49.9
(*a*) X-ray diffraction pattern of aluminum. (*b*) Electron diffraction pattern of a thin film of cesium iodide.

Questions

1. What evidence exists to show the wave nature of X rays?

2. What do we mean when we say that X rays are not really reflected by a rock-salt crystal? If the process is not reflection, what is it?

3. Is it possible for a Compton recoil electron to have a velocity component opposite that of the incident photon? Is it possible for a Compton scattered photon to have a velocity component opposite that of the incident photon? Explain.

4. In terms of the discussion of Sec. 48.8, explain why there are three absorption edges for the L shell and five for the M shell. An additional fact you need to know is that the energy of a state depends on n, l, and j, but not on m_j (unless a magnetic or electric field is applied).

Problems

1. The grating space of calcite is 3.04 Å. Find the wavelength for which the first-order Bragg reflection occurs at 14.7°, that is, when the incident and emergent radiations are inclined 14.7° with respect to the surface of the calcite. What is the angle for second-order reflection?   *Ans.* 1.54 Å (Cu $K\alpha$ radiation); 30.5°

2. Find the angle for first-order Bragg reflection of Mo $K\alpha$ radiation (0.707 Å) from a calcite crystal with a grating space of 3.04 Å. What is the angle for second-order reflection?

3. Calculate the grating space of KBr, which has a molecular weight of 119 and a density of 2,750 kg/m³. *Ans.* 3.30 Å

4. Find the grating space of a KCl crystal which has the same crystal structure as NaCl. The density of KCl is 1,980 kg/m³, and the atomic weights of K and Cl are 39.1 and 35.5, respectively.

5. X rays of wavelength 0.085 Å are scattered by carbon. At what angle will the Compton scattered photons have a wavelength of 0.09 Å? *Ans.* 37.5°

6. Potassium iodide (KI) crystallizes as a cubic crystal of density 3,130 kg/m³ and structure similar to that of NaCl. Find the grating space of the KI crystal.

7. What is the longest wavelength which a photon can have and still transfer one-half its initial energy to a Compton recoil electron? *Ans.* 0.0485 Å

8. Find the speed and energy of a proton which has a de Broglie wavelength of 2 Å.

9. Fifty per cent of a homogeneous beam of X rays is absorbed by an aluminum sheet 0.5 cm thick. What percentage of the beam will pass through 1 cm of Al? Through 2 cm? Through 3 cm? *Ans.* 25, 6.25, and 1.56 per cent

10. An X-ray beam is studied by means of copper plates. It is found that 0.05 cm of Cu passes 50 per cent of the beam, 0.1 cm passes 30 per cent, and 0.2 cm passes 10 per cent. Explain in detail how this result can be reconciled with the results of Prob. 9.

11. Find the momentum and de Broglie wavelength of an electron in the first Bohr orbit of hydrogen. How does the de Broglie wavelength compare with the circumference of the orbit? *Ans.* 2.0×10^{-24} kg-m/sec; 3.31×10^{-10} m; same

12. Find the de Broglie wavelength associated with an electron traveling at a speed of 2×10^6 m/sec.

13. Find the de Broglie wavelength associated with electrons of energies of 1 eV and 1 keV. With neutrons of energies 0.01 eV and 10 eV.
Ans. 12.3 Å; 0.388 Å; 2.86 Å; 0.906 Å

14. Find the de Broglie wavelength of a 2-MeV proton.

15. If the K, L, and M energy levels of platinum lie at roughly 78, 12, and 3 keV, respectively, compute the approximate wavelengths of the $K\alpha$ and $K\beta$ lines. What minimum potential difference across an X-ray tube is required to excite these lines? At approximately what wavelength is the K absorption edge? The three L edges?
Ans. 0.19 Å; 0.17 Å; 78 kV; 0.16 Å; 1 Å

16. Prove that if a photon is scattered through an angle greater than 60° by a free electron, it cannot produce an electron-positron pair after the scattering event, regardless of the initial energy of the photon.

17. Prove that the de Broglie wavelength of an electron cannot exceed the short-wavelength limit of the X-ray photons which could be produced by this electron. *Hint:* $Ve = (m - m_0)c^2$.

CHAPTER 50   *In Chap. 48 we examined the structure and properties of individual atoms.   Atoms join together to form molecules and other assemblages with unique properties.   In earlier chapters we discussed many characteristics of solids and liquids—elastic constants, indices of refraction, thermal and electrical conductivities, and densities—as unrelated phenomena and without any consideration of the contributions of individual atoms to these properties.   In molecular and solid-state physics we seek to understand properties of gases, liquids, and solids in terms of their structure and organization as societies of atoms.   In recent years solid-state physics has been an area of extraordinary activity.   Advances have come rapidly, enlarging our understanding of the behavior of materials.   Research has brought a host of new and improved materials—high-temperature alloys for jet engines; superior phosphors for fluorescent lights and television screens; new materials for construction and for magnets; transistors replacing vacuum tubes; molecular circuits replacing large, heavy, unreliable circuit elements in specialized fields.*

Molecules and Solids

50.1 Gaseous Molecules

What forces hold simple diatomic molecules together?   There is no single answer to this question; there are several kinds of binding, of which we consider two.

Ionic Binding.   Some molecules are composed of a positive ion bound to a negative ion by Coulomb electrostatic attraction.   An example is potassium chloride (KCl), in which a potassium atom surrenders its outer (or valence) electron to a chlorine atom.   The K^+ ion and the Cl^- ion are held together by *ionic* binding.

Covalent Binding.   Many gas molecules are composed of two identical atoms; examples are the hydrogen, oxygen, nitrogen, and chlorine molecules.   Here we can scarcely invoke the concept of ionic binding, since there is no reason for one of two identical atoms to become positive, and the other negative.   The search for an alternative mechanism ended with modern wave mechanics.   The development of the theory is beyond the scope of this book, but in a qualitative way it is possible to discuss some of the results.   In a hydrogen molecule (H_2) the binding comes about from the sharing of two electrons by two hydrogen atoms. This gives rise to an attractive force associated with the electron *exchange*. The occurrence of exchange forces is a strictly wave-mechanical phenomenon for which there is no classical analogue. The pair of electrons involved in the exchange must have oppositely directed spins (Sec. 48.6). If the spins of the two electrons are aligned, the atoms repel one another, and no molecule is formed. In a similar fashion the binding of oxygen and nitrogen diatomic molecules rises from the sharing of pairs of electrons between the atoms. Binding arising from this type of electron sharing is called *covalent,* or *homopolar.*

The extremes of ionic and covalent binding are reasonably well illustrated by potassium chloride and hydrogen molecules, respectively. However, there are many molecules for which the binding is intermediate between covalent and ionic binding. In these molecules the shared electrons are closer to one of the atoms much more of the time than to the other atom.

An important characteristic of any diatomic molecule is its *dissociation energy,* the energy required to break the molecule into its parts. This, in turn, is equal to the binding energy, the energy released when the two atoms are brought together to form the molecule. Typical binding energies of molecules are of the order of a few electron volts. For potassium chloride it is 4.4. eV, for sodium chloride 4.24 eV, and for hydrogen 4.48 eV.

For any pair of atoms there exists an equilibrium interatomic distance at which the energy is minimum (Fig. 50.1). If the two atoms are slightly farther apart, a net restoring force draws them closer. On the other hand, if the atoms approach more closely than the equilibrium distance R_0, strong forces drive them apart.

50.2 The Pauli Exclusion Principle

If the only forces between two atoms were attractive, the atoms would eventually coalesce. Actually, as atoms approach one another, strong repulsive forces arise. Classically, one imagines the atoms to be solid spheres which cannot penetrate one another. However, the atom of modern physics has a tiny nucleus with an electron cloud about it. In terms of this picture we explain the fact that the atoms occupy a well-defined volume in terms of the Pauli exclusion principle (Sec. 48.8). If

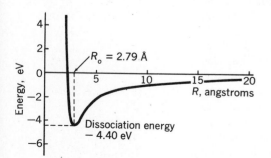

FIGURE 50.1

Energy of a KCl molecule as it varies with the separation of the K^+ and Cl^- ions.

we try to bring a second atom so close that its electrons begin to penetrate the occupied shells of the first atom, the Pauli exclusion principle requires that some of the electrons go to higher energy states. This requires energy and gives rise to a repulsive force.

50.3 Molecular Spectra

In Chap. 48 we considered the spectra emitted by electron transition in individual atoms. Molecules, composed of two or more atoms, also have spectra. Typically, molecular spectra are considerably more complex than atomic spectra, with radiation emitted in three spectral ranges corresponding to different kinds of transitions between molecular energy states. Starting with the longest wavelength region, we explain these spectra as follows:

Rotational Spectra. A simple diatomic molecule can be visualized as a dumbbell (Sec. 20.6). If such a molecule is put into rotation, classically we would expect it to emit radiation of the same frequency as the rotation. However, quantum mechanics limits the rotational energy levels (Fig. 50.2) to those given by the relation

$$E_J = \frac{h^2}{8\pi^2 I} J(J+1) \qquad\qquad \textbf{50.1}$$

where I is the moment of inertia of the molecule about its center of mass, h is Planck's constant, and J is the rotational quantum number, which takes on values 0, 1, 2, 3, ... Radiative transitions occur only when J increases or decreases by 1 ($\Delta J = \pm 1$). The rotational energy levels are spaced in such a way that the rotational lines consist of a fundamental frequency and integral multiples of that frequency, all in the far infrared region.

Vibration-Rotation Spectra. A diatomic molecule is less analogous to a rigid dumbbell than it is to two masses connected by a strong spring. Such masses can perform vibrations relative to one another under the elastic forces which bind them. The frequencies associated with such vibrations are typically much higher than those associated with pure rotation. Consequently, the vibrational spectra appear in the nearer infrared region. Any time its vibrational spectrum is excited, a molecule has much more than enough energy for the rotational spectra; thus we ordinarily observe rotational motion superimposed on the vibrational.

Electronic Spectra. At still higher frequencies we find evidences of transitions of electrons, associated now with the molecule, between allowed quantum states. Since the energies involved are much greater than those associated with either vibration or rotation, electron excitation is generally accompanied by vibrational and rotational excitation. For any single electron state there are many vibrational and rotational states in which the molecule may exist. Consequently, each type of transition between electron energy states produces a large number of closely spaced lines. Such spectra, called *molecular bands* (Fig. 50.3), are often found in the visible and ultraviolet regions.

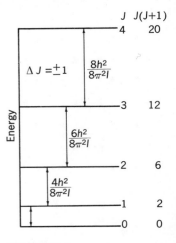

FIGURE 50.2

Lowest rotational levels of a diatomic molecule of moment of inertia I.

FIGURE 50.3

Bands in the spectrum of nitrogen.

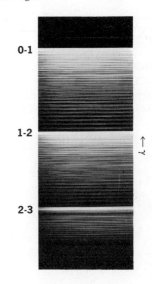

(a)

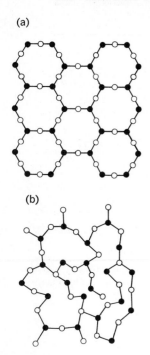

(b)

FIGURE 50.4

Comparison of the lattices (two dimensions only) of (a) a crystal, and (b) a glass.

FIGURE 50.5

NaCl crystal; the Na⁺ ions (dark) have an effective radius 0.525 that of the Cl⁻ ions (light).

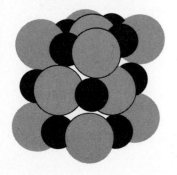

50.4 Amorphous and Crystalline Solids

As we saw in Sec. 21.1, at a sufficiently low temperature the attractive forces between gas molecules typically become great enough for liquefaction to occur; upon further cooling fluid properties disappear, and eventually there remains a block of substance which maintains both its shape and its volume. Such a mass is commonly known as a *solid,* although some scientists prefer to reserve this term for what we shall call a *crystalline solid.* Of a piece of glass, a bar of gold, and a strip of wood, only the gold qualifies as a crystalline solid. The distinction is made on the basis of the kind of order which exists in the material, i.e., on the type of geometrical arrangement in which the atoms fall. By means of X rays we can often locate the relative positions of various kinds of atoms in a material. Suppose for a moment that we could actually see the individual atoms in a piece of glass. If we locate a silicon atom and examine its neighbors, we find that they are not distributed in a random fashion. There is a definite geometrical order. However, if we look at other silicon atoms we find that their neighbors form a somewhat different pattern. For glass there is no orderly arrangement which persists throughout the material; there is *short-range order* (Fig. 50.4), but not *long-range order.* A material which exhibits short-range order and retains its shape is said to be an *amorphous solid,* or sometimes a supercooled liquid.

The geometrical arrangement of atoms in any one region of a crystalline solid is the same as in any other region. The ordering extends in uninterrupted fashion over distances of thousands of atomic diameters. For crystalline solids there exist 14 different possible arrays for three-dimensional lattices. The structure of a given crystal, including the locations of specific kinds of atoms within the lattice, can be studied by X-ray diffraction.

There are many examples of the same kinds of atoms arranging themselves in more than one kind of crystal lattice. In these cases the properties of the solid depend on the crystal structure. This is well illustrated by carbon, which forms crystals both in the diamond lattice and in the graphite lattice. Graphite is opaque and soft, rubbing off on paper, while diamond is translucent and hard enough to scratch glass. Carbon forms a hexagonal lattice in graphite and a type of cubic structure in diamond.

50.5 Crystal Binding

The forces of attraction which hold the atoms of a solid in their regular geometrical array determine not only the type of crystal lattice which is formed, but also other physical properties of the material such as elastic moduli, optical constants, and conductivities, both electrical and thermal. The origin of these forces differs from crystal to crystal; among the many kinds are the following:

Ionic Binding. An ionic crystal is composed of positive and negative ions. For example, a crystal of sodium chloride (NaCl) consists of a regular array of Na⁺ and Cl⁻ ions (Figs. 50.5 and 49.3). The binding forces, which come essentially from the Coulomb attraction between these charged ions, are relatively large. Once a molecule of NaCl becomes part of the crystal, it is no longer possible to identify a particular chlorine ion as belonging to a particular sodium ion. Rather, each ion has a number of equidistant neighbors. Ordinarily, ionic crystals are relatively transparent to visible and ultraviolet light, but show strong absorption in the infrared. At low temperatures they are excellent electrical and thermal insulators; at high temperatures they become electrical conductors by virtue of the motion of ions through the crystal. A crystal formed from ions exhibits *ionic* or *heteropolar* binding.

Covalent Binding. In covalent bonds electrons are exchanged between atoms; the average charge density between the atoms may be relatively high. Examples of crystals exhibiting covalent binding are germanium, silicon, and diamond. In a diamond crystal a single carbon atom shares electrons with four other carbon atoms at alternate corners of a cube. At low temperature, covalent crystals are ordinarily hard and often brittle and have high electrical resistance. As the temperature is increased, there is a marked decrease in resistance. Practical semiconductors (Sec. 50.10) are based on covalent crystals.

Metallic Binding. In metals the valence electrons are not tied to any particular atom or pair of atoms, but are free to wander through the crystal. A metallic crystal may be thought of as an array of closely packed positive ions immersed in a sea of uniformly distributed electrons. This type of binding leads to high electrical and thermal conductivity and to the optical and mechanical properties characteristic of metals.

Hydrogen Binding. The hydrogen atom has a single electron, so one might expect it to form a bond with only one other atom. However, frequently hydrogen forms a strong bond between two atoms. We may think of this bond as primarily ionic in character, since it is formed only with strongly electronegative atoms. The hydrogen atom loses or transfers its electron to one of these atoms, and the proton binds two negative ions, nestling between these very much larger ions. Only hydrogen forms such bonds; no other ion has the very small size of the proton—so small that there are only two nearest neighbors. The hydrogen bond occurs in ice $(H_2O)_n$, solid hydrogen fluoride, and a wide variety of proteins and other organic compounds. Therefore, it is of great interest in biophysics and biochemistry.

Molecular Binding. Atoms of argon, helium, and other inert gases are bound in the solid phase by relatively weak electrostatic forces, known as *van der Waals' forces.* Because of the weakness of these forces, the binding energies are low. The crystals have low melting points and are highly compressible and mechanically weak.

50.6 Thermal Properties of Solids

Quantum mechanics predicts (and experiment confirms) that at $0°K$ there still exists in an atom some vibrational energy, known as the *zero-point energy.* At any higher temperature the energy associated with atomic vibrations is greater. The atoms of a solid do not vibrate independently, since they are joined to one another by elastic forces. The motion of any one atom is influenced by, and in turn influences, the motion of its neighbors. Indeed, the vibration of any individual atom can be thought of as a portion of a wave moving through the crystal. In the crystal only those waves exist which satisfy the boundary conditions at the surface of the material. Calculations of the allowed frequencies show that they are great in number for a solid which contains billions of atoms. Nevertheless, it has been possible to confirm by experiment many of the predictions of the theory.

We have seen that electromagnetic waves come in photons of energy $h\nu$. Similarly, vibrational waves in crystals are quantized, with the minimum energy associated with a frequency given by the same relation $h\nu$. The quanta of vibrational waves are called *phonons*. Near $0°K$ only low-energy phonons are present; as the temperature is raised, phonons of higher frequency come into existence. When we heat a crystal, we excite more phonons. These lattice vibrations make by far the largest contribution to the specific heat, except near $0°K$, where the small contribution to the specific heat from the electrons of the crystal must be taken into account.

The transfer of heat by conduction from one point to another in a solid has been discussed phenomenologically in Sec. 22.2. For the solid as a geometrical assembly of atoms, we can calculate the thermal conductivity in terms of lattice vibrations which transfer energy from atom to atom as waves progress through the crystal. When we raise the temperature in one region of the crystal, phonon waves spreading out from this region of increased amplitude augment the amplitudes at points some distance away. This is equivalent to our phenomenological observation that heat is transferred from one region to another. We can compute the thermal conductivities of crystals with considerable accuracy by the phonon description so long as the crystals are not metallic. We do not get valid predictions for metallic conductors because in metals the primary conduction of heat is by free electrons.

50.7 Imperfections in Crystals

A perfect single crystal is one in which a pattern is repeated without variation over the entire volume. Such a crystal is an idealization; all crystals have *imperfections*. Here the term *imperfection* does not imply anything undesirable. For example, we make steel from iron by deliberately introducing imperfections (see also Sec. 50.10). Many properties of solids—specific heat, thermal conductivity, thermal expansion, and density, for example—are essentially the same for perfect crystals and for those with moderate impurities. On the other hand, some properties of great engineering significance are sensitive to relatively minute imperfections; among these are mechanical strength, resistance to rust, corrosion, and mechanical abrasion, and electrical conductivity in semiconductors. Among the common types of crystal imperfections are the following:

Substitutional Impurities.   No crystal is ever chemically pure.   A substitutional impurity is one in which a foreign atom occupies the site of and plays the role of one of the atoms of the host crystal.   For example, in a *p*-type semiconductor an aluminum atom may replace a germanium atom in the crystal.   If the impurity atom has roughly the same size as the host atom, the regularity of the crystal at the lattice site is disturbed only slightly, and the mechanical properties of the crystal are unchanged.   The change in electrical properties is associated primarily with the fact that the impurity atom brings an electron configuration different from that of a host atom.   The impurity atom also introduces additional electron energy levels into the crystal.   These may play important roles in changing the color and radiation-absorption properties of the crystal.

Interstitials and Vacancies.   A defect in which an atom lies in a crystal lattice at a site which is not ordinarily occupied by atoms is known as an *interstitial* (Fig. 50.6) if the atom is simply a misplaced one of the host material, or as an *interstitial impurity* if it is an impurity atom.   A defect in which a lattice site normally occupied by an atom is unoccupied is called a *vacancy*.   Interstitial atoms and vacancies behave much like chemical impurities in that they too bring new energy levels into the crystal.   They also scatter electrons moving through the crystal and increase the resistivity.

Dislocations.   A crystal with no chemical impurities may contain a region, known as a *dislocation,* in which the atoms are not arranged in the perfect lattice structure.   Dislocations, which play an important role in determining the strength of ductile materials, are produced during solidification from the liquid phase.   Ordinarily the crystal does not grow at a single point as the liquid solidifies.   Rather there are many nuclei from which grow a collection of small crystals oriented more or less at random.   The resulting solid is said to be *polycrystalline*.   At the *grain boundaries* of the small crystals the matching of the crystal pattern is not perfect.   The result is a series of dislocations.

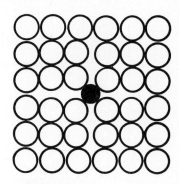

FIGURE 50.6

The imperfection is *interstitial* if it is of the host material, or an *interstitial impurity* if it is an impurity atom.

50.8 Energy Bands in Solids

When a group of atoms is brought together to form a solid, the energy levels associated with each atom undergo shifts, as a result of the presence of the neighboring atoms, which change the potential energy of an electron at any point.   In particular, the potential energies of the outer (or valence) electrons are shifted significantly.   Quantum mechanics reveals that, as a group of atoms is assembled to form a solid, the energy levels which were sharp for individual atoms become broadened to become *energy bands*.   The broadening is particularly great for the higher energy levels (Fig. 50.7).

In a crystal at $0°K$ the individual atoms are as near to rest as they can ever be, and complications associated with thermal vibrations are minimized.   Every electron is in its lowest possible energy state, so the lowest energy levels are filled, and no electron is in an excited state.   Now we can distinguish between metallic conductors, semicon-

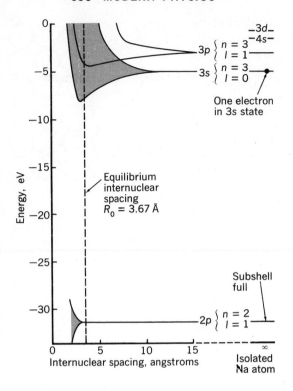

FIGURE 50.7

Energy levels are relatively sharp for gaseous sodium atoms, but when sodium atoms crystallize to form a metal, the presence of other atoms results in a broadening and overlapping of the higher energy levels.

ductors, and insulators by the situations which pertain in the highest energy band as follows:

Metallic Conductors. If the energy-level characteristics of the least tightly bound electrons are such that the energy state permits electrons to move freely about the potential hills, the material is a *metallic conductor.* The energy band contains some electrons but is not completely filled (Fig. 50.8a). An electric field can produce a flow of these electrons, and the material is an excellent electrical conductor at all temperatures.

Semiconductors. If the energy band associated with the outer electrons is completely filled, but within a small energy range there is another band in which electrons could exist and move through the crystal, the material is a good insulator at $0°K$ (Fig. 50.8b). However, as the temperature is raised, thermal agitation gives some electrons enough energy to shift to the higher band. The electrons so excited serve as *conduction electrons.* Further, the *holes* left by the electrons when they move to the higher band also serve as charge carriers. Such an arrangement of energy levels is characteristic of semiconductors, which are insulators at $0°K$ but become poor conductors at somewhat higher temperature. Semiconductors become steadily better conductors as the temperature is raised, because more electrons are transferred to the conduction band. Each electron raised to the conduction band leaves a vacancy in the band below.

Although electrons and holes are separated on an energy diagram, in the crystal itself they exist in the same space. A dynamic equilibrium is achieved between the thermal production of holes and conduction electrons and the destruction of these carrier pairs by electrons dropping to the lower energy state (accessible because of the holes).

Insulators. If the gap between the highest filled band and the next permitted band is large (Fig. 50.8c), modest temperatures are not sufficient to lift electrons to the conduction bands. Electrons in the filled bands are not free, and the material serves as an excellent insulator. Of course, if the temperature is raised sufficiently high, electrons can be excited to conduction levels, so no material is an insulator at extremely high temperatures. However, if the energy gap is reasonably large, practically no electrons are lifted to the conduction band at room temperature.

50.9 The Fermi Level in a Metal

The Pauli exclusion principle requires that free electrons in a metal have a broad range of kinetic energies. The most energetic electrons have a kinetic energy of the order of a few electron volts. The result of calculations due to Fermi is a prediction of the energy distribution of the electrons at $0°K$ similar to that of Figure 50.9. The energy $\mathfrak{W}_f$, the highest state occupied by electrons at $0°K$, is called the *Fermi energy* for the electrons. If the temperature is increased, a few electrons are raised to somewhat higher energies, leaving vacancies in the lower energy levels. Even when the temperature is brought up to $300°K$, the average kinetic energy of the electrons is raised very little; only a small fraction of the heat supplied to warm a metal goes into increasing the kinetic energy of the electrons.

FIGURE 50.8
Comparison of energy bands of (*a*) a metallic conductor, (*b*) a semiconductor, and (*c*) an insulator. At $0°K$ electrons occupy all states indicated in black; energy states in grey are allowed. Some occupied states (such as K and L levels) are at too low an energy level to show on this figure.

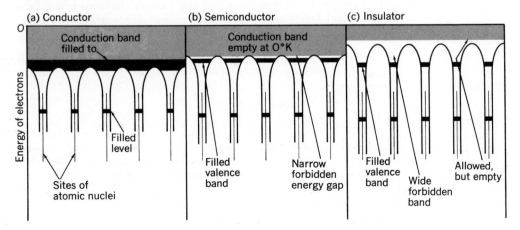

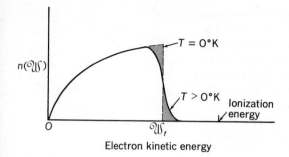

FIGURE 50.9

Fermi distribution showing the relative number of conduction electrons having a given kinetic energy.

In order to remove one of the least tightly bound electrons from a metal at $0°$K, the electron must be supplied enough energy to take it from the Fermi level to the potential just outside the metal (Fig. 50.10). In Sec. 47.2 we found evidence for this statement in the photoelectric effect. We identify the energy $\mathcal{W}_{min}$ in Figure 50.10 as the minimum required by a photon to eject a photoelectron from the Fermi level. Similarly in order to achieve thermionic emission (Sec. 45.1), the temperature must be raised high enough so that electrons escape via thermal excitation.

The Fermi level of a material is of great importance. When two isolated materials are placed in contact, electrons move from the one in which the Fermi level is greater to the other. This lowers the Fermi level in the first and raises it in the second. Charges flow until the Fermi levels become equal in the two materials. If the materials are separated, they bear equal and opposite charges (Sec. 33.2). In general, *the Fermi level in any material at any temperature is defined as the energy level for which there is exactly a 50 per cent probability that an electron occupies any available state at that energy.*

50.10 Semiconductors

Crystals of pure germanium are well known as a semiconductor material. Each atom of germanium has four valence electrons which form four covalent bonds with neighboring atoms. This structure has the

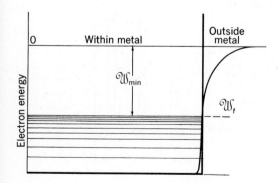

FIGURE 50.10

Energy-level diagram of conduction electrons in metal shows that levels are filled up to Fermi level $\mathcal{W}_f$ at $0°$K, but additional energy $\mathcal{W}_{min}$ is needed to remove an electron. The solid curve at right is the approximate potential energy of an electron just outside the surface of the metal.

semiconductor arrangement of energy states, a completely filled energy band separated from an empty higher-lying conduction level by a small energy gap. Such a crystal is called an *intrinsic semiconductor*.

At any temperature above 0°K a few electrons in the semiconductor are thermally excited to the conduction band. The minimum energy required to move an electron from one of the covalent bonds into the conduction band is called the *energy gap E_g*. For silicon E_g is 1.09 eV; for germanium, 0.72 eV. These are small enough so that at room temperature a significant number of electrons are excited to the conduction band. The resulting holes are available for conduction in the lower band. In this case the Fermi level (Fig. 50.11) is located midway between the top of the valence band and the bottom of the conduction band.

Now consider the effects of adding a small amount of arsenic to a pure germanium crystal. Addition of foreign atoms to an intrinsic semiconductor produces an *impurity semiconductor* (or *extrinsic* or *doped* semiconductor). Most of the important applications of semiconductors call for doped crystals, in which the electrical properties are drastically changed by the impurity atoms. Arsenic impurity atoms occupy sites in the crystal normally filled by germanium atoms (Fig. 50.12a). Each arsenic atom brings a total of five valence electrons, of which four are used in forming covalent bonds with the four nearest germanium neighbors. The fifth electron finds no convenient neighbor with which to form a bond and is very loosely tied to the arsenic ion, even at 0°K. Only a small amount of energy is needed to free this electron and permit it to wander about in the lattice. Room temperature is enough to supply this energy. Almost every arsenic atom introduced into the crystal provides one electron which is available for conduction. The arsenic atoms are called *donors,* since each atom donates an electron to the crystal. An intrinsic semicon-

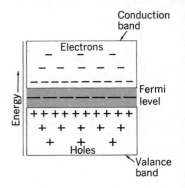

FIGURE 50.11

Some electrons in a semiconductor are excited to the conduction band at room temperature, leaving, in the valence band, vacancies or "holes" which are also available for conduction. Energies in gray are not allowed.

FIGURE 50.12

(*a*) An arsenic atom donates five electrons to a germanium crystal. Four are required to complete the covalent bands with neighboring germanium atoms; the fifth is relatively free and is many lattice distances away from the As nucleus most of the time. (*b*) An indium acceptor atom in a germanium crystal provides only three of four valence electrons needed to complete the covalent bonds. Much of the time, an electron from some other part of the crystal is captured by the indium atom, leaving a hole elsewhere in the crystal.

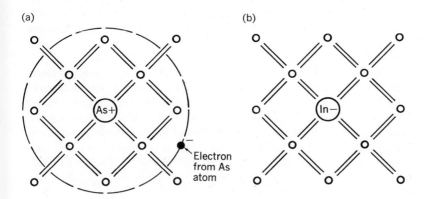

(a)   (b)

Electron from As atom

ductor doped with a donor impurity is called an n-type semiconductor (n stands for negative), because free negative charges have been added. Arsenic is by no means the only donor impurity for n-type semiconductors. Other elements from the same group of the periodic table (such as phosphorus and antimony) are good donor impurities.

Next consider what happens when we add to a germanium crystal atoms of valence 3, such as indium, gallium, aluminum, or boron. Each indium atom (Fig. 50.12b) brings only three electrons to form the four covalent bonds expected from each atom in the germanium crystal. Each indium atom results in a site at which one electron is missing from the four bonds. Such site readily captures a wandering electron and utilizes it to complete the bonding structure. Atoms of valence-3 elements are called *acceptor* impurities. They form p-type semiconductors, since in a crystal with such impurities there are sites at which an electron is missing, and there are positive *holes* available for conduction.

Adding impurity atoms to an intrinsic semiconductor changes the position of the Fermi level. If a donor impurity is added, the semiconductor becomes n-type, since it has more conduction electrons than holes. This raises the Fermi level so that it lies above that of the intrinsic semiconductor. On the other hand, adding acceptor impurities decreases the number of conduction electrons. The center of gravity of the electron-hole system is reduced, and the Fermi level lies lower.

50.11 p-n Junctions

If a region of n-type material is in intimate contact with a region of p-type material, they form a p-n junction. One cannot form such a junction by pressing n-type material against p-type material, since the act of pressing would bring such a tremendous concentration of impurities and imperfections to the interface that the junction would not have the required properties. One way of making a p-n junction is to melt an indium pellet which has been placed on top of an n-type germanium crystal. Where the germanium has been saturated with molten indium, p-type material is produced. A p-n junction is formed at the interface between the indium-saturated p region and the original n material.

When two isolated materials of different Fermi levels are in intimate electrical contact, the Fermi levels shift to the same intermediate energy. As long as the Fermi level is lower in one material than in another, electrons drift from the material with the higher level until equilibrium is established when the Fermi levels of both materials are identical. This does not mean that there is no charge transfer across the junction, but rather that the charge transfers in both directions are equal. At the junction in equilibrium there are still many more electrons in the conduction band in the n material at the right of Figure 50.13 than in the p material at the left; consequently, there is an electron current $I_{n \to p}$ associated with the diffusion of these electrons.

FIGURE 50.13

Electrons in a p-n junction in equilibrium diffuse from n-type material to p-type material at the same rate at which electrons move "downhill" in the reverse direction.

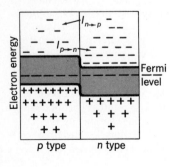

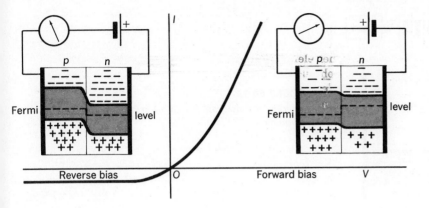

FIGURE 50.14
How current varies with bias potential difference in a *p-n* junction. The addition of bias voltage shifts the Fermi levels in the two semiconductor materials as shown.

At the same time there is an equal electron current $I_{p \to n}$ associated with the electrons which are moving down the "hill." This latter current has a magnitude which depends on the concentration of electrons in the *p*-type material and on the very low rate at which these charges diffuse toward the junction. Hence the current $I_{p \to n}$ has a *saturation* value which is ordinarily small. (The saturation current does not depend on the height of the potential hill any more than the water which goes over a waterfall depends on the height of the fall.) Holes are also exchanged across the boundary; their behavior is directly analogous to that of electrons. (For the sake of brevity we confine our discussion to electron flows.)

When we apply a potential difference across the *p-n* junction, making the *p* material positive relative to the *n* material, the hill down which the electrons slide is reduced. This has essentially no effect on the saturation current $I_{p \to n}$. However, many more electrons from the *n* material diffuse to the *p* materials, so $I_{n \to p}$ is greatly increased by this bias. The current in what is known as the *forward direction* rises rapidly with increasing forward bias (or potential difference), as shown in Figure 50.14. On the other hand, if we make the *n*-type material positive relative to the *p*-type, the hill is increased, and $I_{n \to p}$ is substantially reduced, while the current $I_{p \to n}$ remains essentially at the saturation value. Consequently, with negative or reverse bias there is a very small current essentially independent of bias. Thus a *p-n* junction acts as a rectifier—not quite a perfect one, since there is some current in the reverse direction for reverse bias, but nevertheless an effective one, since we get a substantial current in the forward direction for a modest potential difference and a very small reverse current for the same (magnitude) reverse bias.

50.12 The *n-p-n* Transistor

An extremely important electronic device which is capable of amplifying signals is the *n-p-n* junction transistor (Fig. 50.15). This device consists of a thin layer of weakly *p*-type material known as the *base*

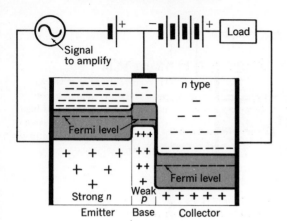

FIGURE 50.15
Energy-level diagram for an *n-p-n* transistor used as an amplifier.

sandwiched between strongly *n*-type material called the *emitter* and relatively weak *n*-type material which comprises the *collector*. Typically, the base is only of the order of a thousandth of an inch in thickness, and the entire transistor may occupy a volume of only a few thousandths of a cubic inch. The base must be sufficiently thin so that the probability of an electron combining with a hole within the base is small compared with the probability of the electron passing completely through the base. Essentially all electrons which leave the emitter pass through the base to the collector, so the electron current to the base is small compared with the electron current to the collector.

The emitter is operated at a small forward bias (~ 0.5 volt) relative to the base, while the collector is reverse-biased by a potential difference of several volts. These potential differences appear almost entirely at the junctions themselves, since both the *n* regions are relatively good conductors. In the emitter, thermal agitation provides a generous and continuous supply of conduction electrons, many of which reach the emitter-base interface and diffuse into and through the base. The electrons lost by the emitter are restored through the emitter electrode.

Since the emitter is forward-biased, a small change in emitter potential results in a substantial change in the electron current from emitter to base to collector and, hence, to a substantial change in the potential difference across the load. Thus a small voltage signal at the emitter leads to a larger change in the potential difference across the load, and the transistor operates as a voltage amplifier.

Among the major advantages of the transistor are its extremely small volume, the small potential differences it requires for operation, its extremely long life, and its ruggedness. There are disadvantages as well, among which is the fact that at sufficiently high temperatures there are enough free electrons in all parts of the transistor so that it fails to function properly.

Questions

1. Why do crystalline solids have sharp melting points while amorphous solids usually soften and melt over a broad temperature range?

2. Why should the disordered region at an edge dislocation be etched away much faster by an acid than a perfectly ordered region?

3. How does the number of conduction electrons compare with the number of holes in (*a*) an ideal intrinsic semiconductor, (*b*) a *p*-type semiconductor, and (*c*) an *n*-type semiconductor? Explain.

4. Why do transistors malfunction or fail if the temperature becomes too great?

5. Draw a *p-n-p* transistor circuit analogous to the *n-p-n* transistor circuit of Figure 50.15. Explain the operation of the *p-n-p* transistor, in which the bias voltages are opposite those of the *n-p-n* transistor.

Problems

1. An experiment on the threshold wavelength for photoelectric emission from tungsten yields the value 270 mμ. Find the energy of the Fermi surface in joules and in electron volts. Compute the maximum energy of photoelectrons ejected by photons of $\lambda = 200$ mμ in both joules and electron volts.
$\qquad$ *Ans.* -7.37×10^{-19} joule; -4.61 eV; 2.57×10^{-19} joule; 1.61 eV

2. The photocurrent of a cell can be cut to zero by a minimum retarding potential of 2 volts when monochromatic light of 200 mμ is incident. (*a*) What is the energy of the Fermi surface? (*b*) What is the maximum kinetic energy of photoelectrons for light of 250 mμ wavelength? (*c*) What is the longest wavelength which can produce photoemission?

3. The moment of inertia of a H_2 molecule in its ground state is about 4.55×10^{-48} kg-m^2. Find the lowest two excited rotational levels for the H_2 molecule and the wavelengths of the first (longest λ) two lines of the rotational spectrum.
$\qquad$ *Ans.* 2.46 and 7.38×10^{-21} joule; 81 and 40.5 μ

4. The moment of inertia of an HCl molecule is about 2.72×10^{-47} kg-m^2. Find the energies of the first two excited states relative to the ground state and the wavelengths of the first (longest λ) two lines of the rotational spectrum.

5. In a NaCl crystal the ions are 2.81 Å from their nearest neighbors. Assuming that each ion is attracted only by the nearest ion in the adjacent layer, calculate the stress (force per unit area) required to pull the crystal apart. Do you expect your answer to be larger or smaller than an experimental determination? Why?
$\qquad$ *Ans.* 3.7×10^{10} newton/m^2; larger; next nearest neighbors repel

6. In a potassium chloride crystal the ions are 3.14 Å apart. Assuming that each ion is attracted only by the nearest ion in the adjacent layer, find the stress (force per unit area) required to pull the crystal apart. Why is the answer smaller than for NaCl (Prob. 5)?

7. Find the average volume occupied by (*a*) a copper atom in a copper bar of density 8,930 kg/m^3, (*b*) an osmium atom in a crystal of osmium, the densest of the metals at 22,500 kg/m^3, and (*c*) a lithium atom in the least dense of metallic crystals at 530 kg/m^3.
$\qquad$ *Ans.* 11.8×10^{-30} m^3; 14×10^{-30} m^3; 21.6×10^{-30} m^3

CHAPTER 51 *The nuclei of atoms are small indeed, but they contain most of the particles which make up the atom and almost all the atomic mass. Since mass is a form of energy, it is in nuclei that most of the energy of atoms is concentrated. The possibility of utilizing some of this energy is a continuing challenge to physicists, and, quite apart from this incentive, the structure of the nucleus and its reactions are of great interest.*

Nuclei and Nuclear Energy

51.1 Building Blocks of Nuclei

In our discussion of atoms thus far, we have been concerned primarily with the energy states of the electrons which are bound to the nuclei by Coulomb attraction. We have attributed to each nucleus a charge Z and a mass number A which is the integer closest to the atomic weight of the nuclear species to which the atom belongs. In this chapter we consider the structure and properties of the nuclei.

The simplest of all nuclei is that of ordinary hydrogen, an atom of which we designate by $_1\text{H}^1$. Note that we shall indicate the atomic number Z of an atomic species with a subscript at the left, and the mass number A with a superscript at the right. The nucleus of the hydrogen atom, called the *proton* (p), bears a positive charge equal to the negative charge on the electron. It has a mass of 1.6725×10^{-27} kg (1,836 times the mass of the electron) or 1.00728 atomic mass units. *One unified atomic mass unit is* $\frac{1}{12}$ *the mass of a carbon-12* ($_6\text{C}^{12}$) *atom.* (A unified atomic mass unit is 0.0318 per cent smaller than the former atomic mass unit based on $\frac{1}{16}$ the mass of the $_8\text{O}^{16}$ atom which was generally used by physicists before the adoption of the carbon-12 scale.)

The proton has an intrinsic spin angular momentum such that the component in the direction of an applied external field is either $\frac{1}{2}h/2\pi$ or $-\frac{1}{2}h/2\pi$. Associated with this spin is a small magnetic moment (Sec. 39.5) of the order of magnitude one would expect from a spinning positive charge the size of the proton, which has a radius of about 10^{-15} m.

Since all nuclei have charges which are integral multiples of the protonic charge, it is reasonable and fruitful to assume that protons are fundamental building blocks of all nuclei. A nucleus of atomic number Z contains Z protons. However, for a typical nucleus only about one-half the mass can be attributed to the protons. It was suggested by Rutherford that there might be a second building block of roughly the same mass as the proton, but having no charge. This particle, the *neutron,* was discovered in 1932 (Sec. 52.2). The neutron mass is 1.00866 amu (atomic mass unit), slightly greater than that of the proton. It has the same intrinsic angular momentum, and, although chargeless, it does have a magnetic moment about 0.7 that of the proton and of opposite sign (as though negative charge were rotating). There is evidence that the neutron has a positive core with enough negative charge in its outer reaches to make it electrically neutral. A spinning neutral system of this kind would have a negative magnetic moment.

Protons and neutrons are the building blocks with which we may construct any nucleus. The number of protons in a nucleus determines the atomic number Z, which is the positive charge on the nucleus in elementary units and the number of electrons associated with the neutral atom. The sum of the number of protons and the number of neutrons is the *mass number A.* Protons and neutrons in a nucleus are collectively referred to as *nucleons.* The mass number A is then the number of nucleons in the nucleus. In the quantum-mechanical treatment of nuclear structure, the strong binding of nuclei can be explained in terms of the exchange of charge between nucleons. A nucleon may be a proton at one instant and become a neutron the next instant by transferring its charge to another nucleon, which transmutes from neutron to proton. In addition to mass, each nucleon contributes angular momentum and magnetic moment to the nucleus. However, these are vector quantities, and their resultant is usually not large—indeed, it is typically zero for nuclei with even numbers of both protons and neutrons. This can be understood by applying the Pauli exclusion principle to nuclei.

The chemical behavior of any atom is determined by its electronic configuration and hence by its atomic number Z. All atoms with $Z = 1$ are hydrogen, all with $Z = 8$ are oxygen, and all with $Z = 92$ are uranium. However, atoms with the same number of protons may have different numbers of neutrons. Atoms with the same atomic number, but different mass number, are *isotopes* (Sec. 44.6). Most elements have at least two stable isotopes; tin has 10, the largest number for any element. In addition to stable isotopes, one or more radioactive isotopes are known for every element.

51.2 The Size of Nuclei

If a typical atom were expanded to a radius of 10 m, its nucleus would have a radius of less than 1 mm. The volume of a nucleus is only about 10^{-12} of the volume of the atom. To put it another way, a nucleus viewed from an outer electron subtends an angle of 1 per cent of the angle subtended by the sun at the earth (0.5°). In a sense an atom is a very open structure comprised largely of empty space through which tiny electrons are passing.

Although nuclei are exceedingly small, several types of measurements have been devised to determine nuclear radii. While there are minor differences in the empirical values, all methods agree on the order of magnitude. The volumes of all nuclei are roughly proportional to the number of nucleons A. If we assume a roughly spherical shape, we find that the radius of a nucleus of mass number A is given by

$$r = 1.2 \times 10^{-15} \sqrt[3]{A} \quad \text{meter} \qquad \textbf{51.1}$$

The heaviest of all common nuclei is that of uranium 238, for which the nuclear radius is somewhat less than 10^{-14} m, as compared with the typical atomic radius of about 10^{-10} m.

The densities of nuclei of all kinds are roughly equal, about 2×10^{17} kg/m³. A pint of packed nucleons would weigh 100 billion tons!

51.3 The Deuteron

In 1932 Urey and his collaborators discovered a stable isotope of hydrogen with mass number 2. Such a hydrogen atom is known as *deuterium* or *heavy hydrogen*. Its nucleus, the *deuteron,* is composed of one proton and one neutron and has a mass of 2.01355 amu. When a proton and a neutron combine to form a deuteron, a mass of 0.00239 amu (1.00728 + 1.00866 − 2.01355) disappears and is transformed to a gamma photon.

According to Einstein's theory of relativity, the mass-energy equivalence is expressed (Sec. 46.8) by

$$\text{Energy} = mc^2 \qquad \textbf{51.2}$$

By Eq. (51.2),

$$1 \text{ amu} = (1.66 \times 10^{-27} \text{ kg})(3 \times 10^8 \text{ m/sec})^2 = 1.49 \times 10^{-10} \text{ joule}$$

Since $1 \text{ eV} = 1.60 \times 10^{-19}$ joule,

$$1 \text{ amu} = 931 \text{ MeV}$$

The mass which disappears when a deuteron is formed corresponds to 2.22 MeV. In order to break a deuteron into a proton and a neutron, we must supply this energy. Indeed, one of our best methods of measuring the neutron mass involves finding the lowest-energy photon which can split the deuteron into a proton and a neutron, a process called *photodisintegration.*

The fact that energy is released in the reaction $_1\text{H}^1 + {_0}n^1 \rightarrow {_1}\text{H}^2$ and is required to break up the deuteron is analogous to the situation in chemical reactions. When carbon and oxygen unite to form carbon dioxide, energy is released. If we wish to decompose carbon dioxide into carbon and oxygen, we must add this amount of energy to the system. The total energy which would be released if we could perform a series of operations to build a nucleus from neutrons and protons is called the *binding energy* of the nucleus. Alternatively, the binding energy is the energy required to tear the nucleus apart into protons and neutrons.

A proton and a neutron are bound together only if their spins are essentially aligned in the same direction. As a result the spin angular momentum of the deuteron is one unit of $h/2\pi$, and the magnetic moment of the deuteron is only about ⅓ that of the proton, because the neutron contributes negative magnetic moment to the system.

There is a third isotopic form of hydrogen, called *tritium,* which has mass number 3. Its nucleus, the *triton,* is composed of one proton and two neutrons. It is unstable, half a given sample transforming to helium 3 in 12 years.

51.4 The Binding Energy of Nuclei

Nuclear forces are so great, and the amount of energy involved when nucleons are brought together to form a new nucleus is so tremendous, that we can observe the difference in masses before and after. We have called the difference between the mass of the component nucleons from which a nucleus is composed and the actual mass of the nucleus the *binding energy* of the nucleus. In practice, mass spectrometers determine the masses of heavy atoms (or ions) rather than the masses of nuclei directly. It is convenient to think of any neutral atom of mass number A and atomic number Z as being composed of Z hydrogen atoms and $A - Z$ neutrons. The hydrogen atoms bring the protons for the nucleus and the electrons for the shells. Then the binding energy is given by the difference between the mass of Z hydrogen atoms plus $A - Z$ neutrons and the mass of the neutral atom:

$$\text{Binding energy} = Zm_\text{H} + (A - Z)m_n - M \qquad \textbf{51.3}$$

where m_H, m_n, and M are the masses of the hydrogen atom, the neutron, and the neutral atom, respectively. Table 51.1 lists the masses of a number of common atomic species.

To obtain the mass of the nucleus from the known atomic mass, one subtracts the mass of the Z electrons.

One electron mass $= 0.0005486$ amu $= 0.511$ MeV

The binding energy increases with the mass number A. For purposes of comparison it is convenient to divide the total binding energy

TABLE 51.1 *Masses of Atoms in amu (Based on C^{12} as 12.00000)*

Element	Z	A	Mass	Element	Z	A	Mass
(Neutron)	0	1	1.00866	Nitrogen	7	14	14.0031
Hydrogen	1	1	1.00782	Oxygen	8	16	15.9949
		2	2.01410	Sodium	11	23	22.9897
		3	3.01604	Sulfur	16	32	31.9721
Helium	2	3	3.01602	Nickel	28	58	57.935
		4	4.00260	Copper	29	63	62.929
Lithium	3	6	6.01506	Tin	50	120	119.902
		7	7.01599	Lead	82	208	207.981
Carbon	6	12	12.0000	Uranium	92	238	238.056

by the number of nucleons to obtain the *binding energy per nucleon*. A plot of the binding energy per nucleon for many stable nuclei is shown in Fig. 51.1.

Example Find the binding energy and the binding energy per nucleon for Li^7; Li^7 is composed of 3 hydrogen atoms and 4 neutrons.

$$3 \times 1.00782 = 3.02346$$
$$4 \times 1.00866 = 4.03464$$
$$7.05810$$
$$Li^7 \qquad 7.01599$$
$$\text{Binding energy} = 0.04211 \text{ amu}$$
$$0.0421 \times 931 = 39.3 \text{ MeV binding energy}$$
$$\text{Binding energy per particle} = \frac{39.3}{7} = 5.6 \text{ MeV/nucleon}$$

51.5 Stable Nuclei

We do not know the exact nature of the forces which hold nucleons together, but we do know what stable nuclei exist in nature and some of the conditions which must be satisfied if a nucleus is to be stable. Among the light elements we never find stable nuclei which have radically different numbers of protons and neutrons. For example, oxygen has three stable isotopes with masses 16, 17, and 18. The 8 protons of the oxygen nucleus form stable configurations with 8, 9, or 10 neutrons, but not with 4 neutrons or with 20 neutrons. As we go up the periodic table, the number of neutrons increases more rapidly than the number of protons, until in U^{238} there are almost 1.6 neutrons for every proton.

The increase in binding energy per nucleon for light elements (Fig. 51.1) is associated in part with the fact that on the average each nucleon has more neighbors to which it is bound. However, the rise is not steady, for example, the binding energy per nucleon is greater for $_2He^4$ and $_8O^{16}$ than for nuclei with one or two more nucleons. This can be explained in terms of a *shell model* of nuclei, which predicts that 2, 8, 20, 50, 82, and 126 nucleons of either type form a particularly stable

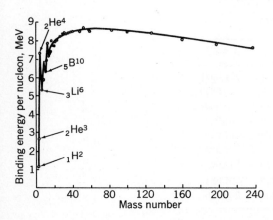

FIGURE 51.1

Binding energy per nucleon as a function of mass number for stable nuclei.

array. Throughout the realm of nuclei there is strong evidence of the pairing of two protons of opposite spin and of two neutrons of opposite spin to form very stable nuclei. Except for hydrogen, elements of even atomic number are several times as abundant as those of odd atomic number. Elements of odd Z have at most two stable isotopes, both of which ordinarily have an even number of neutrons (prominent exceptions: $_1H^2$, $_3Li^6$, $_5B^{10}$, and $_7N^{14}$). On the other hand, elements of even Z often have many isotopes, most of which have also an even number of neutrons.

For the heavier elements the mutual electrostatic repulsion of the protons increases rapidly with Z, and consequently the net binding energy per nucleon falls off. To this Coulomb repulsion we attribute the fact that the number of neutrons exceeds the number of protons for stable nuclei heavier than $_{20}Ca^{40}$. It is also the reason for the instability of the very heavy nuclei. Whenever the arrangement of the nucleons is unstable, the nucleus is radioactive and undergoes one of several kinds of transition. It was in the observation of such transitions that nuclear physics had its birth.

51.6 Natural Radioactivity

Röntgen's discovery of X rays in 1895 stimulated others to search for new kinds of rays. In 1896 Becquerel found that the compounds of uranium emitted radiations that produced a shadow picture on a photographic plate covered with black paper. These radiations had many of the properties of X rays in that they could produce ionization in gases, affect photographic plates, and pass through thin sheets of substances which are opaque to light.

It was soon found that the property of emitting penetrating radiations is not confined to uranium and its compounds. Minerals containing thorium and several other elements have this same property. Such substances are said to be *radioactive*. A few years after Becquerel's discovery of radioactivity Pierre and Marie Curie were able to isolate the highly radioactive element *radium* from the mineral pitchblende. Many other radioactive elements were discovered later.

When the rays from a radioactive material are passed through a strong magnetic field, some are bent in one direction, some are deflected in the opposite direction, and some are undeviated (Fig. 51.2). Thus, three different types of radiation are emitted by radioactive substances. These radiations were named *alpha, beta,* and *gamma rays.* The bending of alpha and beta rays in a magnetic field shows that alpha rays carry positive charge, and beta rays negative charge, while gamma rays are electrically neutral.

51.7 Alpha Particles

The alpha particle is the nucleus of the helium atom. This fact was established by separating an alpha emitter from an evacuated region by means of a thin wall through which alpha particles could pass.

FIGURE 51.2

Gamma rays are undeflected, and alpha and beta particles are deflected in opposite directions, by a magnitude field directed into the page.

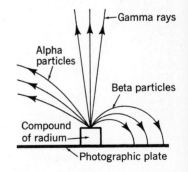

(a)

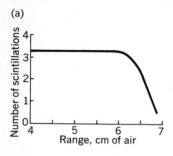

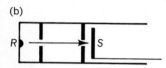

(b)

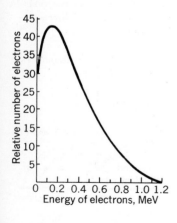

FIGURE 51.3

(*a*) Graph of range of 7.68-MeV alpha particles from $_{84}Po^{214}$ in the air, as measured in apparatus (*b*).

FIGURE 51.4

Beta-ray spectrum of $_{82}Bi^{210}$ showing the relative number of electrons emitted at various energies.

After a few hours enough gas collected in the evacuated region so that its spectrum could be excited. This showed that the gas was helium. Alpha particles have been found to bear a double elementary positive charge, substantiating the fact that they are helium nuclei.

Alpha particles are easily absorbed by metal foils or by a few centimeters of air. They affect a photographic plate, cause many materials to fluoresce brilliantly, and ionize the air through which they pass. When alpha particles strike screens of fluorescent material, they produce tiny flashes of light called *scintillations*. Many of the early researches on alpha particles were carried out in darkened rooms by patient observers who sat for hours counting these flashes. If an alpha emitter is placed at R in Figure 51.3*b*, a fluorescent screen S receives many scintillations each second when it is close to the source. As the screen is moved away from the alpha emitter, the number of scintillations per second remains roughly constant over a considerable distance. Then the number drops off sharply (Fig. 51.3*a*). As the particles move through the gas, they lose energy by ionizing the gas. In passing through the first few centimeters of air, the alpha particles are slowed down significantly, but few are lost. This type of range curve is characteristic of particles which lose energy gradually as they pass through matter. A curve such as that of Figure 51.3*a* suggests that all the alpha particles from the source had the same energy. For any given alpha emitter we find that either all the alpha particles have the same energy or that there are a few groups of alpha particles emitted, each group with its own discrete energy.

In general, a nucleus is unstable against alpha decay if its mass exceeds that of an alpha particle plus that of the residual nucleus. In the reaction

$$_{88}Ra^{226} \rightarrow {}_{86}Rn^{222} + {}_2He^4 + \text{energy}$$

the energy released is the difference between the mass of the radium (226.0312 amu) and the sum of the masses of the radon (222.0233) and the helium (4.0026). This is 0.0053 amu, or 4.9 MeV.

51.8 Beta Emission

Beta particles are electrons ejected from nuclei with speeds which may exceed $0.9c$, where c is the speed of light. These electrons have a penetrating power far greater than that of alpha particles.

The energies of the beta rays from a given radioactive nucleus vary continuously from very low energy to a maximum (Fig. 51.4). There is a *continuous energy spectrum of the beta rays*. This is in sharp contrast with the energy spectrum of the alpha particles, which has at most a few discrete energies. If beta rays were the only particles coming out of a given kind of nucleus, one would expect the energies of the beta rays to be discrete. However, if some other particle were emitted simultaneously with the electron, this particle would share the total energy available, and the electron energy spectrum would be continuous. There is substantial evidence that another particle is ejected from beta emitters along with the electron. It has no charge or rest mass, but has a spin equal in magnitude to that of the electron. This particle was originally called the *neutrino,* meaning "little neutral one," but for reasons suggested in Sec. 52.8 it seems preferable to call it the *antineutrino* (represented by $\bar{\nu}$).

When a nucleus contains too many neutrons for the number of protons present, the unbalance is corrected by the transformation of a neutron into a proton with the emission of a beta ray and an antineutrino:

$$_0n^1 \rightarrow {}_1H^1 + {}_{-1}\beta^0 + \bar{\nu}$$

An isolated neutron is not a stable particle, but decays by the reaction above with a half-life of about 12 min, i.e., in 12 min one-half of any sample of neutrons not bound in nucleus decays (see Sec. 51.10).

The beta-decay process results in a product nucleus of the same mass number A but atomic number Z higher by 1. Beta decay is expected whenever the mass of the product nucleus is less than that of the original nucleus. As an example, the mass of $_6C^{14}$ exceeds that of $_7N^{14}$, and

$$_6C^{14} \rightarrow {}_7N^{14} + {}_{-1}\beta^0 + \bar{\nu}$$

When an element of low to moderate mass has too many protons for the number of neutrons, a transmutation occurs which results in the changing of a proton into a neutron. This may happen in one of two ways: (1) a positron may be emitted or (2) an orbital electron may be captured. In either case a neutrino is also involved. An example of a positron emitter is carbon 11, which decays by the reaction

$$_6C^{11} \rightarrow {}_5B^{11} + {}_1\beta^0 + \text{neutrino } (\nu)$$

where $_1\beta^0$ represents a positron.

51.9 Gamma Rays

High-energy electromagnetic rays are called gamma rays when they are emitted by radioactive nuclei. The properties of gamma rays are identical with those of X rays of the same wavelength.

When a radioactive nucleus emits an alpha or beta particle, it is likely that the residual nucleus will be left not in its most stable arrangement, but in an excited state. Ordinarily, when the nucleus goes to a more stable configuration, the energy released is radiated as a gamma ray. Like the alpha particles, the gamma rays from a given radioactive species have discrete energies.

51.10 The Uranium-Radium Series

The most abundant radioactive nucleus in nature is that of the uranium isotope of mass 238 atomic units, which we abbreviate U^{238}. This material decays by the emission of an alpha particle with a half-life of 5 billion years. *The half-life is the time required for one-half the nuclei in a sample to disintegrate.* For example, the half-life of radon is 3.85 days; one-half of a sample of radon disappears in 3.85 days. At the end of 7.7 days three-quarters of it has disappeared, and one-fourth remains. After 15.4 days, only one-sixteenth of the original radon is present.

The reaction in which U^{238} emits an alpha particle may be written

$$_{92}U^{238} \rightarrow {_2}He^4 + {_{90}}Th^{234}$$

Note that the emission of an alpha particle reduces the atomic number (left subscript) by 2 and the mass number (right superscript) by 4. The Th^{234} decays by beta emission to protactinium 234, which in turn emits a beta ray and becomes U^{234}:

$$_{90}Th^{234} \rightarrow {_{-1}}\beta^0 + {_{91}}Pa^{234}$$
$$_{91}Pa^{234} \rightarrow {_{-1}}\beta^0 + {_{92}}U^{234}$$

U^{234} is an alpha emitter with the daughter Th^{230}. Ultimately the decay series ends with lead 206. The detailed list of reactions and half-lives for the uranium-radium series is presented in Table 51.2.

In addition to the uranium-radium series, three other natural radioactive series exist. The longest-lived member of the *thorium series* is Th^{232}, and the final stable nucleus formed is again lead, but this time Pb^{208}. The *neptunium series* has Np^{237} as its longest-lived member, and the radioactive chain ends with bismuth 209, while the *actinium series* has U^{235} as its longest-lived member and Pb^{207} as its final stable nucleus.

TABLE 51.2 *The Uranium-Radium Series*

Nuclide	Element	Early name	Half-life	Energy of rays, MeV		
				α	β	γ
$_{92}U^{238}$	Uranium	Uranium I	4.5×10^9 yr	4.18		
$_{90}Th^{234}$	Thorium	Uranium X_1	24.1 days		0.103	0.09
$_{91}Pa^{234}$	Protactinium	Uranium X_2	1.18 min		2.32	0.8
$_{92}U^{234}$	Uranium	Uranium II	2.35×10^5 yr	4.76		
$_{90}Th^{230}$	Thorium	Ionium	8×10^4 yr	4.66		
$_{88}Ra^{226}$	Radium	Radium	1,620 yr	4.79		0.19
$_{86}Rn^{222}$	Radon	Ra emanation	3.8 days	5.49		
$_{84}Po^{218}$	Polonium	Radium A	3.05 min	6.00		
$_{82}Pb^{214}$	Lead	Radium B	26.8 min		0.65	0.29
$_{83}Bi^{214}$	Bismuth	Radium C	19.7 min	5.5	3.15	1.8
$_{84}Po^{214}$	Polonium	Radium C'	1.5×10^{-4} sec	7.68		
or						
$_{81}Tl^{210}$	Thallium	Radium C''	1.32 min		1.80	
$_{82}Pb^{210}$	Lead	Radium D	22 yr		0.026	0.047
$_{83}Bi^{210}$	Bismuth	Radium E	5.0 days		1.17	
$_{84}Po^{210}$	Polonium	Radium F	138 days	5.3		0.8
$_{82}Pb^{206}$	Lead	Radium G	Stable			

51.11 Radioactive Dating

Since each alpha particle is a helium nucleus, helium is in the process of formation in all minerals containing alpha-emitting radioactive substances. The number of alpha particles given out by 1 g of uranium in equilibrium with its radioactive products has been found to be 9.7×10^4 per sec. If this helium were all occluded and retained by the mineral, the ratio of the amount of helium to the amount of uranium would give an estimate of the age of the mineral. Without doubt some of the helium escapes, and this estimate of the age of the mineral would be too low. A determination of the uranium and helium in different kinds of rocks has shown that the ratio of the amount of helium to the amount of uranium is largest in those formations which, from geological considerations, are known to be the oldest. Studies of many kinds of radioactive decay point to an age for the earth of the order of 5×10^9 years.

For determining the ages of artifacts of archaeological interest, radioactive carbon 14 has proved to be a highly useful tool. Radiocarbon decays by beta emission with a half-life of 5,570 years. The $_6C^{14}$, produced by the bombardment of atmospheric nitrogen with neutrons, is in equilibrium in the earth's atmosphere and is present in all living matter in equilibrium concentration through exchange with the atmosphere. However, once the matter ceases to live, exchange stops, and the $_6C^{14}$ concentration decreases steadily. Libby has established the dates when life ceased in a wide variety of organic materials. This development is an important tool for geology and archaeology.

51.12 Fusion

The alpha particle is composed of 4 nucleons, 2 protons, and 2 neutrons. The mass of a He^4 atom is 4.00260 amu, while the sum of the masses of 2 hydrogen atoms and 2 neutrons is 4.003296 amu. The binding energy is 0.0304 amu, or 28.2 MeV.

If we could build helium nuclei from protons and neutrons, we would have a source of tremendous energy. Actually, the probability of getting 2 protons and 2 neutrons simultaneously in so small a volume that they would interact to form an alpha particle is small. However, we might well carry out the process by first having a proton and a neutron combine to form a deuteron. Then two deuterons might be brought close enough together to interact. When we do this, so much energy is available that the four particles do not ordinarily stick together. Rather, either a high-energy proton is emitted, leaving us a triton, or a neutron is emitted, leaving us with a He^3 nucleus. The reactions are

$$_1H^2 + {_1H^2} \nearrow {_2He^3} + {_0n^1} + 3.28 \text{ MeV energy}$$
$$\searrow {_1H^3} + {_1H^1} + 4.04 \text{ MeV energy}$$

The energy released in a nuclear reaction such as this is calculated by subtracting the mass of the reaction products from the mass of the interacting particles. One of the many ways in which we can get an alpha particle from these products is to bring a deuteron and a triton together. The resulting reaction is

$$_1H^2 + {}_1H^3 \rightarrow {}_2He^4 + {}_0n^1 + 17.6 \text{ MeV energy}$$

The process of building helium from hydrogen is called *fusion*. As we have seen, 28.2 MeV is released for each helium nucleus built from the building blocks. If we produce fusion reactions on a large scale, we release a colossal amount of energy in a very short time and thus create a great explosion. The hydrogen bomb is an example of a fusion device. If deuterons and tritons are to come in contact with each other in spite of the repulsion between the positive charges, they must have high speeds. In a hydrogen bomb these speeds may be achieved by bringing the particles to an exceedingly high temperature, thereby producing *thermonuclear reactions*. One way to produce temperatures of this magnitude is by a nuclear explosion utilizing fission. An alternative is to pour vast amounts of energy into a plasma of ionized deuterium and tritium. In achieving the temperature needed (tens of millions of Kelvin degrees) in a laboratory fusion experiment, the hot plasma is confined by magnetic fields, since any type of material container would be vaporized by contact with the plasma.

The release of energy by means of the combination of nucleons into heavier particles (fusion) is directly analogous to the release of chemical energy by the combination of atoms. In the nuclear case one may release energy by combining a proton and a neutron to form a deuteron. In the analogous chemical situation one may combine an atom of sodium with an atom of chlorine to form sodium chloride. One great difference between these two reactions lies in the amount of energy released per interacting particle. In the case of proton and neutron the energy resulting from the combination is 2.2 MeV per proton, while in the case of the sodium chlorine reaction the energy is about 4 eV per sodium atom.

51.13 Fission

One can obtain energy from chemical reactions not only by combining atoms of various substances to form molecules, but also by breaking very large and complex molecules, such as trinitrotoluene molecules, into smaller and more tightly bound units. Similarly, heavy and complex nuclei can be made to break up with the release of energy.

When any heavy nucleus is highly excited, it may break up into two roughly equal parts. This process is called *fission*. Some heavy nuclei fission readily; others do not. The excitation can be achieved in several ways. For example, gamma rays may induce fission. The most familiar method is by introducing a neutron into a nucleus of uranium 235. When a slow neutron collides with a U^{235} nucleus, it may be captured. The resulting U^{236} nucleus breaks up into two roughly equal parts, plus a few additional neutrons. A typical reaction is

$$_{92}U^{235} + {}_0n^1 \rightarrow {}_{92}U^{236} \rightarrow {}_{56}Ba^{145} + {}_{36}Kr^{88} + 3{}_0n^1 + \text{energy}$$

The mass of the products is less than that of the fissioning nucleus; thus energy is released, on the average about 200 MeV per fission. The excited U^{236} nucleus may break up in many different ways. Figure 51.5 shows the relative fission yields of the many mass numbers which may be created as fission fragments.

When a heavy nucleus fissions, the product nuclei usually contain several too many neutrons for stability. For example, one common fission product is strontium 95. The heaviest stable isotope of strontium is Sr^{88}. The radioactive Sr^{95} nucleus undergoes three successive beta decays and finally reaches stability as niobium 95. Some fission products transmute through beta decays of long half-life and produce serious contamination after a nuclear explosion.

51.14 Chain Reactions and the Reactor

Since two to three neutrons are released in a typical fission, two or three other atoms may be fissioned if these neutrons are captured by U^{235} nuclei. The neutrons released in these fissions can produce four or five more fissions, and a *chain reaction* is set off if a sufficient supply of U^{235} atoms is present in a small volume. Such a chain reaction does not occur in ordinary uranium because a large fraction of the neutrons are captured by U^{238} nuclei, which are 140 times as abundant in natural uranium as U^{235} nuclei. Few of the U^{238} nuclei fission.

To produce the first nuclear weapons, U^{235} was separated from U^{238} so a large fraction of the neutrons emitted by fissioning nuclei would be captured by U^{235} nuclei and thereby produce additional fissions. However, even pure U^{235} does not support a chain reaction unless an amount known as a *critical mass* is present, because too large a fraction of the neutrons escapes from the surface of a subcritical mass. If two almost critical masses are brought together, the system becomes critical, and an explosion occurs.

The neutrons released in fission are *fast,* with energies of several MeV. They are quickly slowed down by collisions with nuclei. U^{235} does not capture fast neutrons readily, but it captures slow neutrons (energy less than 1 eV) very effectively. On the other hand, U^{238} captures neutrons of intermediate energies more readily than slow ones. If the neutrons from fissions in natural uranium are slowed down in some other material so the U^{238} does not capture them, a sustained reaction using natural uranium can be maintained in a nuclear *reactor* (or *pile*). Figure 51.6 shows a reactor in which carbon is used to slow down or *moderate* the neutrons. (Heavy water, containing deuterium, is another material which is an excellent *moderator*.) Fissions produce fast neutrons which enter the carbon, where they have many collisions and slow down to thermal velocities before they reach another uranium slug. The probability that a slow neutron will be captured by a U^{235} nucleus is much greater than the probability it will be captured by a U^{238} nucleus, even though there are 140 times as many of the latter. Cadmium control rods are moved into or out of the reactor to regulate

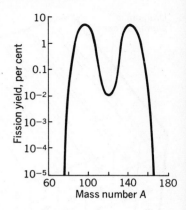

FIGURE 51.5

Fission yield of U^{236} as it varies with the mass numbers of the fragments.

Uranium in
aluminum cans

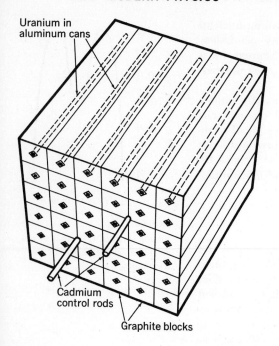

Cadmium
control rods

Graphite blocks

FIGURE 51.6
Uranium-graphite reactor in which uranium slugs are
canned in aluminum; cadmium rods are used to control the
power level at which the reactor operates.

the power level of the pile and keep it from blowing up. Cadmium 113
is an excellent capturer of slow neutrons.

Each fission in a reactor releases about 200 MeV of energy, and the
total energy transformed from mass to thermal energy in a large reactor is great. Nuclear energy is being used for generating electric
power, for heating, for propelling submarines, and for nuclear weapons.
Nuclear power plants for aircraft promise to extend the range and
revolutionize the operation of airplanes. In the next century it is
likely that an ever-increasing fraction of our total energy requirements
will be supplied from nuclear sources.

51.15 Plutonium

When neutrons are captured in U^{238}, fission sometimes occurs, but
usually the U^{239} formed does not split up. However, it does emit a
beta particle (half-life 23 min) to become neptunium 239 (Fig. 51.7).
Np^{239} is a beta emitter with a half-life of 2.3 days and becomes

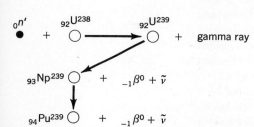

FIGURE 51.7
Production of plutonium from U^{238}.

plutonium 239. Pu^{239} is an alpha emitter with a half-life of 24,400 years. This plutonium fissions readily. Practically no plutonium exists in natural materials. Substantial quantities have been produced for use in nuclear weapons. It is produced in reactors which use natural uranium as fuel.

Questions

1. What are the properties of alpha, beta, and gamma rays?

2. How do atomic number and atomic weight change when a nucleus emits (*a*) an alpha particle, (*b*) a beta particle, (*c*) a gamma ray, and (*d*) a positron?

3. What is meant by the binding energy of a nucleus? How do the binding energies of nuclei vary with atomic number?

4. What is the function of graphite in a typical reactor?

5. Why are fission products ordinarily radioactive while fusion products are not?

6. In a typical fission reaction a neutron is captured by a $_{92}U^{235}$ nucleus, and three neutrons and two fission fragments are formed. If one of the fragments is a $_{55}Cs^{140}$ nucleus, what must the other fragment be?

7. (*a*) A nucleus of thorium 232 ($_{90}Th^{232}$) eventually becomes lead 208 ($_{82}Pb^{208}$). In the series of alpha and beta decays by which this occurs, how many alpha and beta particles are emitted? (*b*) After a series of alpha and beta decays plutonium 239 ($_{94}Pu^{239}$) becomes lead 207 ($_{82}Pb^{207}$). How many alpha and beta particles are emitted in the complete decay scheme?

Problems

1. Find the binding energy and the binding energy per nucleon for $_{20}Ca^{40}$, which has a mass of 39.9627 amu.   *Ans.* 342 MeV; 8.54 MeV/nucleon

2. In Sec. 51.12 three fusion reactions involving interactions of deuterium with deuterium and tritium are written. Check the energy released in each case by finding the mass converted to energy in the reaction.

3. Find the minimum energy required for the photodisintegration of an α particle into (*a*) $He^3 + _0n^1$, (*b*) $H^3 + H^1$, and (*c*) $H^2 + H^2$.
                    Ans. (*a*) 20.6 MeV; (*b*) 19.8 MeV; (*c*) 23.8 MeV

4. Find the binding energy and the binding energy per nucleon for oxygen 16 and for sodium 23.

5. A free neutron is unstable and decays to a proton, an electron, and an antineutrino. The maximum energy of electrons from neutron decay is 785 keV, and the half-life of the neutrons is 11.7 min. Find the difference between the masses of proton and neutron. What fraction of a sample of free neutrons decays in 35.1 min?   *Ans.* 0.00139 amu; ⅛

6. Find the binding energy and the binding energy per nucleon for tritium. The maximum energy of beta rays emitted in the decay of tritium to $_2He^3$ is 18 keV. Find the mass difference between $_1H^3$ and $_2He^3$.

7. At the end of 20 days one-eighth of a sample of radioactive material remains. What is the half-life?   *Ans.* 6.7 days

8. When a U^{238} nucleus captures a slow neutron, uranium 239, with a half-life of 23 min, is produced. If a sample of radioactive material from a nuclear reactor contains 10 g of U^{239}, what mass of this isotope remains at the end of 92 min?

9. The half-life of sodium 24 is 15 hours. What fraction of a sample of Na^{24} remains after a time of 30 hours? 90 hours? *Ans.* 0.25; 0.0156

10. The half-life of iodine 131 is 8 days. What fraction of a given sample of I^{131} remains after 24 days? After 40 days?

11. Uranium 238 decays to thorium 234 by the emission of an alpha particle of energy 4.18 MeV. Assuming that essentially all the energy released in this decay goes to the alpha particle, calculate the mass of thorium 234. *Ans.* 234.049 amu

12. When a slow neutron is captured by a U^{235} nucleus, a fission releasing 200 MeV results. How much mass disappears? What fraction of the mass of the reacting particles is converted into energy?

13. A nuclear reactor converts 1 mg of mass to energy each day. Compute the power output in megawatts. If the average fission yields 200 MeV, how many nuclei fission each second? *Ans.* 1.04 MW; 3.25×10^{16}

14. How many fissions per day are required for a reactor to develop electric power at the rate of 50 MW if 10 per cent of the energy released in fission is converted to electrical energy?

15. The heat of combustion of coal (assume pure carbon) is about 3×10^7 joules/kg. (*a*) When 1 kg of coal burns, what mass is converted to energy? (*b*) How many electron volts are released per atom of carbon burned? (*c*) If all the mass of carbon were annihilated, how many joules could be obtained per kilogram?
Ans. (*a*) 3.3×10^{-10} kg; (*b*) 3.7 eV/atom; (*c*) 9×10^{16} joules

16. It is estimated that the energy released in the atomic-bomb explosion at Hiroshima was about 7.6×10^{13} joules, equivalent to 20,000 tons of TNT. If an average of 200 MeV was released per fission, and if all fissions were by neutron capture in U^{235}, find the number of U^{235} atoms fissioned and the mass of U^{235} consumed. If 20 per cent of the U^{235} atoms fissioned, what mass of U^{235} was needed for the bomb?

17. A Ra^{226} nucleus emits an alpha particle with an energy of 4.79 MeV. Find the speed of the alpha particle and the recoil speed of the Rn^{222} nucleus.
Ans. 1.5×10^7 m/sec; 2.7×10^5 m/sec

18. How close can a 4.00-MeV α particle approach a lead nucleus, assuming the latter remains at rest?

19. A fission fragment of 90 amu mass has an energy of 120 MeV. Find its speed, and find the temperature at which molecules of this mass would have an average energy of 120 MeV. *Ans.* 1.6×10^7 m/sec; $(9.3 \times 10^{11})°$K

CHAPTER 52 *In Chap. 51 we presented many facts concerning nuclei and the particles of which they are formed. But how were these facts established? In this chapter we discuss how physicists have induced reactions by bombarding various nuclear species with particles and how they determine the mechanisms involved from information provided by a wide variety of detectors.*

Nuclear Reactions

52.1 The First Artificial Transmutation

The discovery of radioactivity in 1896 stimulated research activity which led to an understanding of both the decay schemes of the heavy elements such as uranium and the properties of the alpha, beta, and gamma rays arising from these natural transmutations. In 1919 Rutherford found that when alpha particles passed through air, a penetrating charged particle was produced which had a range as great as 40 cm, although the range of the incident alpha particles was only 7 cm. The more penetrating particles were not produced when the alpha particles passed through oxygen or carbon dioxide, but they were observed whenever nitrogen was present. Rutherford showed that the penetrating particles were high-energy protons, produced by the capture of alpha particles by nitrogen nuclei (Fig. 52.1).

When an alpha particle is captured by a nitrogen nucleus, a highly excited fluorine 18 nucleus is produced. This excited nucleus has too much energy to remain together; it breaks up by ejecting one of the protons, leaving a residual $_8O^{17}$ nucleus. We write the reaction as

$$_2He^4 + {_7}N^{14} \rightarrow {_9}F^{18*} \rightarrow {_8}O^{17} + {_1}H^1 + \text{energy}$$

Here the asterisk indicates that the F^{18} nucleus is excited.

Rutherford's discovery of artificial transmutation suggested that physicists could change one element into another by shooting high-speed particles into nuclei. In Rutherford's day alpha particles from radioactive materials were the only convenient high-energy projectiles available. Only high-energy charged particles can enter nuclei, because positive charges repel one another; these repulsive forces become exceedingly great before the two particles are close enough for the attractive nuclear forces to become dominant. Rutherford's discovery was a great stimulus toward the development of accelerators to produce high-energy charged particles. Until such high-voltage machines could be developed, there was always the possibility of using alpha particles from radioactive materials as bombarding projectiles. Here again Rutherford's discovery provided a major stimulus.

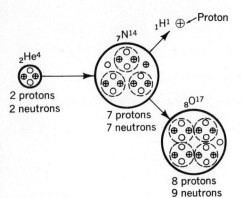

FIGURE 52.1

A nitrogen-14 nucleus captures a bombarding alpha particle to yield a proton and an oxygen-17 nucleus.

52.2 The Discovery of the Neutron

In 1930 Bothe and Becker observed that several of the lighter elements emitted a very penetrating radiation when bombarded by alpha particles from polonium. They thought this radiation consisted of gamma rays, since it was not affected by magnetic fields and was therefore uncharged. The radiation was so penetrating that, when alpha particles bombarded beryllium, it required 2 cm of lead to cut the intensity in half.

Two years later the Joliots found that these penetrating rays were fairly readily absorbed in paraffin, water, or cellophane. They concluded that the penetrating radiation was absorbed through some reaction which resulted in the ejection of protons from hydrogenous materials.

Later that same year Chadwick repeated the Joliot experiment and measured the energy of the ejected protons. He concluded that this energy was much too high to have been received in any sort of gamma-ray reaction. He recalled that 12 years earlier Rutherford had suggested that there might be a neutral particle with approximately the mass of the proton. If the penetrating radiation consisted of high-speed particles of this kind, they should produce not only recoil protons, but also recoils in other nuclei. It turned out that Feather had already published data on the recoil velocities of nitrogen nuclei when they were bombarded by the mysterious particles. By applying the laws of conservation of energy and of momentum to what he assumed were elastic collisions between these particles and target nuclei, Chadwick was able to show that both his own data on proton recoils and those of Feather were consistent with the idea that the penetrating radiation consisted of neutral particles of mass slightly greater than the mass of the proton. These particles are called *neutrons*. The reaction by which neutrons are produced when beryllium is bombarded with alpha particles (Fig. 52.2) is

$$_4\text{Be}^9 + {_2}\text{He}^4 \rightarrow {_6}\text{O}^{13*} \rightarrow {_6}\text{C}^{12} + {_0}n^1 + Q$$

where Q represents the energy released through the conversion of mass.

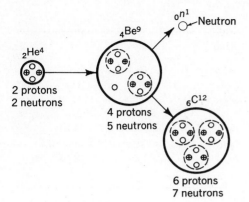

FIGURE 52.2

A neutron may be ejected when an alpha particle is captured by a beryllium-9 nucleus, leaving a carbon-12 nucleus.

52.3 Reactions Induced by Accelerated Particles

Soon after Rutherford's discovery of artificial transmutation, physicists in several countries began to build accelerators to produce high-energy protons. The first device which was successful in accelerating charged particles artificially to produce nuclear reactions was put into operation by Cockcroft and Walton in England in 1930. Their accelerator produced a beam of protons of 0.5 MeV energy by utilizing high-voltage transformers, rectifiers, and capacitors.

Cockcroft and Walton found that when lithium was bombarded with protons of 150 keV energy, alpha particles were emitted with energies of about 8.6 MeV (Fig. 52.3). The following reaction occurred:

$$_3\text{Li}^7 + {}_1\text{H}^1 \rightarrow {}_4\text{Be}^{8*} \rightarrow {}_2\text{He}^4 + {}_2\text{He}^4 + 17.3 \text{ MeV energy}$$

The energy released is shared equally by the alpha particles, since this is the only way in which momentum can be conserved.

The source of the energy released in this and other nuclear reactions is the conversion of mass into energy. The masses of the lithium and hydrogen atoms add to 8.02381 amu (Table 51.1), while the two helium atoms have a total mass of 8.00520 amu. The decrease in mass is 0.0186 amu, which corresponds to 17.3 MeV.

Shortly after Cockcroft and Walton made their discovery, other types of accelerators were put into operation, some of which are described in Secs. 34.8 and 44.9.

When a beam of high-energy particles (electrons, protons, deuterons, alpha particles, or other ions) bombards nuclei, a wide variety of reactions take place in which the bombarding particle is captured to produce a radioactive "compound" nucleus, which then emits one or more particles before it reaches a stable state. So long as the bombarding particles have energies less than about 100 MeV, the reactions can be described in terms of protons, neutrons, electrons, positrons, neutrinos, and antineutrinos. However, when the bombarding particles have energies of hundreds and thousands of MeV, new and strange particles are created—a whole new science of particle physics is born. Before

FIGURE 52.3

A lithium-7 nucleus captures a proton to produce a beryllium-8 nucleus which promptly breaks into two alpha particles.

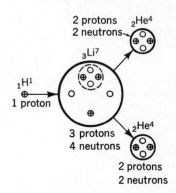

TABLE 52.1   *Some Typical Nuclear Transmutations*

Kind	Example	Kind	Example
(α,p)	$_{13}Al^{27} + {}_2He^4 \rightarrow {}_1H^1 + {}_{14}Si^{30}$	$(d,2n)$	$_1H^3 + {}_1H^2 \rightarrow 2{}_0n^1 + {}_2He^3$
(α,n)	$_{13}Al^{27} + {}_2He^4 \rightarrow {}_0n^1 + {}_{15}P^{30}$	(n,α)	$_{13}Al^{27} + {}_0n^1 \rightarrow {}_2He^4 + {}_{11}Na^{24}$
(p,α)	$_9F^{19} + {}_1H^1 \rightarrow {}_2He^4 + {}_8O^{16}$	(n,p)	$_{48}Cd^{106} + {}_0n^1 \rightarrow {}_1H^1 + {}_{47}Ag^{106}$
(p,n)	$_5B^{11} + {}_1H^1 \rightarrow {}_0n^1 + {}_6C^{11}$	$(n,2n)$	$_{47}Ag^{107} + {}_0n^1 \rightarrow 2{}_0n^1 + {}_{47}Ag^{106}$
(p,γ)	$_{15}P^{31} + {}_1H^1 \rightarrow {}_{16}S^{32} + \gamma$	(n,γ)	$_{48}Cd^{113} + {}_0n^1 \rightarrow {}_{48}Cd^{114} + \gamma$
(d,α)	$_{13}Al^{27} + {}_1H^2 \rightarrow {}_2He^4 + {}_{12}Mg^{25}$	(γ,n)	$_4Be^9 + \gamma \rightarrow {}_0n^1 + {}_4Be^8$
(d,p)	$_7N^{14} + {}_1H^2 \rightarrow {}_1H^1 + {}_7N^{15}$	(γ,p)	$_{13}Al^{27} + \gamma \rightarrow {}_1H^1 + {}_{12}Mg^{26}$
(d,n)	$_{12}Mg^{25} + {}_1H^2 \rightarrow {}_0n^1 + {}_{13}Al^{26}$		

introducing these particles, we consider some of the reactions induced by nuclear projectiles of moderately high energy and describe some of the detection devices which physicists use to study reactions.

52.4 Artificial Transmutations

The development of high-voltage accelerators made it possible to bombard atomic nuclei with a variety of swiftly moving projectiles. When an accelerated particle is captured by a nucleus, the resulting system of nucleons is initially in a state of high excitation. It may get rid of its excess energy by emitting one or more particles. Hundreds of artificial transmutations have been studied. Table 52.1 lists some typical reactions. Figures 52.4 and 52.5 show two reactions in schematic form. A reaction in which a proton is captured and a neutron is emitted is called a (p,n) reaction, etc. In this shorthand the entering particle appears first, and the emitted particle after the comma.

If a target is bombarded by protons (or some other particles), it is common to find that protons of one energy are strongly captured, while

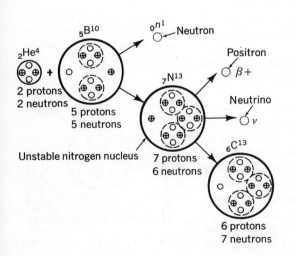

FIGURE 52.4

A boron-10 nucleus captures an alpha particle, producing a neutron and a nitrogen-13 nucleus; the $_7N^{13}$ nucleus is unstable and decays to carbon 13 by the emission of a positron and a neutrino.

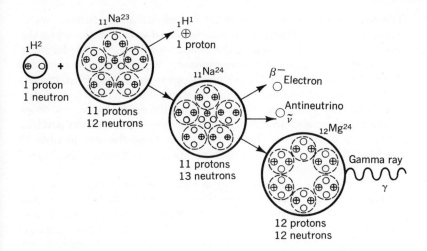

FIGURE 52.5

A sodium-23 nucleus captures a deuteron, emitting a proton and leaving an unstable sodium-24 nucleus which decays to magnesium 24 by the emission of an electron and an antineutrino; the $_{12}Mg^{24}$ nucleus is left in an excited state and emits a gamma photon.

protons of slightly higher or lower energy are rejected. We say that such capture reactions show *resonances*. A proton is likely to be captured if it brings in just the right energy and angular momentum to form a compound nucleus in one of its allowed energy states. A proton with more or less energy than this required amount is not captured.

Many nuclei created by transmutations are unstable and eventually decay. In some cases these unstable nuclei have relatively long half-lives. When a proton is captured by carbon 12, nitrogen 13 is formed. This nitrogen nucleus is unstable, with a half-life of 10.1 min. It decays to C^{13} by the emission of a positron. When tellurium 130 is bombarded with neutrons, Te^{131} is formed, but decays by electron emission to iodine 131. I^{131} is also a beta emitter; its half-life is 8 days. This radioactive isotope is used in treating hyperthyroid conditions.

52.5 The Detection of Nuclear Reactions

In nuclear reactions the target nuclei, the bombarding particle, and the resulting products are far too small to see and too light to weigh on the most sensitive balance. The problem of studying a reaction is a difficult one, since all judgments as to what has happened must be inferred from indirect evidence. However, scientists have developed a number of ingenious methods for studying nuclear reactions and detecting the products of the reactions.

Nuclear Emulsions. The first detector of nuclear reactions was the photographic plate. Gamma rays striking such a plate produce blackening, just as do visible light and X rays. By using an exceedingly fine-grained emulsion, the path of a high-energy proton, alpha particle, or electron may be studied under a microscope.

The Cloud Chamber. The Wilson cloud chamber consists of a cylinder with a glass top and a movable piston at the bottom (Fig. 52.6).

FIGURE 52.6
Wilson cloud chamber.

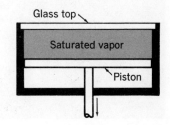

The volume of the chamber is filled with air and saturated water vapor or alcohol. When the piston is moved downward quickly, the mixture expands adiabatically, the temperature falls, and the formerly saturated vapor becomes supersaturated. Vapor molecules condense on any tiny particle which is present to serve as nucleus for a droplet. In particular, droplets form readily on charged ions. If a charged particle is moving through the chamber when the expansion occurs, droplets form on the ions produced by the passage of this charged particle, and a *track* is produced. Figure 52.7 shows cloud-chamber pictures of the breakup of nuclei struck by high-energy neutrons. The ionized fragments leave visible tracks.

When a strong magnetic field is impressed on a cloud chamber, charged particles moving across the field are deflected, producing curved paths. From the radius of curvature of a path, its length, and the number of ion pairs formed per unit path length, it is often possible to determine the mass and charge of the particle responsible for the track. It is not practical to build cloud chambers large enough to show the entire path of an extremely high-energy particle. To observe the paths and the reactions induced by such particles, photographic emulsions or bubble chambers are used.

The Bubble Chamber. In 1952 Glaser invented the bubble chamber, in which a charged particle moves through a superheated liquid rather than a supersaturated gas. The liquid is maintained at a temperature

FIGURE 52.7
Cloud chamber photos of (*a*) two carbon and oxygen atoms breaking apart when struck by a high-energy neutron and (*b*) oxygen stars produced by 90-MeV neutrons in a 14,000 gauss magnetic field.

(a)

(b)

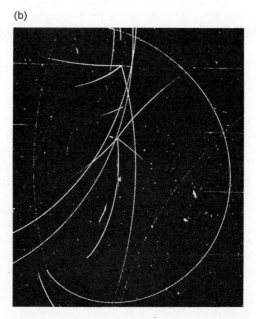

(a)

(b)

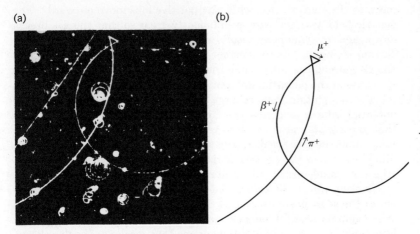

FIGURE 52.8
(*a*) Bubble-chamber photograph showing the path of a π^+ meson entering at the lower left and curving to top center, where it decays into a muon (and a mu neutrino which leaves no track). The μ^+ moves a short distance to the right and down before decaying to a positron, a neutrino, and a mu antineutrino. The positron leaves an almost circular path, while the other particles leave no tracks. There is a magnetic field B perpendicular to the plane of the paper. (*b*) Explanatory sketch.

just under its boiling point at an elevated pressure. When the path of a particle is desired, the pressure is suddenly reduced. Ions produced by the passing particles offer nuclei on which bubbles form preferentially before general boiling begins. The bubble tracks are photographed (Fig. 52.8). Bubble chambers containing liquid hydrogen have proven to be peerless detectors of many high-energy reactions for which the particle tracks are too long to be shown completely in a cloud chamber of reasonable size. A charged particle loses its energy in a much shorter distance in a liquid than in a gas, because it interacts with many more atoms per unit path length.

The Geiger-Müller Counter. A common detector of beta and gamma rays is the Geiger-Müller counter. An elementary counter can be made by stretching an insulated wire along the axis of a conducting metal cylinder (Fig. 52.9). This chamber is evacuated and then filled to a pressure of about 10 cm Hg with a mixture of argon and methyl alcohol. The central wire is made about 1,000 volts positive relative to the metal cylinder. When an ionizing particle passes through this counter, electrons are ejected from atoms. The electrons

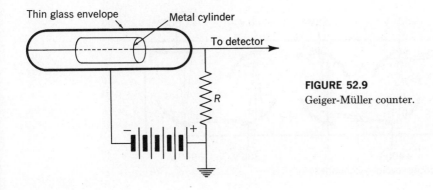

FIGURE 52.9
Geiger-Müller counter.

move to the central wire, while the positive ions move outward. The electric field near the wire is sufficiently great so that the gas breaks down, and an avalanche results during which a large instantaneous current is drawn. As the current rises, the potential difference across the Geiger counter falls, while that across the resistance R (Fig. 52.9) rises. Soon the potential difference across the Geiger counter becomes too low to maintain the discharge. The current drops to zero, and the potential difference across the counter again rises to 1,000 volts, so that the counter is once more ready to detect an incident particle. Each time the gas breaks down in the Geiger counter, the potential difference across the resistor R rises sharply; this rise can be made to trigger a scaling circuit, which automatically counts the pulses.

The Scintillation Detector. A detector which is the modern descendent of the scintillation screen of Sec. 51.7 is the scintillation counter. When gamma rays fall on a crystal of sodium iodide with a little thallium impurity, absorption of the gamma rays results in the fluorescent emission of ultraviolet and visible light. In the scintillation detector shown in Figure 52.10, the gamma-ray energy is absorbed in the crystal, producing light which falls on the photosensitive surface of the cathode of an *electron multiplier tube*. Electrons are ejected by the photoelectric effect and accelerated by a potential difference of the order of 200 volts to electrode 1, which is made of a material which has the property of copious secondary emission. When they strike this electrode, several secondary electrons are ejected for each incident electron. The electrons from electrode 1 are accelerated to electrode 2, where a further multiplication is produced, and so forth. At the final collector an electron pulse is collected which may be 1 million times as great as that from the photocathode. Each time a gamma ray strikes and is absorbed in the crystal, a charge pulse is delivered to the anode. The charge collected is a measure of the energy of the gamma ray. The scintillation counter has the great advantage over the Geiger counter that it not only tells when a gamma ray has been absorbed in the

FIGURE 52.10

Scintillation detector with photomultiplier tube.

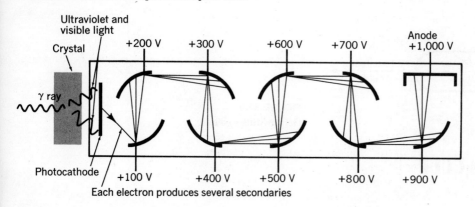

crystal, but it also yields a charge pulse which is a measure of the energy.

Čerenkov Detectors. When a charged particle passes through a medium with a speed greater than the speed of light in the medium, an electromagnetic "shock wave" of light is produced which is closely analogous to acoustic shock waves (Sec. 17.10). For example, electrons with a speed of $0.9c$ produce a bluish glow as they pass through water in which the speed of light is $c/1.33 = 0.75c$. Just as in the acoustic case, the sine of the angle between the path of the particle and the wave front generated is the ratio of the speed of the electromagnetic wave c/n to the speed of the particle. (Here n is, of course, the index of refraction of the material through which the particle is moving.) Measurement of this angle permits the physicist to determine the speed of the particle generating the radiation, called *Čerenkov radiation* in honor of the physicist who made an early investigation of the phenomenon.

52.6 Cosmic Rays

There are many accelerators which give charged particles (chiefly electrons and protons) energies in the range from 300 MeV to 35 GeV (billion electron volts in U.S. usage). In addition to these accelerators, there is another source of high-energy particles which is of great importance in studying nuclear reactions. This source is *cosmic radiation*. The primary cosmic rays consist of charged particles, mostly (85 per cent) protons, with energies as great as 10^{20} eV. Also present are alpha particles, as well as some primary (and many secondary) electrons and positive nuclei with atomic numbers from 3 to 26. Few primary cosmic rays reach the surface of the earth. As they pass through the upper atmosphere, they collide with atmospheric nuclei and blast them apart. At the earth's surface the progeny of the primaries are high-energy photons, electrons, positrons, and other particles (Sec. 52.7). We call these particles *secondary cosmic rays*. A single proton may initiate a "shower" containing thousands of these secondaries.

The cosmic radiation which reaches the earth changes drastically in time, both in intensity and in energy spectrum. The major variations, which occur chiefly in particles with energies below 50 GeV, are closely related to solar magnetic activity. The particles are accelerated by magnetic fields in interstellar space and by accelerating fields associated with disturbances such as solar flares on the sun and other stars.

52.7 Pions and Muons

When cosmic-ray particles collide with nuclei in the upper atmosphere, particles called *pions* (or π mesons) are often produced. Pions, which may be produced equally well by beams of accelerators, may be positive, negative, or neutral. A charged pion has a mass 273 times that of an electron, while the neutral pion is less massive—about 264 electron masses. Neutral π mesons disappear with the emission of two photons, which share the 134 MeV of energy released. Negative pions are strongly attracted to nuclei and are captured quickly. Positive pions are repelled by nuclei and are less likely to be captured. A π^+ decays (Fig. 52.8) in a very short time to a positive *muon* (μ^+) and a *mu neutrino* (ν_μ), while a negative pion decays according to the reaction

$$\pi^- \rightarrow \mu^- + \tilde{\nu}_\mu$$

where the tilde implies an antineutrino. The mu neutrino is similar to, but distinguishable from, the neutrino of beta decay. Both the μ^+ and μ^- particles have a mass of 207 electron masses. Both are short-lived, decaying by the reactions

$$\mu^- \rightarrow \beta^- + \tilde{\nu} + \nu_\mu \qquad \mu^+ \rightarrow \beta^+ + \nu + \tilde{\nu}_\mu$$

TABLE 52.2 *Particles of Modern Physics*

Name	Symbol (charge)	Anti-particle	Rest mass, MeV	Spin, $\frac{h}{2\pi}$	Mean life, sec	Dominant decay modes
Photon	γ	(γ)	0	1		
LEPTONS						
Neutrinos	ν, ν_μ	$\tilde{\nu}, \tilde{\nu}_\mu$	0	½		Stable
Electron	β^-	β^+	0.511	½		Stable
Muon	μ^-	μ^+	105.7	½	2.2×10^{-6}	$\beta^- + \nu_\mu + \tilde{\nu}$
MESONS						
Pion	π°	(π°)	135	0	2×10^{-16}	Two γ rays
	π^+	π^-	139.6	0	2.6×10^{-8}	$\mu^+ + \nu_\mu$
	K^+	K^-	494	0	1.2×10^{-8}	$\mu^+ + \nu_\mu$; $\mu^+ + \nu_\mu + \pi^\circ$
Kaon						$e^+ + \nu + \pi^\circ$; $\pi^+ + \pi^\circ$
						$2\pi^+ + \pi^-$; $\pi^+ + 2\pi^\circ$
	K°	$\tilde{K}^\circ$	498	0	1×10^{-10}	$\pi^+ + \pi^-$; $2\pi^\circ$; also other modes
BARYONS						
Proton	p^+	p^-	938	½		Stable
Neutron	n	$\tilde{n}$	939.5	½	1×10^3	$p + \beta^- + \tilde{\nu}$
Lambda hyperon	Λ	$\tilde{\Lambda}$	1,115	½	2.2×10^{-10}	$p + \pi^-$; $n + \pi^\circ$
Sigma hyperons	Σ^+	$\tilde{\Sigma}^+$	1,189	½	8×10^{-11}	$p + \pi^\circ$; $n + \pi^+$
	Σ°	$\tilde{\Sigma}^\circ$	1,192	½	$(<10^{-11})$	$\Lambda + \gamma$
	Σ^-	$\tilde{\Sigma}^-$	1,196	½	$(\sim 10^{-10})$	$n + \pi^-$
Xi hyperons	Ξ°	$\tilde{\Xi}^\circ$	1,311	½	1.5×10^{-10}	$\Lambda + \pi^\circ$
	Ξ^-	$\tilde{\Xi}^-$	1,318	½	1.3×10^{-10}	$\Lambda + \pi^-$

Pions are intimately linked to the attractive force between nucleons, each of which is sometimes imagined to be surrounded by a virtual pion cloud. In terms of this picture, the binding forces in nuclei are attributed to the exchange of pions much as we attribute covalent binding between hydrogen atoms to electron-exchange forces.

When a beam of protons with energies of several billion electron volts is incident on a target, many other kinds of particles may be produced; indeed, any of the particles listed in Table 52.2 may be generated in this way.

52.8 Particles and Antiparticles

In 1955 a particle identical with the proton except for a negative charge was discovered by Segré, Chamberlain, and their collaborators at the University of California at Berkeley. The negative proton, or *antiproton*, was created by bombarding protons in a target with 6-GeV protons, thereby inducing the reaction

$$p + p + \text{energy} \rightarrow p + p + \bar{p} + p$$

where $\bar{p}$ indicates an antiproton. The energy of the bombarding proton is converted to a proton-antiproton pair plus the kinetic energy of the four residual particles. As soon as the antiproton is slowed down, it is annihilated by a proton; in a typical annihilation reaction the rest mass of the annihilating pair appears as five pions and their kinetic energy (Fig. 52.11):

$$p + \bar{p} \rightarrow \pi^+ + \pi^- + \pi^+ + \pi^- + \pi^0$$

One year later the antineutron $\bar{n}$ was discovered at the same laboratory. Since the neutron bears no charge, the antineutron is also neutral. It is quickly annihilated, either by a proton or a neutron, usually with the production of several pions. If an antineutron is not annihilated by a nucleon, it decays by the reaction $\bar{n} \rightarrow \bar{p} + \beta^+ + \nu$.

(a) (b)

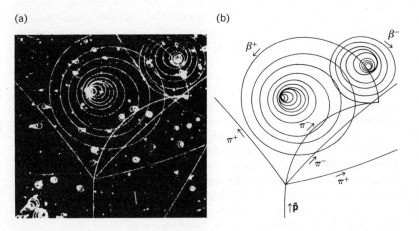

FIGURE 52.11

(*a*) Bubble-chamber photograph showing the path of an antiproton entering from below. Near the bottom of the picture the antiproton annihilated a proton, forming two + pions, two − pions, and a π^0 which leaves no track. In the upper quadrant of the picture a π^- interacted with a proton. Among the resulting products were a positron which formed the counterclockwise spiral at top center and an electron which produced the smaller clockwise spiral. (*b*) Explanatory sketch.

We note a remarkable similarity here to the behavior of the electron and positron, ordinarily created together and disappearing by the annihilation reaction $\beta^- + \beta^+ \rightarrow 2\gamma$. We therefore identify the positron as the *antielectron*. It appears that each particle of modern physics has an antiparticle by which it can be annihilated (Table 52.2). Of course, any antiparticle has a charge opposite to that of the corresponding particle, or else charge would not be conserved in annihilations. Many elementary particles decay in such a short time that they rarely find an antiparticle to annihilate. For example, the π^- is antiparticle to the π^+, and vice versa. However, as we saw in Sec. 52.7, the most common fates for a π^- are (1) capture by a nucleus and (2) decay to a μ^-. Observe that if we know a decay mode of any particle, we can immediately write a corresponding possible decay mode for its antiparticle by changing each particle in the reaction to its antiparticle (just as was done for the muon decays in Sec. 52.7).

There is every reason to believe that a positron and a negative proton could form an atom of antihydrogen, which would have a spectrum similar to that of ordinary hydrogen. Indeed, from a collection of antiprotons, antineutrons, and positrons a world of antimatter could be constructed which would be indistinguishable from our world so long as everything were made of antiparticles. However, if some of this *contraterrene* matter were to come in contact with terrene matter, particle-antiparticle annihilation would occur, and the entire mass of the annihilating particles would be converted to energy of other forms. Contrast this to a fission reaction in which only about 0.1 per cent of the mass is transformed.

When we organize the observed particles of physics into particles and antiparticles, several interesting regularities can be observed. (Of course, this is precisely the reason for this mode of organization.) We classify neutrinos, electrons, and muons as *leptons* or light particles. Then, *in any reaction the total number of leptons is conserved, provided we regard an antiparticle as the absence of a particle.* When a neutron decays according to $n \rightarrow p + \beta^- + \bar{\nu}$, we note that one lepton (β^-) and one antilepton ($\bar{\nu}$) appear, or a net zero leptons. In the μ^- decay we find one electron, one μ neutrino, and one antineutrino— one lepton before the decay and a net one lepton after the decay. The principle of *conservation of leptons* is a key conservation law in modern particle physics.

Pions and kaons are called *mesons,* particles of mass intermediate between leptons and *baryons* or heavy particles. A glance at the decay modes in Table 52.2 shows that there is no conservation of mesons, but the number of baryons is conserved.

The study of the physics of baryons, mesons, and leptons is an area of intense activity in contemporary physics, and many more particles have been discovered. What is the role of these strange new particles in nature? How many particles remain undiscovered? Will important uses be found for the new particles? Are there regions in the universe where stars and planets are composed of antiparticles? All these questions have been speculated upon. Answers may come from further research.

Questions

1. How can nuclear events be detected? Describe as many methods as you can.

2. How are tracks produced in a Wilson cloud chamber?

3. What are cosmic rays? What is the distinction between primary and secondary cosmic rays?

4. What is a meson? A lepton? A baryon?

5. Neutrons incident on the upper atmosphere collide with and are captured by N^{14} nuclei with the subsequent emission in many cases of protons or alpha particles. What nuclei remain in each case?

6. Roughly in what direction do you suppose the π^0 meson produced in the p-$\bar{p}$ annihilation of Figure 52.11 went? Why?

7. When a π^+ meson at rest decays to a μ^+ lepton, the muon always has the same energy, but when a μ^+ lepton decays to a positron, the positron may have any of a broad range of energies. Why?

Problems

1. Find the Q (energy released) in the $_4Be^9$ (α,n) $_6C^{12}$ reaction if the mass of $_4Be^9$ is 9.01243 amu. *Ans.* 5.93 MeV

2. Complete each of the following reactions:

Na^{23} (n,α) ? F^{19} (p,α) ? H^2 (γ,n) ?
Li^7 (p,n) ? $Cu^{58} \to Ni^{58} + ? + ?$ U^{238} (n,γ) ?
B^{11} (γ,α) ? Ag^{109} (n,γ) ? Mg^{24} (d,α) ?

3. The first observed artificial transmutation was reported by Rutherford in 1910. He bombarded $_7N^{14}$ with alpha particles, and protons came out of the reaction. Find the Q (energy released) in the reaction if the mass of $_8O^{17}$ is 16.9991 amu. (In this case Q is negative, meaning that energy must be supplied to the system.) *Ans.* -1.1 MeV

4. Calculate the Q (energy released) in the $_3Li^6$ (n,α) $_1H^3$ reaction.

5. From the masses of Li^6 and Li^7 compute the binding energy of a neutron captured by a Li^6 nucleus. What is the wavelength of the gamma ray emitted in the Li^6 (n,γ) Li^7 reaction? *Ans.* 7.2 MeV; 1.73×10^{-13} m

6. Find the Q (energy released) in the reaction $_9F^{19}$ (p,α) $_8O^{16}$ if the mass of $_9F^{19}$ is 18.9984 amu.

7. A π^0 meson at rest decays into two photons which must have equal and opposite momenta. Find the energy and wavelength of one of the photons. *Ans.* 67.5 MeV; 1.84×10^{-14} m

8. Find the energy released in the decay of a positive muon to a positron (plus neutrino and antineutrino).

9. Find the energy released in the decay of a pion to a muon. When a pion at rest decays, the muon receives about 4.1 MeV of kinetic energy. Find the momentum carried off by the neutrino. *Ans.* 33.9 MeV; 1.57×10^{-20} kg-m/sec

10. A neutron of mass m and initial speed v_i collides head on with a nucleus of mass M at rest. Show that if the collision is elastic, the energy $\mathcal{W}$ transferred to the nucleus is

$2Mm^2v_i{}^2/(M + m)^2$. Find the fraction of the energy of the neutron transferred to (*a*) a proton of mass *m*, (*b*) an alpha particle of mass $4m$, and (*c*) a uranium atom of mass $238m$.

11. A negative muon may be captured by a nucleus and occupy a "Bohr orbit" until it decays or interacts with a proton. Find the radius of the first Bohr orbit of a muon captured by lead, and show that this orbit lies inside the nucleus.

Ans. 3.1×10^{-15} m; nuclear radius is about 7×10^{-15} m

Mathematical Formulas

Trigonometric Relations

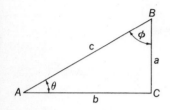

FIGURE A.1

Consider angle θ in the right triangle ABC (Fig. A.1) which has sides of lengths a, b, and c. By definition, the sine of θ is the ratio of the side opposite θ to the hypotenuse, the cosine of θ is the ratio of the side adjacent to θ to the hypotenuse, and the tangent of θ is the ratio of side opposite θ to the side adjacent to θ. The values of these functions are listed in the Table of Trigonometric Functions. The cotangent of θ is the reciprocal of $\tan \theta$.

$$\sin \theta = \frac{a}{c} \qquad \cos \theta = \frac{b}{c} \qquad \tan \theta = \frac{a}{b} \qquad \cot \theta = \frac{b}{a}$$

Angle ϕ is the complement of θ. Clearly,

$$\sin \phi = \frac{b}{c} = \cos \theta = \cos (90° - \phi)$$

and

$$\cos \phi = \frac{a}{c} = \sin \theta = \sin (90° - \phi)$$

By the pythagorean theorem, $c^2 = b^2 + a^2$. From this it follows immediately that $\sin^2 \theta + \cos^2 \theta = 1$. Other trigonometric identities which are useful are

$$\sin (\theta \pm \phi) = \sin \theta \cos \phi \pm \cos \theta \sin \phi$$
$$\cos (\theta \pm \phi) = \cos \theta \cos \phi \mp \sin \theta \sin \phi$$

In any plane triangle having angles α, β, and γ with opposite sides a, b, and c, respectively (Fig. A.2),

$$\frac{\sin \alpha}{a} = \frac{\sin \beta}{b} = \frac{\sin \gamma}{c} \qquad \text{law of sines}$$

and

$$\cos \alpha = \frac{b^2 + c^2 - a^2}{2bc} \qquad \text{law of cosines}$$

If an angle exceeds 90°,

$$\sin \beta = \sin (180° - \beta)$$

and

$$\cos \beta = -\cos (180° - \beta)$$

If an angle θ is expressed in radians,

$$\sin \theta = \theta - \frac{\theta^3}{3!} + \frac{\theta^5}{5!} - \frac{\theta^7}{7!} + \cdots$$

$$\cos \theta = 1 - \frac{\theta^2}{2!} + \frac{\theta^4}{4!} - \frac{\theta^6}{6!} \cdots$$

FIGURE A.2

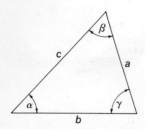

Trigonometric Functions

Angle	Sine	Cosine	Tangent	Angle	Sine	Cosine	Tangent
1°	.0175	.9998	.0175	46°	.7193	.6947	1.0355
2°	.0349	.9994	.0349	47°	.7314	.6820	1.0724
3°	.0523	.9986	.0524	48°	.7431	.6691	1.1106
4°	.0698	.9976	.0699	49°	.7547	.6561	1.1504
5°	.0872	.9962	.0875	50°	.7660	.6428	1.1918
6°	.1045	.9945	.1051	51°	.7771	.6293	1.2349
7°	.1219	.9925	.1228	52°	.7880	.6157	1.2799
8°	.1392	.9903	.1405	53°	.7986	.6018	1.3270
9°	.1564	.9877	.1584	54°	.8090	.5878	1.3764
10°	.1736	.9848	.1763	55°	.8192	.5736	1.4281
11°	.1908	.9816	.1944	56°	.8290	.5592	1.4826
12°	.2079	.9781	.2126	57°	.8387	.5446	1.5399
13°	.2250	.9744	.2309	58°	.8480	.5299	1.6003
14°	.2419	.9703	.2493	59°	.8572	.5150	1.6643
15°	.2588	.9659	.2679	60°	.8660	.5000	1.7321
16°	.2756	.9613	.2867	61°	.8746	.4848	1.8040
17°	.2924	.9563	.3057	62°	.8829	.4695	1.8807
18°	.3090	.9511	.3249	63°	.8910	.4540	1.9626
19°	.3256	.9455	.3443	64°	.8988	.4384	2.0503
20°	.3420	.9397	.3640	65°	.9063	.4226	2.1445
21°	.3584	.9336	.3839	66°	.9135	.4067	2.2460
22°	.3746	.9272	.4040	67°	.9205	.3907	2.3559
23°	.3907	.9205	.4245	68°	.9272	.3746	2.4751
24°	.4067	.9135	.4452	69°	.9336	.3584	2.6051
25°	.4226	.9063	.4663	70°	.9397	.3420	2.7475
26°	.4384	.8988	.4877	71°	.9455	.3256	2.9042
27°	.4540	.8910	.5095	72°	.9511	.3090	3.0777
28°	.4695	.8829	.5317	73°	.9563	.2924	3.2709
29°	.4848	.8746	.5543	74°	.9613	.2756	3.4874
30°	.5000	.8660	.5774	75°	.9659	.2588	3.7321
31°	.5150	.8572	.6009	76°	.9703	.2419	4.0108
32°	.5299	.8480	.6249	77°	.9744	.2250	4.3315
33°	.5446	.8387	.6494	78°	.9781	.2079	4.7046
34°	.5592	.8290	.6745	79°	.9816	.1908	5.1446
35°	.5736	.8192	.7002	80°	.9848	.1736	5.6713
36°	.5878	.8090	.7265	81°	.9877	.1564	6.3138
37°	.6018	.7986	.7536	82°	.9903	.1392	7.1154
38°	.6157	.7880	.7813	83°	.9925	.1219	8.1443
39°	.6293	.7771	.8098	84°	.9945	.1045	9.5144
40°	.6428	.7660	.8391	85°	.9962	.0872	11.4301
41°	.6561	.7547	.8693	86°	.9976	.0698	14.3007
42°	.6691	.7431	.9004	87°	.9986	.0523	19.0811
43°	.6820	.7314	.9325	88°	.9994	.0349	28.6363
44°	.6947	.7193	.9657	89°	.9998	.0175	57.2900
45°	.7071	.7071	1.0000	90°	1.0000	.0000	

Quadratic Equations

Any quadratic equation can be put in the form $ax^2 + bx + c = 0$, for which the solutions are

$$x = \frac{-b \pm \sqrt{b^2 - 4ac}}{2a}$$

Mensuration Formulas

The circumference of a circle of radius r is $2\pi r$ ($\pi = 3.1416$).
The area of a circle of radius r is πr^2.
The area of an ellipse with semiaxes a and b is πab.
The surface area of a sphere of radius r is $4\pi r^2$, and its volume is $\frac{1}{3}\pi r^3$.

Tables of Data

TABLE 1 *Heat Constants of Solids*

Substance	Melting point, °C	Coefficient of linear expansion per C°	Specific heat kcal/(kg)(C°)	Heat of fusion kcal/kg	Heat of fusion Btu/lb
Aluminum	657	0.0000255	0.22	76.8	140
Bismuth	268	0.0000157	0.030	12.6	22.7
Brass		0.0000193	0.090		
Copper	1084	0.0000167	0.093	43	77
Glass		0.0000083	0.20		
Gold	1063	0.0000139	0.030		
Ice	0	0.000051	0.50	79.8	144
Iron	1503	0.0000119	0.11	30	54
Lead	327	0.0000276	0.030	5.4	9.7
Mercury	−38.8		0.033	2.8	5.4
Nickel	1452	0.0000128	0.109	4.6	8.3
Platinum	1756	0.0000089	0.032	27	48.6
Silver	960	0.0000188	0.056	22	39
Steel		0.000012	0.11		
Tungsten	3360	0.0000044	0.034		
Zinc	418	0.0000263	0.092	28.1	50.6

TABLE 2 *Heat Constants of Liquids*

Substance	Boiling point, °C	Cubical expansion per C°	Specific heat, kcal/(kg)(C°)	Heat of vaporization kcal/kg	Heat of vaporization Btu/lb
Ammonia	−34			294	529
Aniline	184		0.514	110	198
Alcohol (ethyl)	78.1	0.0011	0.55	205	369
Benzine	80.3	0.00124	0.34	94.4	170
Chloroform	61	0.00126	0.232	58	106
Ether (ethyl)	34.5	0.00163	0.56	88.4	159
Gasoline	70–90	0.0012		71–81	128–146
Glycerin	290	0.00053	0.58		
Mercury	358	0.000182	0.0332	68	122
Turpentine	159	0.00094	0.42	70	126
Water	100	0.00030	1.00	540	970

Note: Densities are tabulated in Sec. 11.8, page 148.

TABLE 3 *Boiling Point of Water (Boiling points of water at pressures near standard atmospheric pressure. The pressures are given in millimeters of mercury at 0°C.)*

Pressure, mm Hg	Tempera- ture, °C	Pressure, mm Hg	Tempera- ture, °C	Pressure, mm Hg	Tempera- ture, °C
733	98.99	749	99.59	765	100.18
735	99.07	751	99.67	767	100.26
737	99.14	753	99.74	769	100.33
739	99.22	755	99.82	771	100.40
741	99.29	757	99.89	773	100.47
743	99.37	759	99.96	775	100.55
745	99.44	761	100.04	777	100.62
747	99.52	763	100.11	779	100.69

TABLE 4 *Properties of Saturated Water Vapor*

Tem- pera- ture, °C	Pressure		Volume		Heat units per unit mass, kcal/kg		
	kg-wt/cm²	lb/in.²	m³/kg	ft³/lb	Of water	Latent heat	Total heat of vapor
0	0.0063	0.089	204.970	3283.00	0	594.7	594.7
10	0.0125	0.178	106.620	1707.60	10	589.4	599.4
20	0.0236	0.336	58.150	931.48	20	584.1	604.1
30	0.0429	0.61	33.132	530.72	30	578.8	608.8
40	0.0747	1.06		314.77	40.1	573.4	613.5
50	0.125	1.78	12.091	193.68	50.1	567.9	618
60	0.202	2.88	7.695	123.26	60.1	562.4	622.6
70	0.317	4.51	5.050	80.89	70.2	556.8	627
80	0.482	6.86	3.4085	54.60	80.3	551	631.5
90	0.714	10.16	2.3592	37.79	90.4	545.2	635.6
100	1.033	14.70	1.6702	26.754	100.5	539.6	639.7
110	1.462	20.79	1.2073	19.339	101.7	532.9	643.6
120	2.027	28.83	0.8894	14.247	120.9	526.6	647.4
130	2.760	39.26	0.6664	10.675	131.1	520	651
140	3.695	52.56	0.5071	8.123	141.3	513.2	654.5
150	4.868	69.24	0.3917	6.274	151.6	506.2	657.8
160	6.323	89.93	0.3065	4.91	161.9	498.9	660.8
170	8.104	115.27	0.2429	3.891	172.2	491.4	663.7
180	10.258	145.90	0.1945	3.116	182.6	483.7	666.3
190	12.835	182.56	0.1575	2.523	193.1	475.7	668.8
200	15.890	226.00	0.1288	2.063	203.6	467.5	671.1
210	19.490	277.20	0.1063	1.703	214.1	459.1	673.2

Energy Stored in an Inductive Circuit

The energy stored in the magnetic field associated with a circuit for which the coefficient of self-induction is L is equal to the work required to establish the current in the circuit or the energy which will be released when the current is eliminated. The back emf due to the self-inductance in the circuit is

$$e = -L\frac{di}{dt}$$

The work done against this back emf in the time dt is

$$ei \, dt = Li\frac{di}{dt} dt = Li \, di$$

The whole work is

$$\mathcal{W} = \int_0^I ei \, dt = \int_0^I Li \, di = \tfrac{1}{2}LI^2$$

Effective Value of an Alternating Current

By definition the effective value of an alternating current is the steady current which dissipates heat in a resistor at the same average rate as the alternating current. Let the alternating current be

$$i = I_{max} \sin 2\pi \nu t$$

The power developed instantaneously in a resistor R is

$$I_{max}^2 R \sin^2 2\pi \nu t$$

The heat developed during one cycle is

$$I_{eff}^2 RT = \int_0^T I_{max}^2 R \sin^2 2\pi \nu t \, dt$$

where T is the period ($T = 1/\nu$). Therefore,

$$I_{eff}^2 T = I_{max}^2 \int_0^T \sin^2 \frac{2\pi}{T} t \, dt = \frac{I_{max}^2 T}{2}$$

from which

$$I_{eff} = \frac{I_{max}}{\sqrt{2}} = 0.707 I_{max}$$

A-C Series Circuits

Application of Kirchhoff's second law to the circuit of Figure 43.3 yields

$$v = \mathcal{E}_{max} \sin 2\pi \nu t = L\frac{di}{dt}$$

from which

$$i = \int \frac{\mathscr{E}_{\max} \sin 2\pi\nu t \, dt}{L} = -\frac{\mathscr{E}_{\max} \cos 2\pi\nu t}{2\pi\nu L}$$

and

$$I_{\max} = \frac{\mathscr{E}_{\max}}{2\pi\nu L}$$

Similarly, when an alternating potential difference $\mathscr{E}_{\max} \sin 2\pi\nu t$ is applied across a capacitor,

$$\mathscr{E}_{\max} \sin 2\pi\nu t = \frac{q}{C}$$

Since $i = dq/dt$,

$$\frac{i}{C} = \frac{d(\mathscr{E}_{\max} \sin 2\pi\nu t)}{dt} = 2\pi\nu\mathscr{E}_{\max} \cos 2\pi\nu t$$

Therefore,

$$i = \frac{\mathscr{E}_{\max} \cos 2\pi\nu t}{1/2\pi\nu C} \qquad \text{and} \qquad I_{\max} = \frac{\mathscr{E}_{\max}}{1/2\pi\nu C}$$

For an a-c series circuit containing a source of emf $e = \mathscr{E}_{\max} \sin 2\pi\nu t$ and resistance, inductance, and capacitance (Fig. 43.7), application of Kirchhoff's second law at any instant leads to

$$e = \mathscr{E}_{\max} \sin 2\pi\nu t = Ri + L\frac{di}{dt} + \frac{q}{C}$$

If we differentiate with respect to time,

$$2\pi\nu\mathscr{E}_{\max} \cos 2\pi\nu t = R\frac{di}{dt} + L\frac{d^2i}{dt^2} + \frac{i}{C}$$

The solution of this differential equation is

$$i = \frac{\mathscr{E}_{\max} \sin(2\pi\nu t - \theta)}{\sqrt{R^2 + [2\pi\nu L - (1/2\pi\nu C)^2]}}$$

where

$$\tan \theta = \frac{2\pi\nu L - 1/2\pi\nu C}{R}$$

and

$$I = \frac{\mathscr{E}}{\sqrt{R^2 + [2\pi\nu L - (1/2\pi\nu C)]^2}}$$

If either the inductor or the capacitor is removed from the circuit and the circuit is completed once more, the appropriate term vanishes from the equations above. This leads to Eq. (43.4) if the capacitor is removed and to Eq. (43.6) if there is no inductance.

Power in an A-C Circuit

The instantaneous power supplied to an a-c circuit is given by $p = ei$
[Eq. (43.9)]. The average power over a complete cycle is

$$P = \frac{1}{T} \int_0^T p \, dt = \frac{1}{T} \int_0^T ei \, dt = \frac{1}{T} \int_0^T$$

$$\mathcal{E}_{max} \sin 2\pi\nu t \, I_{max} \sin (2\pi\nu t - \theta) \, dt$$

where T is the period $(T = 1/\nu)$. Since

$$\sin (2\pi\nu t - \theta) = \sin 2\pi\nu t \cos \theta - \cos 2\pi\nu t \sin \theta$$

P becomes

$$P = \frac{\mathcal{E}_{max} I_{max}}{T} \int_0^T \left(\sin^2 \frac{2\pi t}{T} \cos \theta + \sin \frac{2\pi t}{T} \cos \frac{2\pi t}{T} \sin \theta \right) dt$$

$$= \frac{\mathcal{E}_{max} I_{max} \cos \theta}{2} = \mathcal{E}I \cos \theta$$

which is Eq. (43.10).

INDEX

PERIODIC TABLE OF THE ELEMENTS (*Based on Carbon-12 as 12.00000*)

n	$s(l=0)$		$d(l=2)$						VIII			s		$p(l=1)$					Inert gases
	I_A	II_A	III_B	IV_B	V_B	VI_B	VII_B				I_B	II_B	III_A	IV_A	V_A	VI_A	VII_A	
1	1 H 1.00797	2 He 4.0026																	2 He 4.0026
2	3 Li 6.939	4 Be 9.0122											5 B 10.811	6 C 12.011	7 N 14.0067	8 O 15.9994	9 F 18.998	10 Ne 20.183
3	11 Na 22.990	12 Mg 24.312											13 Al 26.982	14 Si 28.086	15 P 30.974	16 S 32.064	17 Cl 35.453	18 Ar 39.948
4	19 K 39.102	20 Ca 40.08	21 Sc 44.956	22 Ti 47.90	23 V 50.942	24 Cr 51.996	25 Mn 54.938	26 Fe 55.847	27 Co 58.933	28 Ni 58.71	29 Cu 63.54	30 Zn 65.37	31 Ga 69.72	32 Ge 72.59	33 As 74.922	34 Se 78.96	35 Br 79.909	36 Kr 83.80
5	37 Rb 85.47	38 Sr 87.62	39 Y 88.905	40 Zr 91.22	41 Nb 92.906	42 Mo 95.94	43 Tc (99)	44 Ru 101.07	45 Rh 102.91	46 Pd 106.4	47 Ag 107.870	48 Cd 112.40	49 In 114.82	50 Sn 118.69	51 Sb 121.75	52 Te 127.60	53 I 126.90	54 Xe 131.30
6	55 Cs 132.91	56 Ba 137.34	*	72 Hf 178.49	73 Ta 180.95	74 W 183.85	75 Re 186.2	76 Os 190.2	77 Ir 192.2	78 Pt 195.09	79 Au 196.97	80 Hg 200.59	81 Tl 204.37	82 Pb 207.19	83 Bi 208.98	84 Po (210)	85 At (210)	86 Rn (222)
7	87 Fr (223)	88 Ra (226)	†															

Transition elements

$f(l=3)$

d

* Lanthanide series (*rare earths*)	57 La 138.91	58 Ce 140.12	59 Pr 140.91	60 Nd 144.24	61 Pm (147)	62 Sm 150.35	63 Eu 151.96	64 Gd 157.25	65 Tb 158.92	66 Dy 162.50	67 Ho 164.93	68 Er 167.26	69 Tm 168.93	70 Yb 173.04	71 Lu 174.97
† Actinide series	89 Ac (227)	90 Th 232.04	91 Pa (231)	92 U 238.03	93 Np (237)	94 Pu (244)	95 Am (243)	96 Cm (247)	97 Bk (247)	98 Cf (251)	99 Es (254)	100 Fm (253)	101 Md (256)	102 No (254)	103 Lw (257)